FRIEDLINE.

PROPERITY of
LESLIE ... FRIEDLINE

TRANSISTOR ELECTRONICS

PRENTICE-HALL ELECTRICAL ENGINEERING SERIES

W. L. EVERITT, Ph.D., *Editor*

ANNER *Elements of Television Systems*
BENEDICT *Introduction to Industrial Electronics*
DAVIS AND WEED *Industrial Electronic Engineering*
FICH *Transient Analysis in Electrical Engineering*
GOLDMAN *Information Theory*
GOLDMAN *Transformation Calculus and Electrical Transients*
JORDAN *Electromagnetic Waves and Radiating Systems*
LO, ENDRES, ZAWELS, WALDHAUER, CHENG *Transistor Electronics*
MARTIN *Electronic Circuits*
MARTIN *Ultrahigh Frequency Engineering*
MOSKOWITZ AND RACKER *Pulse Techniques*
PUMPHREY *Electrical Engineering*, 2d ed.
PUMPHREY *Fundamentals of Electrical Engineering*
RIDEOUT *Active Networks*
RYDER *Electronic Engineering Principles*, 2d ed.
RYDER *Electronic Fundamentals and Applications*
RYDER *Networks, Lines and Fields*, 2d ed.
SHEDD *Fundamentals of Electromagnetic Waves*
SKRODER AND HELM *Circuit Analysis by Laboratory Methods*, 2d ed.
STOUT *Basic Electrical Measurements*
THOMSON *Laplace Transformation*
VAIL *Circuits in Electrical Engineering*
VAN DER ZIEL *Noise*
VON TERSCH AND SWAGO *Recurrent Electrical Transients*
WARD *Introduction to Electrical Engineering*, 2d ed.

TRANSISTOR ELECTRONICS

ARTHUR W. LO
R.C.A. Laboratories Div., Princeton, N.J.

RICHARD O. ENDRES
Rese Engineering, Inc., Philadelphia, Pa.

JAKOB ZAWELS
R.C.A. Electronic Products Div., Camden, N.J.

FRED D. WALDHAUER
South African Iron and Steel Corporation

CHUNG-CHIH CHENG
R.C.A. Electronic Products Div., Harrison, N.J.

PRENTICE-HALL, INC.
Englewood Cliffs, N. J.

LIBRARY OF CONGRESS
CATALOG CARD NO.: 55-10875

First printing .... *September, 1955*
Second printing........ *January, 1956*
Third printing .... *March, 1956*
Fourth printing .... *January, 1957*

PRINTED IN THE UNITED STATES OF AMERICA
93010

PREFACE

In the few years since its invention, the transistor has become firmly established as a most important member of the rapidly increasing family of electronic devices. Indeed, the transistor is already competitive and promises to surpass the vacuum tube in many applications in the electronic industry.

To one interested in becoming familiar with the field of transistors and associated devices, certain questions naturally arise. How well is the operation of the transistor understood? Is the design of transistor circuits more complex than the design of vacuum tube circuits? Is an understanding of vacuum tube circuits of direct benefit in the application of transistors? These questions and their answers may logically preface a book on transistor electronics.

With reference to the first question, it may be said that the theory of operation of the transistor has been brought to a remarkable state of advancement, considering the relatively short time the transistor has been known. Theoretical expressions describing the behavior of the transistor agree well with experimentally observed behavior, especially for transistors of relatively simple geometrical construction.

A clear-cut answer cannot be given to our second question, since factors which complicate the design of certain circuits may be of little consequence in the design of other circuits. The transistor, in contrast with the vacuum tube, for example, may often have to be considered a bilateral device even at low frequencies. Analysis of certain linear continuous-wave transistor circuits may thereby be more complicated. On the other hand, large signal characteristics of the transistor approach those of a perfect switching device. Switching circuits utilizing transistors may therefore be simpler in design and structure than vacuum tube circuits which perform the same function.

Knowledge of vacuum tube circuits may be beneficial in applying the transistor to circuits if reasonable care is exercised. In view of the very different mechanisms of operation of transistors and vacuum tubes, it is surprising when certain similarities in their circuit behavior are recognized. However, too rigorous an attempt to develop parallels between vacuum tube and transistor circuits, as for example, literally following the principles of direct analogy or of duality, may obscure unique circuit possibilities of the transistor.

Emphasis is placed here on a basic understanding of the circuit aspects of the transistor, and description and analysis of circuits are directed to the principles governing operation of these circuits. In addition, intelligent use of the transistor is facilitated by knowledge of the physical principles governing transistor operation, so that discussion of these principles is included.

Chapter 1 of this volume treats qualitatively the fundamental concepts of transistor physics. Chapters 2 and 3 introduce the operating characteristics and the general properties of the transistor as a circuit element. Stabilization of the d-c operating point, important in transistor circuits, is described in Chapter 4. Chapters 5 and 6 offer a treatment of low-frequency amplifiers, including the principles of complementary symmetry as applied to these circuits. Chapters 7 and 8 introduce the reader to high-frequency operation of transistors including high-frequency equivalent circuits. Chapter 8, in particular, treats the various physical phenomena of transistor action in the light of their effect on equivalent circuits. This is followed by a study of high-frequency amplifiers in Chapter 9. Chapters 10, 11, and 12 deal with nonlinear operation of the transistor; oscillators are treated in Chapter 10, modulation and demodulation are treated in Chapter 11, and pulse circuits are studied in Chapter 12.

This book is written for advanced undergraduate or graduate students in electrical engineering and associated fields, and as a reference work for the electronics engineer. The sections on circuit design should provide an effective guide for the design engineer, covering many fields from amplifiers to digital computers. Parallels and contrasts between transistor and vacuum tube circuits are included where it is believed they may properly add perspective.

The symbols and notations used in this book conform, in the main, to the I.R.E. standards. A particular deviation is the use of V and v to represent voltages, while the letters E and e are reserved to designate the emitter of the transistor. Since no graphical symbol has become standard for the transistor at this time of writing, the authors have found it desirable to adopt a symbol for the junction transistor for better functional representation and to distinguish it from the point contact transistor. It should be noted that this symbol is of the "building block" type, as recommended by the I.R.E.

The authors wish to acknowledge the helpful cooperation of the Radio Corporation of America. They are indebted to many of their colleagues for valuable suggestions and criticisms, as well as for technical contributions which have been adapted and acknowledged in this volume. In particular, the authors wish to thank T. P. Bothwell, D. E. Deuitch, H. Johnson, H. C. Lin, A. Moore, and W. M. Webster, for their kind assistance.

THE AUTHORS

CONTENTS

Chapter 1

PHYSICAL CONCEPTS

1.1 Introduction

In the application of the transistor to electronic circuits one needs only to treat the transistor as a circuit element whose behavior is defined by its operating characteristics. However, if one is to realize the greatest possible facility in using the transistor, a knowledge of the fundamental principles governing the operation of the device is essential.

Basically, the electron-tube operates by virtue of the flow of electrons in vacuum between the electrodes; the two fundamental problems involved are the liberation of electrons from a solid and the control of these electrons in a vacuum. In transistors, as well as in other related solid-state electronic devices, operation depends upon a flow of electric charge carriers within the solid; here the essential problems are the generation and control of these carriers within the solid. This chapter presents a summary of the physical concepts governing the operation of transistors, phototransistors, and rectifiers in a descriptive and qualitative form without entering into detailed and rigorous discussion of solid-state physics. However, in some specific instances, where circuit analysis requires a more thorough understanding of transistor physics, adequate quantitative treatment of the physical concepts involved is provided in those chapters where such subjects are considered. In particular, Chapters 7 and 8 will discuss the physics of high-frequency operation in detail.

It is practically impossible to review the physics of the transistor without reference to the works of Shockley and others,[1] whose treatments of this subject are adopted in this chapter. The reader is urged to study these references where a more thorough grasp of fundamentals is desired.

1.2 Germanium crystal

Germanium is the material used in most transistors and crystal rectifiers available at present. Some other semiconductors, such as

[1] See references at the end of this chapter.

silicon are also presently being used. Purified germanium usually is in the polycrystalline form, though it is possible and often desirable to prepare a specimen of germanium which is a single crystal. In such a single crystal, the germanium atoms arrange themselves in a regular pattern known as the *lattice structure*. As shown in the symbolic diagram of Fig. 1-1, each atom is bonded to four neighboring atoms in such a manner that the distance between any two neighboring atoms is the same. Each germanium atom consists of a nucleus and 32 electrons. The nucleus and 28 of the electrons form an inert core of net charge of +4 units of the charge of an electron. The inert cores,

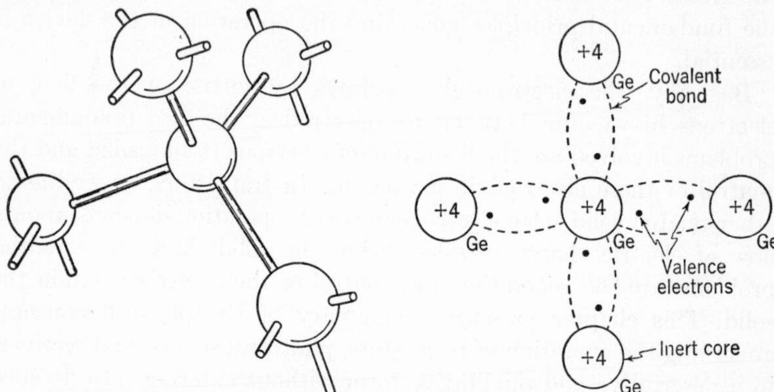

Fig. 1-1. Germanium crystal structure.

Fig. 1-2. Symbolic crystal structure of perfect germanium.

represented by the spheres in the figure, comprise the essential mass of the solid but do not contribute directly to the chemical and electrical properties of the element. The remaining 4 electrons, which constitute the bonds between the atoms (represented by the rods in Fig. 1-1), are the valence electrons and are responsible for the chemical and electrical properties. Two valence electrons, one from each of two neighboring atoms, by virtue of their relative motion cause a binding force to exist between the two atoms. This binding force and the force of electrostatic repulsion of the positively charged cores are in equilibrium, resulting in the specific arrangement of the atoms within the crystal. The electron-pair bonds are referred to as *covalent bonds*.

For a clearer conception of this arrangement, the lattice structure is reproduced symbolically in the two-dimensional picture shown in

Fig. 1-2. In the absence of external disturbances, the covalent bonds are stable and the motion of the valence electrons is restricted to their individual bonds. Although there are enormous numbers of electrons in a germanium crystal, these electrons are bound, either in the cores or in the covalent bonds, and are not free to move from one point to another in the crystal under the influence of an electric field. Thus the germanium crystal behaves like an insulator with a high dielectric constant. This discussion is limited to the ideal case of a perfect crystal in which there is no imperfection whatever in the lattice structure. It will be shown later that the operation of transistors and crystal rectifiers depends on controlled imperfections in the crystal. For the sake of simplicity, in the rest of the book the term "electron," unless specified otherwise, will be reserved for electrons that contribute to the conduction of electricity in the crystal, and will not include electrons in the covalent bonds or in the cores.

1.3 The behavior of an electron in the perfect germanium crystal

Suppose that by some means an electron is injected into a perfect germanium crystal. Since this *excess electron* is situated in an environment of perfect periodicity of electric potential, wave mechanics predicts that the electron will not be affected by the fluctuating electric field inside the crystal. This implies that the electron should either remain at rest or it should move with constant velocity through the crystal. In practice, however, this is not the case. The presence of thermal energy in the crystal, which we can never entirely avoid unless the crystal is kept at absolute zero temperature, causes lattice vibration. This lattice vibration excites the electrons into motion. The mechanism of thermal excitation of electrons may be illustrated by adopting the concept of the *phonon*. In much the same manner that light energy may be considered to be composed of discrete quanta, *photons*, the energy of lattice vibration may be considered as composed of particles of quantized energy, known as the *phonons*. We may consider phonons to be uncharged elastic masses moving with random thermal energies. Successive collisions between the phonons and the electron cause the electron to describe a random zigzag motion as represented in Fig. 1–3a. The random zigzag motion does not create a net displacement of the electron in any one direction; and thus does not contribute to the conduction of electricity in the solid.

A net displacement of electrons in a solid may happen as the result of *drift* or *diffusion*. When an electric field is applied to the solid, the random motion of the excess electron is modified to show a net drift in the direction of the field (Fig. 1-3b). The drift of the electron constitutes an electron current or, in other words, the conduction of electricity in the crystal. The resultant motion is the superimposition of the motion due to the electric field and the random zigzag motion of diffusion. Within the limit that the drift velocity of the electron is small compared with the thermal velocity of the phonon, the drift

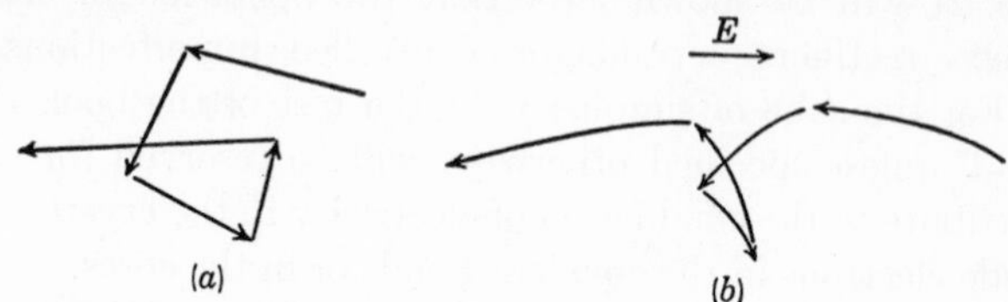

Fig. 1-3. Motion of an electron in a crystal: (a) random motion under no electric field; (b) motion under an electric field E.

velocity is directly proportional to the potential gradient (in other words, the electric field) in the relation,

$$v = \mu E$$

where v is the drift velocity, E is the applied electric field, and μ is the *mobility constant*, which is different in different solids. Consider the example of a solid of uniform cross section with a length l and a potential difference V applied across this length. If there are N electrons per unit length of the solid, the current in the solid is

$$i = Nqv = Nq\mu E = Nq\mu(V/l)$$

where q is the charge of an electron. This implies that the relation between voltage and current in a crystalline solid obeys Ohm's law. This relation, however, no longer holds when the applied electric field is too strong.

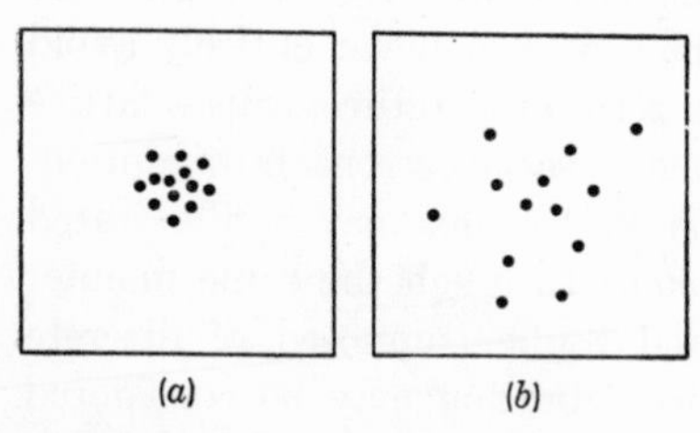

Fig. 1-4. Spreading of electrons by diffusion in a crystal: (a) before diffusion; (b) after diffusion.

When a concentration of electrons is injected at a point in the crystal, in the absence of an externally applied electric field, the random motion of the electrons results in spreading the electrons in all directions (Fig. 1-4). This spreading of electrons, being the result of thermal excitation in the crystal, is referred to as *diffusion*. Consider a sample of unit cross section area in which there is a uniform linear density gradient along the specimen. The diffusion current is

$$i = qD(dp/dx)$$

where q is the charge of an electron, dp/dx is the density gradient, and D is the *diffusion constant* of the solid.

The diffusion constant and the mobility of electrons in a crystal are related by the expression, known as Einstein's relationship,

$$D/\mu = kT/q \tag{1-1}$$

where k is Boltzmann's constant, T is the absolute temperature, and q is the charge of an electron. At room temperature the diffusion constant and mobility of electrons in germanium are approximately $\mu = 3600$ cm/sec per volt/cm, and $D = 93$ cm^2/sec.

1.4 Imperfections in the crystal

Up to this point we have been considering the properties of a perfect crystal whose structure suffers no imperfection. A small number of electrons injected into the crystal does not disturb the crystal structure nor does it appreciably affect the distribution of the electric field in the crystal. However, as far as transistor electronics is concerned, the perfect crystal is but an idealized model. The operation of transistors and crystal rectifiers actually depends on controlled imperfections in the crystal. Imperfections in the crystal provide the electric charge carriers in the solid and also contribute to the control of flow of these carriers. The three main causes of imperfections are radiation energy, chemical impurities, and disordered atomic arrangements. (The term imperfection is used here in the broad sense to include not only atomic imperfections such as atomic dislocations and impurity atoms but also energy imperfections which result from a disturbance of the normal energy state of the crystal.)

1.5 Imperfection by radiation energy

The electrical properties of germanium may change considerably when the element is exposed to light. The incident light is composed of photons, each of which is a quantum of energy, $E = h\nu$, where h is Planck's constant and ν is the frequency of the incident light. When light falls on the crystal, a quantum may be absorbed by the crystal and delivered to one of the covalent bonds. Provided the energy is great enough (i.e., the frequency of the incident light is high enough), an electron may be ejected from the bond. The ejected electron is free to wander in the crystal, like the injected excess electron discussed earlier, and it contributes to the conduction of electricity in the same manner. The empty space in the covalent bond left behind by the ejected electron is called a *hole* (Fig. 1-5). It is quite easy for an electron in a neighboring bond to move into the hole, thereby creating a new hole in its place. In this manner, the hole appears to move through the crystal. In the absence of an electric field, the motion of the hole is random, similar to that of the excess electron. Under the influence of an electric field, however, the hole behaves as an excess electron with a positive electronic charge. In fact, in the study of transistor electronics, we may treat the hole as a positive excess electron. The diffusion and mobility constants of the hole, however, are about half that of the electron. At room temperature in germanium their values are approximately $D = 43$ cm^2/sec, and $\mu = 1700$ cm/sec per volt/cm.

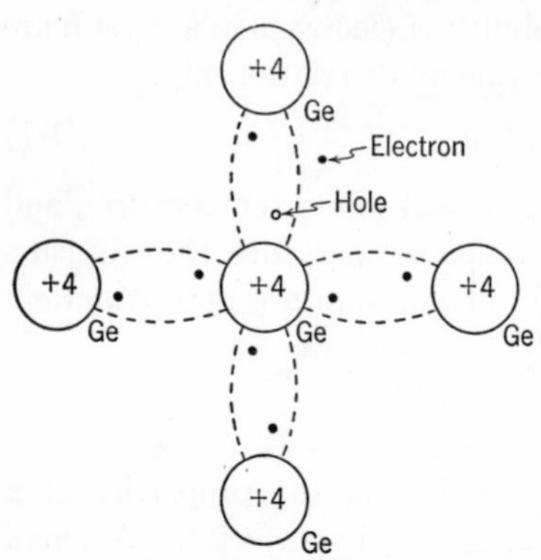

Fig. 1-5. Symbolic crystal structure of intrinsic germanium.

Electrons and holes are referred to as the negative and the positive *carriers*, respectively, and are solely responsible for the conduction of electricity in the crystal. The generation of electron-hole pairs by light is the basic principle of operation of phototransistors and photodiodes. In ordinary transistor and crystal rectifier operation, the crystal is shielded to eliminate the effect of light.

Thermal energy is another cause of crystal imperfection. We have discussed the role of thermal energy as it relates to the motion of the excess electron once the electron is either injected into or generated within the crystal. Thermal energy also assumes an important role in the generation of electron-hole pairs. The average thermal energy of the phonon at room temperature is too small to cause imperfections in the crystal. However, the distribution of thermal energy among individual phonons follows the Maxwell-Boltzmann distribution function and a small percentage of the phonons possess energies high enough to break a covalent bond. These high-energy phonons, when absorbed in the crystal and delivered to the covalent bonds, generate electron-hole pairs in the same manner as incident light energy. It is to be noted that thermal energy, as well as light energy, generates electrons and holes in identical numbers, since they are generated in electron-hole pairs. The conduction of electricity by these electron-hole pairs is called *intrinsic conduction*, and the crystal itself is known as the intrinsic specimen. Once generated a carrier will remain in the crystal for a finite *lifetime*, before recombining with a second carrier of the opposite charge to form a bond again. The average lifetime of the electron-hole pairs in germanium at room temperature is about 10^{-4} second. The generation and recombination of electron-hole pairs is a continuing process. When a germanium specimen reaches any steady temperature, the generation and recombination of electron-hole pairs reach a dynamic equilibrium, resulting in a definite concentration of carriers in the specimen. The concentration varies exponentially with temperature in accordance with the relation,

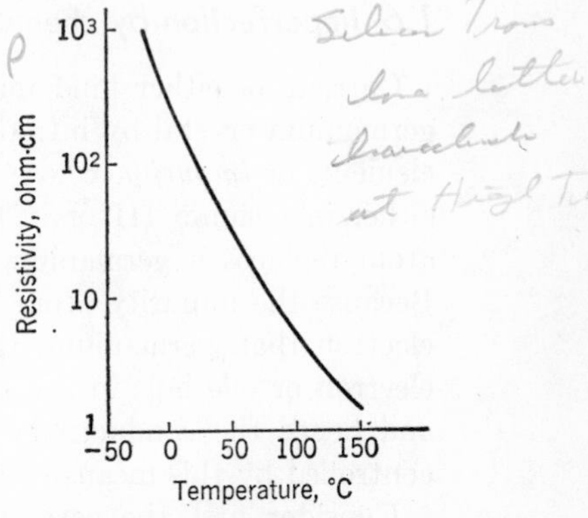

Fig. 1-6. Resistivity of intrinsic germanium as a function of temperature.

$$n_i^2 = K\epsilon^{-E_g/kT}$$

where n_i stands for the concentration of the conduction electrons in the intrinsic specimen, and E_g is the energy required to break a covalent bond. Since there are equal numbers of holes and conduction electrons, the concentration of the total carriers is twice that of n_i. The conductivity of intrinsic germanium, which may serve as a measure of the concentration of the carriers, is shown as a function of temperature in Fig. 1-6.[2] Note that at temperature much above normal room temperature the conductivity increases rapidly. In most solid-state electronic devices the intrinsic conduction, which is affected by the ambient temperature, must be kept small compared with controlled conduction if the device is to be of practical value.

The resistivity of pure germanium at room temperature is about 60 ohm-cm as compared with an insulator, such as mica, having a resistivity of 9×10^{15} ohm-cm, while a conductor, such as copper, has a resistivity of 1.7×10^{-6} ohm-cm. Thus germanium and similar solids are aptly called *semiconductors*.

1.6 Imperfection by chemical impurities

Carriers of either kind may be provided in an otherwise perfect germanium crystal by introduction of a minute amount of a foreign element, or *impurity*, whose position in the periodic table is usually either in Column III or in Column V. In either case, an impurity atom replaces a germanium atom in the perfect lattice structure. Because the impurity atom has either one more or one less valence electron than germanium, the result is the existence of one excess electron or one hole in the structure. The concentration of carriers, and hence the conductivity of the germanium, may be accurately controlled by this means.

Consider first the case in which an element with five valence electrons, such as antimony or arsenic, is added to the perfect crystal. The impurity disturbs the crystal lattice structure in such a manner that the new structure may be represented symbolically by the diagram of Fig. 1-7. Four of the five valence electrons of the impurity atom form covalent bonds with four neighboring germanium atoms, while the fifth valence electron is loosely attached to the antimony core. This fifth valence electron is readily detached from the antimony atom, even at low temperature, and behaves like an excess electron. Since this type of impurity provides excess electrons, it is called a

donor impurity. The presence of donors contributes excess electrons but does not contribute holes. Because of the negative carriers, germanium which is "doped" with donor impurity is called *n-type* germanium.

[2] P. G. Herkart and J. Kurshan, "Theoretical Resistivity and Hall Coefficient of Impure Germanium Near Room Temperature," *RCA Rev.*, Vol. 14, pp. 427–440, Sept. 1953.

If, to a perfect germanium crystal, there is added an impurity of a chemical element with three valence electrons, such as indium or boron, the lattice structure is modified as shown symbolically in Fig. 1-8. Since the impurity atom, say indium, has only three valence electrons, one of the four bonds linking the indium atom to the four neighboring germanium atoms is not complete. Thus there is a hole in the lattice structure. Since this type of impurity contributes holes (which is actually a deficiency of electrons), it is called an *acceptor* impurity. Germanium with added acceptors is called *p-type* germanium as a consequence of the predominating positive carriers.

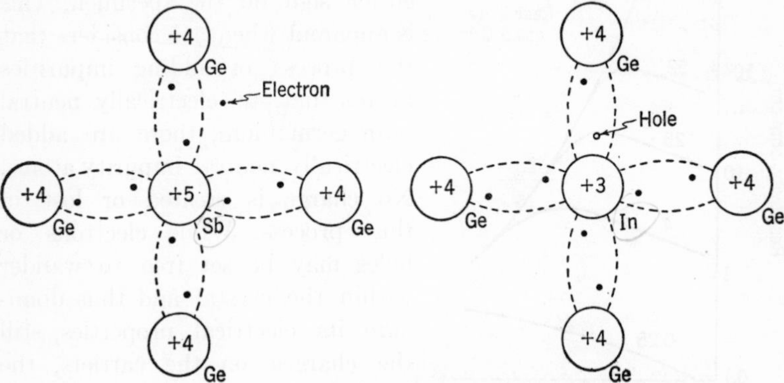

Fig. 1-7. Symbolic crystal structure of n-type germanium.

Fig. 1-8. Symbolic crystal structure of p-type germanium.

By growing single crystals, germanium samples practically free of impurities may be prepared. Pure germanium at room temperature has a resistivity of approximately 60 ohm-cm. The presence of a trace of impurity, too minute to be detected by conventional chemical and spectroscopic means, may affect the conductivity considerably. As an example, the addition of a trace of donor impurity in the amount of one impurity atom for 10^8 germanium atoms will reduce the resistivity of the specimen to 4 ohm-cm. The resistivity of germanium at room temperature (25°C) is used as a measure of the impurity content of the specimen, provided the nature of the impurity is known. The effect of temperature on the resistivity of n-type germanium with different degrees of purity is shown in Fig. 1-9.[3] The resistivity characteristics of p-type germanium closely

[3] Herkart and Kurshan, *loc. cit.*

follow the same pattern. It is to be noticed that at higher temperatures, say 80°C or greater, intrinsic conduction is comparable with p-type or n-type conduction and will seriously handicap transistor operation. Figure 1-10[4] shows a plot of germanium resistivity as a function of impurity concentration. Again, the resistivities of both n-type and p-type germanium follow much the same characteristic.

It should be observed at this point that neither the predominance of excess electrons in n-type germanium nor the predominance of holes in p-type germanium results in the presence of a net charge of either sign on the specimen. This is apparent when one considers that the process of adding impurities means that, to electrically neutral pure germanium, there are added electrically neutral impurity atoms. No charge is created or lost in this process. While electrons or holes may be set free to wander within the crystal and thus dominate its electrical properties, still the charges on the carriers, the bonded electrons, and the inert cores always balance one another, leaving the specimen electrically neutral.

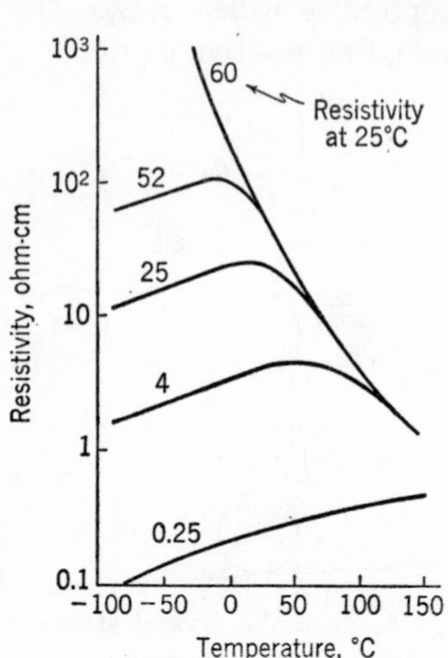

Fig. 1-9. Resistivity of n-type germanium as a function of temperature.

The excess electrons in n-type germanium are called the *majority carriers*; and the holes which might be injected into an n-type specimen in the operation of the device are called the *minority carriers*. Conversely, the holes in p-type germanium are the majority carriers, while injected electrons are the minority carriers. It will be shown later that the minority carriers play the leading role in the operation of transistors.

1.7 Imperfections arising from disordered atomic arrangement

Imperfections in a crystal may be the result of atomic vacancies, interstitial atoms, grain boundaries, and other disordered atomic

[4] *Ibid.*

arrangements. Such imperfections often play an important part in determining the lifetime of the carriers in the semiconductor; they are referred to, by virtue of their functions, as *deathnium centers* and *traps*. The deathnium center may be considered an intermediate stepping stone in the process of generation and recombination of electron-hole pairs. A bonded electron may be elevated to the deathnium center (leaving a hole behind) by a lesser amount of energy than that required to break a covalent bond. This electron may later be excited to leave the deathnium center and become a conduction electron. The reverse process, i.e., the recombination of electrons

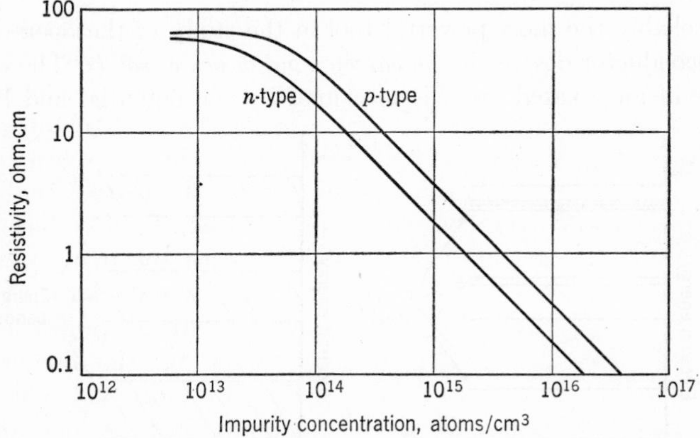

Fig. 1-10. Resistivity vs. impurity content for germanium at 25°C.

and holes through the intermediate step of the deathnium center, takes place with equal frequency. Since less energy is required in each step of the deathnium process, the presence of deathnium catalyzes the generation and recombination of electron-hole pairs.

At a given temperature, more electron-hole pairs are generated per second by thermal energy in a crystal with deathnium than one without deathnium. However, during the same time interval, more electrons and holes recombine in the crystal with deathnium than in the one without deathnium. Thus the presence of deathnium does not affect the concentration of carriers in the crystal, however, the average lifetime of the carriers is shortened. Deathnium centers are often found in germanium crystals in which the atomic arrangement is disordered (i.e., crystals having vacancies in the lattice), and also at the surface of the crystal.

A trap may be considered an imperfection center which can retain either a hole or an electron for a time much longer than that provided by a deathnium center. Hole traps appear in n-type germanium used in point-contact transistors as a result of a "forming" process. The trap has the property of capturing a hole and retaining it for an appreciable time before either releasing it or permitting it to recombine with an electron. In this way, carriers of one kind may be held in some region for an appreciable length of time, and thus substantially affect the charge density in that region.

1.8 Energy bands

Probably the most powerful tool in the study of the operation of semiconductor devices is the *energy band theory of solids*. The energy state of an isolated atom is measured by the potential and kinetic

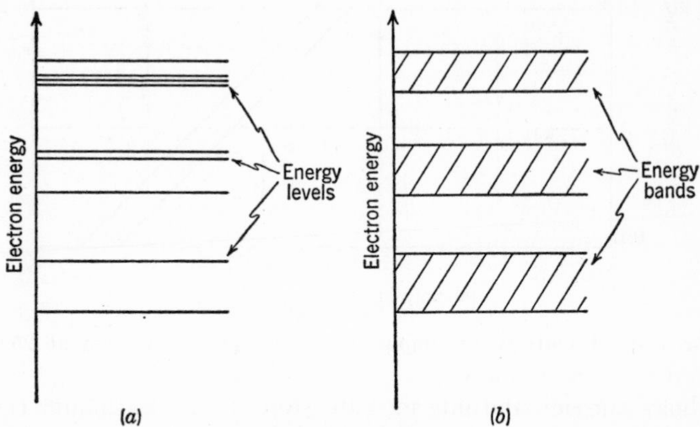

Fig. 1-11. Energy levels and energy bands: (a) isolated atom; (b) crystalline solid.

energy possessed by each electron in the atom. Each electron can possess only certain exact amounts of energy, and hence may exist only in certain discrete *energy levels* (Fig. 1-11a). In an isolated atom there are a finite number of these energy levels, and no more than two electrons may exist in each energy level at the same time. An electron which occupies a lower energy level is strongly attached to the atom, while an electron which occupies a high energy level is only feebly attached to the atom. Between the energy levels are forbidden energy gaps in which no electron may remain, but through which it must pass if it should gain sufficient energy to go from one level to a higher one, or if it should give up enough energy to pass from a given energy level to a lower one.

In the absence of external disturbing influences the electrons of an atom fill all the possible energy levels from the bottom up, and the atom is said to be in its normal state. An atom which has one or more of its electrons raised to a higher than normal energy level is said to be in an excited state. Two identical atoms, of course, have identical energy levels. When the two are brought into close proximity, however, the energy levels are observed to shift slightly with respect to each other; and each energy level of the single-atom system appears to be split into two levels in the two-atom system.

In the case of a solid, enormous numbers of atoms are packed in a small volume, so that interaction between the atoms causes the splitting and merging of energy levels, resulting in the formation of energy bands, where each band consists of an enormous but finite number of energy levels (Fig. 1-11b). Hence, just as the electrons of an isolated atom are restricted to discrete energy *levels*, so the electrons in a solid are restricted to discrete energy *bands*, each of which is separated from the neighboring bands by forbidden gaps.

In the crystalline semiconductor solids under discussion, the valence electrons normally occupy and completely fill the second highest energy band. This band is called the *valence band* or *filled band* (Fig. 1-12b). Excess electrons, whose existence is the consequence of imperfections in the crystal, are in the highest band, which is called the *conduction band* or the *empty band*. The energy bands below the valence band are filled by electrons which constitute the inert cores in the lattice. As mentioned before, these electrons in the inert cores do not contribute directly to the electrical properties of the solid.

To generate an electron-hole pair in a perfect crystal it is necessary to supply to one electron in the filled band sufficient energy to excite it into the empty band, thus depositing a carrier, the electron, in the empty band and creating a second carrier, the hole, in the filled band. The energy required for the generation of the electron-hole pair in this manner is equal to the height of the forbidden energy gap, E_g, the energy which was described as necessary to break a covalent bond. Recombination occurs when an electron drops back from the empty band to the filled band. Energy in the form of a phonon or a photon is released when recombination takes place. The conduction of electricity in the crystal is performed solely by the excess electrons in the empty band and by the holes in the filled band; for a study of the electrical properties of a semiconductor we need only concentrate our attention on these two bands.

It is of interest to note that all crystalline solids with atoms of four valence electrons do not behave alike electrically. For example, diamond (crystalline carbon) is a good insulator, lead is a good conductor, and germanium is a semiconductor. This apparent inconsistency may be readily explained by an examination of the energy band diagrams of these solids. In the case of diamond, the filled band and the empty band are far apart (Fig. 1-12a) so that at normal ambient temperatures an extremely small number of electrons would receive enough energy to be excited from the filled band to the conduction band with the consequent generation of holes in the filled band. Thus the crystal behaves like an insulator. The two energy bands of germanium (Fig. 1-12b), on the other hand, are close enough that, at room temperature, a considerable number of electrons are excited into the empty band, leaving behind them holes in the filled band. The two bands in lead (Fig. 1-12c) actually overlap one another. The valence electrons are therefore free to move in the lattice structure as "free" electrons in a conductor.

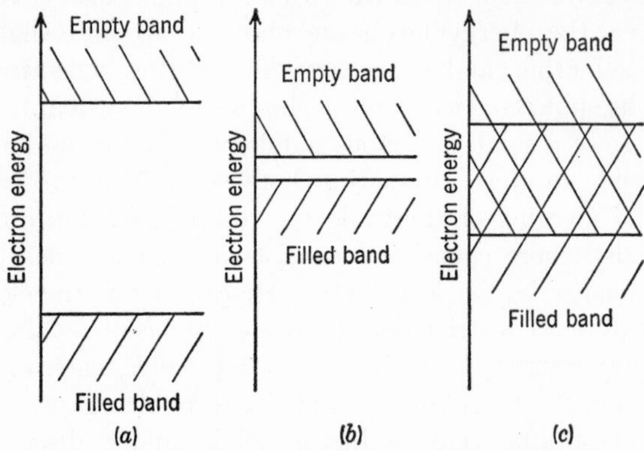

Fig. 1-12. Energy bands of crystalline solids: (a) insulator; (b) semiconductor; (c) conductor.

The generation of electrons and holes by the ionization of chemical impurities may also be illustrated by the energy band diagram, as shown in Fig. 1-13. In n-type germanium, the excess electrons of the donor atoms occupy a narrow band closely below the empty band, and a considerable number of them are excited into the empty band even at very low temperatures. In p-type germanium, the holes attached to the acceptor atoms occupy a narrow band closely above the filled band, and a considerable number of bonded electrons in the filled band move into these holes, leaving holes in the filled band. This may also occur at low temperatures.

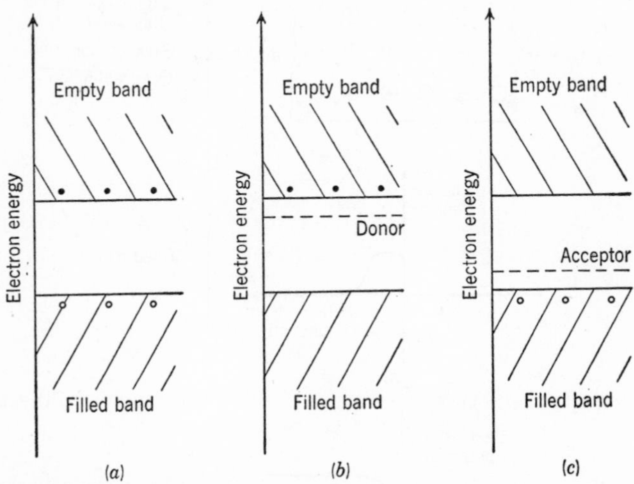

Fig. 1-13. Energy bands of germanium crystals: (a) intrinsic germanium; (b) n-type germanium; (c) p-type germanium.

The energy required to ionize the impurity atoms to generate electrons in n-type germanium and holes in p-type germanium is much lower than that required to generate electron-hole pairs in intrinsic germanium, as is evident in Fig. 1-13. It is observed that the energy required to generate an electron-hole pair in pure germanium is about 0.7 ev; while the energy required to set an electron free from a donor atom or to replace the hole from an acceptor atom is about 0.01 ev. At normal ambient room temperatures, where the thermal energy is about 0.02 ev, almost all the electrons and holes are detached from their donors and acceptors, respectively. Thus, for the temperature range in which transistors and crystal rectifiers may be operated, neglect of intrinsic conduction without loss of rigor is justified. But at higher temperatures intrinsic conduction plays an important part and disrupts the normal behavior of semiconductor devices.

1.9 Junctions

As was pointed out above, there is no net charge in any region of an isolated n-type or p-type germanium specimen, although there is a predominance of negative carriers (electrons) in the former, and

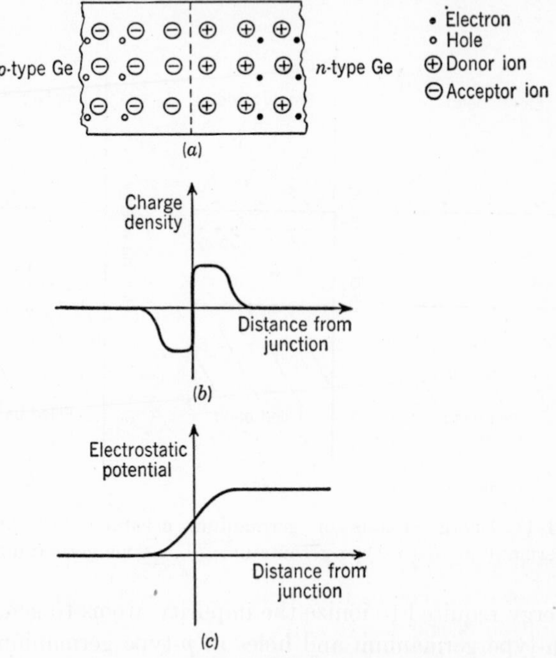

Fig. 1-14. p-n Junction: (a) structure; (b) charge density distribution; (c) electrostatic potential distribution.

a predominance of positive carriers (holes) in the latter. If now a piece of n-type germanium and a piece of p-type germanium are brought together in intimate contact to form a *junction*, while still preserving continuity of the crystal lattice structure at the junction, regions which exhibit net charges will be created (Fig. 1-14). (The junction is usually formed by introducing donor impurities into one side of a single crystal and acceptor impurities into the other side so as to form two regions in a single crystal.)

The excess electrons in the n-type region tend to diffuse and spread across the junction into the p-type region; while holes from the p-type region tend to spread into the n-type region. Thus there is a flow of electrons across the junction in one direction and a flow of holes across the junction in the opposite direction. This migration of charged particles in the specimen, which originally is electrically neutral, results in causing the p side to be electrically more negative than the n side. Thus there arises an electrostatic potential gradient across the junction which tends to oppose further flow of carriers and also affects the distribution of carriers in the neighborhood of the junction.

The system soon reaches a state of equilibrium when the established potential prevents any further flow of net charges across the junction. The *potential barrier* thus created is shown as an electrostatic potential difference in Fig. 1-14c. The carriers in the neighborhood of the junction are directly influenced by the potential gradient, and in the process of attaining equilibrium, move away from the junction until the holes originally at the left of the junction reach the point of lowest electrostatic potential in the p-type region, and the electrons originally at the right of the junction reach the point of highest electrostatic potential in the n-type region. Thus in the vicinity of the junction there is a depletion of carriers of either sign. The donor and acceptor cores, each carrying one unit of unbalanced positive or negative charge, respectively, are bound in the lattice so that they are not able to move away from the junction under the influence of the electric field. These bonded cores constitute the only charges in the area. The charge density distribution is shown in Fig. 1-14b. In a way, the junction appears synonymous to a charged capacitor. Unlike the capacitor, however, conduction current flows through the junction in the operation of the device.

1.10 Diode action

The p-n junction exhibits the unilateral property of allowing an easy path for electric current flow in only one direction. The conduction of electricity through a junction is constituted by the flow of electrons and holes across the junction. In describing the operation of the diode we shall first restrict the discussion to conduction by holes alone, since conduction by electrons is precisely analogous save for a reversal of sign. In this case, when no external voltages are applied to the crystal with a p-type region and an n-type region, we have seen that the electrostatic potential across the junction is that shown in Fig. 1-15a. The potential diagram indicates the amount of energy which a hole must acquire in order to exist physically at any given distance from the junction.[5]

At a given temperature, a number of holes in the p-type region gain enough energy to climb over the potential barrier to combine with electrons in the n-type region. This part of the hole current is represented by I_f, or the *forward current*, in the figure. At the same time thermal agitation generates electron-hole pairs, most probably in deathnium centers, in the n-type region. Some of the holes so gener-

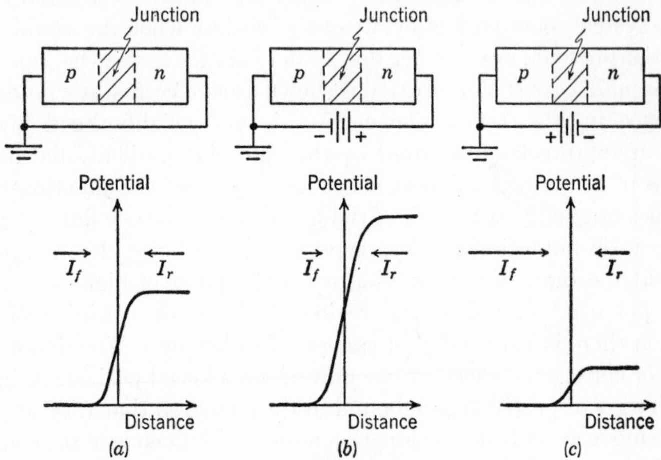

Fig. 1-15. Diode action: (a) p-n junction, not biased; (b) reverse-biased p-n junction; (c) forward-biased p-n junction.

ated will quickly combine with the excess electrons in the vicinity, but others will wander toward the junction and slide downhill over the potential barrier into the p-type region. This part of the hole current is represented by I_r, or the *reverse current*. At any given temperature, the two hole currents balance each other and there is no net current flow across the junction.

Now if a reverse bias is applied as shown in Fig. 1-15b, the potential barrier is raised by the amount of the bias and relatively few holes gain enough energy to climb over the barrier, and I_f is correspondingly small. However, I_r, which represents holes sliding down

[5] See Ref. 1 at the end of this chapter.

the potential hill, is not affected by the height of the barrier and thus remains constant. If the reverse bias is made sufficiently large, I_f will become negligibly small and the net current is practically I_r, which is independent of the bias voltage. This explains the saturation of the reverse current of a junction diode (Fig. 1-16). If a forward bias is applied, the potential barrier is lowered accordingly (Fig. 1-15c). Now more holes will have energy enough to go over the barrier, resulting in a larger current I_f, while the reverse current I_r remains constant as explained before. The net current thus increases with the forward bias (Fig. 1-16).

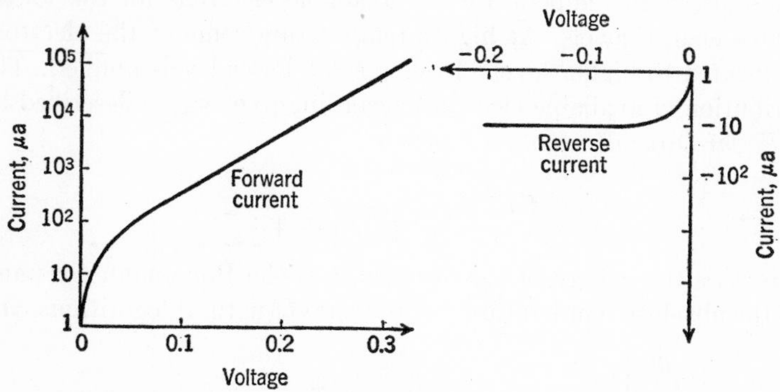

Fig. 1-16. Voltage-current characteristic of a junction diode.

The electron current across the junction follows a pattern similar to that of the hole current. The potential energy curve of an electron across the junction is the exact image of that of a hole. The flows of electrons and holes are in opposite directions and the total current across the junction is, of course, the sum of electron and hole currents.

The observed current-voltage relation of a junction rectifier is shown in Fig. 1-16. (Note that the current is plotted on a logarithmic scale in order to include both the large forward current and the small reverse current in the same diagram.) Theoretical interpretation of junction action gives the formula:

$$I = (\epsilon^{qV/kT} - 1)I_s \tag{1-2}$$

where, I = junction current, q = charge of electron, V = applied voltage, k = Boltzmann's constant, T = absolute temperature, I_s = total saturation (reverse) current for both electrons and holes.

Positive values of V and I represent forward bias voltage and forward current; while negative values of V and I represent reversed bias voltage and current. The formula agrees well with experimental results.

1.11 The Fermi level

The process of the formation of a potential barrier across a junction may be better understood with the concept of the *Fermi level.* As mentioned in Sec. 1.8, there are many more allowable energy levels than there are available electrons in the crystal. In a perfect crystal at absolute zero temperature the available electrons fill the lowest possible energy levels. At higher temperature some of the electrons are elevated to higher levels, leaving some lower levels unfilled. The distribution of available electrons according to energy is described by the *Fermi-Dirac distribution function:*

$$f(E) = \frac{1}{\epsilon^{(E-E_f)/kT} + 1}$$

where E is the energy of the electron, k is the Boltzmann constant, T is the absolute temperature, ϵ is the base of natural logarithms, and

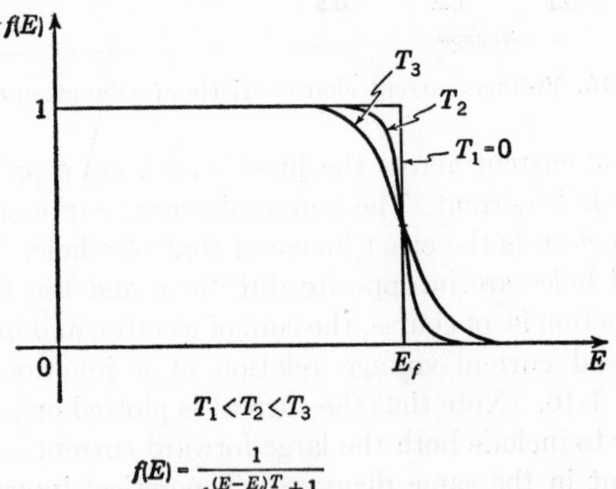

Fig. 1-17. Fermi-Dirac distribution function.

E_f is the energy referred to as the Fermi level. This function gives the probability of finding an electron at an energy level E at temperature T. Graphically the distribution function is shown in Fig. 1-17 for three different temperatures.

At absolute zero temperature the curve may be interpreted that statistically the available electrons fill all the energy levels below E_f, while none of the energy levels above E_f is occupied. At a higher temperature, the thermal energy increases the probability of finding an energy level slightly above E_f occupied by an electron, and also increases the probability of finding an energy level slightly below E_f not occupied by an electron (or we may say occupied by a hole). From the symmetry of the curve about the ordinate at E_f we see that at any given temperature the probability of finding an electron at a level E above E_f is the same as finding a hole E below E_f. This property of the distribution function may serve as a guide in finding the position of the Fermi level.

In intrinsic semiconductors there are as many electrons as holes. The electrons are essentially at the bottom of the conduction band, and the holes are essentially at the top of the filled band. The Fermi level is therefore at the center of the gap between the two bands. In n-type semiconductors the Fermi level lies closer to the empty band, and in p-type semiconductors the Fermi level lies closer to the filled band. Increasing the number of impurity atoms moves the Fermi level further away from the middle of the gap between the two bands, while increasing temperature moves the Fermi level toward the middle of the gap.

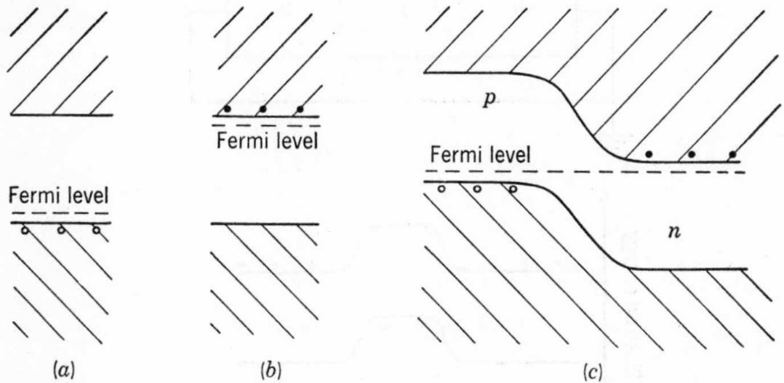

Fig. 1-18. Fermi level in germanium crystal: (a) p-type germanium; (b) n-type germanium; (c) p-n junction.

An important physical property attached to the concept of the Fermi level is that when two solids are in contact at thermal equilibrium the Fermi levels of the two solids are in alignment. The Fermi level of p-type germanium is closer to the filled band; and the Fermi level of n-type germanium is closer to the empty band (Fig. 1-18a, b).

When the two types of germanium are brought together to form a junction, electrons and holes move across the junction, and the accumulated net charges modify the electrostatic potential of the two regions in such a way that the two Fermi levels line up to form a common equilibrium level for the new system (Fig. 1-18c). The potential barrier for the electrons is represented by the elevation of the bottom of the empty band from the *n*-region to the *p*-region. The potential barrier for the holes may be considered as following the top of the filled band with its vertical direction reversed, as the energy bands are plotted for electrons and not for holes. Thus we see that the electrons in the *n*-region have to climb over the potential barrier to go into the *p*-region, and holes in the *p*-region must also climb over the barrier to enter the *n*-region.

1.12 Transistor action

A germanium crystal with *p*-type and *n*-type regions may be arranged to amplify the power of an electric signal. Let us consider the example of the *n-p-n* junction transistor, which consists of a

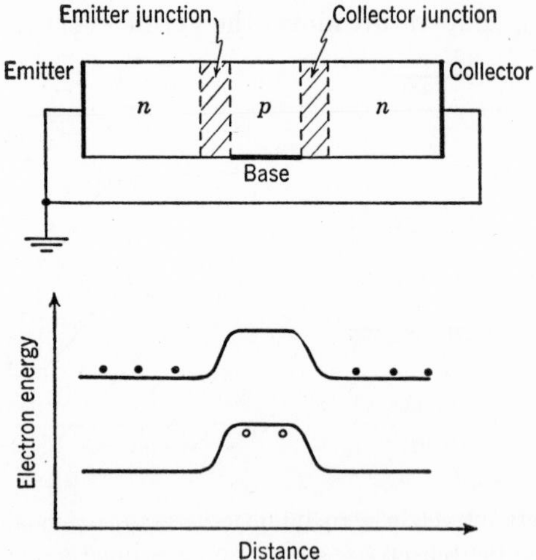

Fig. 1-19. Junction transistor without bias voltages.

germanium crystal with two *n*-type regions separated by a thin layer of *p*-type region (Fig. 1-19). Large-area metal contacts to each of the three regions provide means to connect the transistor to external circuit elements. The contacts to the *n*, *p*, and *n* layers are referred to as the *emitter* terminal (e), the *base* terminal (b) and the *collector* terminal (c), respectively; while the two junctions are termed the *emitter junction* and the *collector junction*.[6] In the absence of external biases, the potential barriers across the two junctions are as shown in Fig. 1-19.

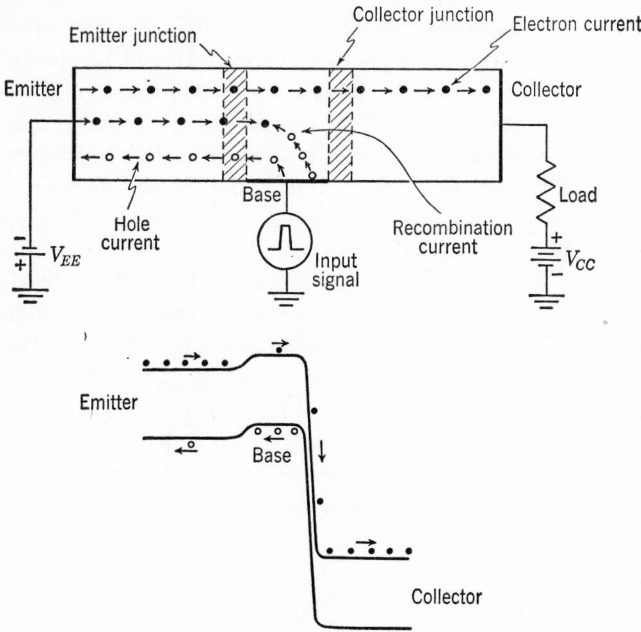

Fig. 1-20. Junction transistor with bias voltages.

Now, consider the case where the transistor is connected to amplify a small-signal a-c input. In a typical amplifier circuit, the emitter is grounded through a source of bias V_{EE}, and a positive voltage is applied through the load resistor to the collector, so that the collector junction is reverse-biased to saturation as shown in Fig. 1-20. The input signal is to be applied at the base. To explain the transistor

[6] J. Bardeen and W. H. Brattain, "The Transistor, A Semi-conductor Triode," *Phys. Rev.*, Vol. 74, pp. 230, 231, July 15, 1944; W. Shockley, "The Theory of *pn* Junctions in Semi-conductors and *pn* Junction Transistors," *Bell System Tech. J.*, Vol. 28, pp. 435–489, July 1949.

action let us first take the simplified case where volume and surface recombination of electrons and holes in the base region is negligible. In the absence of an input signal the current flow in the transistor may be taken in three parts. First there is the current I_{co} (defined as the collector-to-base current with the emitter terminal open-circuited) which is the saturated reverse current of a junction diode, as explained in Sec. 1.9. Since this current remains constant in ordinary transistor operation, we shall exclude it in the rest of the discussion of transistor action in this chapter. It will be shown later, however, that I_{co} is highly temperature dependent and requires serious consideration in practical circuit design. Second, there is a current I_1 composed of electrons flowing from the emitter through the base to the collector. This current is the forward electron current across the emitter junction. Referring to the potential diagram in Fig. 1-20, the electrons in the left-hand n-region that gain enough energy climb over the emitter potential barrier, diffuse through the narrow p-region with negligible loss by recombination, and slide down the collector junction potential barrier into the collector. The magnitude of this current is primarily a function of the height of the emitter junction potential barrier. Third, there is a current I_2 composed of holes flowing from the base to the emitter. The magnitude of this hole current is also governed by the emitter junction potential barrier. The ratio of the magnitudes of the two currents, I_1 and I_2, may be derived theoretically as

$$\frac{I_1}{I_2} = \frac{L\sigma_n}{W\sigma_p} \tag{1-3}$$

where L = diffusion length of a hole in the n-region, W = width of the p-layer, σ_p = conductivity of p-region, σ_n = conductivity of n-region. In a practical transistor, the ratio σ_n/σ_p is deliberately made large to insure that the ratio I_1/I_2 is large. This ratio may exceed 100 in a well-made transistor.

When an input signal is applied to the base, the signal voltage modulates the potential of the base region and thus effectively modulates the potential barrier across the emitter junction. (The collector junction is reverse-biased to saturation by the collector supply voltage, and thus is not materially affected by the small signal voltage.) Assume a positive signal is applied at the base. The signal voltage makes the base region more positive, which effectively lowers the emitter junction potential barrier and allows more electrons to flow over the potential hump and go down to the collector, resulting in an increase of current I_1. At the same time the lowering of the emitter junction potential barrier increases the hole current I_2 by

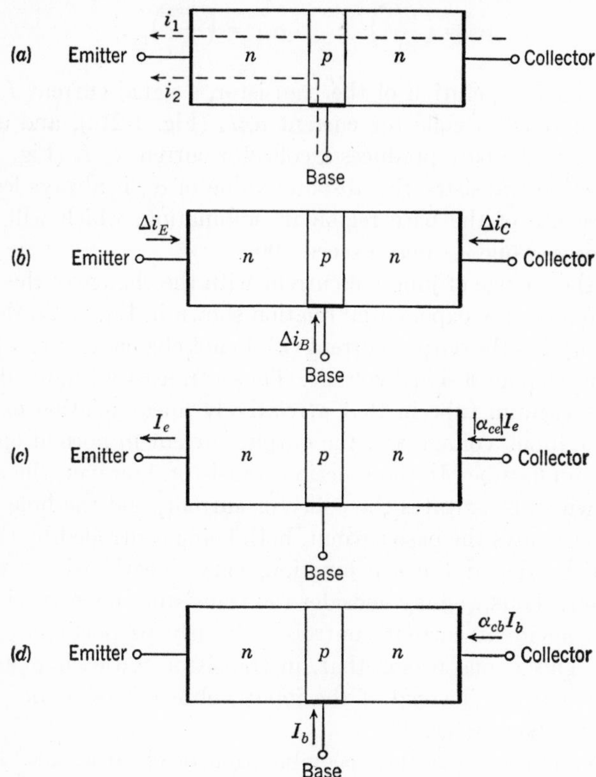

Fig. 1-21. Current relations in a junction transistor.

the same proportion. Thus for a small increment of the input signal voltage the increments of emitter, base, and collector currents are, respectively,

$$\Delta i_E = -(\Delta I_1 + \Delta I_2); \quad \Delta i_B = \Delta I_2 ; \quad \Delta i_C = \Delta I_1$$

where positive current indicates a current flowing into the transistor as is shown in Fig. 1-21b. For a small increment of signal voltage, the relative increments of the three currents are usually expressed by the *collector-to-emitter short-circuit current amplification factor* α_{ce}, and the *collector-to-base short circuit current amplification factor* α_{cb}, where

$$\alpha_{ce} = \left(\frac{\partial i_C}{\partial i_E}\right)_{v_C} ; \qquad \alpha_{cb} = \left(\frac{\partial i_C}{\partial i_B}\right)_{v_C} .$$

Thus, in linear operation of the transistor, a signal current I_e at the emitter produces a collector current $\alpha_{ce}I_e$ (Fig. 1-21c), and a signal current I_b at the base produces a collector current $\alpha_{cb}I_b$ (Fig. 1-21d). In a junction transistor the absolute value of α_{ce} is always less than unity because of the base region recombination, which will be discussed later, while α_{cb} may exceed 100.

Since the change of junction current with the change of the applied voltage follows the exponential relation shown in Eq. (1-2), the input current (i_b) and the output current (i_c) do not change in direct proportion to the change of signal voltage. Thus a transistor is quite different from the vacuum tube in that a relatively linear relation exists between the input voltage and the output current in normal operation of the vacuum tube. In the junction transistor, however, the electron current which constitutes the collector current, and the hole current which constitutes the base current, both being controlled by the same potential barrier at the *n-p* junction, vary linearly with respect to each other. Thus we may consider the transistor an electronic device in which an input current controls a linearly proportionate output current. This is one reason that, in transistor static characteristics, the input current, instead of the input voltage, is generally used as the running parameter.

In a practical transistor, recombination of electrons and holes in the base region affects the operation of the transistor considerably. The effect of carrier recombination in the base region is twofold. A number of the electrons which constitute the electron current I_1 recombine with holes in the base region; hence not all the electrons leaving the emitter reach the collector. Recombination in the base region also causes a hole current to flow from the base terminal into the base region. These effects reduce the efficiency of the transistor, as well as the values of α_{ce} and α_{cb}.

Because of the large collector-to-base current amplification factor, the junction transistor may be operated as a current amplifier. Note that there is a 180° phase shift between the input (base) and the output (collector) voltages in the junction transistor as in the vacuum tube. (We shall see later that the point-contact transistor has the unique property of providing a current gain between the emitter and the collector without phase reversal.) Since the input current and the input impedance are both small, the transistor requires little input power. The output current is relatively large, however, and flows through a high internal impedance; thus the available output power is relatively large. Power gains of as high as 50 db are common with junction transistors which are presently available.

1.13 The point-contact diode

The metal point-contact semiconductor rectifier or, more popularly, the *point-contact diode* or *crystal rectifier*, has been a commercial product well in advance of the invention and subsequent development of the transistor and the junction rectifier. The physical prin-

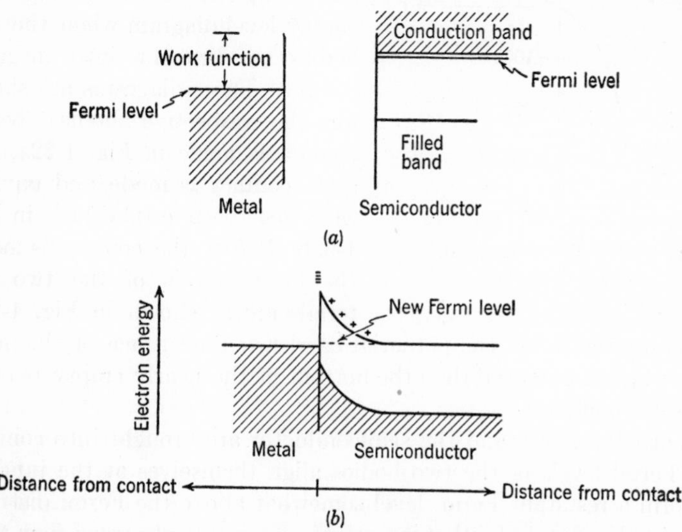

Fig. 1-22. Point-contact diode: (a) metal and semi-conductor before contact; (b) metal to semi-conductor contact after equilibrium is established.

ciples involved in point-contact rectification are, however, closely allied to those principles underlying operation of junction devices which we have discussed here.

We observed that in the case of the semiconductor junction rectifier, and hence the junction transistor as well, operation evolves upon the existence of a potential barrier at the junction of two dissimilar, extrinsic semiconductors. In the junction rectifier the height of this barrier, which controls the flow of electrons and holes, is a function of the voltage applied across the junction. In the junction transistor, the height of a potential barrier is modulated by a signal current which controls the flow of a much larger current across the barrier. The manner by which a potential barrier is formed between a metallic point contact and a semiconductor body is described here.

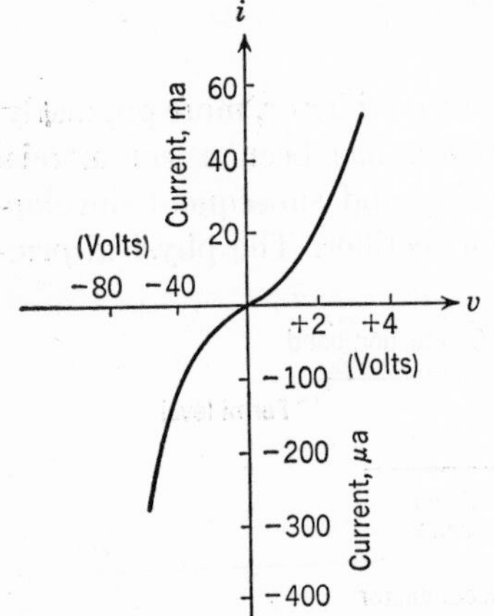

Fig. 1-23. Point-contact diode characteristics.

In the point-contact diode the junction between the metal and the semiconductor, usually *n*-type germanium, may best be described in terms of their respective energy level diagrams and the resultant energy level diagram when the two bodies are brought into intimate contact. These diagrams are shown for the respective bodies before contact is made in Fig. 1-22a, and after contact is made and equilibrium has been established, in Fig. 1-22b. Before the contact is made, the Fermi levels of the two materials are as shown in Fig. 1-22a, assuming the top of the potential barrier at the surface of the metal is at a higher potential than the bottom of the nearly empty band of the semiconductor.

When the metal and the semiconductor are brought into contact, the Fermi levels of the two bodies align themselves at the junction to form a resultant Fermi level somewhat above the Fermi distribution in the metal. In the process of alignment, electrons flow from the semiconductor into the metal. The process continues until a potential barrier formed by the unbalanced donor cores in the semiconductor, and the electrons in the metal at the surface of the junction prevents further flow of electrons. The potential barrier thus created acts precisely as the barrier which is created in the junction of semiconductors. The barrier, however, is not so thick as in the case of a junction made of two semiconductors.

The shape of the voltage-current characteristic of the point contact rectifier is shown in Fig. 1-23. Note that the relationship to the right of the ordinate is again distinctly exponential, since the electrons in the conduction band of the semiconductor follow the Boltzmann distribution of energies. If a reverse potential is applied across the contact, the characteristic is that to the left of the ordinate. For excessively high reverse potential the electric field will cause breakdown resulting in large current flow in the reverse direction.

1.14 The point-contact transistor

The *point-contact transistor* consists of a block of n-type or p-type germanium (which serves as the *base*) and two metallic point contacts in close proximity to one another on the germanium. After a process of forming, one contact whisker serves as the collector and the other

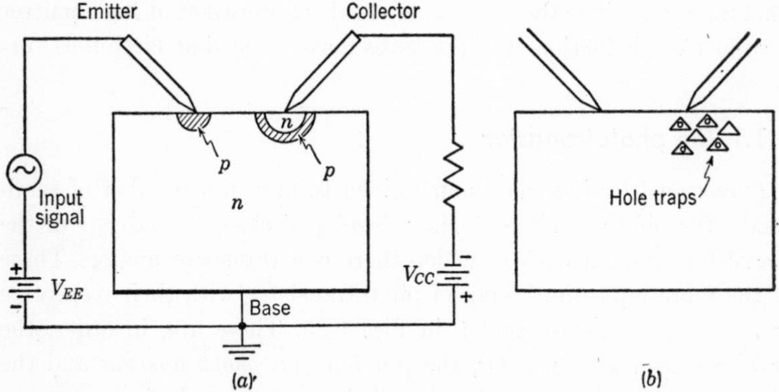

Fig. 1-24. Point-contact transistor: (a) transistor action explained in terms of p-n hook; (b) transistor action explained in terms of hole traps.

serves as the emitter (Fig. 1-24a). (The forming process may consist of the momentary passage of relatively large currents through the collector contact.) With the bias voltage as shown in the diagram for an n-type body, it is observed that there is current amplification between the emitter current and the collector current without phase reversal. One explanation is that, as a result of the forming process, a *p*-type region is formed close to, but not in contact with, the collector. Thus in the neighborhood of the collector there actually is an *n-p-n* configuration. When the input source injects holes through the emitter into the germanium block, the holes flow into the *p*-type region. The hole current acts as the input hole current to an *n-p-n* transistor and results in a larger electron current from base to collector.

Another explanation, which seems to have better experimental verification, is based on the concept of *hole trapping*. It is believed that the forming process creates some imperfections (traps) near the collector point. The trap has the property of capturing a hole and retaining it for an appreciable time before either releasing it or permitting it to recombine with an electron (Fig. 1-24b). The trapped holes around the collector form a cloud of positive "space charges." The longer life of the trapped holes enhances the flow of electrons between the collector and base, resulting in a high collector current. This theory predicts the saturation of collector current at high emitter current as a deduction that the traps may be filled at large hole currents.

1.15 The phototransistor

Phototransistor is a class name given to any of a number of semiconductor photo-sensitive devices developed since the advent of the transistor, and for each of which there is a transistor analog. Three of the more important types of phototransistor with their respective transistor analogs are shown in Fig. 1-25. These are, in order, the *point-contact phototransistor*, the *p-n junction phototransistor* and the *n-p-n junction phototransistor*. In all three of these devices a quanta of light energy, impinging on electrons in the valence band, will raise an electron to the conduction band, leaving behind a hole in the filled band. The effect is described in the energy level diagram of Fig. 1-26.

As we have observed in previous discussions, the operation of transistors evolves upon the injection of minority carriers into germanium. Operation of the phototransistor depends, on the other hand, on the *liberation* of carriers by light energy.

Consider operation of the *p-n* phototransistor of Fig. 1-25. The junction is reverse-biased; that is, a positive d-c voltage is applied to the *n*-side, a negative d-c voltage is applied to the *p*-side. In the absence of light a *dark current* of a few microamperes will flow across the junction. This is the same current that flows across a reverse-biased *p-n* junction diode as a consequence of *thermal liberation* of minority carriers. Light energy incident at, or very near, the *p-n* junction will liberate minority carriers of either sign, which immediately diffuse across the junction, constituting a flow of electric charges. Carriers liberated farther away from the junction, however, tend to recombine before they reach the junction and, hence, do not contribute to the photo current. The absolute quantum yield of the *p-n* phototransistor, hence its sensitivity, is about one electron-hole pair per quantum of light absorbed at the junction.

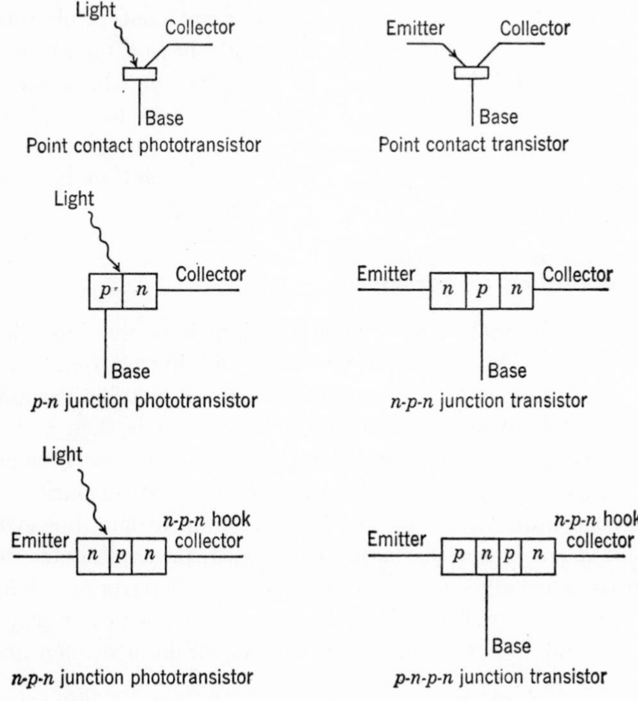

Fig. 1-25. Phototransistors and transistor analogues.

The *n-p-n* junction phototransistor provides a quantum yield of the order of 100 electron-hole pairs per quantum of light absorbed. This is in good agreement with the discussion on the junction transistor, for the effective *n-p-n* configuration provides a current gain of about 100 times the initial photo current.

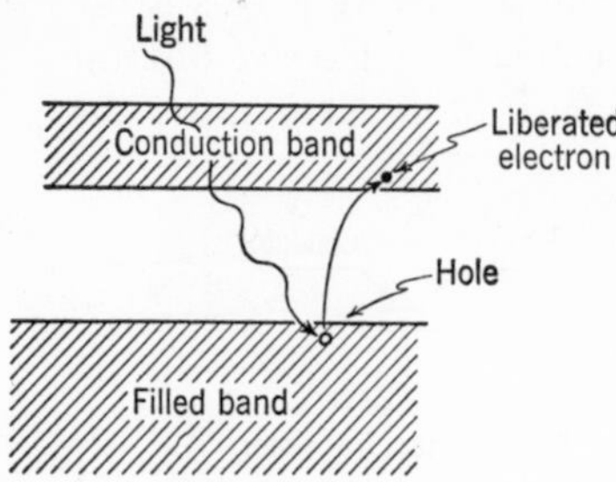

Fig. 1-26. Generation of electrons and holes by light energy.

The point contact phototransistor may have a quantum yield of but two or three electron-hole pairs per light quantum; this again is in general agreement with point-contact transistor theory.

1.16 Preparation of germanium

At present the main source of germanium is germanium dioxide, which is obtained as a by-product of zinc mining or from coal ash. The dioxide is first reduced to a powder form of metallic germanium by firing in a hydrogen atmosphere. The powder is then melted at a higher temperature and formed into ingots. The raw germanium ingot, at this point in the refining process, may have a purity of the order of one impurity atom to 10^7 germanium atoms; however, as was pointed out in the discussion of physical principles, this degree of impurity is usually unacceptable for transistor purposes. A higher degree of purification is required. Purification of the elementary pure ingot and growth of the single crystal germanium specimen are obtained as follows:

The ingot is placed in a special hydrogen atmosphere furnace, and heat is applied to one end of the ingot by induction heating. After this end has become molten the induction coil is moved slowly toward the other end of the ingot, causing progressively more distant points from the original end to become molten and then to solidify after the heating has passed on. The impurity elements tend to remain in the liquid part rather than in the solid, and hence are effectively swept to the end of the ingot as the heated section is progressively moved from one end to the other. This process may be repeated as often as necessary until the desired degree of purification has been obtained. Germanium prepared in this manner may contain as little as one impurity atom for each 10^9 germanium atoms.

The germanium ingot, while now quite pure, is in a polycrystalline form, while as we have seen above, single-crystal germanium is required for transistor applications. The purified germanium ingot is

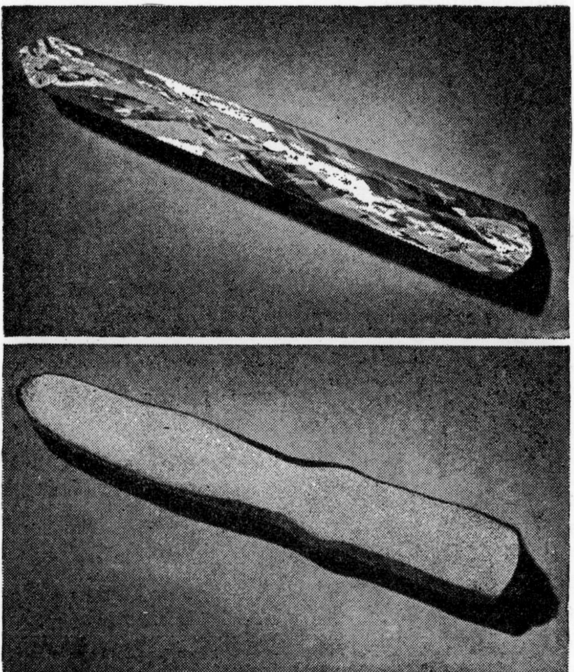

Fig. 1-27. Polycrystalline ingot (top) and monocrystalline ingot (bottom). (*Courtesy Radio Corporation of America.*)

once more subjected to firing in a graphite crucible in a hydrogen atmosphere. Once a melt has been obtained, a single crystal "seed" is introduced into the melt and then withdrawn at the rate of a fraction of an inch per minute, in an environment of constant temperature.

As the original seed is withdrawn from the melt it grows into a large, rodlike single crystal specimen, from which sufficient germanium for several thousands of transistors may be obtained. Figure 1-27 shows photographs of both a polycrystalline ingot and a monocrystalline ingot. The grain boundaries in the polycrystalline ingot are clearly visible. One more step in purification is obtained in this process, since the solidified crystal tends to leave the impurities in the melt. Donor or acceptor impurity of any appropriate amount may be added to the melt to obtain *n*-type or *p*-type germanium in the original "pure" single crystal specimen.

1.17 Junction transistor construction

Two general methods of junction transistor manufacture are in common practice. The first consists of growing a single crystal with alternate *n*, *p*, and *n* layers, or *p*, *n*, and *p* layers. The *p*-type and *n*-type layers are obtained by controlling the nature and the degree of impurity in the melt at different states of the crystal withdrawal. The crystal is then cut into pieces perpendicular to the layers to form *n-p-n* or *p-n-p* transistors such as are shown in Fig. 1-28. Metallic contacts are then soldered or plated to the three regions to which the leads are attached. After leads have been attached, the unit is encased and sealed against contamination and the effect of light.

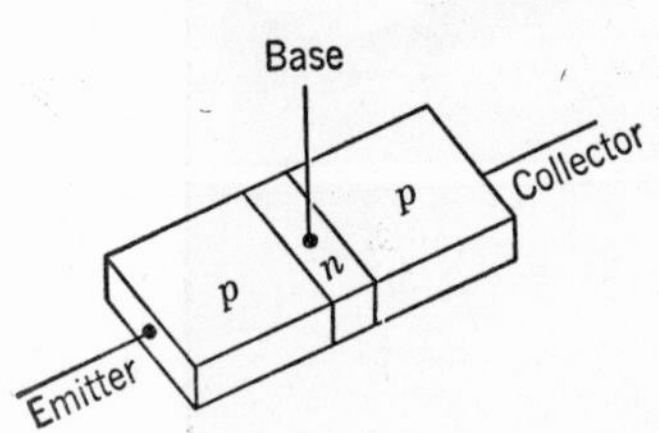

Fig. 1-28. Construction of a *p-n-p* junction transistor made by the crystal growing process.

The second method of junction transistor construction involves the alloying of impurity elements into opposing sides of a thin slab of single crystal germanium. The original slab is chosen to be either *n*-type or *p*-type germanium; acceptor elements may then be alloyed into the opposing sides of the *n*-type specimen to form a *p-n-p* transistor, or donor elements may be alloyed into the opposing sides of the *p*-type specimen to form an *n-p-n* transistor. The physical construction of a junction transistor made by the alloying process is shown in Fig. 1-29. Typical examples of the construction of alloy junction transistors are as follows.

In a *p-n-p* transistor the center piece is a thin wafer of *n*-type single-crystal germanium. Two indium disks are attached to opposing sides of the germanium wafer and the combined structure is placed in a furnace heated to a temperature just high enough to melt the indium disks. The molten indium dissolves the germanium slowly. After an appropriate time interval the structure is cooled to allow germanium to recrystallize out from the indium solution. The recrystallized germanium, with its indium content, forms a p-region on each side of the n-type germanium. The emitter is made the smaller of the two indium disks to insure a high degree of collection at the collector of those carriers leaving the emitter.

In the n-p-n junction transistor, the center piece is p-type single-crystal germanium, as for example, indium-doped germanium; and the two n-regions are formed by alloying donor impurities, say antimony, into the opposite sides of the p-type wafer.

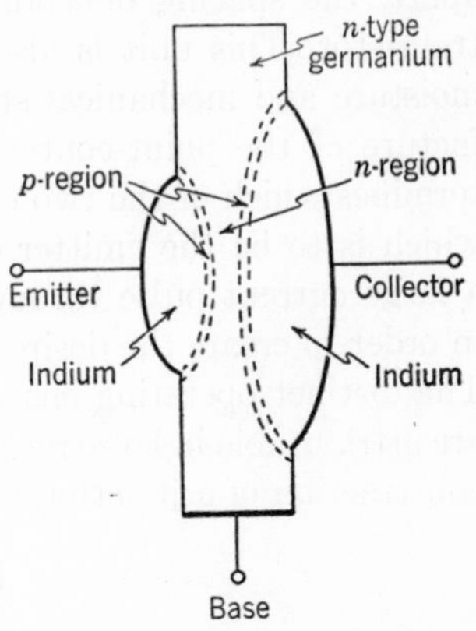

Fig. 1-29. Construction of a p-n-p junction transistor made by the alloy process.

1.18 Point-contact transistor construction

The construction of a point contact transistor is shown in Fig. 1-30a. A pellet of germanium is first soldered to a metal support,

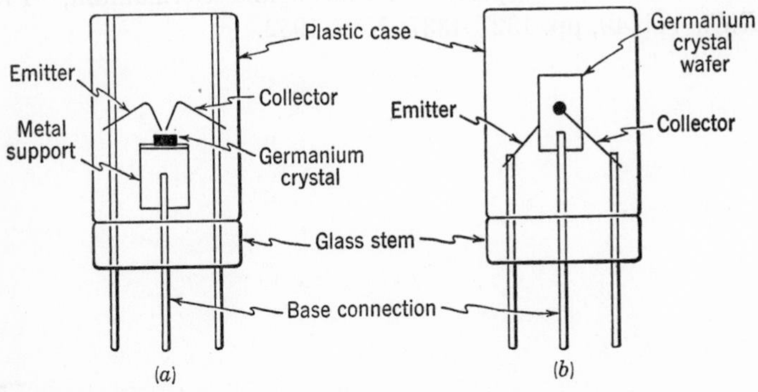

Fig. 1-30. (a) Point-contact transistor; (b) junction transistor. (*Courtesy Radio Corporation of America.*)

which in turn is soldered or welded to the base lead. Two metallic point contacts, or "cat whiskers," are then pressed firmly to the surface of the germanium block, spaced a few thousandths of an inch apart, the spacing depending on the desired characteristics of the transistor. This unit is also encased as a means of protection from moisture and mechanical shock. A final step required in the manufacture of the point-contact transistor is *forming*. This process determines which of the two contacts is to be the collector element and which is to be the emitter element. The process consists of passing a large current pulse through the point assigned to be the collector in order to create the desired imperfections in the germanium crystal. The distinct operating characteristics of the point-contact transistor are attributable in large measure to the forming process. The physical construction of a junction transistor is shown in Fig. 1-30b.

REFERENCES

1. W. Shockley, "Transistor Electronics: Imperfections, Unipolar, and Analog Transistors," *Proc. I.R.E.*, Vol. 40, pp. 1289–1313, Nov. 1952.
2. W. Shockley, "Electrons and Holes in Semiconductors," D. Van Nostrand Co., Inc., New York, 1950.
3. J. Bardeen and W. H. Brattain, "Physical Principles Involved in Transistor Action," *Phys. Rev.*, Vol. 75, p. 1208, 1949.
4. E. M. Conwell, "Properties of Silicon and Germanium," *Proc. I.R.E.*, Vol. 40, pp. 1327–1337, Nov. 1952.

Chapter 2

CHARACTERISTICS, PARAMETERS, EQUIVALENT CIRCUITS

2.1 Introduction

A general description of the physical concepts of transistor operation has been given in the first chapter. We shall proceed in this chapter to treat the transistor as a linear, active, three-terminal circuit element which is subject to the mathematical analysis of four-terminal network theory. The transistor will be treated here as a linear element; nonlinear operation of the transistor will be taken up in later chapters. A detailed description is given first of the static characteristics of the transistor and the low-frequency parameters which may be derived from these characteristics. This is followed by a discussion of equivalent circuits, and certain approximations which may be introduced to simplify such circuits. A systematic analysis of the transistor as a linear four-terminal network is included, and the general principles of complementary symmetry are developed. The major portion of this chapter deals with junction transistors, while point-contact transistors are treated in the last two sections.

2.2 The transistor as a circuit element

The transistor, as a circuit element, may be represented by its terminal voltage and current relations, which completely define its electrical performance. The most common transistors, the triodes, have three terminals; the *base*, the *emitter*, and the *collector*. Some other types have additional terminals in which no signal energy is normally intended to flow. Hence, these additional terminals are usually ignored in small signal linear analysis. Graphical symbols for the common transistor types are shown in Fig. 2-1.

A new symbol is introduced to represent the junction transistor in order to avoid confusion with the point-contact transistor, whose properties and circuit operation are markedly different from those of the junction transistor. The symbol is of the building block type, and can be extended to represent new devices as they are developed. It is seen that the arrow symbol for the emitter is retained, the direction of the arrow indicating the direction of relatively easy current flow across the emitter junction. The collector symbol is nonpolarized to avoid ambiguity with the emitter symbol.

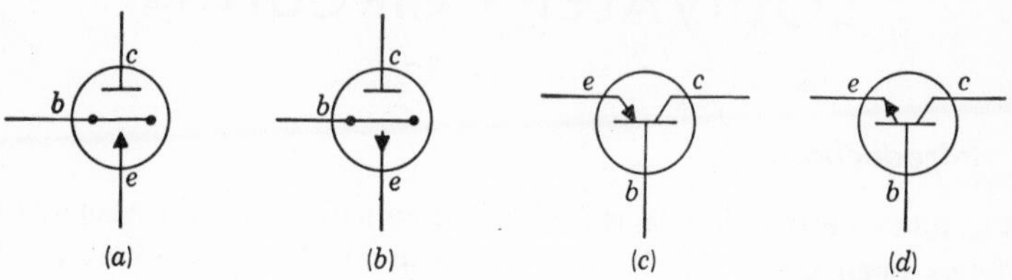

Fig. 2-1. Graphical symbols: (a) *p-n-p* junction transistor; (b) *n-p-n* junction transistor; (c) *n*-type point-contact transistor; (d) *p*-type point-contact transistor.

The electrical behavior of a three-terminal device may be described by the three currents i_1, i_2, i_3 flowing in the terminals, and the three voltages v_1, v_2, v_3 across successive terminal pairs. Only two currents and two voltages need be specified, however, since

$$i_1 + i_2 + i_3 = 0 \tag{2-1}$$

$$v_1 + v_2 + v_3 = 0 \tag{2-2}$$

When the transistor is used as an amplifier, one terminal becomes the input terminal, another becomes the output terminal, and the third terminal is common to input and output circuits. The two currents of interest then are the input and output currents, and the two voltages specified are those existing between the input terminal and the common terminal, and between the output terminal and the common terminal. These currents and voltages, and their assumed positive directions, are shown in Fig. 2-2.

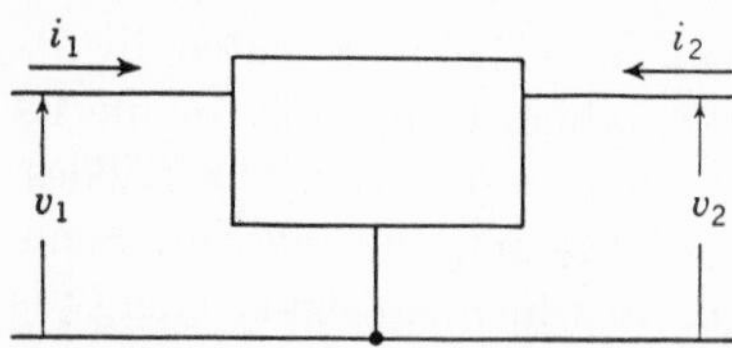

Fig. 2-2. Assumed positive directions of currents and voltages in a four-terminal network.

Each of the three transistor leads may in turn be assigned as the common or grounded terminal, which gives rise to three basic circuit configurations of the transistors, designated as the *common-emitter*, *common-base* and *common-collector* configurations. These configurations are also referred to as the *grounded-emitter*, *grounded-base* and *grounded-collector* circuits. To describe its performance, each configuration uses a different set of four of the six variables given in Eqs. (2-1) and (2-2). The three configurations with corresponding input and output currents and voltages are shown in Fig. 2-3. These three configurations are also referred to as the basic amplifying circuits. In the junction transistor, power gain is realized in only one direction through the device; and in this direction the base must always be one of the two input terminals, and the collector must always be one of the two output terminals. As drawn, therefore, the input is always on the left and the output is on the right in the diagrams of Fig. 2-3.

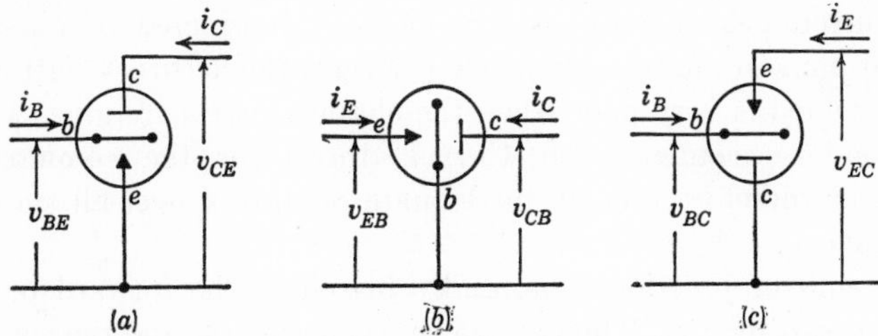

Fig. 2-3. The three basic circuit configurations of the junction transistor.

Graphical characteristics and equivalent circuits are useful aids in understanding the performance of an active device. There are many possible sets of characteristic curves which can be drawn for the transistor. The final choice of a set of characteristics will be based upon the accuracy with which these characteristics can present the required data about the device, and upon the general usefulness of the characteristics in circuit design.

2.3 Junction transistor characteristic curves; general considerations

The relation between the input and output currents and voltages may be represented by a minimum of two sets of characteristic curves for any one of the three transistor configurations, since all other curves may be derived from these two. It is desirable at the outset, therefore, to select those curves which describe the transistor most accurately, and to determine which of the three basic configurations offers the best indication of transistor performance.

In the junction transistor, most of the conduction carriers which are injected by the emitter reach the collector. This means that the base current is small compared with the emitter and collector currents. The base current is an important quantity however, since it is the input current of both the common-emitter and the common-collector circuits as shown in Fig. 2-3. If the two currents specified by the characteristic curves are the emitter and the collector current, as in the case of the common-base configuration, the base current is found by Eq. (2-1) to be

$$i_B = -(i_E + i_C) \tag{2-3}$$

Since i_E and i_C are of opposite polarity (following the convention that currents flowing into the device are considered positive) and differ in magnitude by only a few per cent, the accuracy with which i_B is specified is very poor when the characteristics are given for the common-base configuration. Curves drawn for the common-base transistor therefore give an inadequate picture of over-all transistor performance.

The emitter junction is normally biased in the forward or high-conduction direction. The voltage between the base and the emitter is therefore low compared with the voltage across the collector junction, which is biased in the reverse direction. The collector-to-emitter voltage is the sum of these two voltages, and is practically equal to the voltage across the collector junction. If these latter two voltages are given by the characteristic curves, as they are in the case of the common-collector stage, the voltage between the base and the emitter is given by the small difference between these two large quantities, and cannot be determined accurately. Therefore curves drawn for the transistor in the common-collector configuration are also inadequate to accurately describe over-all transistor performance.

Curves drawn for the transistor in the common-emitter configuration specify the values of base current and base-to-emitter voltage explicitly; therefore they are capable of giving all six quantities of Eqs. (2-1) and (2-2) most accurately. Accordingly, the curves for the common-base and the common-collector configurations of the transistor can be derived accurately from curves of the common-emitter configuration, while the reverse is not usually true. Thus best accuracy of representation is obtained when the common-emitter configuration is used to obtain the characteristics of the junction transistor.

The available power gain of the transistor in the common-emitter configuration is higher than it is in either of the other two configurations. This follows qualitatively from the fact that input voltage and current are small in the common-emitter amplifier. Other unique features of the common-emitter stage are its phase-reversal property, and the fact that the current gain and voltage gain can simultaneously be greater than unity. These properties make the common-emitter stage more widely used than the other circuit configurations, so that common-emitter characteristics not only give the most accurate information about the transistor, but are generally most useful in practice.

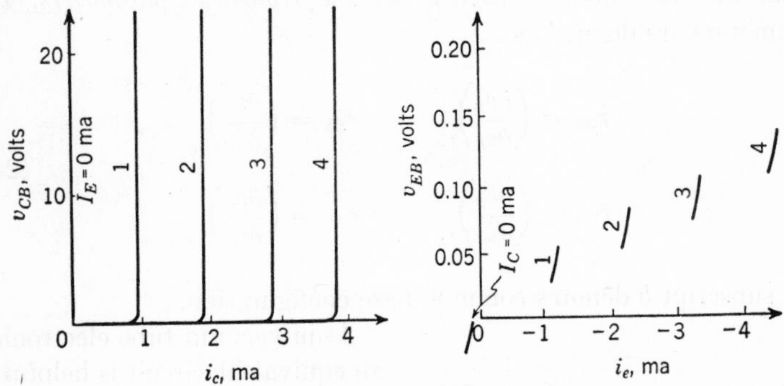

Fig. 2-4. Characteristics of an *n-p-n* junction transistor in the common-base connection.

2.4 Common-base characteristics

In the previous section, the common-emitter characteristic is shown to represent the transistor more accurately than either of the other two characteristics. The common-base characteristics, however, were used extensively in the earlier days, and certain transistor parameters derived from these characteristics still are often referred to in the literature. A brief description of the common-base characteristics is given in this section before going into detailed discussion of the common-emitter characteristics.

The set of common-base characteristics most often used to represent a transistor is shown in Fig. 2-4. Input and output currents are considered as the independent variables; the latter is plotted along the abscissa, and the former becomes the running parameter in these characteristics. Prior to the development of the junction transistor, most point-contact transistors were "short-circuit unstable", so that characteristics were measured by applying currents to the transistor terminals from energizing sources of high impedance. The currents acted as the controlling quantities, and consequently they were considered the independent variables of both the output and input circuits.

A set of low-frequency four-terminal network parameters may be derived from the set of characteristics shown in Fig. 2-4. The set of parameters commonly used is the *low-frequency z parameters.* The parameters are defined as

$$r_{11b} = \left(\frac{\partial v_E}{\partial i_E}\right)_{I_C} \qquad r_{21b} = \left(\frac{\partial v_C}{\partial i_E}\right)_{I_C}$$
$$r_{12b} = \left(\frac{\partial v_E}{\partial i_C}\right)_{I_E} \qquad r_{22b} = \left(\frac{\partial v_C}{\partial i_C}\right)_{I_E} \tag{2-4}$$

The subscript b denotes common-base configuration.

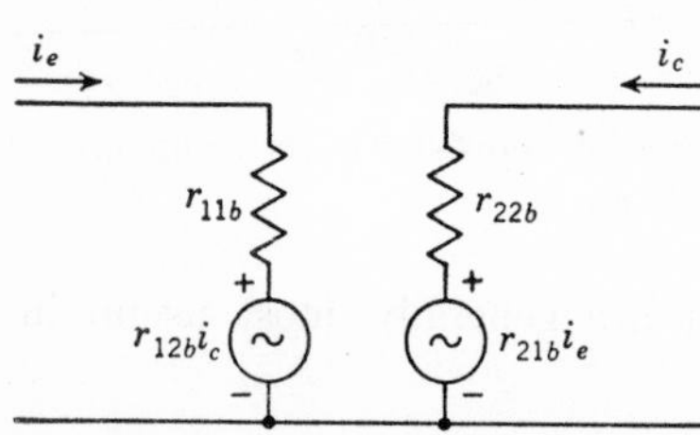

Fig. 2-5. Two-generator equivalent circuit for the common-base transistor.

As in vacuum tube electronics, an equivalent circuit is helpful in analyzing the performance of a transistor. Detailed discussion of transistor equivalent circuits is given in later sections. We shall at present examine a few commonly used equivalent circuits to illustrate the relation between static characteristics and transistor equivalent circuit parameters.

A two-generator common-base equivalent circuit is shown in Fig. 2-5. The resistance parameters r_{11b}, r_{12b}, r_{21b}, and r_{22b} are adopted directly in this equivalent circuit as shown in the figure. Another equivalent circuit, commonly known as the basic T equivalent circuit, is shown in Fig. 2-6a. A new set of equivalent circuit parameters, known as the *common-base T equivalent circuit parameters*, is used here. The relation bweeten the two sets of parameters are as follows:

$$\begin{aligned} r_e &= r_{11b} - r_{12b}, && \text{the emitter resistance} \\ r_b &= r_{12b}, && \text{the base resistance} \\ r_c &= r_{22b} - r_{12b}, && \text{the collector resistance} \\ r_m &= r_{21b} - r_{12b}, && \text{the mutual resistance} \end{aligned} \tag{2-5}$$

These new parameters may therefore be computed from the characteristics of Fig. 2-4. Another form of the basic T equivalent circuit is shown in Fig. 2-6b in which a current generator in parallel with the collector resistance replaces the voltage generator in series with the

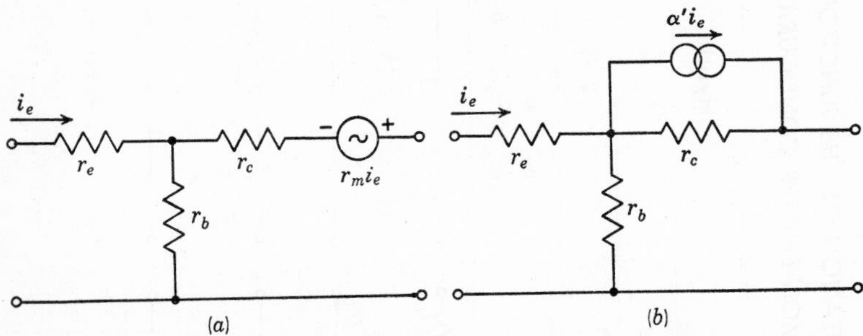

Fig. 2-6. T equivalent circuits for the common-base transistor: (a) voltage generator; (b) current generator.

collector resistance of Fig. 2-6a. This current generator delivers a constant current of amplitude $\alpha' i_E$, where α' is called the *generator current amplification factor*, and is defined, at low frequency, as

$$\alpha' \equiv \frac{r_{21b} - r_{12b}}{r_{22b} - r_{12b}} = \frac{r_m}{r_c} \tag{2-6}$$

It is to be noted that another parameter, the *short-circuit current amplification factor* α, is often used as an approximation of the amplification factor α'. The short-circuit current amplification factor α is defined, at low frequency, as

$$\alpha \equiv \frac{r_{21b}}{r_{22b}} = \frac{r_m + r_b}{r_c + r_b}$$

Table 2-1.

FUNCTIONAL REPRESENTATION OF THE JUNCTION TRANSISTOR IN THE COMMON-EMITTER CONFIGURATION

Parameter	Impedance	Hybrid	Admittance
Independent variables	$i_B,\ i_C$	$i_B,\ v_C$	$v_B,\ v_C$
Dependent variables	$v_B,\ v_C$	$v_B,\ i_C$	$i_B,\ i_C$
Equations	$v_B = r_{11}i_b + r_{12}i_c$ $v_C = r_{21}i_b + r_{22}i_c$	$v_B = h_{11}i_b + h_{12}v_c$ $i_C = h_{21}i_b + h_{22}v_c$	$i_B = g_{11}v_b + g_{12}v_c$ $i_C = g_{21}v_b + g_{22}v_c$
Two-generator equivalent circuit	B, r_{11}, $r_{12}i_c$, R_{22}, $r_{21}i_b$	h_{11}, $h_{12}v_c$, $h_{21}i_b$, h_{22}	g_{11}, $g_{12}v_2$, $g_{21}v_1$, g_{22}
One-generator equivalent circuit	r_b, r_e, r_d, $r_m i_b$	$\frac{1}{g_{11}} - r_e$, r_e, r_d, $\alpha_{cb}\, i_b$	g_{be}, g_{bc}, g_{ce}, $g_m v_b$
Relationship between parameters of two- and one-generator circuits	$r_b = r_{11} - r_{12}$ $r_e = r_{12}$ $r_d = r_{22} - r_{12}$ $r_m = r_{12} - r_{21}$	$(1/g_{11}) - r_e = h_{11} - (h_{12}/h_{22})$ $r_e = h_{12}/h_{22}$ $r_d = 1/h_{22}$ $\alpha_{cb} = h_{21}$	$g_{be} = g_{11} + g_{12}$ $g_{bc} = -g_{12}$ $g_{ce} = g_{22} + g_{12}$ $g_m = g_{21} + g_{12}$

Table 2-1 (concluded)

Parameter	Impedance	Hybrid	Admittance
Typical values	$r_b = 370$ ohms $r_e = 23$ ohms $r_d = 58$ K $r_m = 3$ meg.	$(1/g_{11}) - r_e = 1520$ ohms $r_e = 23$ ohms $r_d = 40$ K $\alpha_{cb} = 49$	$g_{be} = 0.64 \times 10^{-3}$ mho $g_{bc} = 0.25 \times 10^{-6}$ mho $g_{ce} = 0.40 \times 10^{-6}$ mho $g_m = 0.033$ mho
Output circuit characteristics	v_c, I_B, i_c	i_c, I_B, v_c	i_c, V_B, v_c
Input circuit characteristics	v_B, I_c, i_B	v_B, V_C, i_B	i_B, V_C, v_B

The amplification factors α and α' are related by the expression

$$\alpha' = \alpha + \frac{r_b}{r_c}(\alpha - 1)$$

In the linear operation region, where $r_c \gg r_b$, there is little difference between the values of α and α'; and they are often used indiscriminately for each other. The reader will notice that the common-base T equivalent circuit parameters, r_e, r_b, r_c, and r_m (or α), have been used extensively in the literature as basic transistor constants, especially in the earlier work.

The relative sense of the input current i_e and the current generator $\alpha' i_e$ is indicated in Fig. 2-6. Occasionally the term α_{ce} is also used in transistor circuitry work. The definitions of α_{ce} and α'_{ce} are

$$\alpha_{ce} \equiv -\alpha, \qquad \alpha'_{ce} \equiv -\alpha'$$

2.5 Common-emitter characteristics; z parameters

In the common-emitter configuration, the general expression governing the terminal voltages and currents is

$$f(i_B, i_C, v_B, v_C) = 0$$

where i_B and i_C are the input and output currents, and v_B and v_C are the input and output voltages, respectively. The relationship of the four variables in low-frequency operation may be expressed graphically in a set of characteristics. If two of the four variables are taken at a time as the independent variables, there are six possible combinations, yielding six sets of characteristics. Two of these combinations are rarely used in ordinary analysis (those which treat both the current and voltage of either the input circuit or the output circuit as the independent variables), and another has little use for transistors (the one which treats v_B and i_C as independent variables). The remaining three combinations of independent variables are commonly used in the representation of the transistor; they are outlined in Table 2-1. The three sets of characteristic curves drawn in accordance with the choice of independent variables are shown at the bottom of the table. One independent variable is plotted along the abscissa, and the other independent variable serves as the running parameter. The *open-circuit impedance parameters* (the z parameters), the *short-circuit admittance parameters* (the y parameters), and the *hybrid parameters* (the h parameters) are also listed in the table; their low-frequency values can be readily derived from the respective set of characteristic curves.

In this section let us consider the currents i_B and i_C as the independent variables and the voltages v_B and v_C as the dependent variables. Two functional relationships may be written

$$v_B = f_1(i_B, i_C) \tag{2-7}$$

$$v_C = f_2(i_B, i_C) \tag{2-8}$$

A set of *collector characteristics* as shown in Fig. 2-7a represents graphically the function of Eq. (2-8). These curves are also termed

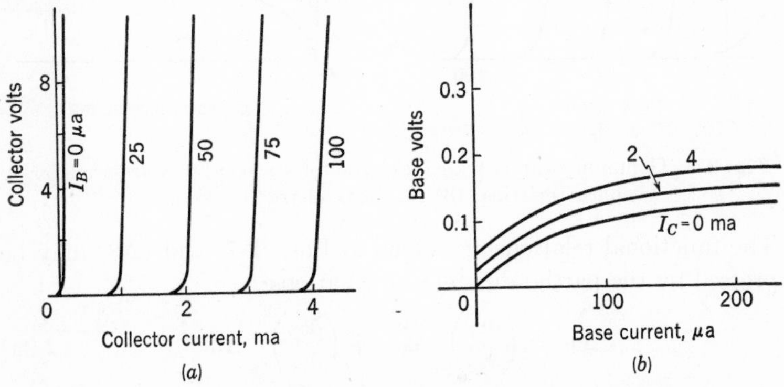

Fig. 2-7. Common-emitter static characteristics: (a) collector characteristics; (b) base characteristics.

the *output static characteristics*, each curve in the family representing the voltage-current characteristic of the output circuit for one quiescent value of the independent variable of the input circuit. The *base characteristics* of Fig. 2-7b, representing the function of Eq. (2-7), are usually referred to as the *input static characteristics.*

These two sets of characteristics are sufficient for the complete specification of the electrical behavior of the transistor at low frequency. As a matter of convenience, the functions of Eqs. (2-7) and (2-8) may be replotted, still using the dependent voltages along the ordinate, but exchanging the roles of the two independent variables. The resulting curves are termed the *transfer characteristics* of the input and output circuits, and are shown in Fig. 2-8. The curves resulting from Eq. (2-8) are termed the *forward transfer characteristics*, and the curves resulting from a plot of Eq. (2-7) are called the *backward transfer*, or *feedback characteristics*. These curves will be used occasionally where the collector and base characteristics fail to give a clear picture of the action of a circuit.

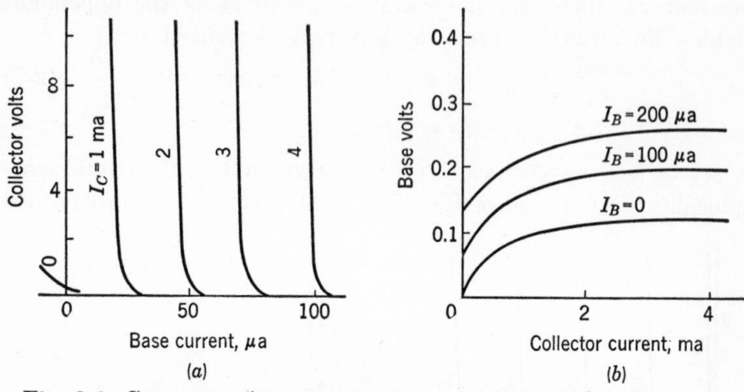

Fig. 2-8. Common-emitter transfer characteristics: (a) forward transfer characteristics; (b) feedback characteristics.

The functional relationships given in Eqs. (2-7) and (2-8) may be expressed by the partial differential equations:

$$\Delta v_B = \left(\frac{\partial v_B}{\partial i_B}\right)_{I_C} \Delta i_B + \left(\frac{\partial v_B}{\partial i_C}\right)_{I_B} \Delta i_C \tag{2-9a}$$

$$\Delta v_C = \left(\frac{\partial v_C}{\partial i_B}\right)_{I_C} \Delta i_B + \left(\frac{\partial v_C}{\partial i_C}\right)_{I_B} \Delta i_C \tag{2-9b}$$

For small-signal operation, where the excursion of the voltages and currents is limited to a linear region around the quiescent operating point, the partial differentials in Eqs. (2-9a) and (2-9b) are constants. These constants are called the *common-emitter z parameters* of the transistor, and they are defined as

$$z_{11e} = \left(\frac{\partial v_B}{\partial i_B}\right)_{I_C}, \quad \text{the input impedance with output open}$$

$$z_{12e} = \left(\frac{\partial v_B}{\partial i_C}\right)_{I_B}, \quad \text{the reverse transfer impedance with input open}$$

$$z_{21e} = \left(\frac{\partial v_C}{\partial i_B}\right)_{I_C}, \quad \text{the forward transfer impedance with output open} \tag{2-10}$$

$$z_{22e} = \left(\frac{\partial v_C}{\partial i_C}\right)_{I_B}, \quad \text{the output impedance with input open}$$

where the subscript e denotes the common emitter configuration. In low-frequency operation these parameters become purely resistive in nature; and they are called the *common-emitter resistance parameters* r_{11e}, r_{12e}, r_{21e}, and r_{22e}. The resistance parameters may be readily derived from the slopes of the four characteristic curves of Fig. 2-7 and Fig. 2-8.

The resistance parameters of the common-emitter configuration are, of course, different from those of the other two configurations. Conversion may be made from one system to the other, as will be shown in a later section.

2.6 Common-emitter characteristics; y parameters

In the preceding section, the currents i_B and i_C were taken as the independent or controlling variables of the transistor characteristics. An alternative representation of the transistor may be made by taking the voltages v_B and v_C as independent variables, and the currents i_B and i_C as dependent variables. Such treatment leads to the representation of the transistor in terms of *common-emitter y parameters*. The y parameters are defined as

$$y_{11e} = \left(\frac{\partial i_B}{\partial v_B}\right)_{V_C}, \quad \text{the input admittance with output short-circuited}$$

$$y_{12e} = \left(\frac{\partial i_B}{\partial v_C}\right)_{V_B}, \quad \text{the reverse transfer admittance with input short-circuited}$$

$$y_{21e} = \left(\frac{\partial i_C}{\partial v_B}\right)_{V_C}, \quad \text{the forward transfer admittance with output short-circuited} \tag{2-11}$$

$$y_{22e} = \left(\frac{\partial i_C}{\partial v_C}\right)_{V_B}, \quad \text{the output admittance with input short-circuited}$$

In an analysis of the mechanism of transistors this representation has been found to possess certain advantages over the z parameter representation. This will be developed further in Chapter 8. In low-frequency operation, to which we limit the present discussion, the y parameters do not appear to offer any distinct advantages over the z parameters in the functional representation of a transistor. A brief description of y parameter representation is summarized in Table 2-1.

2.7 Common-emitter characteristics; h parameters

Before introducing the h-parameters, we shall consider the relative merits of the alternative choices of independent variables in transistor functional representation.

The validity of treating the voltages as the independent variables in transistor circuits at low frequencies will bear some thought. The collector circuit is usually a high-impedance circuit compared with the internal resistance of the energizing source feeding the collector. Consequently, it would seem that the collector voltage is more easily controlled than is the collector current, so that the collector voltage rather than current is more naturally the independent variable. The reason for this is a practical one, since energizing sources which are applied to the collector circuit usually provide relatively constant voltage, as in the case of batteries or rectified energy from the power line.

The base input circuit, on the other hand, presents a different problem. The input resistance of the transistor is low compared with the output resistance, and in fact, is often low compared with the internal resistance of a bias supply connected to the base. It is therefore considerably more difficult to control the input or base-to-emitter voltage than it is to control the base current. In addition, the output voltage and current are nonlinear functions of the base voltage, as mentioned in Chapter 1. Thus a signal from a source of low impedance compared with the impedance of the base circuit will be reproduced with considerable distortion in the output circuit.[1]

A good dual analogy exists between the transistor and the vacuum triode in this respect. The base current in the transistor, and the grid voltage in a tube are the natural controlling quantities, or independent variables. Generally speaking, the tube grid and cathode may be considered as forming a diode which is biased in the reverse direction. Thus the grid voltage is easily controlled, while the grid current is not. The transistor base and emitter, on the other hand, form the elements of a diode which is biased in the forward direction, so that the *current* is easily controlled, while the voltage is not. The output response of a tube to a sinusoidal grid current is nonsinusoidal, as is the output response of the transistor to a sinusoidal base voltage. Hence the roles of current and voltage may be considered to be interchanged in the input circuits of the tube and the transistor.

[1] This statement applies mainly to low-current operation of the transistor. At high values of collector current, several factors modify the characteristics, so that in some cases the output response to base voltage may actually be more nearly linear than the response to base current. These factors will be discussed in greater detail in Chapter 6.

In many ways, therefore, the "natural" independent variables of transistor operation are the collector voltage and the base current. This results in the representation of the transistor by the hybrid parameters.

With the collector voltage v_C and the base current i_B taken as the independent variables in the operation of the transistor in the common-emitter configuration, the two functional relationships for the input and output circuits become

$$v_B = f_1(i_B, v_C) \tag{2-12}$$

$$i_C = f_2(i_B, v_C) \tag{2-13}$$

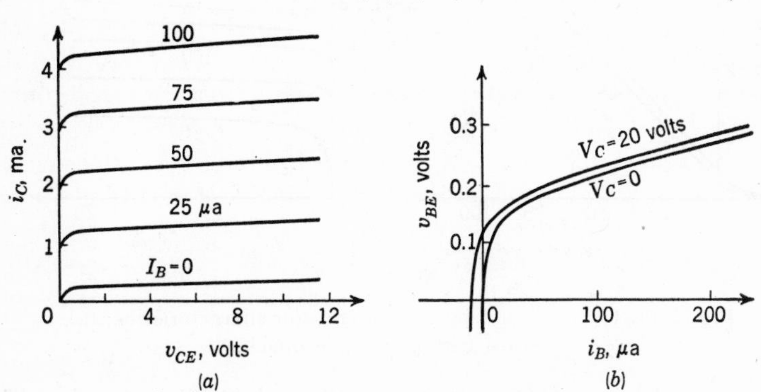

Fig. 2-9. Common-emitter hybrid characteristics: (a) collector characteristics; (b) base characteristics.

In accordance with these equations, the *collector characteristics* are now drawn with collector current along the ordinate, since this is the dependent variable. These characteristics are shown in Fig. 2-9a and are seen to be identical with those of Fig. 2-7, except that the collector voltage and current axes are interchanged. The *base characteristics* are shown in Fig. 2-9b. These characteristics are different from those of Fig. 2-7b in that the collector voltage rather than the collector current is the running parameter. Note particularly that the slope of these curves is greater than the slope of the curves of Fig. 2-7b, indicating that the short-circuit input resistance is greater than the open-circuit input resistance.

The *forward transfer characteristics*, shown in Fig. 2-10a, are found by plotting the collector current *vs.* the base current at various constant values of collector voltage. The slope of these curves is the short-circuit current amplification factor.

The *backward transfer* or *feedback characteristics* shown in Fig. 2-10b give the voltage which appears at the base when a given voltage is applied to the collector at constant values of base current. The slope of these curves is the open-circuit voltage amplification factor in the reverse direction, and is small compared with unity.

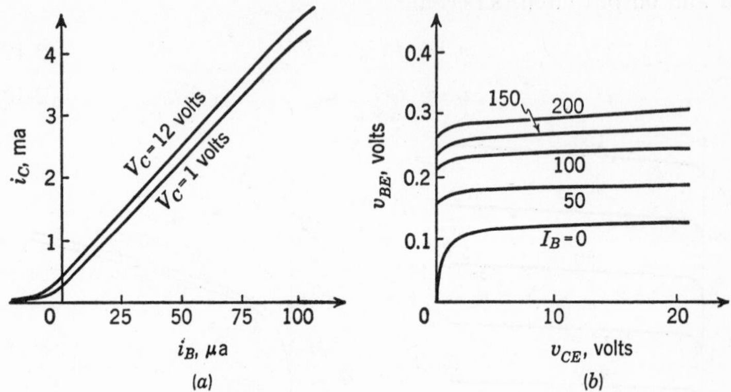

Fig. 2-10. Common-emitter hybrid transfer characteristics: (a) forward transfer; (b) feedback.

Analytically, by expressing Eqs. (2-12) and (2-13) as partial differential equations, we have

$$\Delta v_B = \left(\frac{\partial v_B}{\partial i_B}\right)_{V_C} \Delta i_B + \left(\frac{\partial v_B}{\partial v_C}\right)_{I_B} \Delta v_C \tag{2-14}$$

$$\Delta i_C = \left(\frac{\partial i_C}{\partial i_B}\right)_{V_C} \Delta i_B + \left(\frac{\partial i_C}{\partial v_C}\right)_{I_B} \Delta v_C \tag{2-15}$$

The *common-emitter h parameters* are defined as

$$\left(\frac{\partial v_B}{\partial i_B}\right)_{V_C} = h_{11e} = \frac{1}{y_{11e}}, \quad \text{the input impedance with output shorted}$$

$$\left(\frac{\partial v_B}{\partial v_C}\right)_{I_B} = h_{12e} = \mu_{bc}, \quad \text{the reverse open-circuit voltage amplification factor}$$

$$\left(\frac{\partial i_C}{\partial i_B}\right)_{V_C} = h_{21e} = \alpha_{cb}, \quad \text{the forward short-circuit current amplication factor} \tag{2-16}$$

$$\left(\frac{\partial i_C}{\partial v_C}\right)_{I_B} = h_{22e} = \frac{1}{z_{22e}}, \quad \text{the output admittance with input open}$$

In low-frequency operation, the h parameters are real quantities, and they may be readily derived from the slopes of the four characteristic curves of Fig. 2-9 and Fig. 2-10. It will be shown in Sec. 2.15 that the hybrid parameters are particularly adaptable to precise measurement, and thus assume special importance in describing the performance of the transistor.

2.8 Low-frequency equivalent circuits

Low-frequency equivalent circuits of the transistor in the common-emitter, common-base, and common-collector configurations are derived through a systematic analysis of the transistor as a linear active four-terminal network in Sec. 2.14. The various types of transistor equivalent circuits are summarized in Table 2-2 in Sec. 2.14. At present we shall direct our discussion to several more commonly used low-frequency equivalent circuits in the common-emitter configuration to illustrate their roles in the representation of the transistor.

Referring to Table 2-1 in Sec. 2.5, the two low-frequency equivalent circuits derived from the z parameters are shown in the first column. The two-generator equivalent circuits utilize the common-emitter resistance parameters directly. The one-generator equivalent circuit, commonly known as the common-emitter T equivalent circuit, uses the low-frequency *common-emitter T equivalent circuit parameters*, r_e, r_b, r_d, and r_m. The relation between the z parameters and the T equivalent circuit parameters are shown in the table below the equivalent circuits. It is to be noted that the parameters r_e, r_b, and r_m are identical in both the common-emitter and the common-base configurations. The parameter r_d, representing the open-circuit output resistance of the common-emitter configuration is different, however, from the parameter r_c of the common-base configuration. The relationship between the last two parameters is

$$r_d = r_c - r_m$$

The voltage generator $r_m i_b$ and the series resistance r_d in the one-generator equivalent circuit may be replaced by a current generator $\alpha'_{cb} i_b$ in parallel with the resistance r_d. The common-emitter current generator amplification factor α'_{cb} is defined at low frequencies as

$$\alpha'_{cb} \equiv -\frac{r_{21e} - r_{12e}}{r_{22e} - r_{12e}} = \frac{r_m}{r_d}$$

In linear operation, α'_{cb} differs very slightly in value from the short-circuit current amplification factor α_{cb}, which is defined at low frequencies as

$$\alpha_{cb} \equiv -\frac{r_{21e}}{r_{22e}} = \frac{r_m - r_e}{r_d + r_e}$$

The relation between α_{cb} and α is

$$\alpha_{cb} \cong \frac{\alpha}{1 - \alpha}$$

The low-frequency equivalent circuits derived from the h parameters are shown in the second column of Table 2-1. The two-generator equivalent circuit is of special interest because of its ready application in circuit analysis and design as shown in later chapters, and because of the above-mentioned ease of measurement of the parameters as shown in Sec. 2.15. The other equivalent circuits shown in Table 2-1 are also useful in various applications.

2.9 Approximations in the low-frequency equivalent circuit analysis

In deriving the various equivalent circuits, it was assumed that the characteristics were linear. It must be borne in mind, however, that the characteristics are not exactly linear, even in the so-called linear operating region, and that equivalent circuit analysis is therefore approximate in its basic nature. Great accuracy in the expressions for circuit data such as gain and input and output impedances is therefore rarely warranted in practical circuit applications.

The equivalent circuit analysis of transistor circuits often leads to cumbersome expressions which may be considerably simplified without significant loss of accuracy by use of a few well-formulated assumptions. The basic cause of the unwieldy nature of the equations for transistor circuits as opposed to equations describing the performance of vacuum tube circuits is the presence of (1) a small degree of *signal feed-through* in the transistor, which is present even when the active generator is reduced to zero, and (2) internal *feedback* from output to input.

The first of these effects is extremely small, since the attentuation of the input signal through the passive part of the equivalent circuit network is great, while simultaneously, the amplification due to the active portion of the equivalent circuit is large. Many simplifying assumptions may be made by ignoring the direct signal feed-through component to the output circuit.

The second complicating effect is that of feedback, which causes the transistor to have bilateral properties, as opposed to the vacuum tube, which is essentially unilateral at low frequencies. This feedback may in certain cases be ignored, but it is normally of importance, particularly in the determination of the input and output impedances. For certain standardized applications where a wide range of load impedances need not be accommodated, the effect of feedback may be eliminated from the gain equations with little loss in accuracy. An example of such an application is to be found in cascaded *RC* coupled amplifier circuits, as discussed in Chapter 5.

2.10 Linear four-terminal networks[2]

In the previous sections functional representation of the transistor by characteristic curves, network parameters, and equivalent circuits was described. Here we treat the transistor as a *linear active four-terminal network* and make use of general network theory. A brief review of certain important aspects of the general network theory which are immediately useful in the analysis of transistor circuits is included in this section. This review also clearly defines certain terminology and symbolic convention in order to avoid confusion which might otherwise arise.

A four-terminal network, (also referred to as a *four-pole network*, a *two-terminal-pair network*, or a *four-terminal transducer*) may be simply represented by a "black box" having four externally accessible terminals. The arrangement is shown in Fig. 2-11 in which 1,1′ are input terminals, and 2,2′ are output terminals. The behavior of such a network is completely determined by the relationship among the input and output voltages and currents, denoted by v_1, v_2, i_1, and

[2] Treatments of passive four-terminal network theory will be found in E. A. Guillemin, *Communication Networks*, Vol. 2, John Wiley & Sons, Inc., New York, 1935; of active four-terminal network theory in L. C. Paterson, "Equivalent Circuits of Linear Four-Terminal Networks," *Bell System Tech. J.*, Vol. 27, pp. 593–622, Oct. 1948; of application of the transistor in L. J. Giacoletto, "Terminology and Equations for Linear Active Four-Terminal Networks Including Transistors," *RCA Rev.*, Vol. 14, Mar. 1953.

i_2, respectively. This relationship may be represented analytically by one implicit equation:

$$f(v_1, v_2, i_1, i_2) = 0 \tag{2-17}$$

If two linear equations interrelating the terminal voltages and currents are sufficient to describe completely the properties of a network, the network is called a *linear network*. Several methods of representing the function of Eq. (2-17) by two linear equations are available, depending upon the selection of independent and dependent variables. Three of the more useful selections will be discussed here, leading to the important concepts of the *open-circuit impedance parameters*, the *short-circuit admittance parameters*, and the *hybrid parameters*.

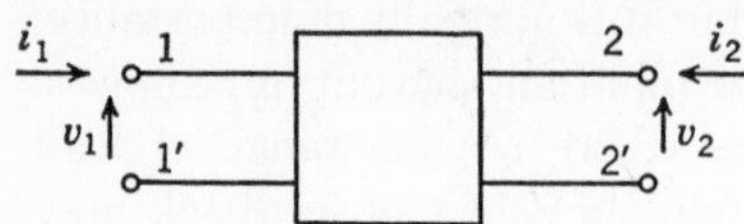

Fig. 2-11. Network representation of a four-terminal network.

If the terminal voltages are chosen as dependent variables, and the terminal currents as independent variables, the linear four-terminal network can be analytically represented by

$$\begin{aligned} v_1 &= z_{11}i_1 + z_{12}i_2 \\ v_2 &= z_{21}i_1 + z_{22}i_2 \end{aligned}, \tag{2-18}$$

which are the general mesh equations for a linear four-terminal network. Represented in matrix form, the mesh equations become

$$\begin{Vmatrix} v_1 \\ v_2 \end{Vmatrix} = \begin{Vmatrix} z_{11} & z_{12} \\ z_{21} & z_{22} \end{Vmatrix} \begin{Vmatrix} i_1 \\ i_2 \end{Vmatrix} \tag{2-18a}$$

The impedance parameters are

$z_{11} = \left(\dfrac{v_1}{i_1}\right)_{i_2=0} = r_{11} + jx_{11}$, the input impedance with output open

$z_{12} = \left(\dfrac{v_1}{i_2}\right)_{i_1=0} = r_{12} + jx_{12}$, the reverse transfer impedance with input open

$z_{21} = \left(\dfrac{v_2}{i_1}\right)_{i_2=0} = r_{21} + jx_{21}$, the forward transfer impedance with output open

$z_{22} = \left(\dfrac{v_2}{i_2}\right)_{i_1=0} = r_{22} + jx_{22}$, the output impedance with input open

If, inversely, the terminal currents are chosen as dependent variables and the terminal voltages as independent variables, the linear four-terminal network can be analytically represented by

$$\begin{aligned} i_1 &= y_{11}v_1 + y_{12}v_2 \\ i_2 &= y_{21}v_1 + y_{22}v_2 \end{aligned}, \tag{2-19}$$

which are the general nodal equations for a linear four-terminal network. The general nodal equations represented in matrix form become

$$\begin{Vmatrix} i_1 \\ i_2 \end{Vmatrix} = \begin{Vmatrix} y_{11} & y_{12} \\ y_{21} & y_{22} \end{Vmatrix} \begin{Vmatrix} v_1 \\ v_2 \end{Vmatrix} \tag{2-19a}$$

The admittance parameters are

$y_{11} = \left(\dfrac{i_1}{v_1}\right)_{v_2=0} = g_{11} + jb_{11}$, the input admittance with output shorted

$y_{12} = \left(\dfrac{i_1}{v_2}\right)_{v_1=0} = g_{12} + jb_{12}$, the reverse transfer admittance with input shorted

$y_{21} = \left(\dfrac{i_2}{v_1}\right)_{v_2=0} = g_{21} + jb_{21}$, the forward transfer admittance with output shorted

$y_{22} = \left(\dfrac{i_2}{v_2}\right)_{v_1=0} = g_{22} + jb_{22}$, the output admittance with input shorted

If the input voltage and the output current are chosen as dependent variables and the output voltage and input current as independent variables, the linear four-terminal network can be represented analytically by

$$\begin{aligned} v_1 &= h_{11}i_1 + h_{12}v_2 \\ i_2 &= h_{21}i_1 + h_{22}v_2 \end{aligned}, \tag{2-20}$$

which, represented in matrix form, becomes

$$\begin{Vmatrix} v_1 \\ i_2 \end{Vmatrix} = \begin{Vmatrix} h_{11} & h_{12} \\ h_{21} & h_{22} \end{Vmatrix} \begin{Vmatrix} i_1 \\ v_2 \end{Vmatrix} \tag{2-20a}$$

The hybrid parameters are

$$h_{11} = \left(\frac{v_1}{i_1}\right)_{v_2=0} = \frac{1}{y_{11}}, \text{ the input impedance with output shorted}$$

$$h_{12} = \left(\frac{v_1}{v_2}\right)_{i_1=0}, \quad \text{the reverse open-circuit voltage amplification factor}$$

$$h_{21} = \left(\frac{i_2}{i_1}\right)_{v_2=0}, \quad \text{the forward short-circuit current amplification factor}$$

$$h_{22} = \left(\frac{i_2}{v_2}\right)_{i_1=0} = \frac{1}{z_{22}}, \text{ the output admittance with input open}$$

It is interesting to note that h_{11} has the dimension of impedance $(1/y_{11})$, and h_{22} has the dimension of admittance $(1/z_{22})$, and h_{12} and h_{21} both represent numerical ratios. The forward short-circuit current amplification factor h_{21} is usually referred to as α_{21}, while the reverse open-circuit voltage gain, h_{12}, is alternately designated as μ_{12}. Two other parameters, α_{12} and μ_{21}, which are members of another set of occasionally used parameters are defined as follows:

$$\alpha_{12} = \left(\frac{i_1}{i_2}\right)_{v_1=0} = \text{reverse short-circuit current amplification factor}$$

$$\mu_{21} = \left(\frac{v_2}{v_1}\right)_{i_2=0} = \text{forward open-circuit voltage amplification factor}$$

Equations 2-20 may now be written

$$v_1 = \frac{1}{y_{11}} i_1 + \mu_{12} v_2, \qquad i_2 = \alpha_{21} i_1 + \frac{1}{z_{22}} v_2 \tag{2-20b}$$

Matrix representation of linear network theory is introduced here because it offers a most powerful shorthand method to the solution of network problems. It simplifies the computational work involved in analyzing networks of a complicated nature such as four-terminal networks connected in cascade, in parallel or in series.[3] It also offers a concise presentation of the network equations and permits easy transformation of the equations from one form to another. The

[3] P. LeCorbeiller, *Matrix Analysis of Electric Network*, John Wiley & Sons, Inc., New York, 1950; Jacob Shekel, "Matrix Representation of Transistor Circuits," *Proc. I.R.E.*, Vol. 40, pp. 1493–1497, Nov. 1952; L. A. Zadeh, "A Note on the Analysis of Vacuum Tube Transistor Circuits," *Proc. I.R.E.*, Vol. 41, pp. 898–992, Aug. 1953.

following transformation between the z, y, and h parameters is obtained by using matrix algebra:

$$\begin{Vmatrix} z_{11} & z_{12} \\ z_{21} & z_{22} \end{Vmatrix} = \begin{Vmatrix} \dfrac{y_{22}}{|y|} & \dfrac{-y_{12}}{|y|} \\ \dfrac{-y_{21}}{|y|} & \dfrac{y_{11}}{|y|} \end{Vmatrix} = \begin{Vmatrix} \dfrac{|h|}{h_{22}} & \dfrac{h_{12}}{h_{22}} \\ \dfrac{-h_{21}}{h_{22}} & \dfrac{1}{h_{22}} \end{Vmatrix} = \begin{Vmatrix} \dfrac{S}{y_{11}} & \mu_{12} z_{22} \\ -\alpha_{21} z_{22} & z_{22} \end{Vmatrix}$$

$$\begin{Vmatrix} y_{11} & y_{12} \\ y_{21} & y_{22} \end{Vmatrix} = \begin{Vmatrix} \dfrac{z_{22}}{|z|} & \dfrac{-z_{12}}{|z|} \\ \dfrac{-z_{21}}{|z|} & \dfrac{z_{11}}{|z|} \end{Vmatrix} = \begin{Vmatrix} \dfrac{1}{h_{11}} & \dfrac{-h_{12}}{h_{11}} \\ \dfrac{h_{21}}{h_{11}} & \dfrac{|h|}{h_{11}} \end{Vmatrix} = \begin{Vmatrix} y_{11} & -\mu_{12} y_{11} \\ \alpha_{21} y_{11} & \dfrac{S}{z_{22}} \end{Vmatrix}$$

$$\begin{Vmatrix} h_{11} & h_{12} \\ h_{21} & h_{22} \end{Vmatrix} = \begin{Vmatrix} \dfrac{1}{y_{11}} & \mu_{12} \\ \alpha_{21} & \dfrac{1}{z_{22}} \end{Vmatrix} = \begin{Vmatrix} \dfrac{|z|}{z_{22}} & \dfrac{z_{12}}{z_{22}} \\ \dfrac{-z_{21}}{z_{22}} & \dfrac{1}{z_{22}} \end{Vmatrix} = \begin{Vmatrix} \dfrac{1}{y_{11}} & \dfrac{-y_{12}}{y_{11}} \\ \dfrac{y_{21}}{y_{11}} & \dfrac{|y|}{y_{11}} \end{Vmatrix}$$

$$|z| = z_{11} z_{22} - z_{12} z_{21} = \frac{1}{|y|} = \frac{h_{11}}{h_{22}}$$

$$|y| = y_{11} y_{22} - y_{12} y_{21} = \frac{1}{|z|} = \frac{h_{22}}{h_{11}}$$

$$|h| = h_{11} h_{22} - h_{12} h_{21} = \frac{y_{22}}{y_{11}} \tag{2-21}$$

$$\mu_{21} = \frac{z_{21}}{z_{11}} = -\frac{y_{21}}{y_{22}} = \frac{1}{\mu_{12}}\left(1 - \frac{1}{S}\right)$$

$$\alpha_{12} = -\frac{z_{12}}{z_{11}} = \frac{y_{11}}{y_{22}} = \frac{1}{\alpha_{21}}\left(1 - \frac{1}{S}\right)$$

$$S = 1 - \mu_{12}\alpha_{21}y_{11}z_{22}$$

If a linear four-terminal network has both a nonzero reverse transfer parameter and a nonzero forward transfer parameter (i.e., $z_{12} \neq 0$, $z_{21} \neq 0$; $y_{12} \neq 0, y_{21} \neq 0$: or $h_{12} \neq 0$, $h_{21} \neq 0$), it is defined as a *bilateral network*. If the network has either a zero reverse transfer parameter or a zero forward transfer parameter, however, it is defined as a *unilateral network*.

A linear four-terminal network requires four independent parameters for its complete specification. However, if equality exists for a given network between its forward and reverse transfer impedances (or admittances), only three parameters are required to define the network. Networks having such properties are referred to as reciprocal *passive networks*, and are composed solely of passive elements. Networks containing active elements, referred to as *active networks*, do not have such properties.

2.11 Equivalent circuits for passive linear four-terminal networks

The equivalent circuits for passive linear four-terminal networks are comparatively simple because $z_{12} = z_{21}$ and $y_{12} = y_{21}$; and a simple T circuit can be derived from the rearranged forms

$$v_1 = (z_{11} - z_{12})i_1 + z_{12}(i_1 + i_2)$$

$$v_2 = z_{12}(i_1 + i_2) + (z_{22} - z_{12})i_2$$

and a simple π circuit can be derived from the rearranged forms

$$i_1 = (y_{11} + y_{12})(v_1) + (-y_{12})(v_1 - v_2)$$

$$i_2 = (-y_{12})(v_2 - v_1) + (y_{22} + y_{12})v_2$$

Figures 2.12a and 2.12b illustrate, respectively, the simple T and π equivalent circuits which are derived from the above equations.

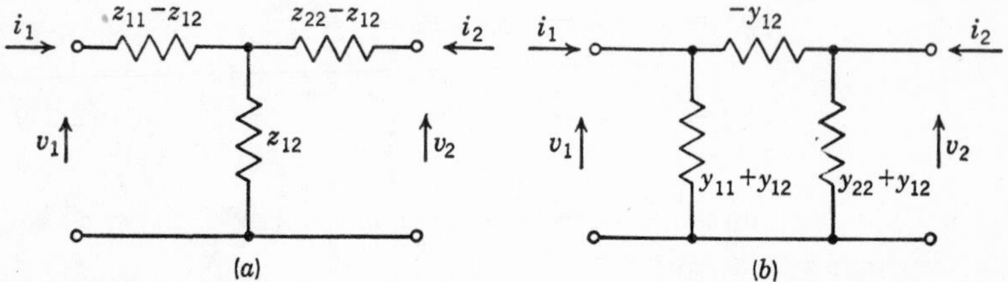

Fig. 2-12. (a) T equivalent circuit for passive linear four-terminal networks; (b) π equivalent circuit for passive linear four-terminal networks.

The negative sign of the circuit element in the series arm of the simple π circuit is the result of the voltage and current sign convention.

2.12 Two-generator equivalent circuits for active linear four-terminal networks

Active linear four-terminal networks require more complicated equivalent circuits for their representation; since $z_{12} \neq z_{21}$ and $y_{12} \neq y_{21}$, fictitious voltage and/or current generators are needed.

The two-generator equivalent circuits can be derived from Eqs.

(2-18), (2-19), and (2-20) by designating $z_{12}i_2$ and $z_{21}i_1$ as voltage generators in Eqs. (2-18), (2-19), and (2-20); and $y_{12}v_2$ and $y_{21}v_1$ as current generators in Eq. (2-19); and $h_{12}v_2$ ($=\mu_{12}v_2$) as a voltage generator, and $h_{21}i_1$ ($=\alpha_{21}i_1$) as a current generator in Eq. (2-20). The equivalent circuits derived in this manner are illustrated in Figs. 2-13a, b, and c, respectively.

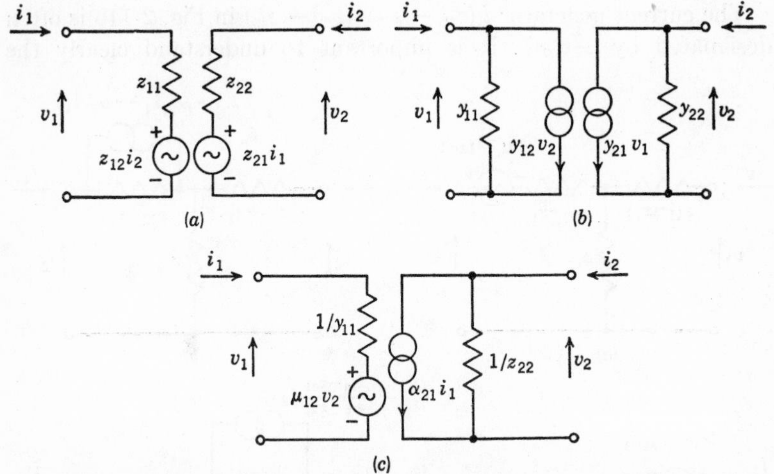

Fig. 2-13. Two-generator equivalent circuits for active linear four-terminal networks: (a) two-voltage generator; (b) two-current generator; (c) one-voltage generator, one-current generator.

2.13 One-generator equivalent circuits for active linear four-terminal networks

One-generator equivalent circuits may be derived from the rearranged forms of Eqs. (2-18), (2-19), and (2-20). Equation (2-18) can be rearranged in the following manner, from which four one-generator T equivalent circuits (Fig. 2-14) are derived.

$$(a)\quad \begin{cases} v_1 = (z_{11} - z_{12})i_1 + z_{12}(i_1 + i_2) \\ v_2 = z_{12}(i_1 + i_2) + (z_{22} - z_{12})i_2 + (z_{21} - z_{12})i_1 \end{cases}$$

$$(b)\quad \begin{cases} v_1 = (z_{11} - z_{12})i_1 + z_{12}(i_1 + i_2) \\ v_2 = z_{12}(i_1 + i_2) + (z_{22} - z_{12})\left[i_2 + \dfrac{z_{21} - z_{12}}{z_{22} - z_{12}}\, i_1\right] \end{cases}$$

$$\cong z_{12}(i_1 + i_2) + (z_{22} - z_{12})[i_2 - \alpha_{21}i_1],$$

$$\text{if } z_{21} > z_{12},\ z_{22} > z_{12}$$

$$(c) \begin{cases} v_1 = z_{21}(i_1 + i_2) + (z_{11} - z_{21})i_1 + (z_{12} - z_{21})i_2 \\ v_2 = z_{21}(i_1 + i_2) + (z_{22} - z_{21})i_2 \end{cases}$$

$$(d) \begin{cases} v_1 = z_{21}(i_1 + i_2) + (z_{11} - z_{21}) \left[i_1 + \dfrac{z_{12} - z_{21}}{z_{11} - z_{21}} i_2 \right] \\ v_2 = z_{21}(i_1 + i_2) + (z_{22} - z_{21})i_2 \end{cases}$$

The current generator $i_1(z_{21} - z_{12})/(z_{22} - z_{12})$ in Fig. 2-14b is often designated by $-\alpha'_{21}i_1$. It is important to understand clearly the

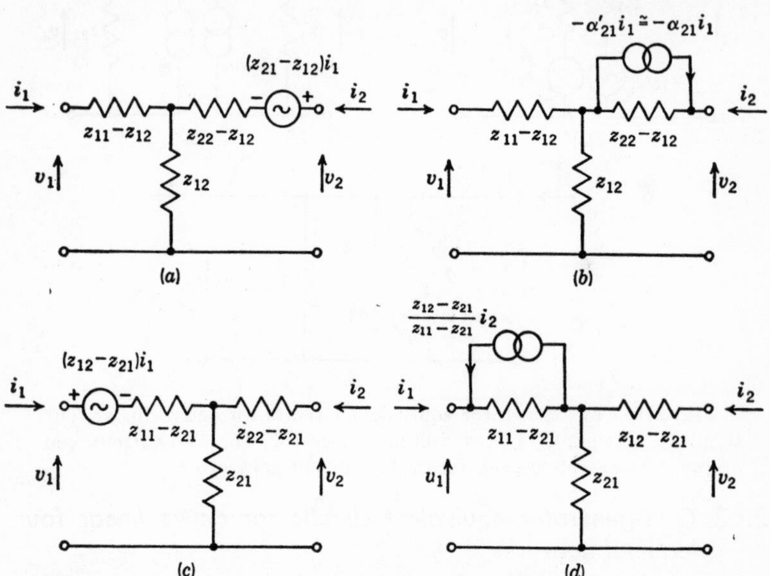

Fig. 2-14. One-generator T equivalent circuits for active linear four-terminal networks.

definitions of α'_{21} and α_{21} and their differences. The former term is defined as the *T circuit current generator amplification factor* of the transistor; $\alpha'_{21}i_1$ represents the fictitious current generator of the T circuit. The other term, α_{21}, is defined as the *short-circuit current amplification factor* of the transistor. By definition, they are

$$\alpha'_{21} \equiv -\frac{z_{21} - z_{12}}{z_{22} - z_{12}}, \qquad \alpha_{21} \equiv -\frac{z_{21}}{z_{22}}$$

It is readily seen that $\alpha_{21} \doteq \alpha'_{21}$ when $z_{12} \ll z_{21}$ and $z_{12} \ll z_{22}$. In the linear region of operation, the two terms are negligibly different. Hence the relationship $\alpha_{21} = \alpha'_{21}$ will be used throughout the re-

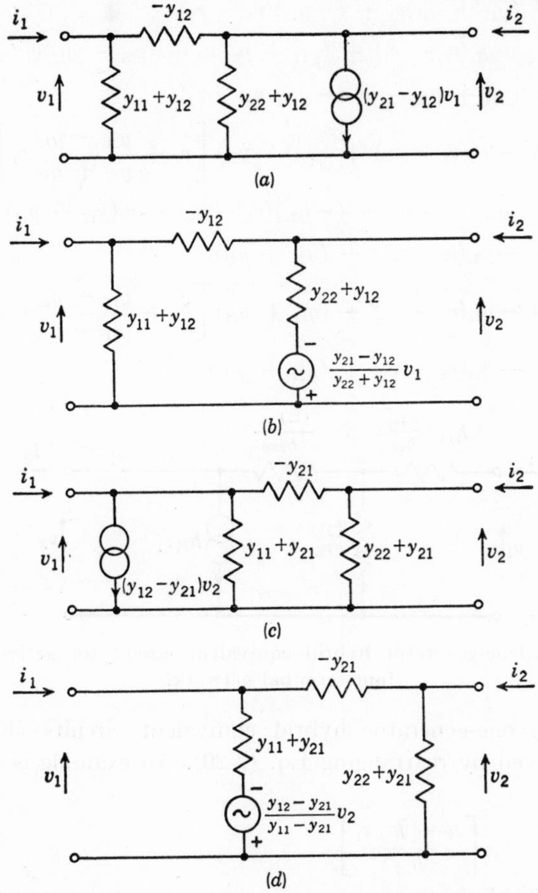

Fig. 2-15. One-generator π equivalent circuits for active linear four-terminal networks.

mainder of the book unless otherwise specified. Where operation extends into the region of saturation, (i.e., high current and low voltage), this approximation no longer holds. This will be considered further in Chapter 12.

As in the case of the one-generator T circuits, four one-generator π equivalent circuits (Fig. 2-15) may be derived by rearranging Eq. (2-19) in the following manner:

$$(a)\quad \begin{cases} i_1 = (y_{11} + y_{12})v_1 + (-y_{12})(v_1 - v_2) \\ i_2 = -y_{12}(v_2 - v_1) + (y_{12} + y_{22})v_2 + (y_{21} - y_{12})v_1 \end{cases}$$

$$(b)\quad \begin{cases} i_1 = (y_{11} + y_{12})v_1 + (-y_{12})(v_1 - v_2) \\ i_2 = -y_{12}(v_2 - v_1) + (y_{12} + y_{22})\left[v_2 + \dfrac{y_{21} - y_{12}}{y_{22} + y_{12}}\, v_1\right] \end{cases}$$

$$(c)\quad \begin{cases} i_1 = (y_{11} + y_{21})v_1 + (-y_{21})(v_1 - v_2) + v_2(y_{12} - y_{21}) \\ i_2 = -y_{21}(v_2 - v_1) + (y_{22} + y_{21})v_2 \end{cases}$$

$$(d)\quad \begin{cases} i_1 = -y_{21}(v_1 - v_2) + (y_{11} + y_{21})\left[v_1 + \dfrac{y_{12} - y_{21}}{y_{11} + y_{21}}\, v_2\right] \\ i_2 = -y_{21}(v_2 - v_1) + (y_{22} + y_{21})v_2 \end{cases}$$

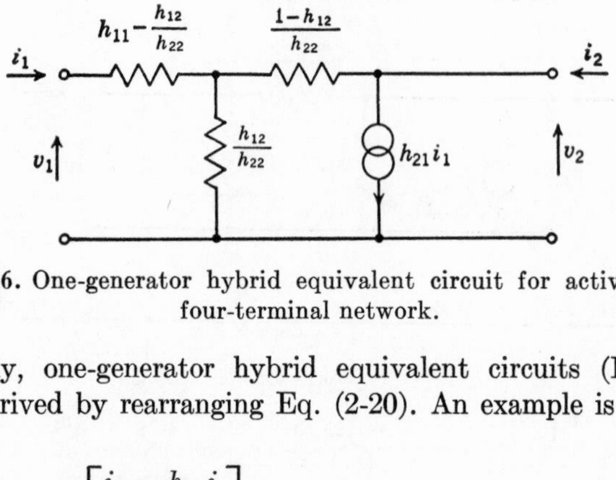

Fig. 2-16. One-generator hybrid equivalent circuit for active linear four-terminal network.

Similarly, one-generator hybrid equivalent circuits (Fig. 2-16) can be derived by rearranging Eq. (2-20). An example is shown as follows:

$$v_1 = h_{11}\, i_1 + h_{12}\left[\frac{i_2 - h_{21}\, i_1}{h_{22}}\right]$$

$$= \left(h_{11} - \frac{h_{12}}{h_{22}}\right) i_1 + \frac{h_{12}}{h_{22}}\, [i_1 + i_2 - h_{21}\, i_1]$$

$$v_2 = \frac{1}{h_{22}}\, (i_2 - h_{21}\, i_1)$$

$$\cong \left(\frac{1 - h_{12}}{h_{22}}\right)(i_2 - h_{21}\, i_1) + \frac{h_{12}}{h_{22}}\, (i_1 + i_2 - h_{21}\, i_1), \text{ if } h_{12}\, i_1 \ll i_2 - h_{21}\, i_1.$$

2.14 The transistor as a linear active four-terminal network

Active linear network theory previously discussed may be applied directly to all transistor circuits provided that a set of four network parameters can be obtained. Determination of these network parameters for the various transistor configurations are therefore most important in solving transistor network problems. When these parameters are obtained, they may be substituted into the equations derived from network theory. Circuit behavior may then be readily obtained by simple algebraic means which will be shown in Chapter 3.

It has been customary to use the common-base T equivalent circuit parameters, z_e, z_b, z_c, and z_m, or the common-emitter equivalent circuit parameters, z_e, z_b, z_d, and z_m, as the basic transistor constants. The z parameters of the transistor for the three configurations may be derived from these basic transistor constants as follows:

	Common-emitter circuit	Common-base circuit	Common-collector circuit
z_{11}	$z_b + z_e$	$z_b + z_e$	$z_c + z_b$
z_{12}	z_e	z_b	z_d
z_{21}	$-z_m + z_e$	$z_m + z_b$	z_c
z_{22}	$z_d + z_e$	$z_c + z_b$	$z_d + z_e$

All the impedance parameters may be considered to be purely resistive at low frequency, and they may be determined from the slopes of the appropriate static characteristics as described in Sec. 2.4 and in Sec. 2.5.

Often the hybrid parameters of the common emitter configuration,

$$h_{11e} \equiv \frac{1}{y_{11e}} \qquad h_{12e} \equiv \mu_{bc}$$

$$h_{21e} \equiv \alpha_{cb} \qquad h_{22e} \equiv \frac{1}{z_{22e}}$$

are selected, in place of the T circuit parameters, as the basic transistor constants. The relationship between the transistor T circuit parameters and the h parameters are derived by using Eqs. (2-21),

Table 2-2

TRANSISTOR EQUIVALENT CIRCUITS

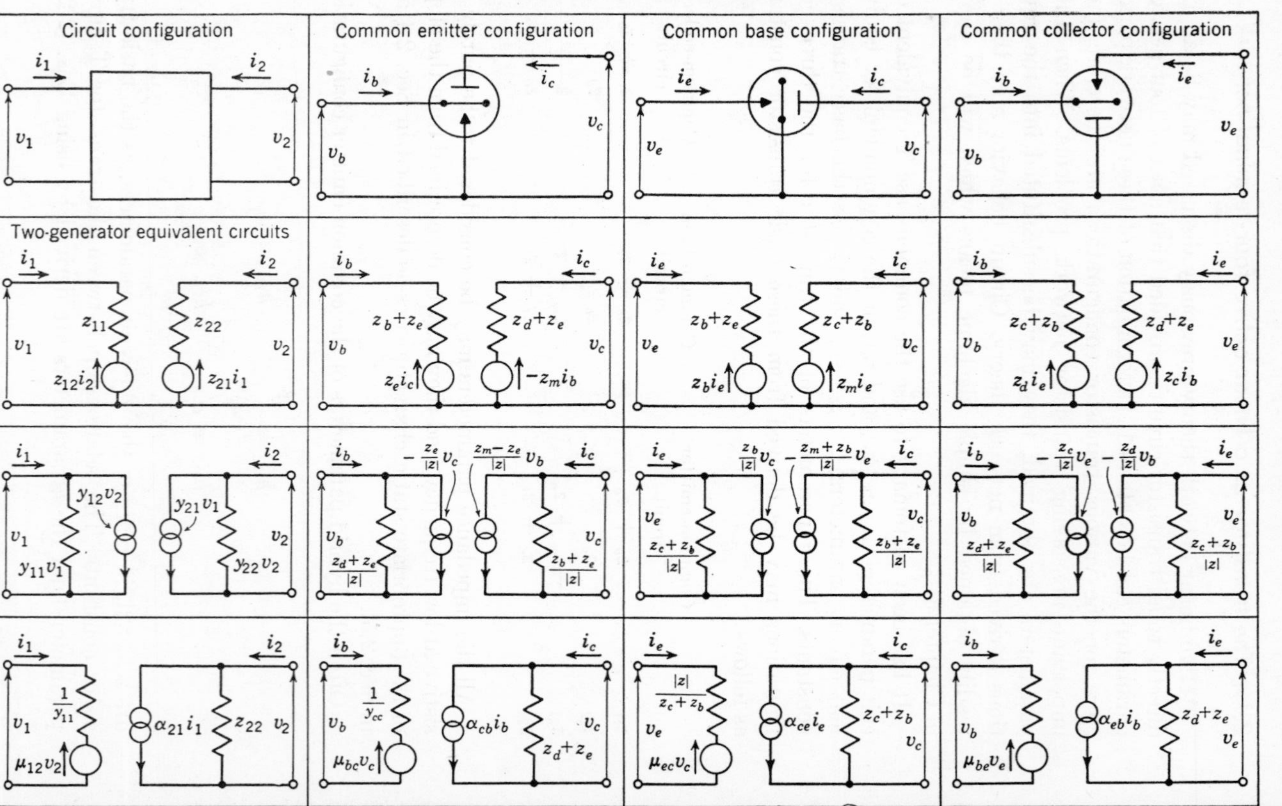

Table 2-2 (concluded)

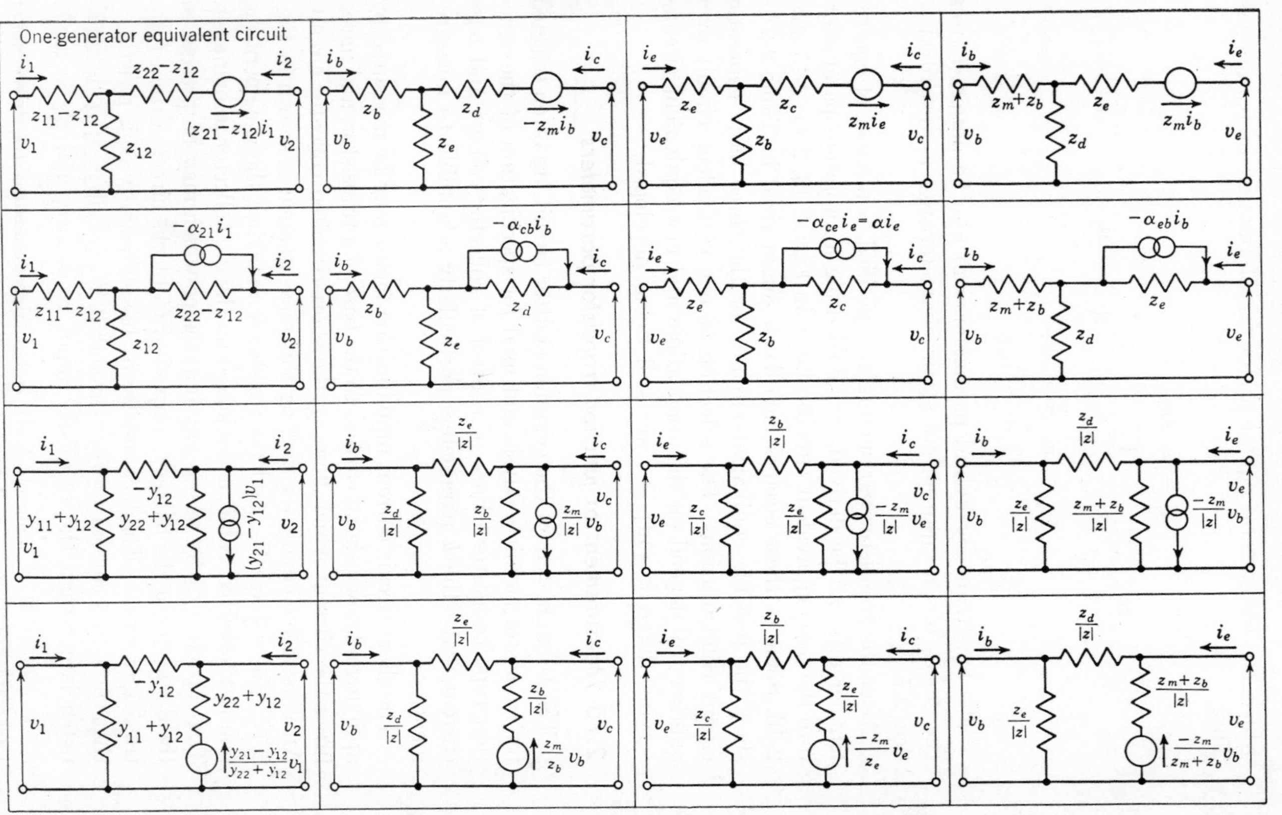

which are the general equations for transformation of parameters. Thus

$$z_e = \mu_{be}\, z_{22e}$$

$$z_b = \frac{1}{y_{11e}} - (1 + \alpha_{cb})\mu_{bc}\, z_{22e}$$

$$z_m = (\mu_{bc} + \alpha_{cb})z_{22e}$$

$$z_c = (1 + \alpha_{cb})z_{22e}$$

The low-frequency hybrid parameters can also be obtained from the slopes of the appropriate static characteristics as described in Sec. 2.7.

After the transistor parameters are specified, a number of equivalent circuits can be derived by substituting appropriate parameters into the basic equivalent circuits shown in Figs. 2-13, 2-14, 2-15, and 2-16. Some of these circuits have been summarized in Table 2-2 to show the possible equivalent circuits for the three basic transistor circuit configurations. The selection of one equivalent circuit over another will depend on the application, and new equivalent circuits serving different purposes are still being developed.

2.15 Measurement of junction transistor parameters

The h parameters of the common-emitter circuit are often selected for transistor circuit analysis and used for specification of the junction type transistor.[4] Ease of control of collector voltage and base current make the h parameters particularly adaptable to measurement.

The short-circuit current amplification factor may be measured by applying a known signal current to the base of a transistor, and measuring the current which flows in the short-circuited collector circuit. An illustrative circuit for making this measurement is shown in Fig. 2-17. The voltage V_{CC} and the resistor R_B establish the d-c operating point at a desired value, as indicated on the d-c collector milliameter. The capacitor C_2 by-passes any impedance which may be present in the d-c meter or the battery. Capacitor C_1 blocks direct current from the signal source. The bias resistor R_B has sufficiently high resistance that the signal current flowing through it is negligible. If R_g is made much larger than the transistor input resistance, and R_L is made

[4] G. Knight, R. A. Johnson, R. B. Holt, "Measurement of the Small Signal Parameters of Transistors," *Proc. I.R.E.*, Vol. 41, pp. 983–989, Aug. 1953.

much smaller than the transistor output resistance, the value of α_{cb} will be given by

$$\alpha_{cb} = \frac{V_2}{V_1} \cdot \frac{R_G}{R_L} \tag{2-22}$$

If three of these four quantities are fixed, the fourth may be calibrated directly in terms of α_{cb}. As a practical case, R_g might be

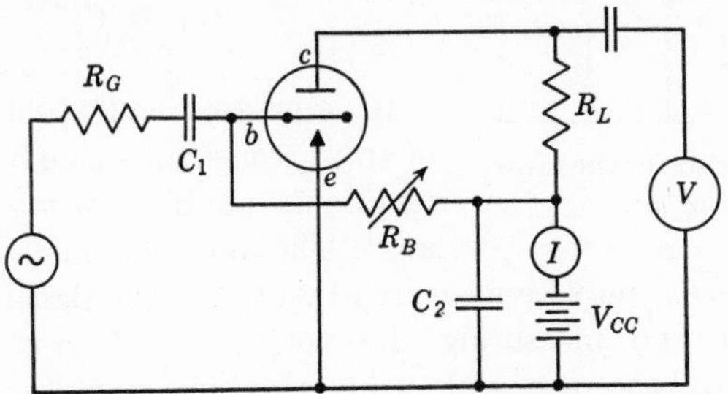

Fig. 2-17. Circuit for measurement of α_{cb} and $1/g_{11e}$.

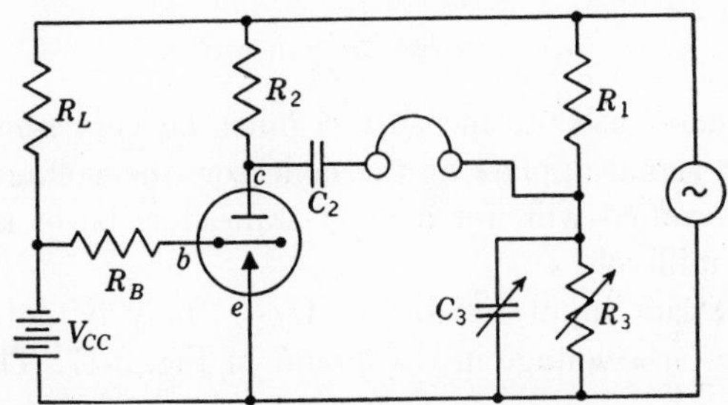

Fig. 2-18. Bridge circuit for the determination of r_d.

100,000 ohms, R_L might be 100 ohms, and the input voltage 1 volt. The reading of V_2 in millivolts would then be numerically equal to α_{cb}.

The open-circuit output resistance r_{22e}, which is almost equal to the collector-emitter resistance r_d, may be measured by incorporating the collector circuit as an arm of a Wheatstone bridge, as shown in Fig. 2-18. The circuit elements which establish the d-c operating point are so proportioned that they have negligible effect on the a-c circuit. When the bridge is balanced,

$$r_{22e} = \frac{R_2 R_3}{R_1} \tag{2-23}$$

Some capacitance will be present in the output impedance of the transistor, so that perfect balance will require the addition of a shunt capacitance C_3, across R_3. The value of the transistor shunt output capacitance C_{22e} may also be determined with this bridge.

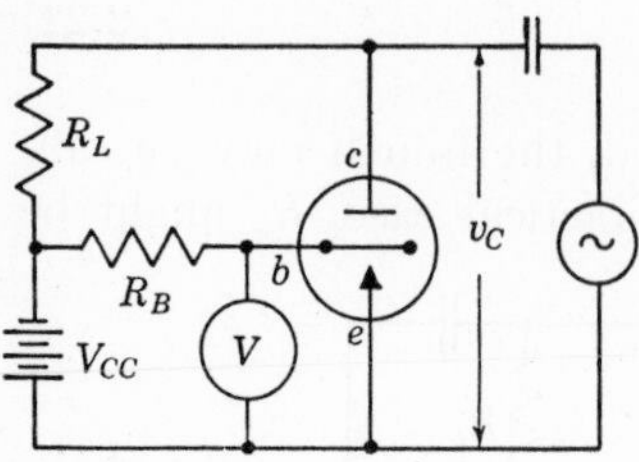

Fig. 2-19. Circuit for the measment of μ_{bc}.

$$C_{22e} = C_3 \frac{R_1}{R_2} \tag{2-24}$$

In order to complete the description of transistor small-signal behavior, two remaining parameters must be measured. The open-circuit voltage amplification factor μ_{bc} may be measured by applying a signal voltage to the collector and measuring the voltage which appears at the open-circuited base terminal, using the circuit of Fig. 2-19. The open-circuit voltage amplification factor is given by

$$\mu_{bc} = \frac{v_b}{v_c} \tag{2-25}$$

The a-c voltmeter used to measure v_b must be very sensitive, since for a one-volt signal applied at the collector, the voltage appearing at the base terminal will, for a good transistor, be of the order of tenths of one millivolt.

The short-circuit input resistance, $1/g_{11e}$, may be determined by measuring the base voltage in the circuit of Fig. 2-17. The value is

$$\frac{1}{g_{11e}} = \frac{v_b}{v_1} R_G \tag{2-26}$$

With four known parameters, the transistor is completely specified. Any other set of parameters, such as the resistance parameters, or the parameters of the T circuit, may be derived from these h parameters, as shown above. At high frequencies, reactive effects become of interest. The hybrid parameters remain among the easiest to measure, but the circuits of Figs. 2-17 and 2-19 must be modified to provide reactive information. This subject will be treated in greater detail in Chapter 7.

2.16 Complementary symmetry

The availability of transistors of opposite conductivity types permits certain design freedoms for which there are no counterparts in tube circuits.[5] Comparing the collector characteristics of transistors of opposite conductivity types (Fig. 2-20), we notice that the characteristics of the *n-p-n* transistor lie in the first quadrant, while those of the *p-n-p* transistor lie in the third quadrant. The complementary symmetry property of these two types of transistors, when they are made to have identical characteristics (except that the polarities of all voltages and currents are reversed), can be used in a number of ways. Complementary symmetry of the static characteristics may yield certain advantages in biasing. Examples of such circuits will be given in later chapters.

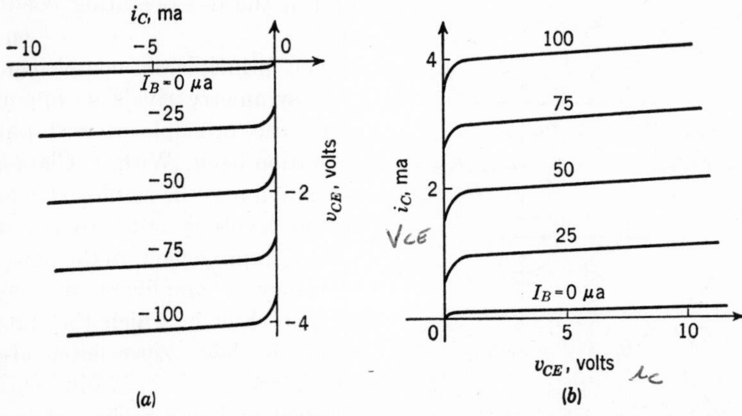

Fig. 2-20. The complementary characteristics of (a) a *p-n-p* transistor, and (b) an *n-p-n* transistor.

The principle of complementary symmetry in dynamic operation is based on the fact that if a positive signal current is introduced in the base of an *n-p-n* transistor, the collector current will increase, while a positive signal introduced in the base of the *p-n-p* transistor will cause its collector current to decrease. This phenomenon may be used to produce a push-pull system in which the two transistors are in parallel for the input a-c signal, and in which no phase inversion is required.

While detailed discussion of circuits employing complementary symmetry is reserved for later chapters, an illustrative example is shown in Fig. 2-21. The collector direct current circulates in series through the two transistors. At zero input signal, the same current

[5] G. C. Sziklai, "Symmetrical Properties of Transistors and Their Applications," *Proc. I.R.E.*, Vol. 41, p. 71, June 1953.

flows through both transistors, and thus no direct current flows through the load. The system operates in push-pull because an input signal will decrease the magnitude of collector current in one transistor while simultaneously increasing the magnitude of collector current in the other. Bias power supply and bias resistance may be arranged at the bases to provide proper base current bias for either Class A or Class B operation. In cases where a very high voltage gain is required, the load resistance may be made high or even eliminated altogether, since this resistance is not required to establish the d-c operating conditions.

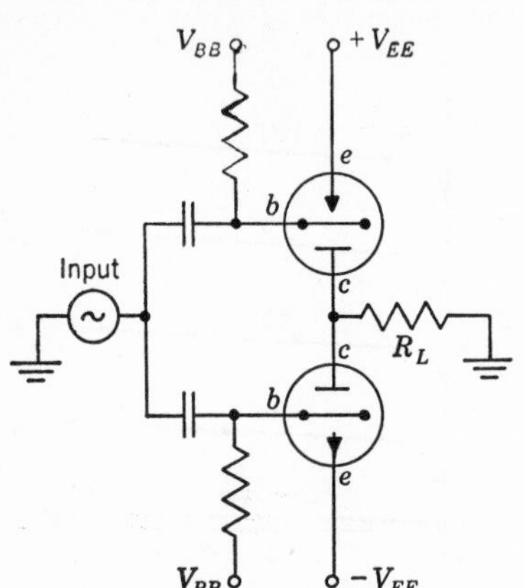

Fig. 2-21. Push-pull single-ended complementary symmetry amplifier.

The principle of complementary symmetry rivals in importance the principle of push-pull operation itself. With it, Class B operation may be employed even at low levels in order to obtain a great improvement in the power efficiency of amplifiers, particularly in cases in which the duty cycle is low. Zero-center d-c amplifiers may be built with efficient and uncomplicated coupling networks, in which the buildup of supply voltages from stage to stage is absent. In audio applications, the well-known advantages of push-pull operation may be enjoyed, as well as the simplicity of single-ended circuits, combined with the low load impedance requirement of parallel operation. In this connection, for instance, it is feasible to operate a low-impedance loud-speaker directly from a push-pull, single-ended complementary symmetry amplifier. It is difficult at present to produce *p-n-p* and *n-p-n* transistors of identical characteristics over the entire operable region. Nevertheless, a number of complementary circuits are practical, especially when negative feed-back is employed.

2.17 The symmetrical transistor

There need be no essential difference in construction between the emitter and collector junctions of a junction transistor. The electron tube, on the other hand, must have a heated cathode for the emitting surface, making the tube operable with current flow in only one direction. In the transistor, the emitter and collector junctions are of essentially the same type. The collector junction is often of larger area than the emitter junction in order to increase the collection efficiency. A transistor can be built, however, in which the collector and emitter junction are physically identical. Such a device is termed a symmetrical transistor.[6] If one junction is biased in the

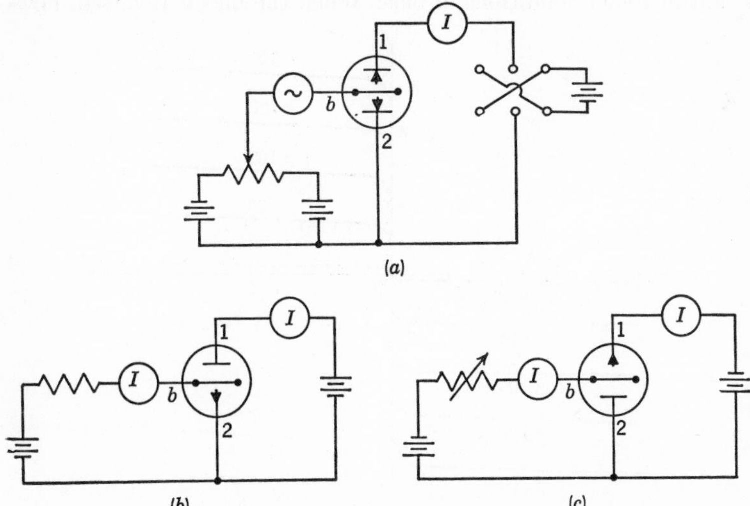

Fig. 2-22. Symmetrical *n-p-n* transistor: (a) measurement circuit; (b) and (c) effective circuits of (a) under two conditions of bias.

reverse direction, and the other in the forward direction, the first junction becomes the collector and the second becomes the emitter of the transistor. If both junctions are biased in the same direction, either forward or reverse, there is no transistor action associated with the resulting circuit.

The circuit of Fig. 2-22 may be used to measure the characteristics of the symmetrical transistor.[7] The circuit is provided with means

[6] Sziklai, *loc. cit.*

[7] The graphical symbol for the symmetrical transistor as shown in Fig. 2-22 is formed by combining the symbols for the collector and emitter elements of the normal junction transistor symbol. The figure shows an *n-p-n* symmetrical transistor. The symbol for a *p-n-p* unit would be similar except that the emitter arrow would be reversed.

for reversing the polarities of the energizing sources. In order to show clearly the action of this measuring circuit, it is drawn for two conditions of polarity of the energizing sources in parts b and c of the figure. The external connections of the transistor are marked with *b* for the base, and 1 and 2 for the indistinguishable junction leads. With the polarities as shown in Fig. 2-22b, a set of output characteristics for a grounded-emitter stage may be drawn, since lead 2 of the transistor, the common element in the circuit, becomes an emitter under conditions of bias. When the bias is reversed, how-

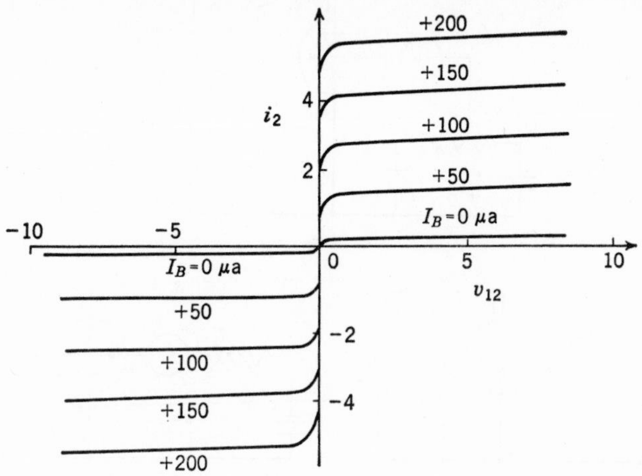

Fig. 2-23. Output characteristics of the symmetrical transistor.

ever, as shown in Fig. 2-22c, lead 2 becomes a collector, and lead 1 becomes an emitter. The output characteristics, therefore, will be those of a common-collector stage, and will be similar in appearance to the common-emitter characteristics of the same transistor. The complete output characteristics of the symmetrical transistor are shown in Fig. 2-23. The output characteristics would not be the same under the conditions of parts b and c of Fig. 2-22, since the base-to-collector voltage of part c will be substantially higher than the base-to-emitter voltage in part b. This apparent nonsymmetry results in the input circuit because the input is measured relative to one of the junction leads, in this case lead 2. The base current return could be made to a center tap in the output load circuit in order to make the circuit completely symmetrical.

A symmetrical transistor has many applications, particularly in switching circuits. The transistor may be used as a bidirectional switch, or as a balanced modulator, a phase detector, or an FM detector. These and other uses for the symmetrical transistor will be treated in later chapters.

2.18 Transistors of the current multiplication type

The point-contact type transistor uses metallic point contacts for its emitter and collector connections. Proper treatment of the point contacts in this type of transistor leads to the formation of a unit

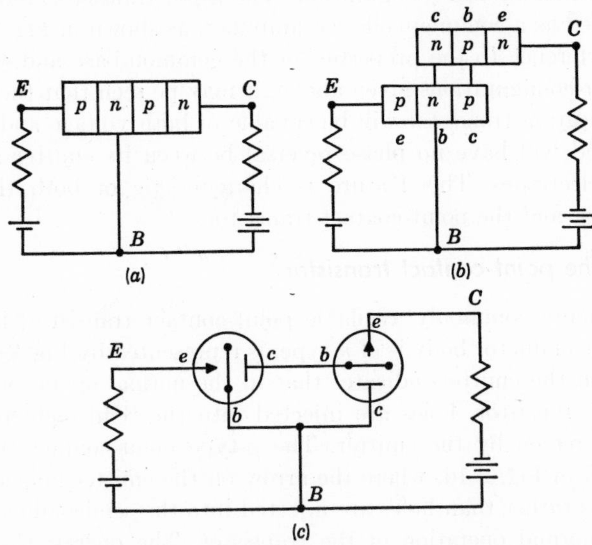

Fig. 2-24. Current multiplication junction transistor and equivalent in terms of the simple junction transistor.

in which the collector current exceeds the emitter current, and in which an incremental change in emitter current will produce a significantly greater incremental change of collector current. It is to be noted that output signals at the collector are in phase with input signals applied to the emitter.

A form of junction transistor in which current multiplication is present is the "*hook*" *transistor*, in which an extra *p-n* junction is provided at the collector of a regular junction triode transistor.

Such a configuration of junctions is shown in Fig. 2-24a. The *p-n-p-n* arrangement thus formed may be considered a combination of a *p-n-p* transistor and an *n-p-n* transistor connected as shown diagrammatically in Figs. 2-24b and 2-24c. Consideration of the bias directions shows that the *p* region on the left becomes the emitter of the *p-n-p* unit, and the *n* region on the right becomes the emitter of the *n-p-n* unit (although this electrode is termed the collector of the composite transistor). Hence, if the composite transistor is connected in the common-base configuration in order to measure the collector-emitter current gain, the *p-n-p* portion is seen also to be in the common-base configuration. The *n-p-n* transistor, however, is connected as a common-collector amplifier, as shown in Fig. 2-24c.

By reference to the properties of the common-base and common-collector configurations given above, it may be seen that the current multiplication transistor will be capable of both voltage and current gain, and will have no phase reversal between its emitter and collector electrodes. This feature is characteristic of both the hook transistor and the point-contact transistor.

2.19 The point-contact transistor

The more commonly available point-contact transistor, in which the semiconductor body is of *n* type, is represented by Fig. 2-1c. The arrow on the emitter indicates that in the normal operation of this type of transistor, holes are injected into the semiconductor body or base region by the emitter. The *p*-type point-contact transistor is shown in Fig. 2-1d, where the arrow on the emitter indicates that electrons rather than holes are injected into the semiconductor body in the normal operation of the transistor. The operation of these two types of transistors is similar except that the polarity of all energizing or bias sources must be opposite in sign. The *p*-type is useful for high-frequency applications, where the higher electron mobility (approximately double that of holes) may be utilized to advantage.

In linear amplifiers the point-contact transistor has the advantage of good frequency response on account of its physical structure. Superior frequency response in the point-contact transistor is a result of smaller internal capacitance and smaller transit time of minority carriers. The smaller internal capacitance is a result of the smaller contact area, while the smaller transit time is a result of the presence of an electric field in the semiconductor body of the point-contact transistor. Unlike the junction transistor, where the motion of minority carriers in the base region depends almost solely on diffusion (as there is very little electric field), the minority carriers in the base region of a point-contact transistor are swept to the collector by this electric field. The transit time is approximately proportional to the cube of the distance between the emitter and collector points and inversely proportional to the resistivity of the germanium.

2.20 Characteristics and equivalent circuits for the point-contact transistor

Common-base static characteristics are shown in Fig. 2-25 for the emitter and collector circuits of a typical point-contact transistor. An examination of these characteristics shows the following features which differentiate the point-contact transistor from the junction

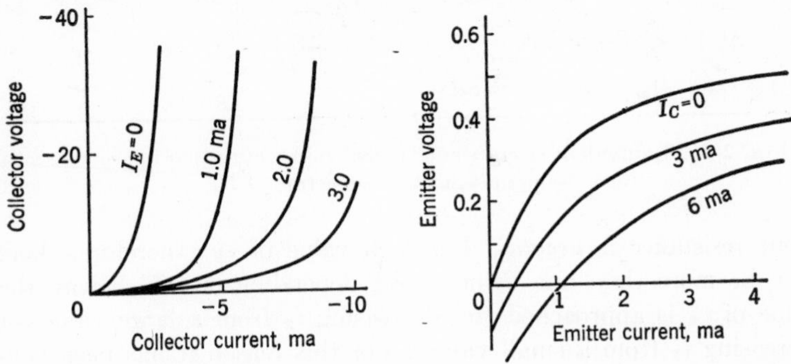

Fig. 2-25. Static characteristics of a point-contact transistor.

transistor in the common-base configuration: (1) the characteristics deviate from linearity over the operable region to a greater extent than those of the junction transistor; (2) the output resistance (given by the slope of the collector characteristics) is lower, and (3) the collector-emitter current gain is greater than unity over a substantial portion of the characteristics.

The basic T equivalent circuit may be used to represent a point-contact transistor at low frequencies, and the equivalent circuit parameters may be derived from the characteristics in the manner shown in Sec. 2.15. The high degree of nonlinearity in the characteristic curves indicates that these parameters are far from being constant over the operable region. Typical values of the parameters in the active region of a point-contact transistor are shown in Fig. 2-26.

To illustrate the internal positive feedback in a point-contact transistor with a normal value of r_b, the emitter voltage v_E is plotted against the emitter current i_E, at a constant value of collector *voltage* (Fig. 2-27) instead of a constant value of collector *current*, as in the case of Fig. 2-25. For smaller values of i_E, the value of v_E increases with in increase in i_E, indicating that the input resistance is positive. However, for larger values of i_E, the value of v_E actually decreases with an increase of i_E, indicating that the

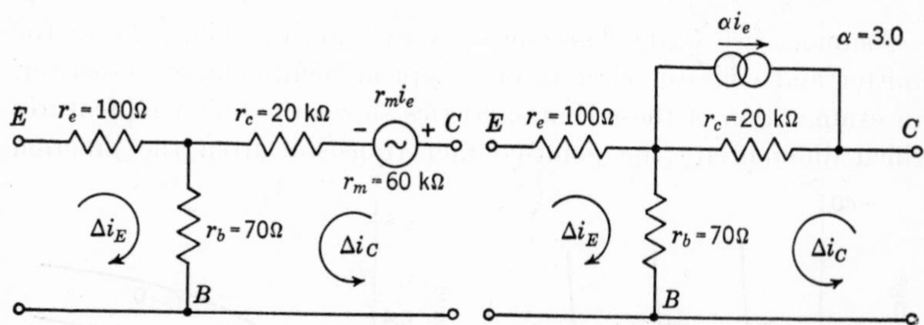

Fig. 2-26. Equivalent circuits and typical values of the parameters for a point-contact transistor.

input resistance is *negative*. For each value of v_E, therefore, there may be more than one value of i_E, depending on which way the value of v_E is approached (by decreasing i_E from a large value, or increasing i_E from a small value). For this reason it has been conventional to plot the emitter characteristics with collector current rather than collector voltage as the running parameter. It is also for this reason that current is treated as an independent variable and plotted along the abscissa, while the voltage is treated as a dependent variable, and plotted along the ordinate.

If the positive feedback (provided by the emitter-to-collector current gain and the resistance in the base circuit) is large enough to overcome the circuit losses, the unit may be unstable in the operating region. In this case, the collector current can increase spontaneously until either the nonlinearity of the characteristics limits the currents from increasing further, or the transistor is damaged. This effect is discussed in detail in Chapter 10. Care must be taken in circuit design for this type of transistor to avoid the latter possibility.

For stable operation, therefore, it is essential that the resistance in the base circuit be kept to a low value. In this respect, considerable manufacturing emphasis is directed toward reduction of internal base resistance. A "short-circuit stable" point-contact transistor is one designed to have such low internal base resistance (by using high-conductivity germanium) that with short-circuited emitter and collector branches the circuit is still stable.

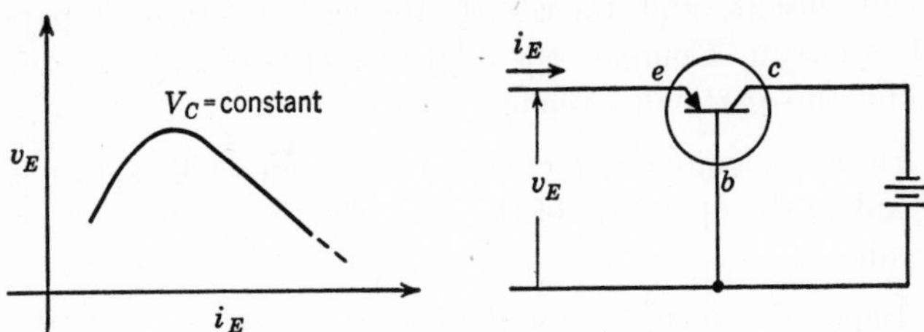

Fig. 2-27. Emitter characteristic of a point-contact transistor showing negative input resistance.

In order to keep the base circuit resistance low, the common-base configuration is the only one ordinarily employed in linear amplifier circuits. Some special amplifier circuits may occasionally employ the other two configurations to advantage; oscillators and switching circuits may use any one of the three configurations to take advantage of the instability property of the point-contact transistor. The significance of negative input resistance in the point-contact transistor will be treated in Chapter 10 and in Chapter 12.

PROBLEMS

2-1. Define the transistor parameters α, α_{ce}, α_{cb}, and α_{eb}, in terms of transistor terminal voltages and currents. Express these parameters in terms of the common-base T-equivalent circuit parameters r_e, r_b, r_c, and r_m. Show the relationships between the alpha parameters, and discuss their relative magnitudes.

2-2. Define the transistor parameters α and α', and illustrate their distinctions. Under what circumstances are the two parammeters almost equal in magnitude?

2-3. Compare the junction transistor characteristics shown in Figs. 2-7 and 2-8 with the characteristics of a vacuum tube pentode. Considering the general differences between the characteristics of the two devices, what modifications in circuit design are essential in "transistorizing" a pentode vacuum tube circuit?

2-4. The transistor described in Table 2-1 is used in its common-emitter configuration to deliver an output signal of 5 v across a load resistance of 10,000 ohms. Find the required input current and voltage. Solve this problem first with the two-generator hybrid equivalent circuit, and then with the one-generator z parameter equivalent circuit. Compare the relative merits of the two equivalent circuits for this particular application.

2-5. Draw an equivalent circuit for the amplifier shown in Fig. 2-21. Explain the operation of the circuit with the aid of the equivalent circuit.

2-6. Repeat Problem 2-5 for the circuit shown in Fig. 2-24c.

2-7. Compare the characteristics of a point-contact transistor (Fig. 2-25) with that of a junction transistor (Fig. 2-4). Discuss the basic differences between the two transistors.

2-8. From the equivalent circuit shown in Fig. 2-26 derive the short-circuit stability criterion of a point-contact transistor. Is this transistor, whose parameter values are listed in the figure, short-circuit stable? What is the maximum base resistance that will permit short-circuit stable operation?

Chapter 3

BASIC AMPLIFIER CONFIGURATIONS

3.1 Introduction

The transistor as a circuit element represented by its static characteristics, small-signal parameters, and equivalent circuits has been discussed in the previous chapter. The performance of basic amplifier configurations will now be studied in light of these discussions. A transistor amplifier circuit in its simplest form consists of a transistor having a signal source (a generator and its internal impedance) connected to its input terminals, and a load impedance connected to its output terminals. For linear operation, to which we limit the present discussion, the transistor may be adequately represented as a linear, active four-terminal network characterized by a set of transistor parameters. The performance of the amplifier, as determined by the value of the parameters and the terminating impedance, can readily be computed by conventional linear network analysis. The more important properties which govern the usefulness of an amplifier are, generally speaking, the *gains* (current gain, voltage gain, and power gain) and the effective *impedances* (input and output impedances, and matching impedances). Other amplifier properties, such as the frequency response, the limits of linear operation, and the power handling capabilities, will be studied in later chapters.

As mentioned in Chapter 2, a transistor may be connected in one of three configurations, resulting in the three basic types of amplifiers—the *common-base* amplifier, the *common-emitter* amplifier, and the *common-collector* amplifier, each of which has certain unique, useful properties. A comprehensive study of the relative merits of these amplifier circuits in various applications is made possible by generalized network analysis of these circuits, whereby such pertinent properties as gains, effective impedances, and matching conditions may be computed. The results of such a systematic analysis are summarized and listed in Table 3-1 and Table 3-2 in Sec. 3.7 and Sec. 3.8 respectively. The reader will find the information valuable as a reference in circuit design and analysis, as well as an aid in understanding the roles of the different basic amplifiers. A certain amount of ambiguity in terminology often exists in generalized network analysis. In order to avoid such ambiguity a resume of the analysis is included preceding each table.

While the properties of these basic amplifiers are adequately and precisely represented by the analytical expressions, it is also desirable that the circuit engineer have an intuitive grasp of the operation of the basic circuits without performing lengthy analysis. This may be achieved by an examination of the amplifier circuits in which the transistor is represented by an equivalent circuit, and by making appropriate approximations based upon the relative magnitudes of the transistor parameters and the terminating impedances. In this way, one may attain a general impression of the properties of the basic amplifier circuits to facilitate his study of the more elaborate circuits. The first part of this chapter is devoted to this purpose.

As the main emphasis of this chapter is to illustrate fundamentals of operation of the three basic amplifier configurations, the discussion in this chapter is limited to low-frequency linear operation of the transistor. Since junction transistors are generally used for such operation, the first six sections of this chapter deal with this type of transistors exclusively. The treatment in the rest of the chapter is general and includes both junction and point-contact transistors. Various aspects of low-frequency amplification circuitry will be discussed in Chapters 4, 5, and 6; and high-frequency operation of the transistor will be discussed in Chapters 7, 8, and 9. A comparison of transistor and vacuum tube circuits is often helpful to the reader who is familiar with vacuum tube circuits. A discussion of direct analogy and dual analogy between transistor and vacuum tube circuits will be described in Sec. 3.6. Noise in transistor circuits will be discussed in Secs. 3.9 and 3.10.

3.2 The basic amplifiers

All three basic amplifiers are used extensively in practical transistor circuits. The three amplifiers are closely interrelated both in structure and function, so that we may treat one of the three amplifiers as the "standard" configuration and consider the other two amplifiers as auxiliary configurations related to the standard form. A close examination of the three amplifiers reveals that in taking the common-emitter amplifier as the standard configuration, the common-base amplifier and the common-collector amplifier appear to be feedback versions of the standard configuration. In this respect a good analogy exists between the vacuum tube amplifier and the transistor amplifier. As illustrated in Fig. 3-1, the common-emitter, common-base, and common-collector transistor amplifiers are, respectively, the direct analogy of the grounded-cathode, grounded-grid, and grounded-plate (cathode follower) vacuum tube amplifiers. Generally speaking,

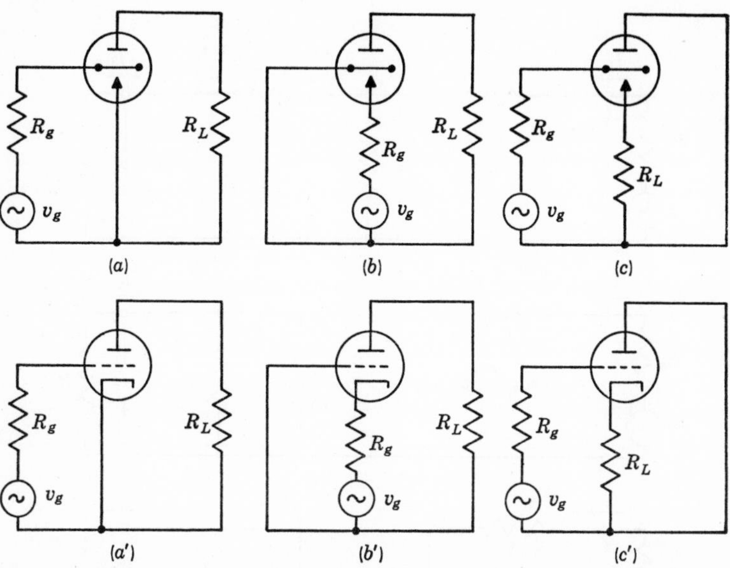

Fig. 3-1. Basic transistor and vacuum tube amplifiers: (a) common-emitter; (b) common-base; (c) common-collector; (a′) grounded-cathode; (b′) grounded-grid; (c′) cathode-follower.

the common-emitter amplifier is more often used than the other two configurations. The available power gain of a transistor in common-emitter operation is higher than it is in either of the other two connections. Furthermore, the common-emitter amplifier is capable of amplifying both current and voltage at the same time, while the current gain of the common-base amplifier is always less than unity, and the voltage gain of the common-collector amplifier is always less than unity. These properties of the three basic amplifiers will be illustrated in detail in the rest of the chapter.

As shown in Chapter 2, the performance of a transistor is accurately and conveniently predicted by the static characteristics and the transistor parameters in common-emitter operation. In design and analysis, the operation of the three amplifiers may be derived from these characteristics and parameters equally well. This is in accordance with vacuum tube circuit practice where the grounded-cathode characteristics and parameters are used for the design and analysis of all three types of amplifiers.

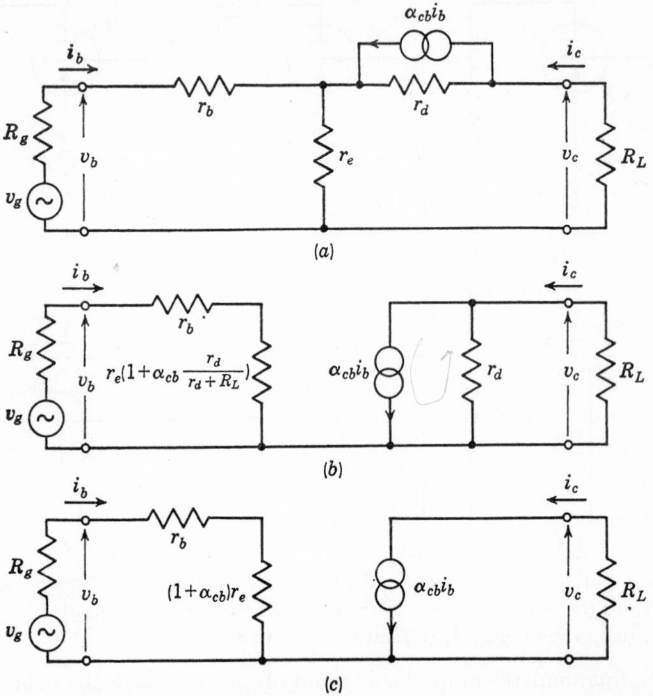

Fig. 3-2. The common-emitter amplifier: (a) equivalent circuit; (b) simplified equivalent circuit; (c) approximate equivalent circuit for $R_L \ll r_d$.

3.3 The common-emitter amplifier

The basic common-emitter amplifier, where the transistor is replaced by a T equivalent circuit, is shown in Fig. 3-2a. The d-c energizing circuits, which establish the operating point of the transistor in the desired linear region, are omitted in this and other figures in this chapter. These biasing circuits will be discussed in detail in Chapters 4 and 5. For illustrative purposes the following typical parameter values for a general-purpose junction transistor in normal operation are given:

$$r_e = 25 \text{ ohms}, \quad r_b = 500 \text{ ohms}, \quad r_d = 40{,}000 \text{ ohms}, \quad \alpha_{cb} = 50$$

The analytical expressions for the gains and the effective impedances of the basic amplifier, as listed in Tables 3-1 and 3-2, are long and complicated as compared with those of vacuum tube amplifier circuits. The complexity of the analytical expressions arises from the inherent properties of the transistor as a circuit element. In particular, the following two properties contribute to complexity:

1. A portion of the input signal *feeds through* the transistor to the output circuit even when the equivalent generator in the transistor is omitted.

2. A portion of the output signal *feeds back* through some internal element in the transistor into the input circuit.

These properties are well illustrated in the equivalent circuit of Fig. 3-2a. Even in the absence of the equivalent generator $\alpha_{cb}i_b$, part of the input current will flow in the load R_L, although the shunt resistance r_e causes the feed-through current to be small in magnitude. With the presence of the equivalent generator, the output current i_c is usually large compared with the input current i_b; and the feedback through the resistance r_e, which is common to both the input and the output circuit, may play a significant part in the operation of the amplifier. We shall see later that the feed-through and feedback properties play a more important part in the operation of the common-base and the common-collector amplifiers.

The gain and effective impedance expressions of the amplifier may be substantially simplified by making certain approximations which are justified in most practical applications. As far as the output circuit is concerned, it makes very little difference if r_e is short-circuited, since the magnitude of r_e is much smaller than that of r_d. This results in the simplified output circuit shown in the right-hand portion of Fig. 3-2b. The current gain of the amplifier, defined as the ratio of the output current i_c to the input current i_b, may be readily derived from the simplified output circuit, where the current source, $\alpha_{cb}i_b$, feeds the two resistances, r_d and R_L, in parallel. Thus, we have

$$\text{current gain, } K_i \equiv \frac{i_c}{i_b} \cong \alpha_{cb} \frac{r_d}{r_d + R_L} \tag{3-1}$$

Looking into the input circuit of Fig. 3-2a, one sees that the voltage across the input terminals is made up of the voltage drop across r_b and the voltage drop across r_e. For a given input current i_b, the current flowing in r_e is, from Eq. (3-1), approximately $[1 + \alpha_{cb}r_d/(r_d + R_L)]i_b$. Thus the input circuit may be simplified to the form shown in the left-hand portion of Fig. 3-2b. The input resistance of the amplifier is therefore

$$\text{input resistance, } R_i \equiv \frac{v_b}{i_b} \cong r_b + \left(1 + \alpha_{cb} \frac{r_d}{r_d + R_L}\right) r_e \tag{3-2}$$

The voltage gain of the amplifier may be computed from the current gain and the input resistance as follows:

$$\begin{aligned} \text{voltage gain, } K_v &\equiv \frac{v_c}{v_b} = -\frac{i_c R_L}{i_b R_i} = -K_i \frac{R_L}{R_i} \\ &\cong -\alpha_{cb} \frac{r_d}{r_d + R_L} \frac{R_L}{r_b + [1 + \alpha_{cb} r_d/(r_d + R_L)]r_e} \end{aligned} \tag{3-3}$$

The negative sign preceding the expression for K_v implies that an increment of the instantaneous input voltage results in a decrement of the instantaneous output voltage. In other words, the input signal voltage and the output signal voltage are 180° out of phase.

The power gain[1] of the amplifier is the product of the current gain and the voltage gain in absolute values. Thus

$$\begin{aligned} \text{power gain, } K_a &\equiv |K_v|\,|K_i| \\ &\cong \left(\alpha_{cb} \frac{r_d}{r_d + R_L}\right)^2 \frac{R_L}{r_b + [1 + \alpha_{cb} r_d/(r_d + R_L)]r_e} \end{aligned} \tag{3-4}$$

One remaining property of the amplifier, the output resistance, unfortunately cannot be so easily derived from the simplified circuit in Fig. 3-2b, without a little analytical manipulation. The analytical expression is in the form:

[1] The power gain K_a, which is defined as the ratio of the power delivered to the load to the power sent into the input circuit of the amplifier, should not be confused with the operating power gain K_P discussed in Secs. 3-7 and 3-8. The operating power gain K_P is defined as the ratio of the power delivered to the load to the available power from the signal source generator.

output resistance, $$R_o = (r_d + r_e)\left(1 + \frac{r_e}{r_b + r_e + R_g}\alpha_{cb}\right) \qquad (3\text{-}5)$$

$$\cong r_d \quad \text{if} \quad R_g > \alpha_{cb} r_e\,,\ r_d \gg r_e \qquad (3\text{-}5a)$$

$$\cong r_d\left(1 + \frac{r_e}{r_b + r_e}\alpha_{cb}\right) \qquad (3\text{-}5b)$$

$$\text{if} \quad R_g \ll r_b + r_e\,,\ r_d \gg r_e$$

In other words, the magnitude of R_o is in the same order of r_d. It approaches the value of r_d when R_g is very large compared with $\alpha_{cb} r_e$; and it may become several times as large as r_d when R_g is small.

In many practical applications, the load resistance of the common-emitter amplifier is low compared with r_d. Examples of such operation are applications wherein the load of the amplifier consists of the input circuit of a common-emitter or a common-base amplifier, or a low-impedance transducer such as the voice coil of a loudspeaker. Under such conditions the approximate expressions may be further simplified, as illustrated in the simplified circuit in Fig. 3-2c, as follows:

current gain, $$K_i \cong \alpha_{cb}\,, \quad \text{if} \quad R_L \ll r_d \qquad (3\text{-}6)$$

voltage gain, $$K_v \cong -\frac{R_L\,\alpha_{cb}}{r_b + (1 + \alpha_{cb})r_e}\,, \quad \text{if} \quad R_L \ll r_d \qquad (3\text{-}7)$$

power gain, $$K_a \cong \frac{R_L\,\alpha_{cb}^2}{r_b + (1 + \alpha_{cb})r_a}\,, \quad \text{if} \quad R_L \ll r_d \qquad (3\text{-}8)$$

input resistance, $$R_i \cong r_b + (1 + \alpha_{cb})r_e\,, \quad \text{if} \quad R_L \ll r_d \qquad (3\text{-}9)$$

output resistance, $$R_o \cong r_d\left(1 + \frac{r_e\,\alpha_{cb}}{r_b + r_e + R_g}\right) \qquad (3\text{-}10)$$

Using the typical values of transistor parameters listed earlier in this section, and a load resistance which is one-twentieth of r_d, representative values of the gains and the effective impedances of the common-emitter amplifier are:

$$K_i = 50$$

$$K_v = 55$$

$$K_a = 2800$$

$$R_i = 1800 \text{ ohms}$$

$$R_o = 40{,}000 \text{ ohms to } 100{,}000 \text{ ohms}$$

These representative values, as well as the simplified equivalent circuit shown in Fig. 3-2c, provide a "visual impression" in practical applications of the common-emitter amplifiers.

3.4 The common-base amplifier

In transistor operation, the base current may be considered as the control current. This is in accord with our use of the common emitter static characteristic where the base current is used as the controlling quantity.

In the common-emitter amplifier, in which the load is connected between the collector and the emitter, the signal source input current is identical with the base or control current. If the load is re-

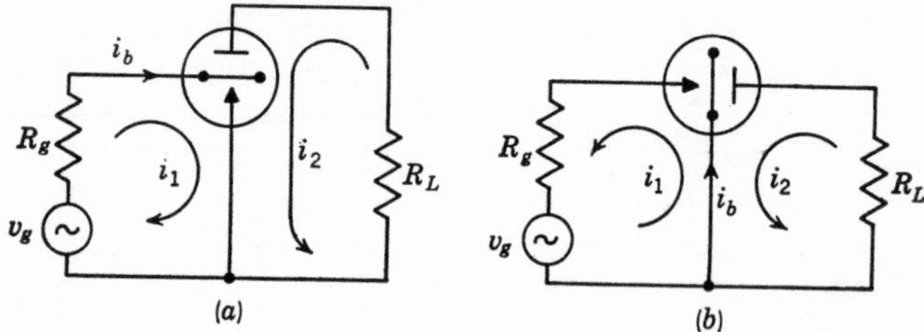

Fig. 3-3. The common-base amplifier as a feedback version of the common-emitter amplifier: (a) common-emitter, $i_b = i_1$; (b) common-base, $i_b = i_1 - i_2$.

turned to the base rather than to the emitter, the base becomes common to both input and output circuits. In this common-base amplifier, the control current is the difference between the signal source input current and the output load current. Since the output load current is fed back in its entirety through the signal source input circuit, the common-base amplifier is a feedback amplifier with respect to the common-emitter amplifier, having 100 per cent negative current feedback, as illustrated in Fig. 3-3.

Consider a given amplifier with gains K_i, K_v, and K_a. If 100 per cent negative current feedback is introduced in this amplifier, the gains of the feedback amplifier will be

$$\text{current gain} = -\frac{K_i}{1 + K_i}$$

$$\text{voltage gain} = 1 - K_v$$

$$\text{power gain} = \left| \frac{K_i}{1 + K_i} (1 - K_v) \right|$$

Comparing with the common-emitter, we see that the current gain of the common-base amplifier is reduced to a value always less than unity. The voltage gain of the common-base amplifier is approximately the same as that of the common-emitter amplifier; while the power gain of the former is approximately $1/\alpha_{cb}$ that of the latter.

The input and output impedances of the feedback amplifier, however, cannot be so easily derived from the standard amplifier, except for certain extreme impedance termination conditions. Roughly speaking, the input impedance of the feedback amplifier is reduced by a factor of $1 + \alpha_{cb}$ if the load resistance is very small; and the output resistance is increased by a factor of $1 + \alpha_{cb}$ if R_g is very large as compared with the standard amplifier.

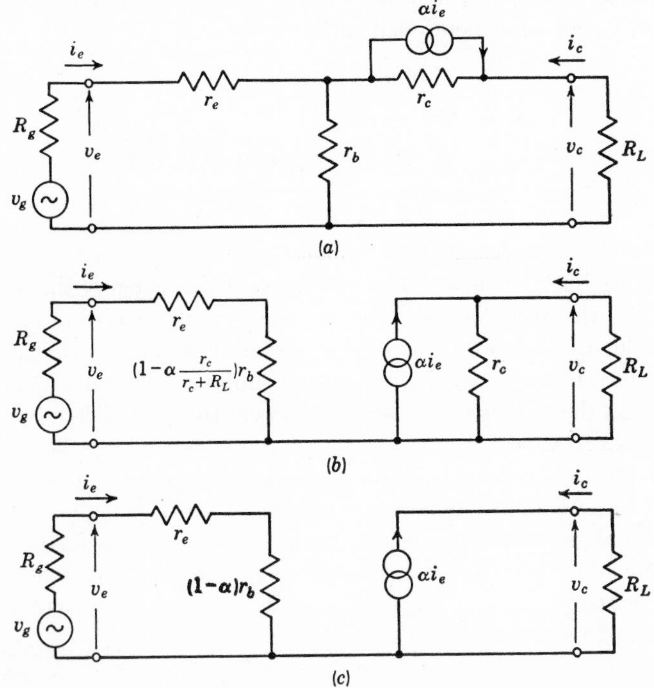

Fig. 3-4. The common-base amplifier: (a) equivalent circuit; (b) simplified equivalent circuit; (c) approximate equivalent circuit for $R_L \ll r_c$.

The common-base amplifier has considerable isolation between its output and input terminals. In the normal range of load resistance used, the input resistance of this amplifier is less affected by output loading than either of the other two amplifiers. This amplifier is often used as an impedance transformation device to couple a low-impedance circuit to a high-impedance load. As is well known in circuit analysis, negative feedback arrangements stabilize the gain of an amplifier and reduce nonlinear distortion. Because of the high output impedance, the available power gain of the amplifier is high, but this is rarely realized in untuned amplifiers, since the unavoidable shunt capacitance in the output circuit outweighs the merit of using a very high load resistance.

The performance of the common-base amplifier may be derived directly from the equivalent circuit shown in Fig. 3-4a, where the transistor is replaced by its common-base T equivalent circuit. Typical values of the common-base T equivalent circuit parameters for the same transistor mentioned earlier are

$$r_e = 25 \text{ ohms}$$

$$r_b = 500 \text{ ohms}$$

$$r_c = (1 + \alpha_{cb})r_d = 2{,}000{,}000 \text{ ohms}$$

$$\alpha = \frac{\alpha_{cb}}{1 + \alpha_{cb}} = 0.98$$

The feedback element in this case is r_b, which is many times larger than r_e, the feedback element in the common-emitter amplifier. The value of r_b, however, is still very small compared with r_c, which is of the order of megohms. Thus a simplified circuit (Fig. 3-4b) similar to the one used for the common-emitter amplifier is adopted. Similar expressions for the gains and the effective impedances may be readily derived from the simplified circuit. As mentioned earlier, the value of the load resistances R_L cannot be very high in practice because of capacitance consideration. The expressions for the gains and the effective impedances for the common-base amplifier, under the condition $R_L \ll r_c$ may be derived from the equivalent circuit in Fig. 3-4c as follows:

$$\text{current gain, } (K_i)_b \cong -\alpha, \quad \text{if } R_L \ll r_c \tag{3-11}$$

$$\text{voltage gain, } (K_v)_b \cong \frac{R_L\alpha}{r_e + (1-\alpha)r_b}, \quad \text{if } R_L \ll r_c \tag{3-12}$$

$$\text{power gain, } (K_a)_b \cong \frac{R_L\alpha^2}{r_e + (1-\alpha)r_b}, \quad \text{if } R_L \ll r_c \tag{3-13}$$

$$\text{input resistance, } (R_i)_b \cong r_e + (1 - \alpha)r_b\,, \quad \text{if} \quad R_L \ll r_c \tag{3-14}$$

$$\text{output resistance, } (R_o)_b \cong r_c\left(1 - \frac{r_b\,\alpha}{r_b + r_e + R_g}\right) \tag{3-15}$$

The voltage gain expression of this amplifier gives a positive value, indicating that the input and output signal voltages are in phase.

Based on the typical parameter values listed earlier and a load resistance of the magnitude of one-fiftieth of r_c, the representative values of the gains and the effective impedances of the amplifier are

$$
\begin{aligned}
(K_i)_b &= 0.98 \\
(K_v)_b &= 1200 \\
(K_a)_b &= 1200 \\
(R_i)_b &= 35 \text{ ohms} \\
(R_o)_b &= 2{,}000{,}000 \text{ ohms}, \quad \text{for} \quad R_g \gg \alpha r_b \\
&= 100{,}000 \text{ ohms}, \quad \text{for} \quad R_g \ll r_b
\end{aligned}
$$

3.5 The common-collector amplifier

With reference to the common-emitter amplifier, if the signal source is returned to the collector rather than to the emitter, as in Fig. 3-5, the collector becomes common to both the input and output circuits. In this amplifier the entire output voltage appears in series with the signal source voltage. Thus the common-collector amplifier is a feedback amplifier with respect to the common-emitter amplifier, having 100 per cent negative voltage feedback.

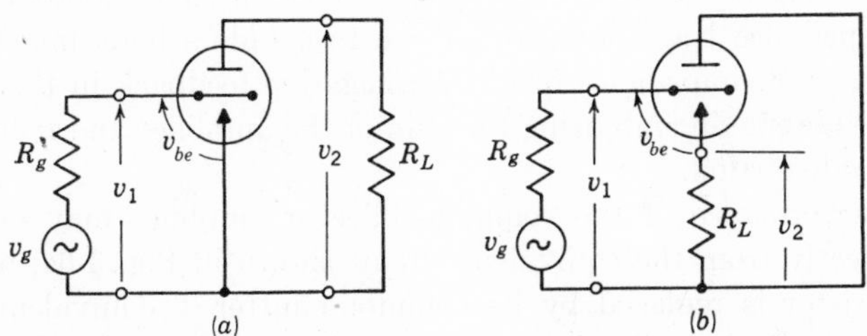

Fig. 3-5. The common-collector amplifier as a feedback version of the common-emitter amplifier: (a) common-emitter, $v_{be} = v_1$; (b) common-collector, $v_{be} = v_1 - v_2$.

Consider a given amplifier with gains K_i, K_v, and K_a. If 100 per cent negative voltage feedback is introduced in this amplifier, the gains of the feedback amplifier will be

$$\text{current gain} = -(1 + K_i)$$

$$\text{voltage gain} = \frac{-K_v}{1 - K_v}$$

$$\text{power gain} = \left| \frac{-K_v}{1 - K_v}(1 + K_i) \right|$$

From these expressions we see the current gain of the common-collector amplifier is about the same as that of the common-emitter amplifier. The voltage gain of the common-collector amplifier is always less than unity; and the power gain of this amplifier is much smaller than that of the other two amplifiers. Further analysis reveals that the input resistance of the amplifier is approximately $\alpha_{cb}(R_L + r_e)$; and the output resistance is approximately $r_e + (R_g + r_b)/(1 + \alpha_{cb})$. In comparison with the other two amplifiers, the input and output resistances of the common-collector amplifier depend much more heavily on the load and source resistances, respectively. This lack of isolation between the input and the output circuits is characteristic of the common-collector amplifier. The input resistance may be very high when R_L is large; and the output resistance may be low when R_g is small. This amplifier is often used as an impedance transformation device to couple a high-impedance circuit to a low-impedance load. The negative feedback in this amplifier is valuable in stabilizing the gain of the amplifier and reducing nonlinear distortion.

The performance of the common-collector amplifier may be derived directly from the equivalent circuit shown in Fig. 3-6a, where the transistor is replaced by its common-emitter T equivalent circuit. In practical applications R_L is usually much smaller than r_d. In such cases the simplified equivalent circuit, Fig. 3-6b may be used. The approximate expressions for the gains and the effective impedances of the amplifier are as follows:

$$\text{current gain, } (K_i)_c \cong -(1 + \alpha_{cb}), \quad \text{if} \quad R_L \ll r_d \tag{3-16}$$

$$\text{voltage gain, } (K_v)_c \cong 1, \quad \text{if} \quad R_L \ll r_d \tag{3-17}$$

$$\text{power gain, } (K_a)_c \cong 1 + \alpha_{cb}, \quad \text{if} \quad R_L \ll r_d \tag{3-18}$$

$$\text{input resistance, } (R_i)_c \cong (1 + \alpha_{cb})(R_L + r_e), \quad \text{if} \quad R_L \ll r_d \tag{3-19}$$

$$\text{output resistance, } (R_o)_c \cong r_e + \frac{R_g + r_b}{1 + \alpha_{cb}} \tag{3-20}$$

The input and output signal voltages of the amplifier are in phase. Typical values of the gains and the effective impedances of the am-

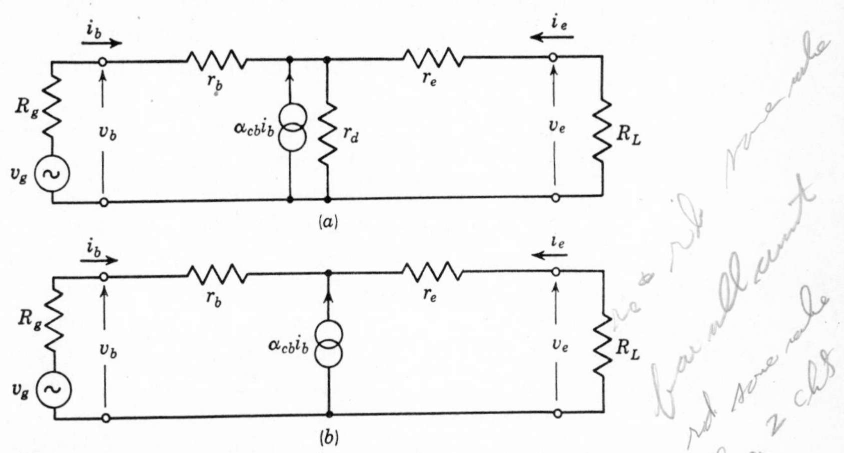

Fig. 3-6. The common-collector amplifier: (a) equivalent circuit; (b) approximate equivalent circuit for $R_L \ll r_d$.

plifier, for the same transistor mentioned earlier and a load resistance of the magnitude of one-twentieth of r_d, are as follows:

$$\begin{aligned}
(K_i)_c &= 50 \\
(K_v)_c &= 1 \\
(K_a)_c &= 50 \\
(R_i)_c &= 50\, R_L \text{ ohms} \\
(R_o)_c &= 35 \text{ ohms} \quad \text{if} \quad R_g \ll r_b \\
&= R_g/50 \text{ ohms,} \quad \text{if} \quad R_g \gg r_b
\end{aligned}$$

3.6 Direct analogy and dual analogy of transistor and vacuum tube circuits

As illustrated in Fig. 3-1, each of the three basic transistor amplifiers has a direct analogy in one of the three basic vacuum tube amplifiers. The common-emitter amplifier is analogous to the grounded cathode amplifier as the "standard" configuration. The common-base amplifier is directly analogous to the grounded-grid amplifier as the current feedback configuration; and the common-collector amplifier is directly analogous to the cathode-follower amplifier as the voltage-feedback configuration. The relative performances of the three transistor amplifiers, in terms of their gains and effective impedances, are to a certain extent also analogous to that of the three vacuum tube amplifiers, as illustrated in previous sections.

There are, however, certain basic distinctions between transistor and vacuum tube circuits which limit the usefulness of the direct analogy. The major difference lies in the fact that the operation of the transistor is based on the linear relation between the input signal *current* and the output signal voltage or current, while the operation of the vacuum tube is based on the linear relation between the input signal *voltage* and the output signal current or voltage. This was discussed in detail in Chapter 2 in the discussion of transistor characteristics. In normal operation of the transistor, the base-to-emitter resistance is much smaller than the collector-to-emitter resistance; while in normal operation of the vacuum tube, the grid-to-cathode resistance is much larger than the plate-to-cathode resistance. These contrasting properties suggest that *dual analogy*, instead of *direct analogy*, may be a more effective means of comparing the transistor circuit with the vacuum tube circuits.[2]

The principle of duality will be briefly described here; more complete treatments of this subject may be found in the literature.[3, 4] Duality refers to a reciprocal quality which exists between voltages and currents in circuits and circuit elements. Consider, for example, the following pairs of equations:

$$v = iR, \qquad i = vG \tag{3-21}$$

[2] R. L. Wallace, Jr. and G. Raisbeck, "Duality as a Guide in Transistor Circuit Design," *Bell System Tech. J.*, Vol. 30, pp. 331–417, Apr. 1951; R. L. Wallace, Jr., "Duality, a New Approach to Transistor Circuit Design," *Proc. I.R.E.*, Vol. 39, pp. 702, June 1951.

[3] Guillemin, *Communication Networks*, Vol. 2, John Wiley & Sons, Inc., New York, 1935.

[4] Gardner and Barnes, *Transients in Linear Systems*, Vol. 1, John Wiley & Sons, Inc., New York, 1942.

and
$$v = L\frac{di}{dt}, \qquad i = C\frac{dv}{dt} \tag{3-22}$$

The equations of each pair are of the same form; the currents and voltages, however, are interchanged. The two constants of proportionality in each of these pairs of equations are dimensionally different from each other and are dual circuit elements.

The dual relationship between the first of these pairs of equations may be extended to nonlinear circuits by means of the following graphical definition of duality: Two circuit elements are duals if the voltage-current plot of one can be made identical in form to the current-voltage plot of the other. Dual circuit elements in accordance with this definition are shown in the graphs of Fig. 3-7, in which

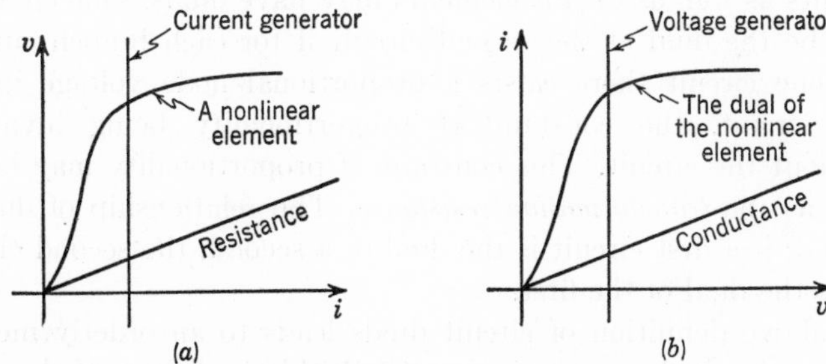

Fig. 3-7. Dual analogue of non-reactive circuit elements.

it is seen that conductance is the dual of resistance, and a current generator is the dual of a voltage generator. In addition, the two nonlinear devices of Figs. 3-7a and 3-7b are duals in accordance with the above definition.

The graphical method of defining duality may be extended to include the second pair of equations, Eq. (3-22), if the element of time or frequency is introduced. Thus if a *current* driving force of fixed amplitude and variable frequency is made to flow through a two-terminal network, the dependance on frequency of the voltage across this network may be expressed in a graph such as that shown in Fig. 3-8a. Likewise, a *voltage* driving force of fixed amplitude and variable frequency may be applied to another two-terminal network, and the dependance on frequency of the current through this element may be plotted as shown in Fig. 3-8b. If the curves of Figs.

3-8a and 3-8b are of the same shape, then the two elements described by these curves are duals. From this description it is apparent, for instance, that inductance and capacitance are dual quantities.

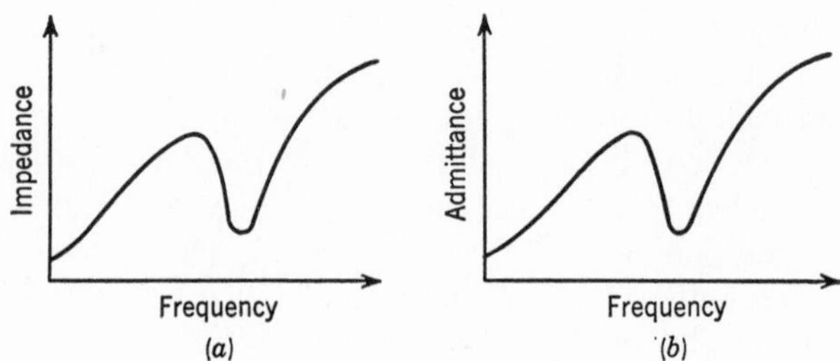

Fig. 3-8. Dual analogue of reactive circuit elements.

Circuits as well as circuit elements may have duals. One circuit is said to be the dual of the second circuit if for each branch current of the one circuit there exists a proportional node voltage in the second circuit, the constant of proportionality being invariant throughout the circuit. This constant of proportionality may be expressed as the *transformation resistance*. The relationship of duality is mutual; if a first circuit is the dual of a second, the second circuit must be the dual of the first.

The above definition of circuit duals leads to an orderly method of finding the dual of a given circuit.[5] Within each loop of the original circuit there will be a node of the dual. The first step, therefore, in finding the dual of a given circuit is to place a point corresponding to the node of the new circuit within each loop of the original circuit, and in addition, one point external to the original circuit. Connecting each of these node points in the dual circuit, there will be a number of circuit elements in parallel. The number of elements connecting two node points is equal to the number of elements in the branch of the original circuit which is common to the two loops encircling these nodes. The new circuit elements will be dual to the corresponding ones of the original circuit. The value of these elements, W_R is equal to

$$W_R = \frac{r^2}{W_O} \tag{3-23}$$

where W_O is the value of the element in the original circuit, and r is the transformation resistance. An example of dual circuits is shown

[5] This method appears in Gardner and Barnes, *loc. cit.*

in Fig. 3-9, which outlines the method of obtaining the dual of circuit *a*, shown as circuit *b*.

As an illustrative example of dual relationship, let us consider the vacuum tube amplifier circuit shown in Fig. 3-10a. The dual analogy of this circuit, as shown in Fig. 3-10b, is in the form of a common-emitter transistor amplifier. Note that a feedback element R_{pg} is intentionally included in the vacuum tube circuit in order to account

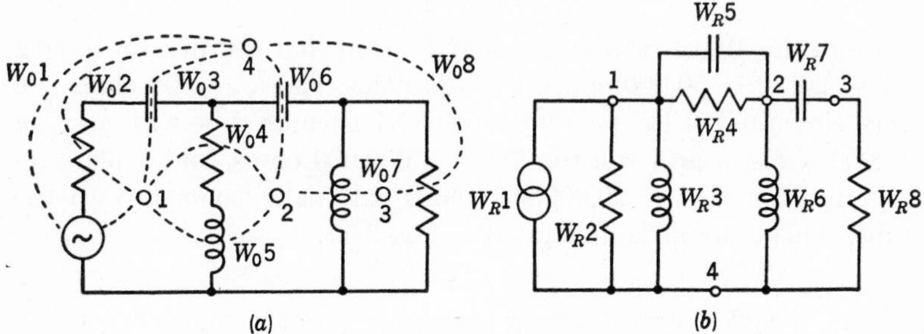

Fig. 3-9. A circuit and its dual.

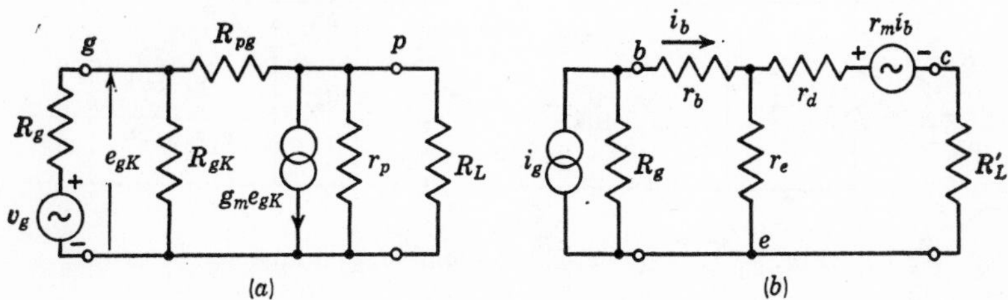

Fig. 3-10. Dual analogue between vacuum tube circuit and transistor circuit.

for the feedback element r_e in the transistor circuit. A grid resistance R_{gk} is also included in the vacuum tube circuit, as in practical circuit design, to account for the finite input resistance of the transistor circuit.

The circuit parameters of the dual vacuum tube circuit may be expressed in terms of the circuit parameters of the transistor circuit. Given the plate resistance of the tube, r_p, and the collector-to-emitter resistance of the transistor, r_d, the other parameters may be derived from the transformation resistance r, which is defined as

$$r = \sqrt{r_p r_d}$$

The parameters of the dual vacuum tube circuit are therefore,

$$r_{gk} = \frac{r^2}{r_b} = \frac{r_p r_d}{r_b}$$

$$r_{gp} = \frac{r^2}{r_e} = \frac{r_p r_d}{r_e}$$

$$g_m = \frac{r_m}{r^2} = \frac{r_m}{r_p r_d}, \quad \text{or} \quad \mu = \alpha_{cb}$$

From the above relations, it may be seen that a transistor having $\alpha_{cb} = 20$, $r_d = 50{,}000$ ohms, $r_e = 25$ ohms, and $r_b = 500$ ohms is a very close dual of the popular type 6SN7 vacuum tube with an r_p of 10,000 ohms, a grid resistor $R_{gk} = 1{,}000{,}000$ ohms, and a plate-to-grid resistor $R_{pg} = 20{,}000{,}000$ ohms externally connected to the tube. This example is illustrated in Fig. 3-11.

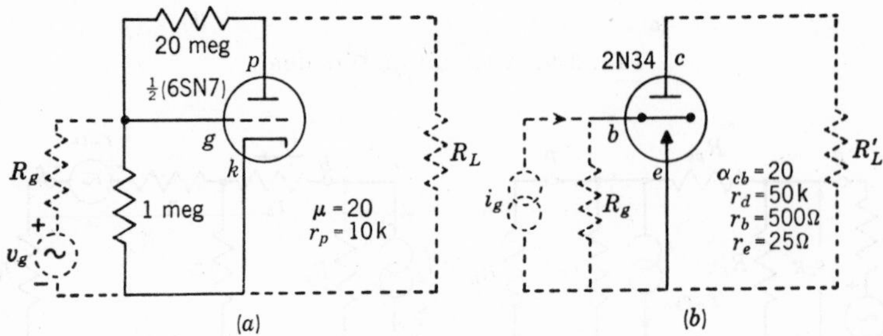

Fig. 3-11. A numerical example of dual analogy.

The grid-to-cathode resistance of 1 megohm is, by coincidence, the maximum value of grid circuit resistance which should be used with this type of tube. This resistance therefore imposes no additional restriction upon the normal operation of the tube. The base resistance of the transistor (from which we derived the grid-to-cathode resistance in the tube circuit) is therefore normally no more a restriction on the operation of this transistor than is the 1-megohm maximum grid resistance rating of the 6SN7 vacuum tube.

The grid-to-plate resistor constitutes a negative feedback connection. The main effect of this feedback is to reduce the open-circuit input resistance of the grid circuit from 1 megohm to $\frac{1}{2}$ megohm by the additional shunting of approximately r_{gp}/μ. In most amplifier applications this effect would be negligible. Practically, then, isolation between the output and the input circuit still exists, as in the vacuum tube without feedback. The design of cascaded amplifiers, even in the presence of this resistance, would proceed on a stage-by-stage basis. Similarly, design of practical transistor circuits is not greatly affected by the presence of a small amount of feedback due to r_e. Stage-by-stage design of transistor circuits is therefore also practical.

3.7 Analysis of transistor amplifiers using z parameters

General Analysis. If a signal source having a voltage generator v_g and an internal impedance Z_g is connected to the input terminals of a four-terminal network, and a load impedance Z_L is connected to the output terminals, then the equations relating these external conditions are

$$v_g = i_1 Z_g + v_1, \qquad v_2 = -i_2 Z_L \tag{3-24}$$

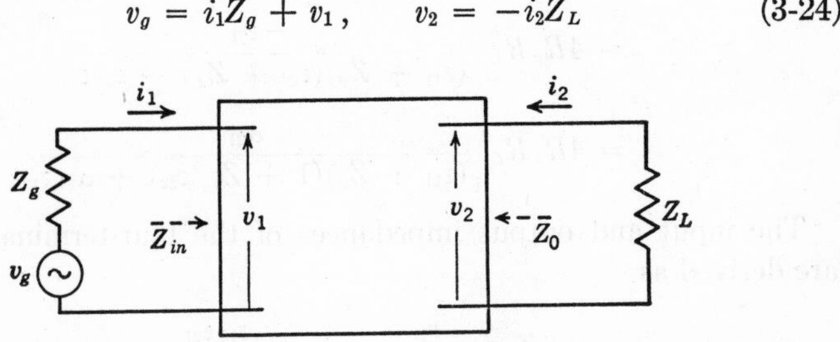

Fig. 3-12. A four-terminal network with external connections.

By representing the four-terminal network by its open-circuit impedance parameters, the circuit equations, referring to Fig. 3-12, are

$$\begin{aligned} v_g &= (z_{11} + Z_g)i_1 + z_{12}i_2 \\ 0 &= z_{21}i_1 + (z_{22} + Z_L)i_2 \end{aligned} \tag{3-25}$$

The input and output currents can be derived from Eq. (3-25) as

$$\begin{aligned} i_1 &= \frac{v_g}{z_{11} + Z_g - [z_{12}z_{21}/(z_{22} + Z_L)]} \\ i_2 &= -\frac{z_{21}}{z_{22} + Z_L}\, i_1 = \frac{-z_{21}}{(z_{11} + Z_g)(z_{22} + Z_L) - z_{12}z_{21}}\, v_g \end{aligned} \tag{3-26}$$

Solving Eqs. (3-24) and (3-26), we find the current gain of the circuit is

$$\frac{i_2}{i_1} = K_i = -\frac{z_{21}}{z_{22} + Z_L} \tag{3-27}$$

and the voltage gain is

$$\frac{v_2}{v_1} = K_v = \frac{z_{21} Z_L}{z_{11} z_{22} - z_{12} z_{21} + z_{11} Z_L}$$

$$= \frac{-\alpha_{21} Z_L}{z_{11} + \alpha_{21} z_{12} + (z_{11}/z_{22}) Z_L} \tag{3-28}$$

The operating power gain K_p of the network is defined as the ratio of the power delivered to the load to the available power from the generator. According to this definition, the power gain K_p becomes

$$K_p = \frac{|i_2|^2 R_L}{|v_g|^2/4R_g} = 4R_g R_L \left| \frac{i_2}{v_g} \right|^2$$

$$= 4R_g R_L \left| \frac{-z_{21}}{(z_{11} + Z_g)(z_{22} + Z_L) - z_{12} z_{21}} \right|^2$$

$$= 4R_g R_L \left| \frac{\alpha_{21}}{(z_{11} + Z_g)(1 + Z_L/z_{22}) + \alpha_{21} z_{12}} \right|^2 \tag{3-29}$$

The input and output impedances of the four-terminal network are derived as

$$Z_{in} = \frac{v_1}{i_1} = z_{11} - \frac{z_{12} z_{21}}{z_{22} + Z_L}$$

$$Z_o = \frac{v_2}{i_2} = z_{22} - \frac{z_{12} z_{21}}{z_{11} + Z_g} \tag{3-30}$$

Matched Conditions. Three specific terminating conditions are of special interest in the study of the linear, active four-terminal network. They are the *conjugate matched*, the *image matched*, and the *iterative matched* conditions. Analysis of these terminating conditions will be carried out in terms of the impedance parameters; however, the admittance parameters or the hybrid parameters may be used as well.

(a) *Conjugate Match.* A linear four-terminal network is *conjugate matched* if the generator impedance is the complex conjugate of its input impedance and the load impedance is the complex conjugate of its output impedance. It is under this terminating condition that maximum power amplification is obtained. The conjugate matched input impedance Z_{im} and the matched output impedance Z_{om} can be derived from Eq. (3-30) by equating $Z_{in} = Z_g^*$ and $Z_o = Z_L^*$ where

$$Z_g^* = R_g - jX_g = \text{conjugate of generator impedance}$$

$$Z_L^* = R_L - jX_L = \text{conjugate of load impedance}$$

and

$$Z_{im} = R_{im} + jX_{im} = z_{11} - \frac{z_{12}z_{21}}{z_{22} + Z_L} = Z_g^*$$

$$Z_{om} = R_{om} + jX_{om} = z_{22} - \frac{z_{12}z_{21}}{z_{11} + Z_g} = Z_L^* \tag{3-31}$$

Thus

$$z_{12}z_{21} = (z_{11} - Z_g^*)(z_{22} + Z_L^*) = (z_{11} + Z_g)(z_{22} - Z_L^*) \tag{3-32a}$$

and

$$\frac{z_{11} - Z_g^*}{z_{11} + Z_g} = \frac{z_{22} - Z_L^*}{z_{22} + Z_L} \tag{3-32b}$$

By simple algebraic manipulation, we obtain

$$\frac{z_{11} + Z_g}{R_g} = \frac{z_{22} + Z_L}{R_L}$$

Equating the real and imaginary terms independently, we obtain the required condition for the conjugate matched network:

$$z_{12}z_{21} = (z_{11} - Z_g^*)(z_{22} + Z_L) = (z_{22} - Z_L^*)(z_{11} + Z_g)$$

$$\frac{z_{11} - Z_g^*}{z_{11} + Z_g} = \frac{z_{22} - Z_L^*}{z_{22} + Z_L}$$

$$\frac{z_{11} + Z_g}{R_g} = \frac{z_{22} + Z_L}{R_L} \tag{3-32c}$$

$$\frac{R_L}{R_g} = \frac{R_{om}}{R_{im}} = \frac{r_{22}}{r_{11}} = \frac{x_{22} + X_L}{x_{11} + X_g}$$

For abbreviation let us introduce two new composite parameters η_r and η_x, where

$$\eta_r = \frac{R_g}{r_{11}} = \frac{R_L}{r_{22}}$$

$$\eta_x = \frac{X_g + x_{11}}{r_{11}} = \frac{X_L + x_{22}}{r_{22}}$$

The generator and load impedances may be rewritten as

$$Z_g = r_{11}(\eta_r + j\eta_x) - jx_{11}$$
$$Z_L = r_{22}(\eta_r + j\eta_x) - jx_{22}$$

Substituting these two equations into Eq. (3-32a):

$$\begin{aligned} z_{12}z_{21} &= r_{11}r_{22}(1 - \eta_r + j\eta_x)(1 + \eta_r + j\eta_x) \\ &= r_{11}r_{22}(A + jB) \end{aligned} \tag{3-33}$$

where
$$\begin{aligned} A &= \frac{r_{12}r_{21} - x_{12}x_{21}}{r_{11}r_{22}} = 1 - \eta_r^2 - \eta_x^2 \\ B &= \frac{r_{12}x_{21} + r_{21}x_{12}}{r_{11}r_{22}} = 2\eta_x \end{aligned} \tag{3-34}$$

Now η_x and η_r become

$$\begin{aligned} \eta_x &= \frac{r_{12}x_{21} + r_{21}x_{12}}{2r_{11}r_{22}} = \frac{B}{2} \\ \eta_r &= \sqrt{1 - A - (B/2)^2} \end{aligned} \tag{3-35}$$

The matched power gain K_{pm} and the matched input and output impedances Z_{im} and Z_{om} can be derived as

$$\begin{aligned} K_{pm} &= \frac{i_2 i_2^* R_L}{i_1 i_1^* R_g} \\ &= \left(\frac{z_{21}}{z_{22} + Z_L}\right)\left(\frac{z_{21}^*}{z_{22}^* + Z_L^*}\right)\frac{R_L}{R_g} \\ &= \frac{|z_{21}|^2}{r_{11}r_{22}[(1 + \eta_r)^2 + \eta_x^2]} \end{aligned} \tag{3-36}$$

$$\begin{aligned} Z_{im} &= r_{11}(\eta_r - j\eta_x) + jx_{11} \\ Z_{om} &= r_{22}(\eta_r - j\eta_x) + jx_{22} \end{aligned} \tag{3-37}$$

The foregoing equations completely describe the conjugate matched condition including power gain and input and output impedances in terms of four open-circuit impedances.

(b) *Image Match.* A linear four-terminal network is *image matched* if the generator impedance is equal to its input impedance and the load impedance is equal to its output impedance, i.e.,

$$
\begin{aligned}
Z_g &= Z_{in} = z_{11} - \frac{z_{12} z_{21}}{z_{22} + Z_L} \\
Z_L &= Z_o = z_{22} - \frac{z_{12} z_{21}}{z_{11} + Z_g}
\end{aligned}
\tag{3-38}
$$

Solving Eq. (3-38), we obtain independent expressions for Z_g and Z_L.

$$
\begin{aligned}
Z_g &= Z_{in} = z_{11} \sqrt{1 - \frac{z_{12} z_{21}}{z_{11} z_{22}}} \\
Z_L &= Z_o = z_{22} \sqrt{1 - \frac{z_{12} z_{21}}{z_{11} z_{22}}}
\end{aligned}
\tag{3-39}
$$

and

$$\frac{Z_g}{Z_L} = \frac{Z_{in}}{Z_o} = \frac{z_{11}}{z_{22}} \tag{3-40}$$

These are the fundamental relationships which must be satisfied in the image-matched condition. This condition does not enjoy the general importance attributed to the conjugate matched conditions, since the image match does not offer maximum power amplification except at low frequencies where reactive effects can be neglected. Under these conditions, of course, the conjugate match is the same as the image match and it is usually referred to simply as the *matched condition.*

(c) *Iterative Match.* If a series of identical four-terminal networks is connected in cascade (i.e., under the iterative matched conditions, where $Z_L = Z_{in}$ and $Z_g = Z_o$), Eq. (3-30) becomes

$$Z_{in} = z_{11} - \frac{z_{12} z_{21}}{z_{22} + Z_{in}}$$

$$Z_o = z_{22} - \frac{z_{12} z_{21}}{z_{11} + Z_o}$$

Solving for Z_{in} and Z_o, we obtain

$$
\begin{aligned}
Z_{in} &= \frac{z_{11} - z_{22}}{2} \left[1 \pm \sqrt{1 + \frac{4(z_{11} z_{22} - z_{12} z_{21})}{(z_{11} - z_{22})^2}} \right] \\
Z_o &= \frac{z_{22} - z_{11}}{2} \left[1 \pm \sqrt{1 + \frac{4(z_{11} z_{22} - z_{12} z_{21})}{(z_{11} - z_{22})^2}} \right]
\end{aligned}
\tag{3-41}
$$

which are the basic requirements for the iterative matched network.

Low-Frequency Operation. It is clear that at low frequencies, where all reactive effects are neglected, the loop equations (3-25) as well as the expression for the various gains and impedances, Eqs. (3-28) to (3-41), may be modified simply by replacing r_{11} for z_{11}, r_{12} for z_{12}, etc. Of particular interest are the expressions which hold under matched conditions, as these are simplified considerably. Thus, under matched conditions the input and output resistances are:

$$R_{im} = r_{11}\sqrt{1 - \frac{r_{12}\,r_{21}}{r_{11}\,r_{22}}} = r_{11}\sqrt{1 - \alpha_{21o}\,\alpha_{12o}} = \frac{\sqrt{S_o}}{g_{11}} \tag{3-42}$$

$$R_{om} = r_{22}\sqrt{1 - \frac{r_{12}\,r_{21}}{r_{11}\,r_{22}}} = r_{22}\sqrt{1 - \alpha_{21o}\,\alpha_{12o}} = \frac{r_{22}}{\sqrt{S_o}} \tag{3-43}$$

The matched voltage gain K_{vm}, the matched current gain K_{im}, and the matched power gain K_{pm} are:

$$K_{vm} = \frac{r_{21}}{r_{11}[1 + \sqrt{1 - \alpha_{21o}\,\alpha_{12o}}} = \frac{-\alpha_{21o}\,g_{11}\,r_{22}}{S_o(1 + 1/\sqrt{S_o})} \tag{3-44}$$

$$K_{im} = \frac{\alpha_{21o}}{1 + \sqrt{1 - \alpha_{21o}\,\alpha_{12o}}} = \frac{\alpha_{21o}}{1 + 1/\sqrt{S_o}} \tag{3-45}$$

$$K_{pm} = \frac{r_{22}}{r_{11}}\,\frac{\alpha_{21o}^2}{(1 + \sqrt{1 - \alpha_{21o}\,\alpha_{12o}})^2} = \frac{g_{11}\,r_{22}\,\alpha_{21o}^2}{S_o(1 + 1/\sqrt{S_o})^2} \tag{3-46}$$

Finally we introduce the *insertion gain*, K_s, which is defined as

$$K_s = \frac{\text{power delivered to the load with network inserted}}{\text{power delivered to the load without network inserted}}$$

For the resistive case the insertion gain is

$$\begin{aligned} K_s &= \frac{\left[\dfrac{r_{21}\,v_g}{(r_{11} + R_g)(r_{22} + R_L) - r_{12}\,r_{21}}\right]^2 R_L}{\left[\dfrac{v_g}{R_g + R_L}\right]^2 R_L} \\ &= \left[\frac{r_{21}(R_g + R_L)}{(r_{11} + R_g)(r_{22} + R_L) - r_{12}\,r_{21}}\right]^2 \\ &= \left[\frac{\alpha_{21o}(R_g + R_L)}{(r_{11} + R_g)(1 + R_L/r_{22}) + \alpha_{21o}\,r_{12}}\right]^2 \end{aligned} \tag{3-47}$$

T-equivalent Circuit Representation. A convenient approach to the analysis of any amplifier is to consider it in terms of an equivalent circuit with externally connected signal generator and load impedance. Two such equivalent circuits of the T type which are applicable at low frequencies only are shown in Figs. 3-2a and 3-4a. At high frequencies the elements must be replaced by complex impedances, viz., z_e, z_b, z_c, z_d and z_m. The open-circuit impedances, z_{11}, z_{12}, z_{21} and z_{22} may now be expressed in terms of these elements. Next, the analytic expressions for the performance of the three basic amplifier configurations may be written down as shown in Table 3-1. Conversion of the open-circuit impedance parameters (the z parameters) to the short-circuit admittance parameters (the y parameters) for each of the amplifier configurations is also shown in this table.

For low-frequency operation, the impedance parameters in the general expressions in Table 3-1 may be replaced by the corresponding resistance parameters. Matched conditions at low-frequency operation are also listed in the table to give the matched input and output resistances and the corresponding gains. The general criterion of stability and the short-circuit stability criterion of the basic amplifiers in low-frequency operation are also listed.

It is to be noted that, for the convenience of analytical manipulation, we have introduced two forward short-circuit current amplification factors for common-base operation. They are

$$\alpha_{ce} \equiv \left(\frac{i_c}{i_e}\right)_{v_c}, \qquad \alpha \equiv -\left(\frac{i_c}{i_e}\right)_{v_c} = -\alpha_{ce}$$

The introduction of the parameter α is partly for conforming to some existing literature, and partly in making both α_{cb} and α positive quantities at low frequency operation. Since

$$\alpha_{cb} = \frac{z_m - z_e}{z_d - z_e}, \qquad \alpha_{ce} = -\frac{z_m + z_b}{z_c + z_b}$$

for low-frequency operation,

$$\alpha_{cbo} = \frac{r_m - r_e}{r_d + r_e}, \quad \text{a positive quantity}$$

$$\alpha_{ceo} = -\frac{r_m + r_b}{r_c + r_b}, \quad \text{a negative quantity}$$

By adopting the parameter α, we have

$$\alpha_{cbo} = \frac{r_m - r_e}{r_d + r_e}, \quad \text{a positive quantity}$$

$$\alpha_o = \frac{r_m + r_b}{r_c + r_b}, \quad \text{a positive quantity}$$

As discussed in Chapter 2, there is a clear distinction between the short-circuit current amplification factor and the current-generator amplification factor. The distinction is apparent as illustrated in the following expressions:

$$\alpha_{cb} = \frac{z_m - z_e}{z_d + z_e}, \qquad \alpha'_{cb} = \frac{z_m}{z_d}$$

$$\alpha_{ce} = -\frac{z_m + z_b}{z_c + z_b}, \qquad \alpha'_{ce} = -\frac{z_m}{z_c}$$

$$\alpha = \frac{z_m + z_b}{z_c + z_b}, \qquad \alpha' = \frac{z_m}{z_c}$$

In normal linear operation of the transistor, the operating voltage and current is in such range that

$$z_e \ll z_m, \qquad z_e \ll z_d$$

$$z_b \ll z_m, \qquad z_b \ll z_c$$

Thus for linear operation we have $\alpha_{cb} \doteq \alpha'_{cb}$, $\alpha_{ce} \doteq \alpha'_{ce}$, $\alpha \doteq \alpha'$. This approximation is adopted throughout the expressions in Table 3-1. For large-signal operation, such as applications in oscillators and pulse circuits where the operation extends to the saturation region, these approximations no longer hold. The exact expressions must therefore be used for such applications. A discussion of the amplification factors when the transistor is operated in the saturation region is given in Chapter 12.

Table 3-1.
ANALYSIS OF THE THREE BASIC AMPLIFIER CONFIGURATIONS USING z PARAMETERS[1]

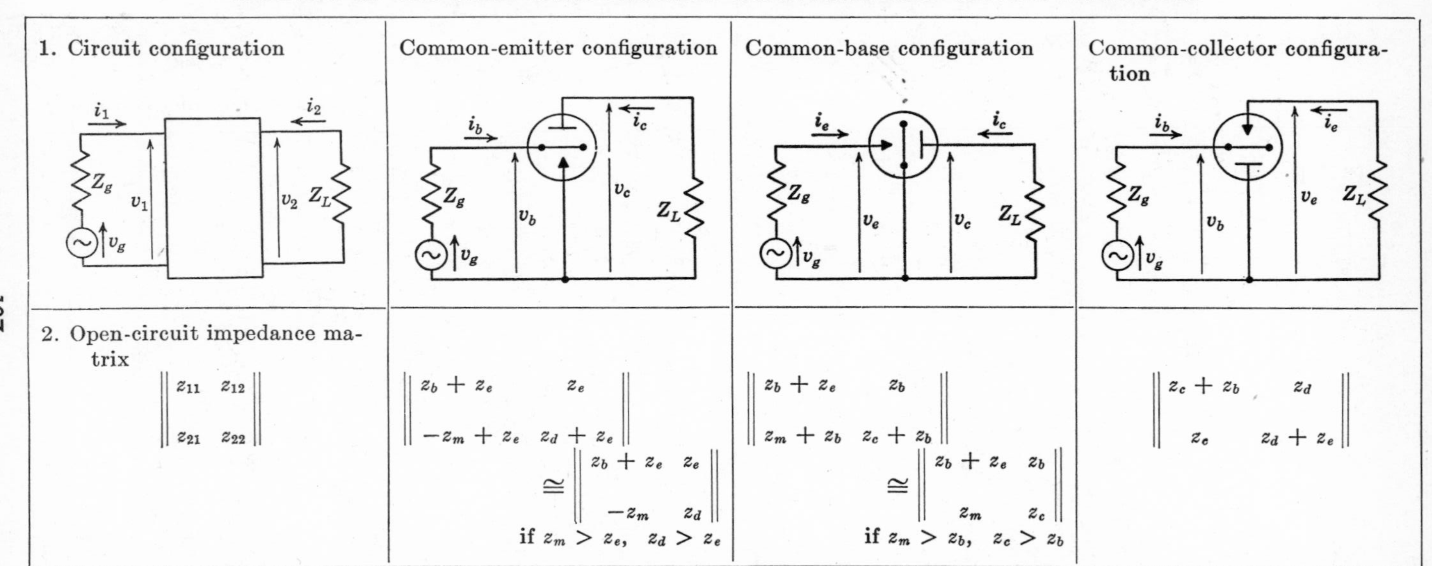

1. Circuit configuration	Common-emitter configuration	Common-base configuration	Common-collector configuration
2. Open-circuit impedance matrix $\begin{Vmatrix} z_{11} & z_{12} \\ z_{21} & z_{22} \end{Vmatrix}$	$\begin{Vmatrix} z_b + z_e & z_e \\ -z_m + z_e & z_d + z_e \end{Vmatrix} \cong \begin{Vmatrix} z_b + z_e & z_e \\ -z_m & z_d \end{Vmatrix}$ if $z_m > z_e$, $z_d > z_e$	$\begin{Vmatrix} z_b + z_e & z_b \\ z_m + z_b & z_c + z_b \end{Vmatrix} \cong \begin{Vmatrix} z_b + z_e & z_b \\ z_m & z_c \end{Vmatrix}$ if $z_m > z_b$, $z_c > z_b$	$\begin{Vmatrix} z_c + z_b & z_d \\ z_c & z_d + z_e \end{Vmatrix}$

Determinant of open-circuit impedance matrix = $|z|$

$|z| = z_b(z_d + z_e) + z_e z_c \cong z_b z_d + z_e z_c$
$\equiv$ determinant in three-circuit configurations

Table 3-1 (continued)

3. Short-circuit admittance matrix $\begin{Vmatrix} y_{11} & y_{12} \\ y_{21} & y_{22} \end{Vmatrix}$	$\begin{Vmatrix} \frac{z_d + z_e}{\lvert z \rvert} & \frac{-z_e}{\lvert z \rvert} \\ \frac{z_m - z_e}{\lvert z \rvert} & \frac{z_b + z_e}{\lvert z \rvert} \end{Vmatrix} \cong \begin{Vmatrix} \frac{z_d}{\lvert z \rvert} & \frac{-z_e}{\lvert z \rvert} \\ \frac{z_m}{\lvert z \rvert} & \frac{z_b + z_e}{\lvert z \rvert} \end{Vmatrix}$	$\begin{Vmatrix} \frac{z_c + z_b}{\lvert z \rvert} & -\frac{z_b}{\lvert z \rvert} \\ -\frac{z_m + z_b}{\lvert z \rvert} & \frac{z_b + z_e}{\lvert z \rvert} \end{Vmatrix} \cong \begin{Vmatrix} \frac{z_c}{\lvert z \rvert} & -\frac{z_b}{\lvert z \rvert} \\ -\frac{z_m}{\lvert z \rvert} & \frac{z_b + z_e}{\lvert z \rvert} \end{Vmatrix}$	$\begin{Vmatrix} \frac{z_d + z_e}{\lvert z \rvert} & -\frac{z_d}{\lvert z \rvert} \\ -\frac{z_c}{\lvert z \rvert} & \frac{z_c + z_b}{\lvert z \rvert} \end{Vmatrix}$
4. Short-circuit current gain $\alpha_{21} = -\frac{z_{21}}{z_{22}}$ $\alpha_{12} = -\frac{z_{12}}{z_{11}}$	$\alpha_{cb} = \frac{z_m - z_e}{z_d + z_e} \cong \frac{z_m}{z_d} \cong \frac{\alpha}{1 - \alpha}$ $\alpha_{bc} = \frac{-z_e}{z_b + z_e}$	$\alpha_{ce} = \frac{-(z_m + z_b)}{z_c + z_b} \equiv -\alpha$ $\alpha_{ec} = \frac{-z_b}{z_b + z_e}$	$\alpha_{eb} = \frac{-z_c}{z_d + z_e} \cong \frac{-z_c}{z_d} \cong \frac{-1}{1 - \alpha}$ $\alpha_{be} = \frac{-z_d}{z_c + z_b} \cong -(1 - \alpha)$
5. Open-circuit voltage gain $\mu_{21} = \frac{z_{21}}{z_{11}}$ $\mu_{12} = \frac{z_{12}}{z_{22}}$	$\mu_{cb} = \frac{-z_m + z_e}{z_b + z_e} \cong \frac{-z_m}{z_b + z_e}$ $\mu_{bc} = \frac{z_e}{z_d + z_e} \cong \frac{z_e}{z_d}$	$\mu_{ce} = \frac{z_m + z_b}{z_b + z_e} \cong \frac{z_m}{z_b + z_e}$ $\mu_{ec} = \frac{z_b}{z_c + z_b} \cong \frac{z_b}{z_c}$	$\mu_{eb} = \frac{z_c}{z_c + z_b}$ $\mu_{be} = \frac{z_d}{z_d + z_e}$

6. Input impedance $Z_{in} = z_{11} - \dfrac{z_{12}z_{21}}{z_{22} + Z_L}$	$Z_{in} = z_b + z_e - \dfrac{z_e(-z_m + z_e)}{z_d + z_e + Z_L}$ $\cong z_b + (1 + \alpha_{cb})z_e; \quad z_e \ll z_m$ $Z_L \ll z_c$	$Z_{in} = z_e + z_b\left(1 - \dfrac{\alpha}{1 + \dfrac{Z_L}{z_c + z_b}}\right)$ $\cong z_e + (1 - \alpha)z_b;$ $Z_L \ll z_c$	$Z_{in} = z_c + z_b - \dfrac{z_d z_c}{z_d + z_e + Z_L}$ $= z_b + \dfrac{1}{\dfrac{1}{z_c} + \dfrac{1 - \alpha}{z_e + Z_L}}$ $\cong z_b + (1 + \alpha_{cb})(z_e + Z_L)$
7. Output impedance $Z_0 = z_{22} - \dfrac{z_{12}z_{21}}{z_{11} + Z_g}$	$Z_0 = z_d + z_e - \dfrac{z_e(-z_m + z_e)}{z_b + z_e + z_g}$ $\cong (z_d + z_e)\left(1 + \dfrac{\alpha_{cb}z_e}{z_b + z_e + Z_g}\right)$ $\cong z_d(1 + \alpha_{cb})$ if $z_b + Z_g \ll z_e$	$Z_0 = z_c + z_b - \dfrac{z_b(z_m + z_b)}{z_b + z_e + Z_g}$ $= (z_c + z_b)\left(1 - \dfrac{\alpha z_b}{z_b + z_e + Z_g}\right)$ $\cong z_c\left(1 - \dfrac{\alpha}{1 + \dfrac{z_e + Z_g}{z_b}}\right)$	$Z_0 = z_d + z_e - \dfrac{z_d z_c}{z_c + z_b + Z_g}$ $\cong z_e + \dfrac{1}{\dfrac{1}{z_d} + \dfrac{1 + \alpha_{cb}}{z_b + Z_g}}$ $\cong z_e + (1 - \alpha)(z_b + Z_g);$ $z_d \gg z_b + Z_g$

Table 3-1 (continued)

8. Voltage gain $K_v = \frac{v_2}{v_1} = \frac{-\alpha_{21} Z_L}{z_{11} + z_{12}\alpha_{21} + \frac{z_{11}}{z_{22}} Z_L}$	$K_v = \frac{\alpha_{cb} Z_L}{z_b + (1 + \alpha_{cb}) z_e + \frac{z_b + z_e}{z_d + z_e} Z_L}$ $\cong \frac{-\alpha_{cb} Z_L}{z_b + (1 + \alpha_{cb}) z_e}$	$K_v = \frac{\alpha Z_L}{z_e + (1 - \alpha) z_b + \frac{z_b + z_e}{z_c + z_b} Z_L}$ $\cong \frac{\alpha Z_L}{z_e + (1 - \alpha) z_b}$	$K_v = \frac{-\alpha_{eb} Z_L}{z_e + z_b + \alpha_{eb} z_d + \frac{z_c + z_b}{z_d + z_e} Z_L}$ $\cong \frac{1}{1 + (1 - \alpha) \frac{z_b}{Z_I}} = 1$
9. Current gain $K_i = \frac{i_2}{i_1} = \frac{\alpha_{21}}{1 + \frac{Z_L}{z_{22}}}$	$K_i \cong \frac{\alpha_{cb}}{1 + \frac{Z_L}{z_d}}$	$K_i \cong \frac{-\alpha}{1 + \frac{Z_L}{z_c}}$	$K_i \cong \frac{-1}{1 - \alpha + \frac{Z_L}{z_c}}$
10. Power gain $K_p = 4R_g R_L \left\| \frac{\alpha_{21}}{(z_{11} + Z_g)\left(1 + \frac{Z_1}{z_{22}}\right) + \alpha_2 z_{12}} \right\|^2$	$K_p = 4R_g R_L \left\| \frac{\alpha_{cb}}{Z_g + z_b + (1 + \alpha_{cb}) z_e + (z_b + z_e + Z_g) \frac{Z_L}{z_d}} \right\|^2$ $\cong 4R_g R_L \left\| \frac{\alpha_{cb}}{Z_g + z_b + (1 + \alpha_{cb}) z_e} \right\|^2$	$K_p = 4R_g R_L \left\| \frac{-\alpha}{Z_g + z_e + (1 - \alpha) z_b + (z_b + z_e + Z_g) \frac{Z_L}{z_c}} \right\|^2$ $\cong 4R_g R_L \left\| \frac{\alpha}{Z_g + z_e + (1 - \alpha) z_b} \right\|^2$	$K_p \cong 4R_g R_L \left\| \frac{1}{z_e + (1 - \alpha)(z_b + Z_g) + Z_L} \right\|^2$

11. Low-frequency matched condition[2]			
(a) Matched input resistance $R_{im} = r_{11}\sqrt{1 - \alpha_{12}\alpha_{21}}$	$R_{im} = (r_b + r_e)\sqrt{\dfrac{r_b + (1 + \alpha_{cb})r_e}{r_b + r_e}}$	$R_{im} = (r_b + r_e)\sqrt{\dfrac{r_e + (1 - \alpha)r_b}{r_e + r_b}}$	$R_{im} = (r_c + r_b)\sqrt{\dfrac{r_b}{r_c + r_b}}$
(b) Matched output resistance $R_{om} = r_{22}\sqrt{1 - \alpha_{12}\alpha_{21}}$	$R_{om} = (r_d + r_e)\sqrt{\dfrac{r_b + (1 + \alpha_{cb})r_e}{r_b + r_e}}$	$R_{om} = (r_c + r_b)\sqrt{\dfrac{r_e + (1 - \alpha)r_b}{r_e + r_b}}$	$R_{om} = (r_d + r_e)\sqrt{\dfrac{r_b}{r_c + r_b}}$
(c) Ratio $\dfrac{R_{om}}{R_{im}} = \dfrac{r_{22}}{r_{11}}$	$\dfrac{R_{om}}{R_{im}} = \dfrac{r_d + r_e}{r_b + r_e}$	$\dfrac{R_{om}}{R_{im}} = \dfrac{r_c + r_b}{r_e + r_b}$	$\dfrac{R_{om}}{R_{im}} = \dfrac{r_d + r_e}{r_c + r_b}$
(d) Matched voltage gain $K_{vm} = \dfrac{r_{21}}{r_{11}(1 + \sqrt{1 - \alpha_{12}\alpha_{21}})}$	$K_{vm} = \dfrac{-r_m}{r_b + r_e} \dfrac{1}{1 + \sqrt{\dfrac{r_b + (1 + \alpha_{cb})r_e}{r_b + r_e}}}$	$K_{vm} = \dfrac{r_m}{r_b + r_e} \dfrac{1}{1 + \sqrt{\dfrac{r_e + (1 - \alpha)r_b}{r_e + r_b}}}$	$K_{vm} = \dfrac{r_c}{r_c + r_b} \dfrac{1}{1 + \sqrt{\dfrac{r_b}{r_c + r_b}}}$
(e) Matched current gain $K_{im} = \dfrac{-r_{21}}{r_{22}(1 + \sqrt{1 - \alpha_{12}\alpha_{21}})}$	$K_{im} = \alpha_{cb} \dfrac{1}{1 + \sqrt{\dfrac{r_b + (1 + \alpha_{cb})r_e}{r_b + r_e}}}$	$K_{im} = \dfrac{-\alpha}{1 + \sqrt{\dfrac{r_e + (1 - \alpha)r_b}{r_e + r_b}}}$	$K_{im} = \dfrac{1}{1 - \alpha} \dfrac{1}{1 + \sqrt{\dfrac{r_b}{r_c + r_b}}}$

Table 3-1 (concluded)

(f) Matched power gain $K_{pm} = \frac{r_{22}}{r_{11}} \frac{\alpha_{21}^2}{(1 + \sqrt{1 - \alpha_{12}\alpha_{21}})^2}$	$K_{pm} = \frac{r_d}{r_b + r_e} \frac{\alpha_{cb}^2}{\left(1 + \sqrt{\frac{r_b + (1 + \alpha_{cb})r_e}{r_b + r_e}}\right)^2}$	$K_{pm} = \frac{r_c}{r_e + r_b} \frac{\alpha^2}{\left(1 + \sqrt{\frac{r_e + (1 - \alpha)r_b}{r_e + r_b}}\right)^2}$	$K_{pm} \cong \frac{1}{(1 - \alpha)\left(1 + \frac{r_b}{r_c + r_b}\right)^2} \cong \frac{1}{1 - \alpha}$
12. Low-frequency short-circuit stability criterion $\alpha_{12}\alpha_{21} < 1$	$\frac{r_m}{r_d} < 1 + \frac{r_b}{r_e} + \frac{r_b}{r_d}$	$\frac{r_m}{r_c} < 1 + \frac{r_e}{r_b} + \frac{r_e}{r_c}$	$\frac{r_m}{r_c} < 1 + \frac{r_e}{r_b} + \frac{r_e}{r_c}$
13. Low-frequency stability criterion with external connections	$\frac{r_m}{r_d + R_L} < 1 + \frac{r_b + R_g}{r_e} + \frac{r_b + R_g}{r_d + R_L}$	$\frac{r_m}{r_c + R_L} < 1 + \frac{r_e + R_g}{r_b} + \frac{r_e + R_g}{r_c + R_L}$	$\frac{r_m}{r_c} < 1 + \frac{r_e + R_L}{r_b + R_g} + \frac{r_c + R_L}{r_c}$

[1] The general expressions are in terms of the z parameters, z_b, z_e, z_c, z_m, and z_d.

[2] The expressions for low frequency operation may be obtained by substituting the resistance parameters, r_b, r_e, r_c, r_m, and r_d for the z parameters in the general expressions.

3.8 Analysis of transistor amplifiers using h parameters

General Analysis. As was shown in Chapter 2, the h parameters are the most convenient to measure in transistors. Thus, it is important to express the performance of the three basic amplifiers in terms of these parameters; such performance is summarized in Table 3-2. As stated in Sec. 3.2, we consider the common-emitter configuration to be the "standard" and, hence, the h parameters for this configuration are treated as the fundamental quantities in terms of which the other configurations are expressed. Table 3-2 also expresses the h parameters, the z parameters, and the y parameters in terms of the common-emitter h parameters.

In a completely analogous manner to that in Sec. 3.7, the general expressions for the gains, the input and output impedances may be derived in terms of the h parameters. The circuit equations are

$$v_g = (h_{11} + Z_g)i_1 + h_{12}v_2 = [(1/y_{11}) + Z_g]i_1 + \mu_{12}v_2$$
$$0 = h_{21}i_1 + (h_{22} + Y_L)v_2 = \alpha_{21}i_1 + [(1/z_{22}) + Y_L]v_2$$

From this, expressions for gain and input and output impedance are derived and are summarized in Table 3-2.[6]

Matched Conditions. The conjugate-matched, image-matched and iterative-matched power gains, and the input and output impedances are also found in a manner which is analogous to the procedure given in Sec. 3.7. These expressions are developed below.

(a) *Conjugate Match.* Let $Z_g^* = R_g - jX_g$ = the conjugate of generator impedance, and let $Y_L^* = G_L - jB_L$ = the conjugate of load admittance. Furthermore, the real part of an h parameter shall be denoted by symbol m and the imaginary part by n. Thus,

$$h_{11} = m_{11} + jn_{11} \qquad h_{12} = m_{12} + jn_{12}$$
$$h_{21} = m_{21} + jn_{21} \qquad h_{22} = m_{22} + jn_{22}$$

Accordingly, we may write for an input impedance $Z_L = m_i + jn_i$, etc. Now, from the circuit equations it follows directly that the input impedance and the output admittance (which must be matched) are

$$Z_{in} = m_{im} + jn_{im} = h_{11} - \frac{h_{12}h_{21}}{h_{22} + Y_L} = Z_g^* \qquad \text{(3-48a)}$$

[6] C. C. Cheng, "Transistor Equations Using *H*-Parameters," *Electronics*, Vol. 27, Apr. 1954.

$$Y_o = m_{om} + jn_{om} = h_{22} - \frac{h_{12}h_{21}}{h_{11} + Z_g} = Y_L^* \qquad (3\text{-}48b)$$

Thus

$$h_{12}h_{21} = (h_{11} - Z_g^*)(h_{22} + Y_L) = (h_{11} + Z_g)(h_{22} - Y_L) \qquad (3\text{-}49a)$$

and

$$\frac{h_{11} - Z_g^*}{h_{11} + Z_g} = \frac{h_{22} - Y_L}{h_{22} + Y_L} \qquad (3\text{-}49b)$$

By simple algebraic manipulation we now obtain

$$\frac{h_{11} + Z_g}{R_g} = \frac{h_{22} + Y_L}{G_L}$$

Equating the real and imaginary parts independently, we obtain the required condition for the conjugate matched network.

$$\frac{G_L}{Rg} = \frac{m_{om}}{m_{im}} = \frac{m_{22}}{m_{11}} = \frac{n_{22} + B_L}{h_{11} + X_g} \qquad (3\text{-}49c)$$

For abbreviation let us introduce two new composite parameters η_m and η_n, where

$$\eta_m = R_g/m_{11} + G_L/m_{22}$$
$$\eta_n = (X_g + n_{11})/m_{11} = (B_L + n_{22})/m_{22}$$

Thus, the generator impedance and load admittance may be re-written as

$$Z_g = m_{11}(\eta_m + j\eta_n) - jn_{11} \qquad (= Z_{i\,m}^*)$$
$$Y_L = m_{22}(\eta_m + j\eta_n) - jn_{22} \qquad (= Y_{o\,m}^*)$$

Substituting these two equations into Eq. 3-49a:

$$h_{12}h_{21} = m_{11}m_{22}\,(1 - \eta_n + j\eta_n)\,(1 + \eta_m + j\eta_m) \qquad (3\text{-}50)$$

Equating real and imaginary parts, it follows that

$$\eta_n = \frac{m_{12}n_{21} + m_{21}n_{12}}{2m_{11}m_{22}} \qquad (3\text{-}51a)$$

and

$$\eta_m = \sqrt{1 - A' - \eta_n^2} \qquad (3\text{-}51b)$$

where

$$A' = \frac{m_{12}m_{21} - n_{12}n_{21}}{m_{11}m_{22}} \qquad (3\text{-}52)$$

The matched power gain K_{pm} and the matched input impedance and output admittance can now be derived as

$$K_{pm} = \frac{v_2 v_2^* G_L}{i_1 i_1^* R_g} = \frac{h_{21}}{(h_{22} + Y_L)} \frac{h_{21}^*}{(h_{22}^* + Y_L^*)}$$

that is,

$$K_{pm} = \frac{|h_{21}|^2}{m_{11} m_{22} [(1 + \eta_m)^2 + \eta_n^2]} \qquad (3\text{-}53a)$$

$$K_{pm} = \frac{|\alpha_{21}|^2}{m_{11} m_{22} [(1 + \eta_m)^2 + \eta_n^2]} \qquad (3\text{-}53b)$$

$$Z_{im} = m_{11} (\eta_m - j\eta_n) + jn_{11} \qquad (3\text{-}54a)$$

$$Y_{om} = m_{22} (\eta_m - j\eta_n) + jn_{22} \qquad (3\text{-}54b)$$

(b) *Image Match.* Analogous to the derivation of the generator and load impedance for image matching as shown in Sec. 3-7, we may derive the generator impedance and load admittance in terms of the h parameters as

$$Z_g = Z_{in} = h_{11} \sqrt{1 - \frac{h_{12} h_{21}}{h_{11} h_{22}}} \qquad (3\text{-}55a)$$

$$Z_{in} = \frac{1}{y_{11}} \sqrt{1 - \mu_{12} \alpha_{21} y_{11} z_{22}} \qquad (3\text{-}55b)$$

$$Y_L = Z_o = h_{22} \sqrt{1 - \frac{h_{12} h_{21}}{h_{11} h_{22}}} \qquad (3\text{-}55c)$$

$$Z_o = \frac{1}{z_{22}} \sqrt{1 - \mu_{12} \alpha_{21} y_{11} z_{22}} \qquad (3\text{-}55d)$$

(c) *Iterative Match.* Analogous to the derivation of the input and the output impedances for iterative matching as shown in Sec. 3.7, we may derive the input impedance and output admittance in terms of the h parameters as follows:

$$Z_{in} = h_{11} - \frac{h_{12} h_{21}}{h_{22} + (1/Z_{in})}, \qquad Y_0 = h_{22} - \frac{h_{12} h_{22}}{h_{11} + (1/Y_0)}$$

These equations are somewhat different in form from those preceding Eq. 3-41 and, hence, the forms of Z_{in} and Y_o differ from Eq. 3-41, viz.

$$\frac{1}{Z_{in}} = \frac{1 - (h_{11} h_{22} - h_{12} h_{21})}{2h_{11}} \cdot \left(1 \pm \sqrt{1 + \frac{4h_{11} h_{22}}{[1 - (h_{11} h_{22} - h_{12} h_{21})]^2}}\right) \qquad (3\text{–}56a)$$

or

$$\frac{1}{Z_{in}} = \frac{1 - h_{11}h_{22}S}{2h_{11}}\left(1 \pm \sqrt{1 \pm \frac{4h_{11}h_{22}}{(1 - h_{11}h_{22}S)^2}}\right) \qquad (3\text{–}56b)$$

$$\frac{1}{Y_0} = \frac{1 - (h_{11}h_{22} - h_{12}h_{21})}{2h_{22}} \cdot\left(1 \pm \sqrt{1 + \frac{4h_{11}h_{22}}{[1 - (h_{11}h_{22} - h_{12}h_{21})]^2}}\right) \qquad (3\text{–}56c)$$

or

$$\frac{1}{Y_0} = \frac{1 - h_{11}h_{22}S}{2h_{22}}\left(1 \pm \sqrt{1 + \frac{4h_{11}h_{22}}{(1 - h_{11}h_{22}S)^2}}\right) \qquad (3\text{–}56d)$$

where $$S \equiv 1 - \frac{h_{12}h_{21}}{h_{11}h_{22}}$$

Low-Frequency Operation. Table 3-2 gives the input and output resistances and the various gains for the special case of low-frequency matched conditions. The symbol S is used in the table to simplify the tabulation. It is defined as:

$$S \equiv 1 - \frac{h_{12}h_{21}}{h_{11}h_{22}} \equiv 1 - \mu_{12}\alpha_{21}y_{11}z_{22} \qquad (3\text{–}57a)$$

and may be shown also to be equal to

$$S = \frac{z_{11}z_{22}}{z_{11}z_{22} - z_{12}z_{21}} = \frac{1}{1 - \dfrac{z_{12}z_{21}}{z_{11}z_{22}}} \qquad (3\text{–}57b)$$

The term S is seen to be the inverse of the normalized circuit determinant, and its low-frequency value S_0 is therefore directly related to the short-circuit stability conditions of the amplifier. Thus the circuit is short-circuit stable if $S_0 \geq 0$, and the circuit is short-circuit unstable if $S_0 < 0$.

Table 3-2.

ANALYSIS OF THE THREE BASIC AMPLIFIER CONFIGURATIONS USING h PARAMETERS[1]

1. Circuit configuration	Common-emitter configuration	Common-base configuration	Common-collector configuration
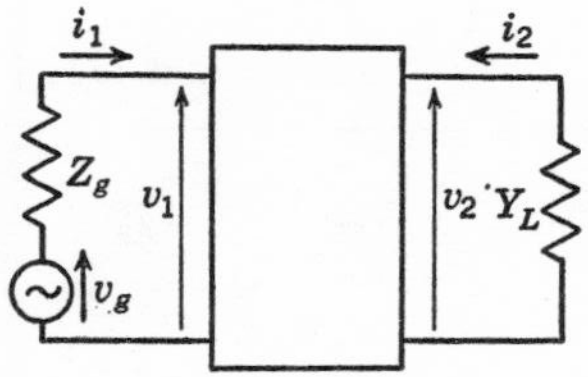	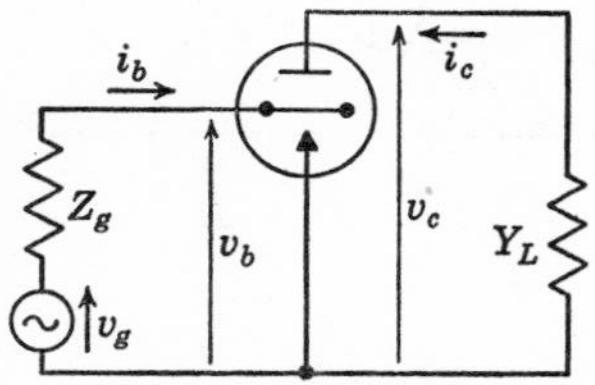	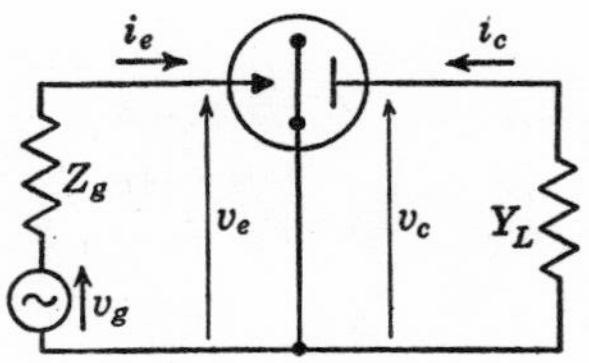	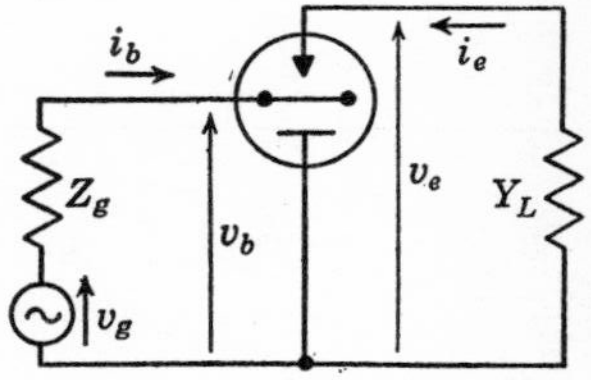
2. *h* parameter $y_{11} = 1/h_{11}$ $\mu_{12} = h_{12}$ $\alpha_{21} = h_{21}$ $z_{22} = 1/h_{22}$ $S = 1 - \mu_{12}\alpha_{21}y_{11}z_{22}$	y_{11e} μ_{bc} α_{cb} z_{22e} $S_e = 1 - \mu_{bc}\alpha_{cb}y_{11e}z_{22e}$	$(1 + \alpha_{cb})y_{11e}$ $\mu_{ec} = \mu_{bc}S_e/(1 - S_e)$, if $\lvert \alpha_{cb} \rvert \gg 1$ $\alpha_{ce} = -\alpha_{cb}/(1 + \alpha_{cb}) = -\alpha$, $\alpha \equiv -\alpha_{ce}$ $(1 + \alpha_{cb})z_{22e}$ $S_b = 1 + (1 + \alpha_{cb})S_e$	y_{11e} $\mu_{be} = 1 - \mu_{bc} \cong 1$, $\lvert \mu_{bc} \rvert \ll 1$ $\alpha_{eb} = -(1 + \alpha_{cb})$ z_{22e} $S_c = 1 + (1 - \mu_{bc})(1 + \alpha_{cb})y_{11e}z_{22e}$ $\cong 1 + \alpha_{cb}y_{11e}z_{22e}$, $\lvert \alpha_{cb} \rvert \gg 1$, $\lvert \mu_{bc} \rvert \ll 1$

Table 3-2 (continued)

3. z parameters $z_{11} = \frac{S}{y_{11}}$ $z_{12} = \mu_{12} z_{22}$ $z_{21} = -\alpha_{21} z_{22}$ z_{22}	$\frac{S_e}{y_{11e}}$ $\mu_{bc} z_{22e}$ $-\alpha_{cb} z_{22e}$ z_{22e}	$\frac{S_b}{(1 + \alpha_{cb}) y_{11e}} \cong \frac{S_e}{y_{11e}}$ $\frac{S_e}{y_{11e}} - \mu_{bc} z_{22e}$ $\alpha_{cb} z_{22e}$ $(1 + \alpha_{cb}) z_{22e}$	$\frac{S_c}{y_{11e}} \cong \frac{1}{y_{11e}} + \alpha_{cb} z_{22e}$ $(1 - \mu_{bc}) z_{22e} \cong z_{22e}$ $(1 + \alpha_{cb}) z_{22e} \cong \alpha_{cb} z_{22e}$ z_{22e}
4. y parameters y_{11} $y_{12} = -\mu_{12} y_{11}$ $y_{21} = \alpha_{21} y_{11}$ $y_{22} = \frac{S}{z_{22}}$	y_{11e} $-\mu_{bc} y_{11e}$ $\alpha_{cb} y_{11e}$ $\frac{S_e}{z_{22e}}$	$(1 + \alpha_{cb}) y_{11e}$ $\cong \frac{S_e}{z_{22e}}$ $-\alpha_{cb} y_{11e}$ $\frac{1 + (1 + \alpha_{cb}) S_e}{(1 + \alpha_{cb}) z_{22e}} \cong \frac{S_e}{z_{22e}}$	y_{11e} $-(1 - \mu_{bc}) y_{11e} \cong -y_{11e}$ $-(1 + \alpha_{cb}) y_{11e}$ $\frac{S_c}{z_{22e}} = \frac{1}{z_{22e}} + \alpha_{cb} y_{11e}$
5. Other parameters $\alpha_{12} = \frac{1}{\alpha_{21}}\left(1 - \frac{1}{S}\right)$ $\mu_{21} = \frac{1}{\mu_{12}}\left(1 - \frac{1}{S}\right)$	$\frac{1}{\alpha_{cb}}\left(1 - \frac{1}{S_e}\right)$ $\frac{1}{\mu_{bc}}\left(1 - \frac{1}{S_e}\right)$	$\alpha_{ec} = \frac{-\alpha_{cb} S_e}{1 + (1 + \alpha_{cb}) S_e}$ $\mu_{ce} \cong -\frac{1}{\mu_{bc}}\left(1 - \frac{1}{S_e}\right)$	$\alpha_{be} = \frac{-1}{1 + \alpha + \frac{1}{y_{11e} z_{22e}}}$ $\mu_{eb} = \frac{1}{1 - \mu_{bc} + \frac{1}{(1 + \alpha_{cb}) y_{11e} y_{22e}}}$

6. Input impedance $Z_{in} = \frac{1}{y_{11}} - \frac{\mu_{12}\,\alpha_{21}}{Y_L + \frac{1}{z_{22}}}$	$Z_{in} = \frac{1}{y_{11e}} - \frac{\mu_{bc}\,\alpha_{cb}}{Y_L + 1/z_{22e}}$ $\cong \frac{1}{y_{11e}} - \frac{\mu_{bc}\,\alpha_{cb}}{Y_L}, \quad Z_L \ll z_{22e}$	$Z_{in} = \frac{1}{(1+\alpha_{cb})y_{11e}}, \quad Y_L \gg \frac{1}{z_{22e}}$	$Z_{in} = \frac{1}{y_{11e}} + \frac{(1+\alpha_{cb})}{Y_L}; \quad Y_L \gg \frac{1}{z_{22e}}$
7. Output admittance $Y_0 = \frac{1}{z_{22}} - \frac{\mu_{12}\,\alpha_{21}}{Z_g + \frac{1}{y_{11}}}$ $= \frac{S}{z_{22}}, \quad Z_g < \frac{1}{y_{11}}$	$Y_0 = \frac{1}{z_{22e}} - \frac{\mu_{bc}\,\alpha_{cb}}{Z_g + \frac{1}{y_{11e}}}$ $\cong \frac{S_e}{z_{22e}}, \quad Z_g < \frac{1}{y_{11e}}$	$Y_0 = \frac{\frac{1}{1+\alpha_{cb}} + S_e}{z_{22e}},$ $Z_g < \frac{1}{y_{11e}(1+\alpha_{cb})}$	$Y_0 \cong \frac{1 + \alpha_{cb}\,y_{11e}\,z_{22e}}{z_{22e}}$ $\lvert \mu_{be} \rvert \ll 1, \quad \lvert \alpha_{cb} \rvert \gg 1$
8. Voltage gain $K_v = \frac{-y_{11}}{SY_L - \frac{1}{z_{22}}}$ $\cong -\frac{y_{11}}{S_e\,Y_L}, \quad \text{if } Y_L \gg \frac{1}{z_{22}}$	$K_v = \frac{-y_{11e}}{S_e\,Y_L - \frac{1}{z_{22e}}}$ $\cong -\frac{y_{11e}}{S_e\,Y_L}$	$K_v = \frac{-y_{11e}}{S_e\,Y_L + \frac{Y_L}{1+\alpha_{cb}} - \frac{1}{z_{22e}(1+\alpha_{cb})^2}}$ $\cong \frac{-y_{11e}}{S_eY_L + \frac{1}{1+\alpha_{cb}}}$	$K_v \cong \frac{-y_{11e}}{Y_L + \alpha_{cb}\,y_{11e}\,z_{22e}}$
9. Current gain $K_i = \frac{\alpha_{21}\,Y_L}{\frac{1}{z_{22}} + Y_L}$	$K_i = \frac{\alpha_{cb}\,Y_L}{Y_L + \frac{1}{z_{22e}}}$	$K_i = \frac{-\alpha_{cb}Y_L}{(1+\alpha_{cb})Y_L + \frac{1}{z_{22e}}}$	$K_i = \frac{-(1+\alpha_{cb})Y_L}{Y_L + \frac{1}{z_{22e}}}$

Table 3-2 (concluded)

10. Power gain $K_p = 4R_gR_L \left\| \dfrac{\alpha_{21}Y_L}{\left(Z_g + \dfrac{1}{y_{11}}\right)\left(Y_L + \dfrac{1}{z_{22}}\right) - \mu_{12}\,\alpha_{21}} \right\|^2$	$K_p = 4R_gR_L \left\| \dfrac{\alpha_{cb}Y_L}{\left(Z_g + \dfrac{1}{y_{11e}}\right)\left(Y_L + \dfrac{1}{z_{22e}}\right) - \mu_{bc}\,\alpha_{cb}} \right\|^2$	$K_p = 4R_gR_L \left\| \dfrac{\alpha_{cb}Y_L}{\left[Z_g + \dfrac{1}{(1+\alpha_{cb})y_{11e}}\right]\left[(1+\alpha_{cb})Y_L + \dfrac{1}{z_{22e}}\right]} \right\|^2$	$K_p \cong 4R_gR_L \left\| \dfrac{(1+\alpha_{cb})Y_L}{\left(Z_g + \dfrac{1}{y_{11e}}\right)\left(Y_L + \dfrac{1}{z_{22e}}\right) + \alpha_{cb}} \right\|^2$
11. Low frequency matched condition[2]			$S_{co} = 1 + (1 + \alpha_{cbo})(1 - \mu_{bco})g_{11e}r_{22e}$ $\cong \alpha_{cbo}g_{11e}r_{22e}$
(a) Matched input resistance $R_{im} = \dfrac{\sqrt{S_0}}{g_{11}}$	$R_{im} = \dfrac{\sqrt{S_{eo}}}{g_{11e}}$	$R_{im} = \dfrac{\sqrt{S_{eo}}}{g_{11e}} \dfrac{1}{\sqrt{1 + \alpha_{cbo}}}$	$R_{im} = \dfrac{\sqrt{S_{co}}}{g_{11e}}$
(b) Matched output resistance $R_{om} = \dfrac{r_{22}}{\sqrt{S_0}}$	$R_{om} = \dfrac{r_{22e}}{\sqrt{S_{eo}}}$	$R_{om} = \dfrac{r_{22e}}{\sqrt{S_{eo}}} \sqrt{1 + \alpha_{cbo}}$	$R_{om} = \dfrac{r_{22e}}{\sqrt{S_{co}}}$
(c) Ratio $\dfrac{R_{om}}{R_{im}} = \dfrac{r_{22}}{r_{11}} = \dfrac{r_{22}g_{11}}{S_0}$	$\dfrac{R_{om}}{R_{im}} = \dfrac{r_{22e}g_{11e}}{S_{eo}}$	$\dfrac{R_{om}}{R_{im}} = \dfrac{r_{22e}g_{11e}}{S_{eo}}(1 + \alpha_{cbo})$	$\dfrac{R_{om}}{R_{im}} = \dfrac{r_{22e}g_{11e}}{S_{co}} \cong \dfrac{1}{\alpha_{cbo}}$

(d) Matched voltage gain $K_{vm} = \dfrac{-\alpha_{21o}\, g_{11}\, r_{22}}{S_o + \sqrt{S_o}}$	$K_{vm} = \dfrac{-\alpha_{cbo}\, g_{11e}\, r_{22e}}{S_{eo} + \sqrt{S_{eo}}}$	$K_{vm} = \dfrac{\alpha_{cbo}(1+\alpha_{cbo})g_{11e}r_{22e}}{1 + (1+\alpha_{cbo})S_{eo} + \sqrt{1 + (1+\alpha_{cbo})S_{eo}}} = \dfrac{\alpha_{cbo}\, g_{11e}\, r_{22e}}{S_{eo} + \sqrt{\dfrac{S_{eo}}{(1+\alpha_{cbo})}}}$	$K_{vm} = \dfrac{(1+\alpha_{cbo})g_{11e}\, r_{22e}}{S_{co} + \sqrt{S_{co}}}$
(e) Matched current gain $K_{im} = \dfrac{\alpha_{21o}}{1 + \dfrac{1}{\sqrt{S_o}}}$	$K_{im} = \dfrac{\alpha_{cbo}}{1 + \dfrac{1}{\sqrt{S_{eo}}}}$	$K_{im} \cong \dfrac{-\alpha_{cbo}}{(1+\alpha_{cbo})\left(1 + \sqrt{\dfrac{1}{\alpha_{cb}\, S_{eo}}}\right)}$	$K_{im} = \dfrac{-(1+\alpha_{cbo})}{1 + \dfrac{1}{\sqrt{S_{co}}}}$
(f) Matched power gain $K_{pm} = \dfrac{g_{11}\, r_{22}\, \alpha_{21o}^2}{S_o\left(1 + \dfrac{1}{\sqrt{S_o}}\right)^2}$	$K_{pm} = \dfrac{g_{11e}\, r_{22e}\, \alpha_{cbo}^2}{S_{eo}\left(1 + \dfrac{1}{\sqrt{S_{eo}}}\right)^2}$	$K_{pm} \cong \dfrac{g_{11e}\, r_{22e}\, \alpha_{cbo}^2}{\dfrac{S_{eo}}{\alpha_{cbo}}\left(1 + \sqrt{\dfrac{1}{\alpha_{cb}\, S_{eo}}}\right)^2}$	$K_{pm} = \dfrac{g_{11e}\, r_{22e}(1+\alpha_{cbo})^2}{S_{co}\left(1 + \dfrac{1}{\sqrt{S_{co}}}\right)^2}$

[1] The general expressions are in terms of the h parameters for common-emitter operation. They are:

$$h_{11e} = 1/y_{11e}, \quad h_{12e} = \mu_{bc}, \quad h_{21e} = \alpha_{cb}, \quad h_{22e} = 1/z_{22e}$$

At low frequencies the h parameters are:

$$h_{11e} = 1/g_{11e}, \quad h_{12e} = \mu_{bco}, \quad h_{21e} = \alpha_{cbo}, \quad h_{22e} = 1/r_{22e}$$

The term S in common-emitter operation is

$$S_e = 1 - \frac{h_{12e}h_{21e}}{h_{11e}h_{22e}} = 1 - \alpha_{cb}\mu_{bc}y_{11e}z_{22e}$$

$$S_{eo} = 1 - \alpha_{cbo}\mu_{bco}g_{11e}r_{22e}.$$

[2] The expressions for low-frequency operation may be obtained by substituting the low-frequency parameters g_{11e}, α_{cbo}, μ_{bco}, r_{22e}, and S_{eo} for the high-frequency parameters y_{11e}, α_{cb}, μ_{bc}, z_{22e}, and S_e in the general expressions.

3.9 Transistor noise

An important factor which characterizes the performance of an electronic device is its associated noise. The theory of noise generation from various kinds of electronic components has been extensively developed. Thermal noise from resistors (attributed to random motion of electrons), shot noise from vacuum diodes (caused by random emission of electrons by the cathode), flicker noise from vacuum triodes (due to low-frequency fluctuation in the emission current), and partition noise from multielectrode tubes (introduced by random distribution of electrons between electrodes) are all fairly well understood. Readers are referred to an excellent treatment on general noise study by A. van der Ziel.[7]

Noise problems associated with transistors and other semiconductor devices have been investigated recently; however, a sound fundamental theory is still lacking. We shall here summarize the available theory on the generation of noise in the transistor and will also present experimental data on noise of some common types of transistors. Equivalent circuits of noisy transistors (i.e., the transistor as a circuit element in the presence of transistor noise) will be derived, and conditions of operation will be discussed. Sufficient information will be given to the circuit engineer so that the noise performance of specific transistor circuits can be predicted.

Junction-type transistors are, in general, less noisy than the point-contact type. As the manufacturing techniques of junction transistors have been improved, some low-noise transistors have become even quieter than low-noise vacuum tubes at audio frequencies. The use of junction transistors in low-noise audio applications, such as input stage of hearing aids, microphone and phonograph preamplifiers, etc., faces a promising future. At the high frequencies, however, vacuum tubes are still quieter and have higher gain than the presently available transistors; thus the application of the transistor to this field is limited at present.

Some of the important properties of transistor noise are illustrated by its frequency spectrum.[8] Figure 3-13 shows the generalized noise spectrum of a typical junction transistor connected as an amplifier. It can be seen that the noise behavior is quite different in

[7] A. van der Ziel, *Noise,* Prentice-Hall, Inc., New York, 1954.

[8] P. L. Bargellini and M. B. Herscher, "Investigations of Noise in Audio Frequency Amplifiers Using Junction Transistors," *Proc. I.R.E.,* Vol. 43, pp. 217-226, Feb. 1955.

different frequency ranges. In the low-frequency range, $f < f_1$, the noise factor[9] decreases as the frequency increases according to the $1/f^\gamma$ law. Experimental results show that γ varies from 0.9 to 1.2, and f_1 varies from 50 kc to 1 kc for many junction transistors; while some newly developed transistors have even lower values of f_1. In the medium-frequency range, $f_1 < f < f_2$, the noise factor remains approximately constant. In the high-frequency range, $f > f_2$, the noise factor increases with the frequency. Experimental results show that f_2 varies from 100 kc to 500 kc for most junction transistors. The trend of improving noise performance of audio frequency junction transistors has been to reduce f_1; and the improvement in high frequency junction transistors has been to increase f_2.

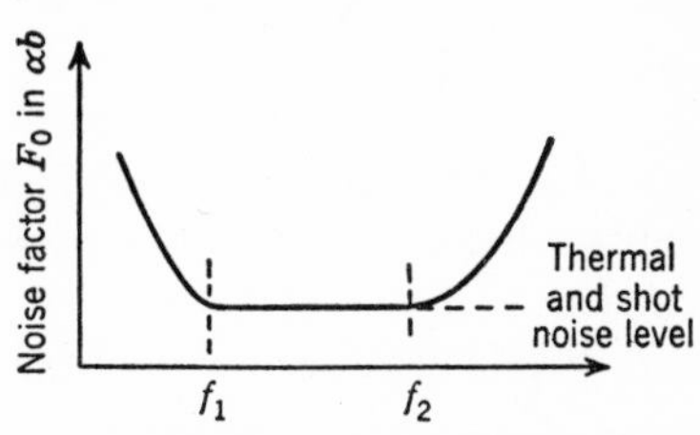

Fig. 3-13. Frequency spectrum of transistor noise.

The more important sources of transistor noise are summarized here as follows:

1. Thermal noise emf, $v_{th,b}$, contributed by the base resistance r_b,

$$\overline{v_{th,b}^2} = 4kTr_b\,df \tag{3-58}$$

where k is Boltzmann's constant, T is the temperature in degrees Kelvin, and df is the effective noise bandwidth.

2. Shot noise emf, $v_{sh,e}$, associated with the emitter-base junction,

$$\overline{v_{sh,e}^2} = 2eI_e r_e^2\,df \tag{3-59}$$

where e is the electronic charge, and I_e is the total emitter direct current.

[9] The noise factor of a four-terminal network is defined as the ratio of the signal-to-noise ratio at the input terminals to the signal-to-noise ratio at the output terminals. Analytically, noise factor, $F = \dfrac{S_i/N_i}{S_o/N_o} = 10 \log_{10} \dfrac{S_i/N_i}{S_o/N_o}$ db where S_i, S_o are the signal power at the input and the output terminals, respectively; and N_i, N_o are the noise power at the input and output terminals, respectively.

3. Shot noise emf, $v_{sh,c}$, associated with the collector-base junction as a result of the current I_{co} of the collector junction,

$$\overline{v_{sh,c}^2} = 2eI_{co}r_c^2\,df \tag{3-60}$$

4. Partition noise current, i_{par}, contributed[10] by the random distribution of the hole current between the collector and the base

$$\overline{i_{par}^2} = 2e\alpha I_e(1 - \beta)\,df \tag{3-61}$$

where α is the current amplification factor, and β is the ratio of the emitter hole current that arrives at the collector to the emitter hole current.

5. Semiconductor noise emf, v_{sc},

$$\overline{v_{sc}^2} = K_c V^\alpha R_c^\beta f^{-\gamma} \tag{3-62}$$

where K_c is a factor dependent on the material used, V is the applied direct voltage, R_c is the d-c resistance, and α, β, are constants.

Equation (3-62) shows the frequency-dependent relation of transistor noise at low frequency. Recent advancements in manufacturing technique have reduced this noise considerably.

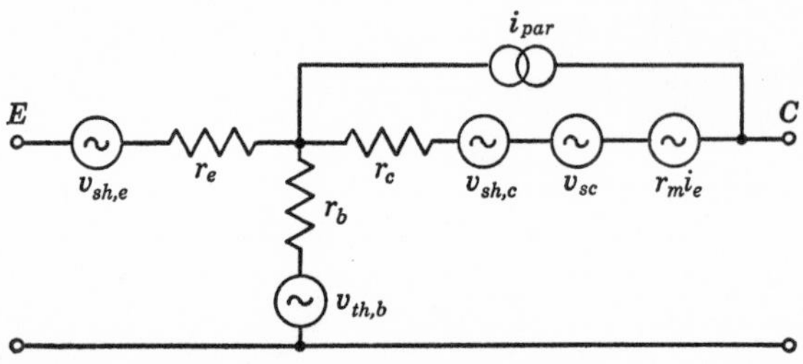

Fig. 3-14. Equivalent circuit of a transistor including transistor noise.

In accordance with the above-mentioned noise sources in a junction transistor, an equivalent circuit for the noise transistor in common-base operation is derived as shown in Fig. 3-14.

3.10 Network representation of transistors in the presence of noise

It has been shown previously that, without the consideration of transistor noise, the transistor can be represented by a four-terminal

[10] A. van der Ziel, "Notes on Shot and Partition Noise in Junction Transistors," *J. Appl. Phys.*, Vol. 25, June 1954.

network characterized by a set of four parameters. If transistor noise is to be included, the "noisy" transistor may be considered as a "noisy" four-terminal network characterized by a set of six parameters, where two noise generators are present with the four transistor parameters. This is illustrated in Fig. 3-15.

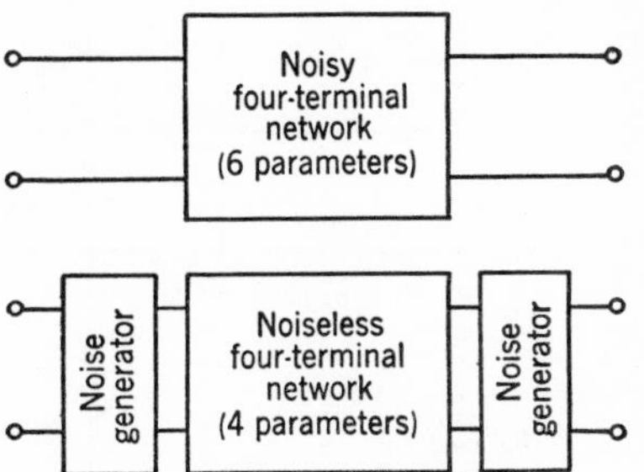

Fig. 3-15. Representation of noisy four-terminal network.

If two voltage generators, v_{n1} in the input circuit and v_{n2} in the output circuit, are selected to represent the noise source, the "noisy" four-terminal network may be represented by the equivalent circuit shown in Fig. 3-16. Equivalent circuits for the three basic amplifier configurations are shown in Fig. 3-17.

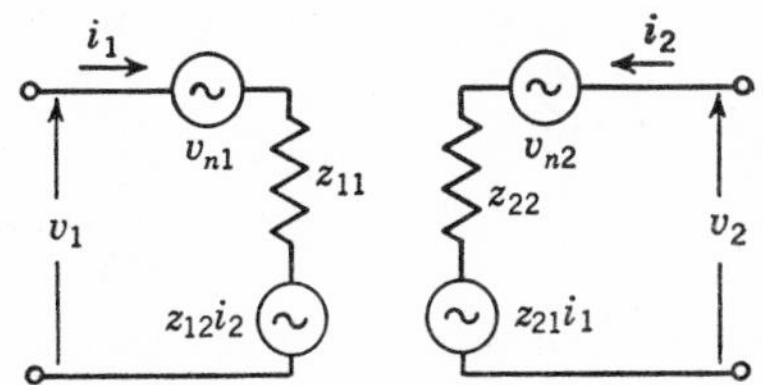

Fig. 3-16. Equivalent circuit of a noisy four-terminal network.

The noise factors of the three basic amplifiers can be obtained easily from the equivalent circuit:

For the common-emitter amplifier,

$$F = 1 + \frac{1}{4KTR_g\Delta f} \cdot \left[\overline{v_{ne}^2}\left(\frac{r_m + r_b + R_g}{r_m - r_e}\right)^2 + \overline{v_{nc}^2}\left(\frac{r_e + r_b + R_g}{r_m - r_e}\right)^2\right] \tag{3-63}$$

For the common-base amplifier,

$$F = 1 + \frac{1}{4KTR_g\Delta f}\left[\overline{v_{ne}^2} + \overline{v_{nc}^2}\left(\frac{r_e + r_b + R_g}{r_m + r_b}\right)^2\right] \tag{3-64}$$

For the common-collector amplifier,

$$F = 1 + \frac{1}{4KTR_g\Delta f}\left[\overline{v_{ne}^2}\left(\frac{r_b + r_c + R_g}{r_c}\right)^2 + \overline{v_{nc}^2}\left(\frac{r_b + R_g}{r_c}\right)^2\right] \tag{3-65}$$

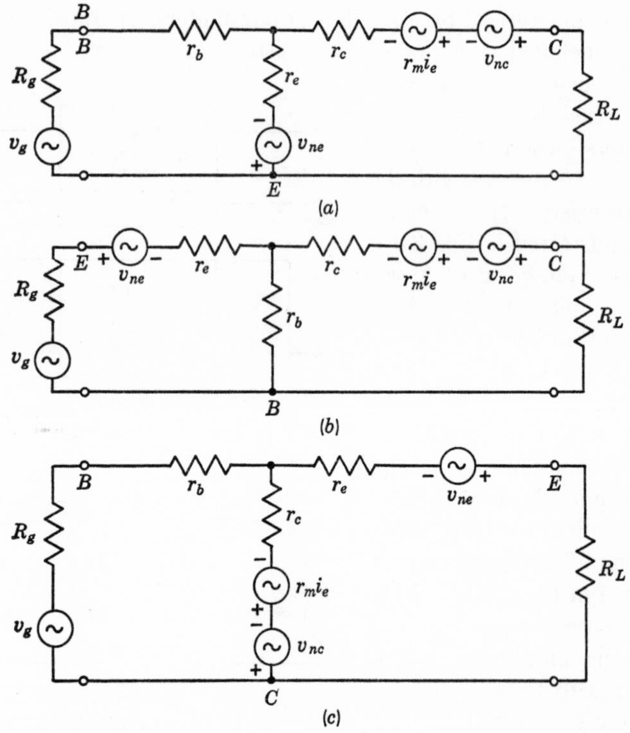

Fig. 3-17. Equivalent circuits of the three basic amplifiers including transistor noise: (a) common-emitter; (b) common-base; (c) common-collector.

For a practical junction transistor, we know that

$$r_e \ll r_c, \qquad r_e \ll r_m, \qquad r_b \ll r_c, \qquad r_b \ll r_m$$

and if the generator resistance used satisfies the condition that

$$r_g \ll r_c, \qquad r_g \ll r_m$$

then Eqs. (3-63), (3-64), and (3-65) can be further simplified as

$$F \cong 1 + \frac{1}{4KTR_g\Delta f}\left(\overline{v_{ne}^2} + \frac{\overline{v_{nc}^2}\,(r_e + r_b + R_g)^2}{r_m^2}\right) \tag{3-63a}$$

$$F \cong 1 + \frac{1}{4KTR_g\Delta f}\left(\overline{v_{ne}^2} + \frac{\overline{v_{nc}^2}\,(r_e + r_b + R_g)^2}{r_m^2}\right) \tag{3-64a}$$

$$F \cong 1 + \frac{1}{4KTR_g\Delta f}\left(\overline{v_{ne}^2} + \overline{v_{nc}^2}\frac{(r_b + R_g)^2}{r_c^2}\right)$$

$$\cong 1 + \frac{1}{4KTR_g\Delta f}\left(\overline{v_{ne}^2} + \alpha_o^2\frac{\overline{v_{nc}^2}}{r_c^2}\right)$$

$$\cong 1 + \frac{1}{4KTR_g\Delta f}\left(\overline{v_{ne}^2} + \frac{\overline{v_{nc}^2}}{r_c^2}\right), \quad \text{if} \quad \alpha_o \cong 1 \tag{3-65a}$$

An inspection of Eqs. (3-63a), (3-64a), and (3-65a) discloses the fact that the noise factors of transistor amplifiers are approximately equal for the three connections.

The spot frequency noise factors (F_o) of the three basic amplifiers are obtained simply by using one cycle as the effective noise bandwidth (Δf), and Eqs. (3-63), (3-64), (3-65), become

$$F_o = 1 + \frac{1}{4KTR_g} \cdot \left[\overline{v_{ne}^2}\left(\frac{r_m + r_b + R_g}{r_m - r_e}\right)^2 + \overline{v_{nc}^2}\left(\frac{r_e + r_b + R_g}{r_m - r_e}\right)^2\right] \tag{3-66}$$

$$F_o = 1 + \frac{1}{4KTR_g}\left[\overline{v_{ne}^2} + \overline{v_{nc}^2}\left(\frac{r_e + r_b + R_g}{r_m + r_b}\right)^2\right] \tag{3-67}$$

$$F_o = 1 + \frac{1}{4KTR_g}\left[\overline{v_{ne}^2}\left(\frac{r_b + r_c + R_g}{r_c}\right)^2 + \overline{v_{nc}^2}\left(\frac{r_b + R_g}{r_c}\right)^2\right] \tag{3-68}$$

The integrated noise factor (F_{int}) over a frequency range can be obtained from the following integration:

$$F_{int} = \frac{1}{f_a - f_b}\int_{f_b}^{f_a} F_o(f)\, df$$

where $f_a - f_b$ is the frequency range of interest.

The noise mean squared voltages ($\overline{v_{ne}^2}$, $\overline{v_{nc}^2}$) can be calculated from the results of spot frequency noise factor measurements. The following data have been obtained:

$$v_{ne} = 1\ \mu\text{v},$$

$$v_{nc} = 100\ \mu\text{v};$$

at 1 kc for point-contact transistors and

$$v_{ne} = 0.005 \text{ to } 0.04\ \mu\text{v},$$

$$v_{nc} = 10 \text{ to } 40\ \mu\text{v};$$

at 1 kc for junction transistors.

The above data show that the noise generators in both the emitter circuit and the collector circuit of point-contact transistors have higher open-circuit voltages than the corresponding generators of the junction transistors. If the mutual resistance (r_m) of both types is about the same, then generally speaking, the point contact transistor amplifiers are much more noisy than the junction transistor amplifiers.

The optimum generator resistance $R_{g,\text{opt}}$ for the minimum noise condition of the three amplifiers can be determined simply if we set

$$\frac{\partial F_o}{\partial r_g} = 0$$

and solve for R_g. Results are listed as follows:

For the common-emitter amplifier

$$R_{g,\text{opt}} \cong \sqrt{r_b^2 + (v_{ne}/v_{nc})^2 r_m^2} \tag{3-69}$$

For the common-base amplifier

$$R_{g,\text{opt}} \cong \sqrt{(v_{ne}/v_{nc})^2(r_b + r_m)^2 + (r_e + r_b)^2} \tag{3-70}$$

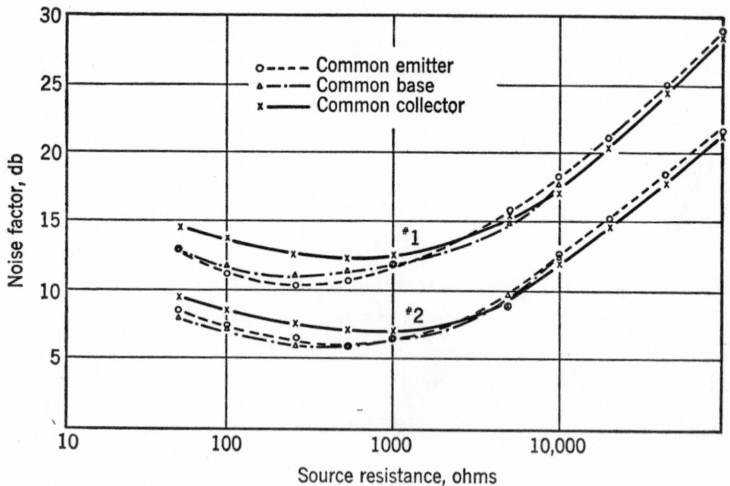

Fig. 3-18. Noise factor vs. source resistance for two junction transistors. $V_C = -6$ volts, $I_c = 1$ ma, $R_L = 10{,}000$ ohms, $f = 1$ kc.

For the common-collector amplifier

$$R_{g,\text{opt}} \cong \sqrt{r_b^2 + (v_{ne}/v_{nc})^2 r_c^2} \tag{3-71}$$

These optimum signal source resistances are different from the matched input resistances of the corresponding amplifiers shown in the earlier section.

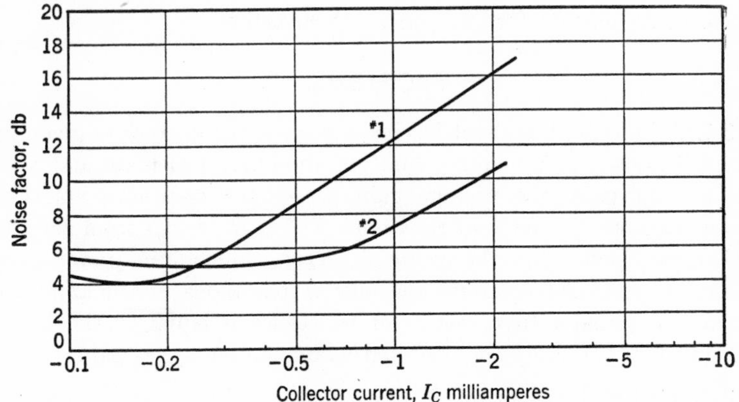

Fig. 3-19. Noise factor vs. collector current for two junction transistors, common-emitter connection. $V_C = -6$ volts, $R_g = 450$ ohms, $R_L = 10{,}000$ ohms, $f = 1$ kc.

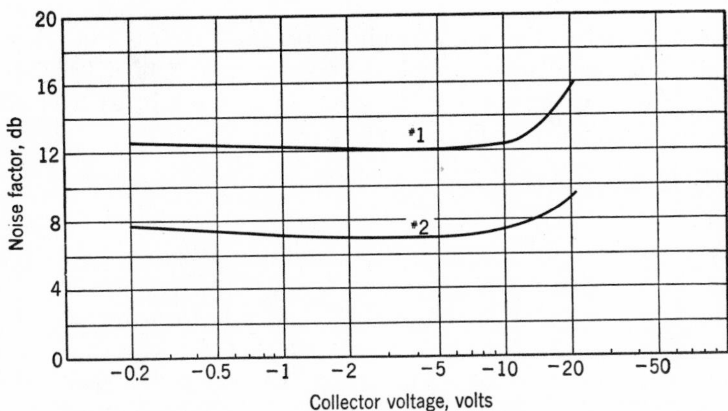

Fig. 3-20. Noise factor vs. collector voltage for two junction transistors, common-emitter connection. $R_g = 450$ ohms, $R_L = 10{,}000$ ohms, $f = 1$ kc, $I_C = 1.0$ ma.

Experimental verification of Eqs. (3-69), (3-70), and (3-71) is shown in Fig. 3-18, where noise factor vs. source resistance R_g is plotted for the three basic amplifiers using typical junction transistors.

The noise factor of a transistor amplifier depends also on its d-c operating condition. Figure 3-19 shows the noise factor vs. collector direct current at constant collector direct voltage. Figure 3-20 shows the noise factor vs. collector direct voltage at constant collector direct current for two junction transistors.

PROBLEMS

3-1. A junction transistor having the same parameters as given in Sec. 3.3 is used as a common-emitter amplifier. Calculate and plot the current gain, the voltage gain, the input resistance and the power gain versus the load resistance R_L, if R_L varies from zero to 10^6 ohms. Determine the value of R_L for maximum power gain from the plot, and compute the output resistance of the amplifier when the signal source generator resistance is equal to the input resistance of the amplifier operated at maximum power gain.

3-2. Repeat Problem 3-2 if the transistor is used as a common-base amplifier and the load resistance varies from zero to 10^7 ohms.

3-3. Repeat Problem 3-1 if the transistor is used as a common-collector amplifier.

3-4. Determine the open-circuit impedance matrix, the short-circuit admittance matrix, and the hybrid matrix of a transistor having the same parameters as given in Sec. 3.3 in each of the three basic amplifier configurations.

3-5. Derive Eqs. 3-63, 3-64, and 3-65.

3-6. Determine the 1 kc spot-frequency noise factor of the three basic amplifiers, using a transistor with the same parameters as given in Sec. 3.3, and $v_{ne} = 0.01\ \mu\text{v}$ and $v_{nc} = 20\ \mu\text{v}$. The signal source has a generator resistance of 1000 ohms at room temperature. Determine the optimum generator resistance for minimum noise condition for the three basic amplifiers. Compare these results with the corresponding generator resistances for maximum power-gain conditions obtained in Problems 3-1, 3-2, and 3-3.

Chapter 4

DIRECT-CURRENT BIAS CIRCUITS

4.1 Introduction

In this and the following two chapters, low-frequency amplifiers utilizing junction transistors will be investigated. This chapter will describe the limitations within which the transistor will perform satisfactorily, and will develop in some detail the methods by which the d-c operating point is established and stabilized. Because of temperature induced variations in the characteristics of transistors, stabilization of the operating point (by means of d-c feedback) is often necessary. Several methods for accomplishing this stabilization are analyzed. Design methods are given for circuits which keep the operating point within prescribed limits, while accommodating relatively large variations in transistor characteristics. Operation of transistors interchangeably in a circuit of fixed components is a basic requirement of practical electronic design.

It will be noted that the bias methods presented are developed with reference to the static characteristics drawn as collector-to-emitter voltage vs. collector current with the *base current* as the running parameter. This is in keeping with the philosophy of treating the common emitter connection of the transistor as the basic one, much as we treat the common cathode connection of the tube as basic.

Since we shall be concerned with d-c values of voltage and current in this chapter, it should be noted that capital letter subscripts designate these d-c values; B is used for base, E for emitter, and C for collector. Therefore I_C designates the direct collector current.

4.2 Establishment of the operating point

The choice of a suitable operating point for a Class A amplifier is made primarily by consideration of the magnitude of the signal to be handled, the requirement being that the largest signal contemplated should not drive the transistor collector current or voltage quite to zero, or to a region of nonlinearity. Other considerations in the choice of the operating point might be noise performance (the noise factor of a transistor is a function of the d-c operating condition), and constancy of performance (which may suffer at high collector voltages and high temperature).

The operating point, taken as (V_C, I_C), may be established by placing a source of direct voltage and a load resistance in series with the collector and emitter terminals of the transistor. A graphical representation of this arrangement is shown in Fig. 4-1. The *load*

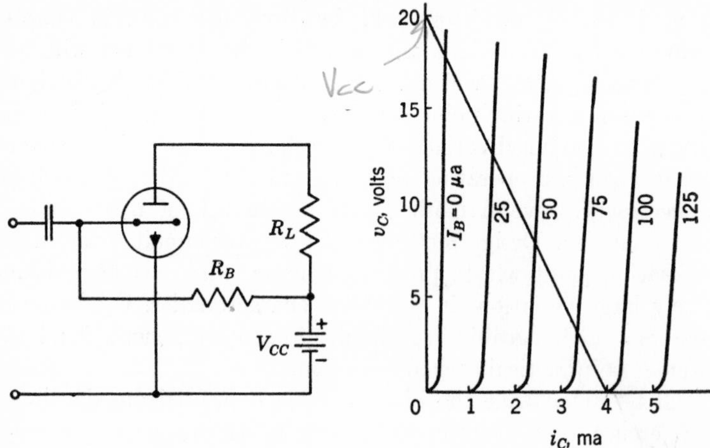

Fig. 4-1. Fixed-bias operation.

line has a slope of $-R_L$, and it intersects the voltage axis at the supply voltage, V_{CC}. The position of the operating point on this load line is determined by the value of bias current flowing to the base of the transistor.

The normal direction of base current bias is positive for the *n-p-n* transistor, and since the collector is fed from a source of positive voltage, the required base current may be conveniently derived by connecting a resistor between the collector supply voltage source and the base, as shown in Fig. 4-1. The value of this resistance is

$$R_B = \frac{V_{CC} - V_B}{I_B} \tag{4-1}$$

where I_B is the desired base current bias, V_{CC} is the collector supply voltage, and V_B is the voltage appearing between the base and the emitter at the operating point. Voltage V_B is usually small compared with the supply voltage, so that it may be neglected in Eq. (4-1), making the base current bias dependent only on quantities external to the transistor. This method of bias is therefore called *fixed base current bias*.

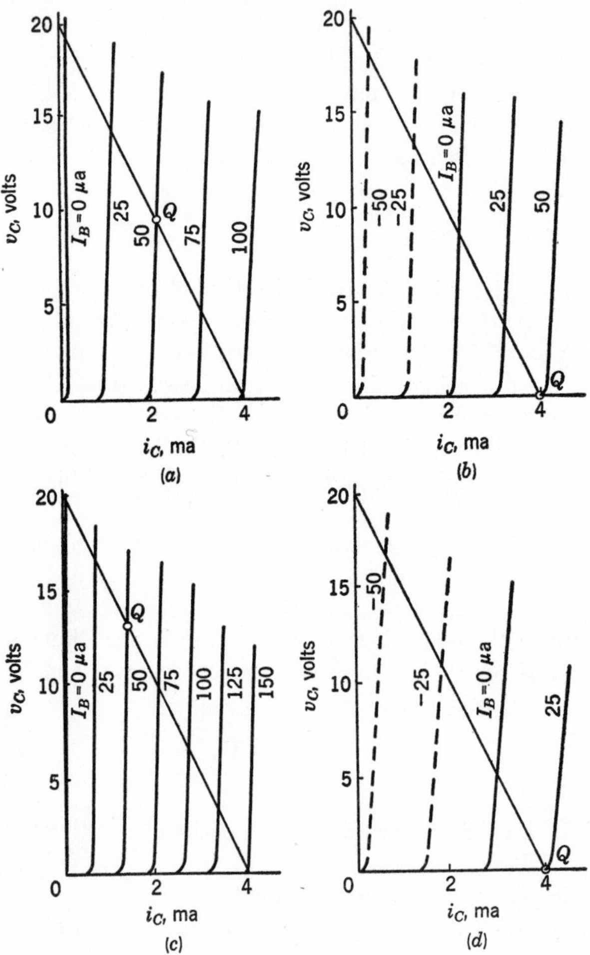

Fig. 4-2. Variation of operating point for several transistors with fixed bias.

The disadvantage of the method is that the operating point is quite sensitive to changes in the transistor. This circuit will not allow for large variations among transistors or for variations in a given transistor. This is illustrated in Fig. 4-2, which shows the location of the operating point on the collector characteristics for several transistors. The operating point is chosen, and the value of base bias current selected for the transistor of part (a) of the figure. When any of the other transistors of parts (b), (c), or (d) are inserted in the same circuit instead of the transistor of part (a), the resulting operating point may be considerably different from that anticipated, and may render the circuit inoperative. A system of self-bias which automatically compensates for transistor variations is therefore necessary.

4.3 Self-bias

If the bias resistor is connected directly between the base and the collector, rather than to the collector supply, as shown in Fig. 4-3, a certain degree of direct current degeneration is introduced, thereby stabilizing the operating point of the transistor. If, because of variation in transistor characteristics, the collector voltage tends to be low, as in parts (b) and (d) of Fig. 4-2, the base bias current will be reduced accordingly, tending to restore the desired bias condition. Likewise, if the collector voltage tends to be high, as in part (c) of the figure, the base current will be higher than normal, and the operating point will move down along the load line toward the desired condition.

To establish the operating point of a transistor of known characteristics, a resistor R_F is connected between collector and base, as in Fig. 4-3; the value is given by

$$R_F = \frac{V_C - V_B}{I_B} \tag{4-2}$$

where V_C is the collector voltage at the desired operating point, I_B is the reqiured base bias current, and V_B is the base voltage, which may usually be neglected in this equation. Hence, to establish the operating point with self-bias, the load line is determined by the method outlined in Sec. 4.2, and the proper value of base current is obtained by connecting a resistor between collector and base of the value indicated in Eq. (4-2).

When circuit values which give the desired operating point for a given transistor are determined, it is often desirable to know the operating condition which obtains when a different transistor is inserted in the circuit. This is the converse of the problem of establishing the operating point. The new operating condition is found by drawing a bias curve on the characteristics of the transistor in question, as shown in Fig. 4-4. This curve is formed by noting that at every value of collector voltage, a certain value of base current, given by the relation of Eq. (4-2), flows through R_F. On each base current line of the collector characteristics, there will be a point on the bias curve at the collector voltage corresponding to this base current. The point at which this bias curve intersects the load line is then the operating point of the transistor in question. The bias curve may be drawn on the collector characteristics shown in Fig. 4-2, to show the improvement in operating point stability gained by use of this form of self-bias. This is done in Fig. 4-5, which shows the operating points for both fixed and self-bias.

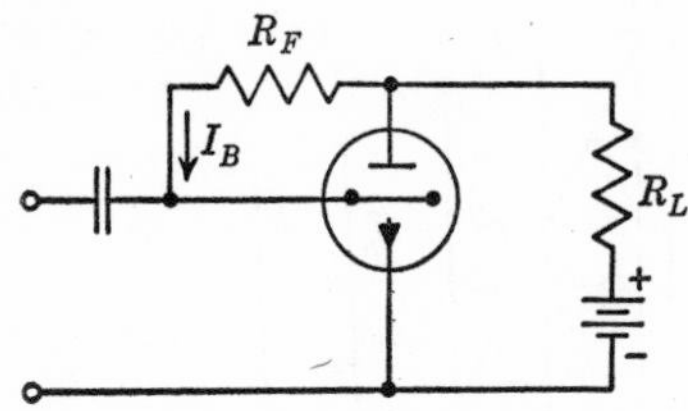

Fig. 4-3. Circuit providing self-bias.

The self-bias connection to obtain base current amounts to d-c negative feedback from the collector to the base. The effectiveness of the system in stabilizing the quiescent point is dependent upon the d-c gain of the system, or more exactly, the change in output voltage for a given change in base current. This will be high if the load resistance in the collector circuit is relatively high. If the d-c load resistance is low, as in the case of a transformer-coupled stage utilizing a low-resistance supply source, the method reverts essentially to a fixed-bias system with little stabilization. At low levels, it is quite

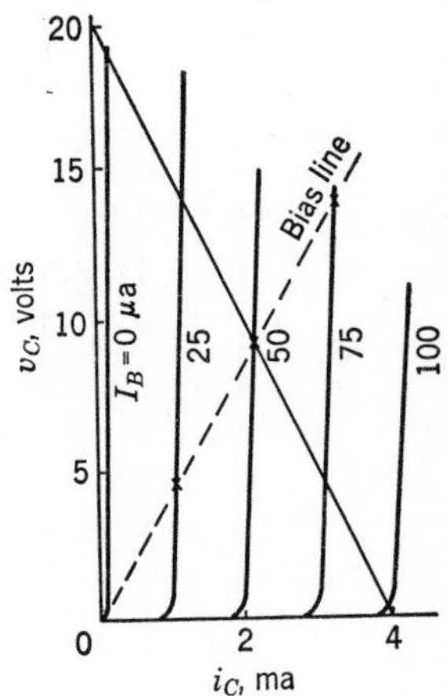

Fig. 4-4. Bias curve plotted on the static characteristics.

common to couple transistors with resistors and capacitors. For this type of coupling, the d-c load resistance is usually high enough to make this simple stabilization method provide a satisfactory degree of interchangeability of transistors in a circuit of fixed components.

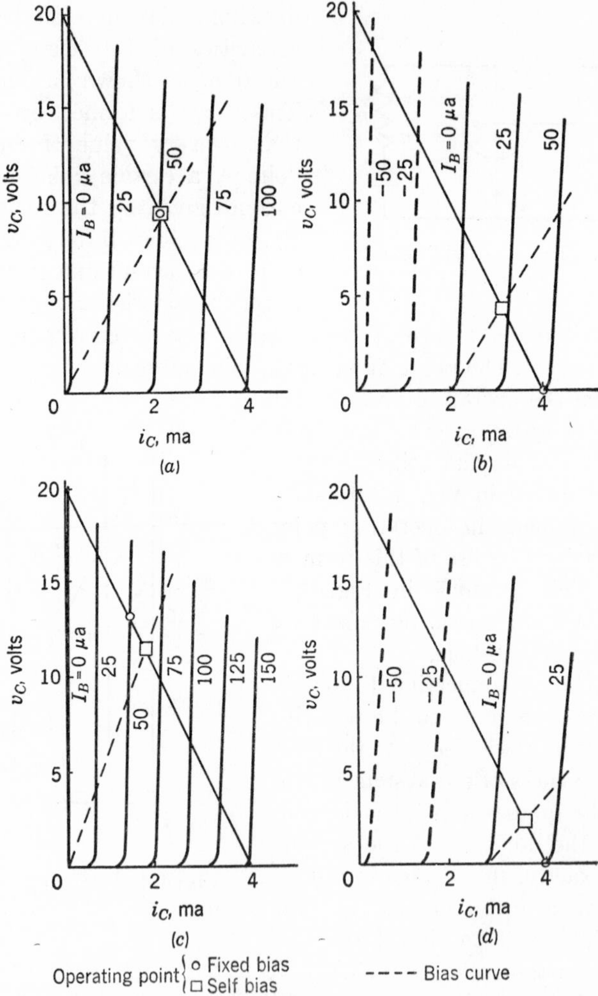

Fig. 4-5. Comparison between self-bias and fixed-bias operating points for several transistors.

One of the effects of applying self-bias in the common emitter amplifier connection of a junction transistor is the degeneration of signal due to the feedback path from collector to base. The amount of degeneration is dependent upon the total a-c load impedance, so that if the collector is fed into a low-impedance load, such as the base of a succeeding transistor stage, little signal voltage appears on the collector, and the degeneration will be relatively small. In cases where this small amount of degeneration is not tolerable, or in cases where the total a-c load impedance is high (and the degeneration consequently high), the signal may be eliminated from the feedback loop by splitting the bias resistor into two series resistors, and shunting the feedback signal through a capacitor to ground from the junction of these two resistors, as shown in Fig. 4-6. The amount of degeneration as a function of the circuit values and transistor parameters will be derived in Chapter 5.

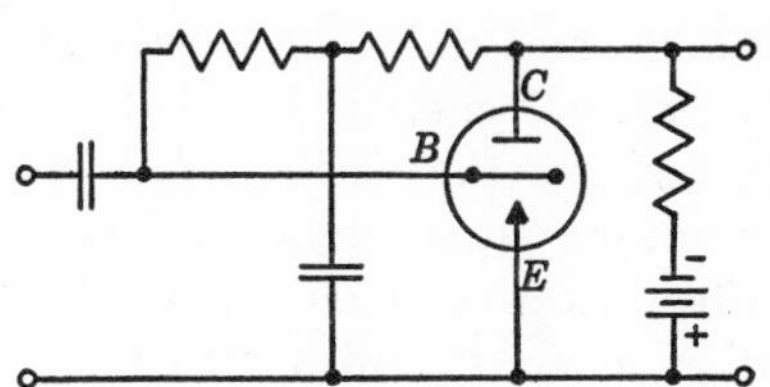

Fig. 4-6. Elimination of a-c degeneration from self-bias feedback path.

4.4 Variable factors affecting the operating point

Primary among the factors which adversely affect operating point stability is the reverse current which flows across the collector junction when a voltage is applied across it and the emitter circuit is opened. This current, termed I_{CO}, is usually very low in value, of the order of tenths of a microampere in most germanium transistors, and less in silicon transistors at room temperature. It increases greatly with temperature, however, and may vary markedly among otherwise similar transistors.

The current I_{CO} should theoretically be nearly independent of applied voltage, although in most transistors it increases with applied voltage due to leakage paths across the junction at the surface of the semiconductor. When the voltage applied across a junction approaches the breakdown voltage for that junction, the reverse current will increase greatly. The variation of I_{CO} with collector voltage for a typical transistor operating well below its breakdown voltage is depicted in Fig. 4.7.

Since the variation of I_{CO} is approximately linear with collector voltage, we may utilize a "linearized" analysis to describe the effect of changes in I_{CO} upon the operating point. If we assume that the curve of Fig. 4-7 is a straight line at relatively high values of collector voltage, extend this straight line to the current axis, and term the current axis intercept I'_{CO}, then

$$I_{CO} = I'_{CO} + \frac{V_C}{r_{CO}} \tag{4-3}$$

where V_C is the collector-to-base voltage, and r_{CO} is the slope of the "linearized" curve of Fig. 4-7. Note that r_{CO} is the small signal open circuit output resistance of the transistor in the common base configuration, operating with zero emitter current.

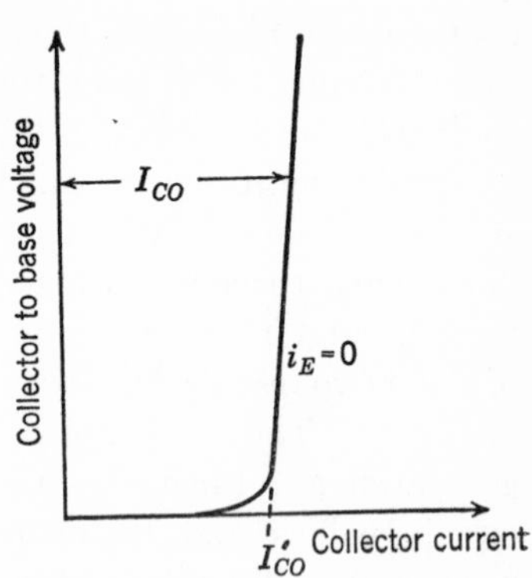

Fig. 4-7. Graphical representation of the conductive path between collector and base.

An "ideal" transistor might be postulated in which I_{CO} is negligible. The actual transistor could then be represented as this perfect transistor with a direct current generator, I'_{CO} and a resistance r_{CO} connected in parallel between its base and collector, as shown in Fig. 4-8.

If the emitter circuit is closed and the base circuit opened, as shown in Fig. 4-8b the current I_{CO} will bias the base of the "ideal" transistor, thereby causing a larger collector current to flow. The collector current I_O under conditions of zero external base current will then be

$$I_O = (1 + \alpha_{cb})I_{CO} \tag{4-4}$$

where the term I_O is used to designate the total current from collector to *emitter* with the base open-circuited. The variation of I_O with collector voltage is shown in Fig. 4-9. The equation for this curve is approximately

$$I_O = I'_O + \frac{V_C}{r_{DO}} \tag{4-5}$$

where I'_O is the current axis intercept of I_O, V_C is the direct collector-to-emitter voltage, and r_{DO} is the slope of the collector characteristics at zero base current bias. For purposes of the "linearized analysis," we assume the curves of Figs. 4-7 and 4-9 to be straight lines intersecting the axis respectively at I'_{CO} and I'_O. Hence

$$I'_O = (1 + \alpha_{cb})I'_{CO} \tag{4-6}$$

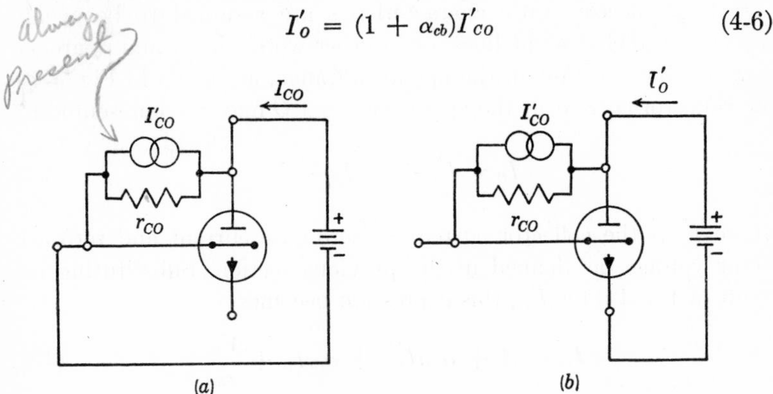

Fig. 4-8. Equivalent circuit representation for collector current at (a) zero emitter current, and (b) zero base current.

Since α_{cb} is usually a large number, the collector current for zero base current bias, I_O, may be appreciable, particularly at high temperatures. If I_O increases, the collector characteristics will shift to a region of high current, while the relative spacing will remain constant, as shown in Fig. 4-2b.

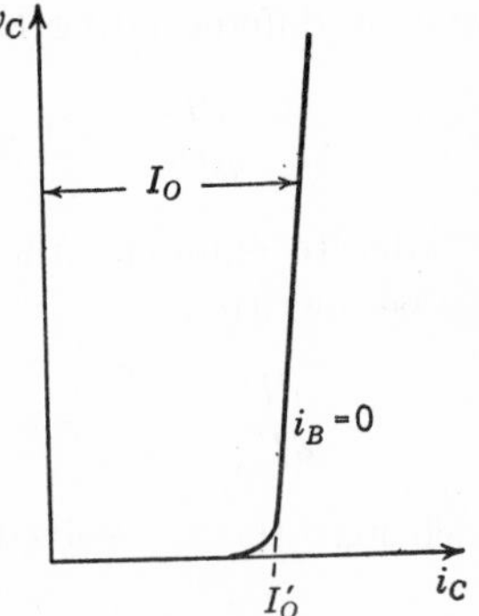

Fig. 4-9. Zero base current bias line.

The current amplification factor α_{cb} is also important in determining freedom from drift of the operating point. The effect of variation in α_{cb} on the position of the operating point is shown in Fig. 4-2. The difficulty is not that the value of α_{cb} will change in a given transistor, but that a circuit will not accommodate various transistors having a range of values of α_{cb}.

Although variations in some of the other characteristics of transistors will affect the operating point, variation in I_{CO} and in α_{cb} are generally the most important in Class A amplification and in similar applications.

4.5 The effect of I_{CO} upon the quiescent current

If the collector static characteristics are assumed to be evenly spaced, parallel straight lines, or in other words, if α_{cb} and r_d are assumed to be constant in the operating range, as shown in Fig. 4-10, the collector current at the operating point Q may be represented by

$$I_C = I'_O + \alpha_{cb} I_B + \frac{V_C}{r_d} \tag{4-7}$$

where I'_O is the collector current at zero base current and zero collector voltage, as defined in the previous section. Substituting the result of Eq. 4-6 for I'_O, this expression becomes

$$I_C = (1 + \alpha_{cb}) I'_{CO} + \alpha_{cb} I_B + \frac{V_C}{r_d} \tag{4-8}$$

This is the collector current in terms of the basic transistor parameters.

The sensitivity of the collector current to changes in I'_{CO} may be found by differentiating Eq. (4-8) with respect to I'_{CO}. Thus,

$$\frac{dI_C}{dI'_{CO}} = (1 + \alpha_{cb}) + \alpha_{cb} \frac{dI_B}{dI'_{CO}} + \frac{1}{r_d} \frac{dV_C}{dI'_{CO}} \tag{4-9}$$

In order to eliminate the dependency on I'_{CO} in this expression, it may be rewritten as

$$\frac{dI_C}{dI'_{CO}} = (1 + \alpha_{cb}) + \alpha_{cb} \frac{dI_B}{dI_C} \frac{dI_C}{dI'_{CO}} + \frac{1}{r_d} \frac{dV_C}{dI_C} \frac{dI_C}{dI'_{CO}} \tag{4-10}$$

which may then be solved for dI_C/dI'_{CO}, yielding

$$\frac{dI_C}{dI'_{CO}} = \frac{(1 + \alpha_{cb})}{1 - \alpha_{cb}(dI_B/dI_C) - (1/r_d)(dV_C/dI_C)} \tag{4-11}$$

To a good degree of approximation, none of the terms in this expression depend upon I'_{CO}, so that the rate of change of I_C with respect to I'_{CO} is a constant. The differential terms in the denominator may be evaluated by consideration of the circuit associated with the transistor. This will be done for the fixed bias and self-bias circuits studied earlier in this chapter. The term dI_B/dI_C represents the amount by which the base current bias changes when the collector current changes by a given amount. In other words, it is the current gain of the bias network in the reverse direction through the amplifier, or from the output terminals (collector and emitter) to the input terminals (base and emitter). If passive elements are used in the bias network, this current gain must always be less than unity.

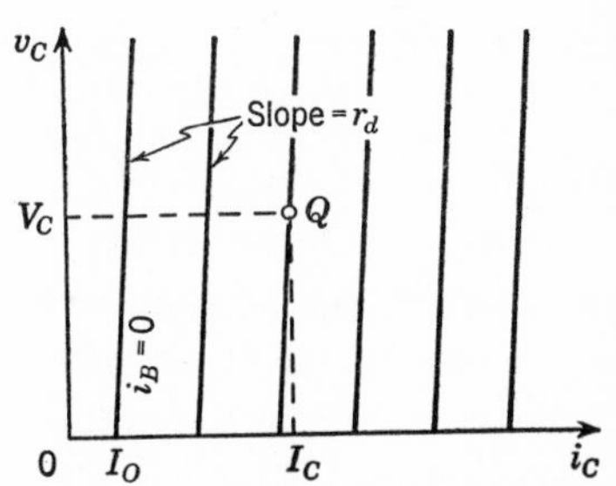

Fig. 4-10. Linear approximation of the collector characteristics.

For the fixed bias circuit, no external connection exists between the collector and the base, so that dI_B/dI_C is zero. The dV_C/dI_C term in Eq. (4-11) is the slope of the load line drawn on the collector characteristics. For the fixed bias system, the collector voltage is given by

$$V_C = V_{CC} - I_C R_L \tag{4-12}$$

and

$$\frac{dV_C}{dI_C} = -R_L \tag{4-13}$$

The sensitivity of the collector current to a change in I_{CO} is obtained by substitution of Eq. (4-13) in Eq. (4-11).

$$\frac{dI_C}{dI'_{CO}} = \frac{1 + \alpha_{cb}}{1 + R_L/r_d} \tag{4-14}$$

for fixed bias.

In the self-bias system of Fig. 4-7, the current gain to the base from the collector may be found by developing the expression given in Eq. (4-2). Neglecting the base to emitter voltage in this expression,

$$I_B = \frac{V_C}{R_F} \tag{4-15}$$

but

$$V_C = V_{CC} - (I_B + I_C)R_L \tag{4-16}$$

since both I_C and I_B produce a voltage drop in R_L. Substituting the value of I_B given in Eq. (4-15) and solving for V_C,

$$V_C = \frac{V_{CC} - I_C R_L}{1 + R_L/R_F} \tag{4-17}$$

and
$$I_B = \frac{V_{CC} - I_C R_L}{R_F + R_L} \tag{4-18}$$

The current gain to the base from the collector may be found by differentiating this expression with respect to I_C:

$$\frac{dI_B}{dI_C} = -\frac{R_L}{R_F + R_L} \tag{4-19}$$

Inspection of the circuit of Fig. 4-7 shows that if the collector current increases, the base current must decrease, which accounts for the negative sign in the expression.

Equation (4-17) may be differentiated with respect to I_C.

$$\frac{dV_C}{dI_C} = -\frac{R_L}{1 + R_L/R_F} = -\frac{R_L R_F}{R_L + R_F} \tag{4-20}$$

This quantity again represents the slope of the load line, since the load on the transistor is composed of the parallel resistance of R_L and R_F. Since R_F is usually considerably larger than R_L, Eq. (4-11) may be written

$$\frac{dI_C}{dI'_{CO}} = \frac{1 + \alpha_{cb}}{1 + \alpha_{cb}R_L/(R_F + R_L) + R_L/r_d} \tag{4-21}$$

for self-bias. The third term in the denominator of this expression is usually very small compared with the other terms, so that the approximation is justified. Comparison of Eqs. (4-14) and (4-21) shows the improvement in d-c stability which accrues by use of the self-bias system.

The rate of change of collector current with I'_{CO} given by Eq. (4-11) is a constant provided that linear passive resistances are used, and that the resistance of the network feeding the base is high compared with the base input resistance. Both of these conditions are usually met in practice. Since dI_C/dI'_{CO} is a constant, Eq. (4-11), and its solution given for particular circuit configurations in Eqs. (4-14) and (4-21), may be integrated to give the change in collector current with a given change in I'_{CO}.

4.6 The effect of changes in α_{cb} upon the quiescent current

The effect of variation in α_{cb} from transistor to transistor was discussed in Sec. 4.4. The sensitivity of the operating point to changes in α_{cb} can be found by differentiating Eq. (4-8) with respect to α_{cb}, and solving for $dI_C/d\alpha_{cb}$, using the method by which Eq. (4-11) was obtained. When this is done, the following result is obtained:

$$\frac{dI_C}{d\alpha_{cb}} = \frac{I'_{CO} + I_B}{1 + \alpha_{cb}(dI_B/dI_C) + (1/r_d)(dV_C/dI_C)} \tag{4-22}$$

This expression depends upon I_B and α_{cb}. If I_B is high, the change in I_C which accompanies a change in α_{cb} will be larger than if I_B is low, a fact which is apparent from inspection of Fig. 4-10. Also, if α_{cb} is high, a change in its value will not affect the collector current so much as if it is low, which is indicated by the fact that α_{cb} appears in the denominator of Eq. (4-22). Because of the dependency of $dI_C/d\alpha_{cb}$ on α_{cb} and I_B (this latter is usually a function of α_{cb}), Eq. (4-22) cannot be integrated easily. In order to find the change in the operating point which occurs when the value of α_{cb} changes, the general Eq. (4-8) should be solved for the circuit in question. For the fixed bias circuit, Eq. (4-12) may be substituted in Eq. (4-8). Then, solving for I_C,

$$I_C = \frac{(1 + \alpha_{cb})I'_{CO} + \alpha_{cb} I_B + V_{CC}/r_d}{1 + R_L/r_d} \tag{4-23}$$

for the fixed bias circuit. In the case of the self-bias method, both I_B and V_C of Eq. (4-8) depend upon I_C. This equation then becomes

$$I_C = (1 + \alpha_{cb})I'_{CO} + \alpha_{cb}\frac{V_C}{R_F} + \frac{V_C}{r_d} \tag{4-24}$$

An expression for the collector voltage in the self-bias circuit was obtained in Eq. (4-17). Putting this value of V_C in Eq. (4-24) yields the following:

$$I_C = (1 + \alpha_{cb})I'_{CO} + \frac{V_{CC} - I_C R_L}{R_F + R_L}\left(\alpha_{cb} + \frac{R_F}{r_d}\right) \tag{4-25}$$

Extracting I_C from this expression,

$$I_C = \frac{(1 + \alpha_{cb})I'_{CO} + V_{CC}(\alpha_{cb} + R_F/r_d)/(R_F + R_L)}{1 + \alpha_{cb} R_L/(R_F + R_L) + R_L R_F/[r_d(R_L + R_F)]} \tag{4-26}$$

The approximation used in Eq. (4-21) for the third term in the denominator is equally valid here. Hence

$$I_C = \frac{(1 + \alpha_{cb})I'_{CO} + V_{CC}(\alpha_{cb} + R_F/r_d)/(R_F + R_L)}{1 + \alpha_{cb} R_L/(R_F + R_L) + R_L/r_d} \tag{4-27}$$

This equation can be used to analyze the effect of changes in α_{cb} on the quiescent current for the simple self-bias system. Since this expression is fairly complex, the analysis is often simpler when the graphical method of determining the operating point, outlined in Sec. 4.3, is used.

4.7 Collector voltage stability

In some circuits, the drift in quiescent collector voltage is of greater importance than the drift in collector current. To find the amount by which the collector voltage changes when α_{cb} or I_{CO} shift in value, the following relationship may be used:

$$\frac{dV_C}{dI'_{CO}} = \frac{dI_C}{dI'_{CO}} \frac{dV_C}{dI_C} \tag{4-28}$$

Combining this relationship with that of Eq. (4-11), the following result is obtained:

$$\frac{dV_C}{dI'_{CO}} = -\frac{1 + \alpha_{cb}}{(1/r_d) + \alpha_{cb}(dI_B/dV_C) - (dI_C/dV_C)} \tag{4-29}$$

If the circuit elements are passive and linear, dV_C/dI'_{CO} is a constant, and must have the dimensions of resistance. If there is a change in I'_{CO} of magnitude $\Delta I'_{CO}$, the change in collector voltage will be $\Delta I'_{CO}$ times this resistance. The last two terms in the denominator of Eq. (4-29) are constants of the circuit, and will be evaluated for both the fixed and self-bias systems.

Since the base current is constant for fixed bias, dI_B/dV_C is zero. The third term in the denominator of Eq. (4-29) is the negative reciprocal of the load resistance. Hence

$$\frac{dV_C}{dI'_{CO}} = -\frac{1 + \alpha_{cb}}{(1/r_d) + (1/R_L)} \tag{4-30}$$

for the fixed bias system, which may be considered as $(1 + \alpha_{cb})$ times the resistance of r_d and R_L in parallel. For self-bias, Eq. (4-15) holds, so that

$$\frac{dI_B}{dV_C} = \frac{1}{R_F} \tag{4-31}$$

The term dI_C/dV_C is found by inverting Eq. (4-20) so that

$$\frac{dI_C}{dV_C} = -\left(\frac{1}{R_L} + \frac{1}{R_F}\right) \tag{4-32}$$

The sensitivity of the collector voltage to a change in I'_{CO} is therefore given by

$$\frac{dV_C}{dI'_{CO}} = -\frac{1 + \alpha_{cb}}{1/r_d + (1 + \alpha_{cb})/R_F + 1/R_L} \tag{4-33}$$

for the self-bias system. This expression may be considered $(1 + \alpha_{cb})$ times the resistance of r_d, R_L, and $R_F/(1 + \alpha_{cb})$ all in parallel. The improvement of the self-bias system over the fixed bias system may be found by comparing Eq. (4-33) with Eq. (4-30).

The rate of change of collector voltage with respect to α_{cb} may be found by applying Eq. (4-28) to the relationship given in Eq. (4-22). The result is dependent upon α_{cb} and I_B, however, and is not easily integrated. The expression for collector voltage in terms of α_{cb} and I'_{CO} may be derived for any circuit under consideration. For the fixed-bias circuit,

$$V_C = V_{CC} - I_C R_L \tag{4-17}$$

Substituting the general expression for I_C given by Eq. (4-8) in this equation, and solving for V_C,

$$V_C = \frac{V_{CC}/R_L - (1 + \alpha_{cb})I'_{CO} - \alpha_{cb} I_B}{1/R_L + 1/r_d} \tag{4-34}$$

Note that if this expression is differentiated with respect to I'_{CO}, the result of Eq. (4-30) is obtained. For the self-bias circuit,

$$V_C = V_{CC} - (I_C + I_B)R_L \tag{4-13}$$

Substituting the general expression of Eq. (4-8) in this equation,

$$V_C = V_{CC} - \left[(1 + \alpha_{cb})I'_{CO} + \alpha_{cb} I_B + \frac{V_C}{r_d} + I_B\right] R_L \tag{4-35}$$

Using the value V_C/R_F for I_B in this expression, and solving for V_C,

$$V_C = \frac{V_{CC}/R_L - (1 + \alpha_{cb})I'_{CO}}{1/r_d + (1 + \alpha_{cb})/R_F + 1/R_L} \tag{4-36}$$

which gives the collector voltage for the self-bias circuit. Similar expressions may be derived for other bias methods by straightforward circuit analysis.

The expressions developed in this and the previous section may be used to analyze the behavior of the operating point under the influence of two simple bias methods. They may also be extended to apply to both the design and analysis of other bias methods to be investigated.

4.8 Separate control of stabilization and bias

The self-bias method performs the dual function of providing bias and stabilization for the transistor. Normally, the collector supply voltage and the load resistance are determined by factors other than the d-c stability of the stage. Since the feedback resistor is the only remaining variable in this circuit, separate control of the sta-

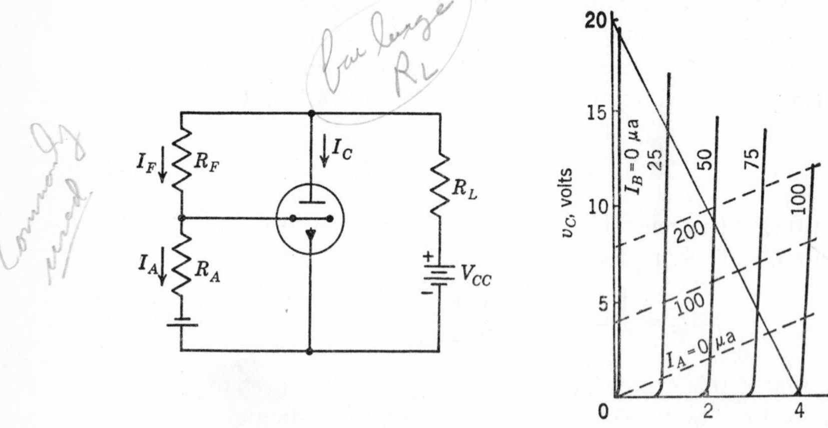

Fig. 4-11. Circuit for providing separate control of stabilization and bias.

Fig. 4-12. Family of bias curves for the circuit of Fig. 4-11.

bilization and the bias is not possible. Separate control may be achieved by the addition of a fixed bias current path to the base of the self-bias circuit. A circuit utilizing this scheme is shown in Fig. 4-11, in which the added fixed bias is in such a direction to reduce the magnitude of the base current. The stabilizing bias current from the collector may therefore be increased.

The simple self-bias method described earlier would not allow the bias to reverse. This method does allow the bias to reverse at the point where the fixed bias current equals the feedback current.

A family of bias curves may be drawn for this circuit with the fixed bias current I_A as the parameter. Three such curves are shown in Fig. 4-12. These bias curves may be drawn from the relationship

$$I_B = \frac{V_C}{R_F} + I_A \tag{4-37}$$

The main purpose of this method is to allow the design of a circuit with a preassigned degree of quiescent point stability. The worst cases for which the operating point must be stabilized occur (1) when a transistor with the highest values of α and/or I_{CO} to be accommodated is inserted in the circuit, giving an extreme condition of low voltage, and (2) when a transistor having the lowest values of α and/or I_{CO} to be accommodated is inserted in the circuit, giving the extreme condition of high collector voltage. Assuming that static characteristics for these two limit transistors or worst cases are available, and assuming that the collector supply voltage and output load resistance are given as well as the maximum variation which can be tolerated in the collector voltage, the values of the feedback resistance R_F and the fixed bias current may be found.

A graphical method which may be used for this purpose is outlined in Fig. 4-13. On the static characteristics for each of the limit transistors, the load line is drawn. The extremes of collector voltage which are to be tolerated, $V_{C\,max}$ and $V_{C\,min}$, are added on the appropriate set of characteristics. The intersection of the load line with $V_{C\,max}$ gives the high-voltage limiting position of the operating point. The value of base current $I_{B\,max}$ required to establish this operating point is found from the characteristics. For the other transistor, $I_{B\,min}$ is found in like manner. These values of base current are then located on a plot of collector voltage versus base current as shown in Fig. 4-13c. The limit values of collector voltage are also plotted on this graph. The intersection of the line of minimum base current with the line of minimum collector voltage will give the operating point of the low voltage transistor; the intersection of the line of maximum base current with the line of maximum collector voltage will give the operating point for the high-voltage transistor. On these coordinates, the bias curve must be a straight line, since the bias curve is given by the relation shown in Eq. (4-37). Since the circuit is fixed, both operating points must lie on the same bias line, which therefore can be drawn through the two operating points. The slope of this bias line is equal to R_F and it intersects the current axis at the required fixed bias current I_A.

This method is slightly in error because the loading on the collector by R_F is not taken into account. The exact result may be obtained by the more complete analysis of the previous sections.

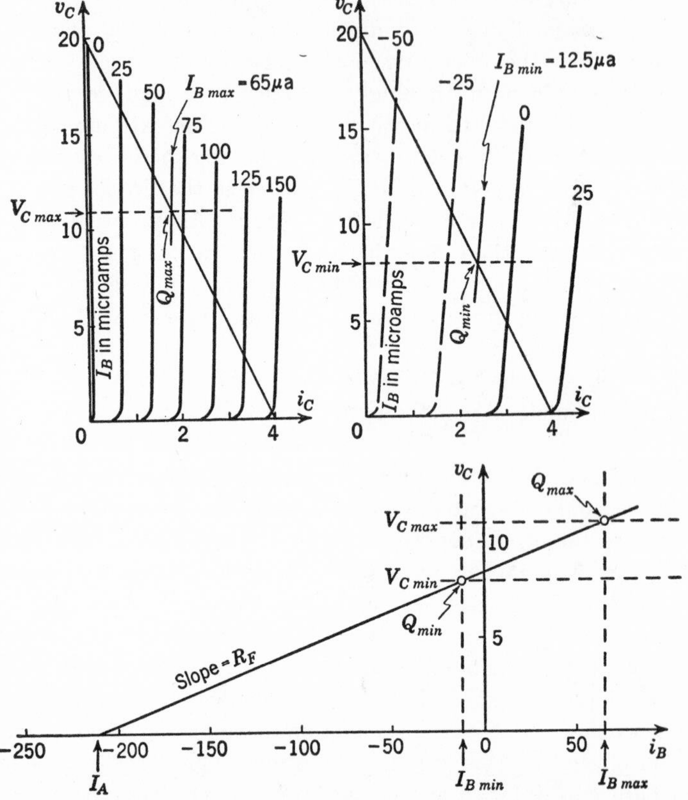

Fig. 4-13. Graphical design method for circuit which holds the collector voltage within prescribed limits. Given: R_L, V_{CC}, $V_{C\,max}$, $V_{C\,min}$, and the characteristics of two "limit" transistors. Find: values of R_F and I_A.

The cost or size of the added battery is sometimes prohibitive. Some benefit can be achieved by eliminating the battery and connecting R_A directly to ground. The added resistor will reduce the bias current even without the extra battery because of the potential existing across the emitter junction. This potential, although not large, is in the proper direction to cause a reverse bias current to flow, so that R_F may be reduced and the stabilization increased somewhat. The dynamic input resistance is relatively low, so that most of the stabilizing feedback current flows into the base circuit. The d-c input impedance is somewhat higher, however, so that part of the direct current flowing through R_F also flows through R_A. The difference between these two input resistances is shown in Fig. 4-14, which plots base-to-emitter voltage vs. base current for the transistor in question. The dynamic input resistance is the slope of the curve at the operating point, which is seen to be lower than the d-c resistance given by the slope of the dashed line in the same figure.

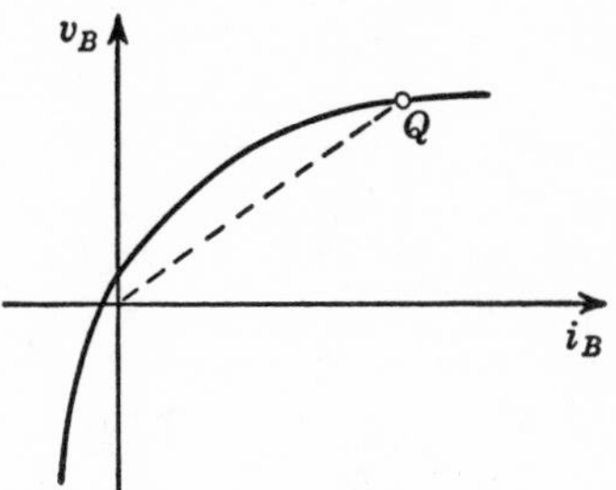

Fig. 4-14. Input characteristic of an *n-p-n* transistor.

4.9 Stabilization by current feedback

The methods of stabilization investigated in the previous sections are based upon feeding back a variable base current which is proportional to collector voltage. In other words, the change in bias current which stabilizes the operating point is derived from a change in collector voltage caused by the variable factors I_{CO} and α_{cb}. In a stage in which the d-c load resistance is high, such as an RC coupled amplifier, a relatively large change in voltage is available at the collector for use in stabilization of the operating point. In a case where the d-c load resistance is low in value, as in a transformer coupled stage, the collector voltage will remain relatively unchanged when I_{CO} and α_{cb} vary, so that the amount of feedback which can be obtained is limited. The collector current in such a circuit will vary with changes in the transistor variables, however, so that stabilization is needed.

This stabilization may be provided by supplying a base bias current which varies in accordance with the value of the collector current and in the proper direction to reduce the variation in collector current. This amounts to negative current feedback, and may be provided by connecting a resistance R_E in series with the emitter circuit, as shown in Fig. 4-15. The voltage drop across R_E is essentially proportional to the collector current. This voltage tends to stabilize the collector current, and is in the proper direction to apply reverse bias to the transistor. The resistance R_F, connected to the other side of the battery, also applies stabilizing current to the base, but in a direction to apply forward bias to the transistor. Hence, with a given value of R_E, decreasing the resistance of the parallel combination of R_A and R_F increases the stabilization, while decreasing R_F relative to R_A increases the base bias current. Separate control is thereby exercised over the two functions of stabilization and bias. The limitation in the amount by which the parallel resistance of R_A and R_F can be reduced is set by the amount of loading which can be tolerated across the input terminals, and by the amount of d-c power which can be dissipated in these resistors.

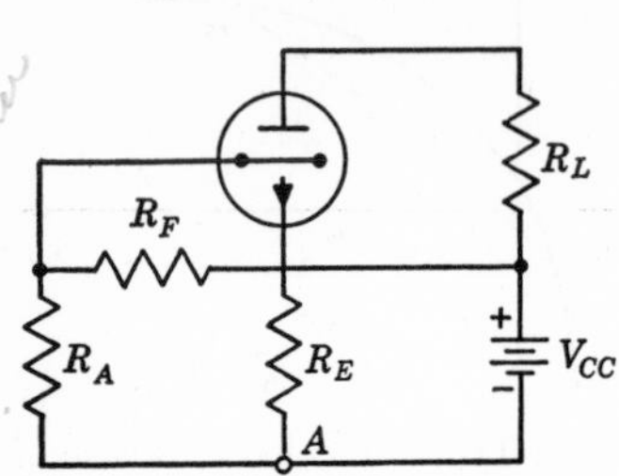

Fig. 4-15. Current-feedback stabilization.

The circuit may be analyzed by making the assumptions of Sec. 4.5. The collector current is again given by

$$I_C = (1 + \alpha_{cb})I'_{CO} + \alpha_{cb} I_B + \frac{V_C}{r_d} \tag{4-8}$$

The base current is given by

$$I_B = I_F - I_A \tag{4-38}$$

where I_F and I_A are the currents flowing through R_F and R_A, respectively. Assuming that V_{BE} is zero,

$$I_F = \frac{V_{CC} - (I_C + I_B)R_E}{R_F} \tag{4-39}$$

and

$$I_A = \frac{(I_C + I_B)R_E}{R_A} \tag{4-40}$$

then

$$I_B = \frac{(V_{CC}/R_F) - I_C[(R_E/R_F) + (R_E/R_A)]}{1 + (R_E/R_F) + (R_E/R_A)} \tag{4-41}$$

If the parallel resistance of R_F and R_A is designated R_P, then Eq.

(4-41) becomes

$$I_B = \frac{(V_{CC}/R_F) - I_C(R_E/R_P)}{1 + R_E/R_P} \tag{4-42}$$

The third term of Eq. (4-8) requires an evaluation of the collector voltage:

$$V_C = V_{CC} - I_C(R_L + R_E) \tag{4-43}$$

approximately (the small term $I_B R_E$ was left out in this expression). Equation (4-8) then becomes

$$I_C = (1 + \alpha_{cb})I'_{CO} + \alpha_{cb}\left(\frac{(V_{CC}/R_F) - I_C(R_E/R_P)}{1 + R_E/R_P}\right) + \frac{V_{CC} - I_C(R_L + R_E)}{r_d} \tag{4-44}$$

which is solved for I_C.

$$I_C = \frac{(1 + \alpha_{cb})I'_{CO} + \alpha_{cb} V_{CC} R_P/[R_F(R_P + R_E)] + V_{CC}/r_d}{1 + \alpha_{cb} R_E/(R_P + R_E) + (R_L + R_E)/r_d} \tag{4-45}$$

The current feedback circuit is best suited for use where the required collector current is fairly high, as in transformer coupled power output stages. In such cases, the terms involving r_d are very small, as may be seen by observation of the static characteristics at high currents. Thus for operation in this region,

$$I_C = \frac{(1 + \alpha_{cb})I'_{CO} + \alpha_{cb} V_{CC} R_P/[R_F(R_P + R_E)]}{1 + \alpha_{cb} R_E/(R_E + R_P)} \tag{4-46}$$

Equation (4-46) or (4-45) may be used to analyze the operation of an existing circuit.

Design of a stage which uses current feedback stabilization will depend upon the circuit features specified. Often there is only a certain amount of collector supply voltage available, and the quiescent collector voltage and current are given. In this case, the voltage drop across the emitter resistance is known, and R_E may be obtained directly. The required base bias current at the operating point may be determined from the static characteristics or from Eq. (4-11). A relationship may then be established between R_A and R_F to give the proper value of bias current for the transistor. If the stabilization is specified as a maximum amount by which the collector current is to drift with certain changes in α_{cb} and I_{CO}, another relationship may be established between R_A and R_F for the new bias current which is required. Simultaneous solution of the two equations relating R_A and R_F will then give the values for these resistances.

4.10 Combination self-bias

The simple self-bias method of Sec. 4.3 is unique in that it requires no more circuit elements than the fixed-bias circuit, unless the a-c degeneration is to be eliminated. There is little range of design freedom, however; the amount of stabilization is not usually one of the initial design criteria when this circuit is to be used. In this sense, the circuit is similar to cathode resistor bias used in tube circuits. If the amount of stabilization is to be controlled in this circuit, a method such as that given in Sec. 4.8 must be used. Furthermore, as mentioned in the previous section, the voltage feedback methods are limited in usefulness when the d-c resistance in the collector circuit is low.

The current feedback method described in Sec. 4.9, on the other hand, requires a minimum of two components more than the fixed bias circuit. It has a great range of design freedom for circuits with low resistance d-c loads. If the d-c load is high, however, this method loses its effectiveness, since changes in α_{cb} and I_{CO} will have a relatively small effect upon the collector current. In this case, use of one of the voltage feedback methods is desirable.

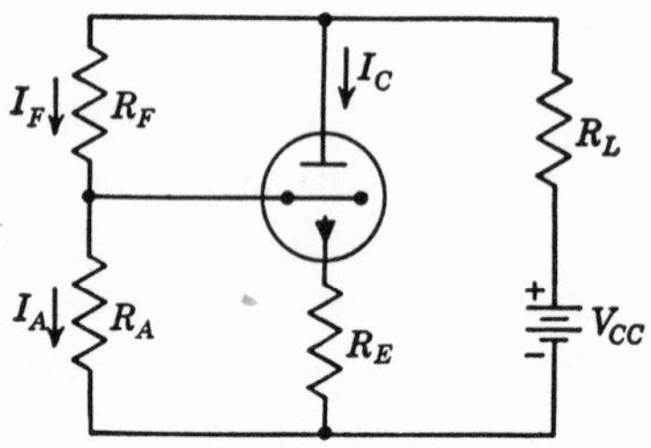

Fig. 4-16. Combination of current- and voltage-feedback self-bias.

A combination of the two methods of self-bias may be used. The circuit arrangement is that shown in Fig. 4-16. If the d-c load resistance is high, the current feedback contributes little to the total stabilization. The main purpose of the emitter resistance is to provide reverse bias so that the voltage feedback can be increased. In other words, at the expense of d-c power used in the emitter resistor, the separate battery in the circuit of Fig. 4-11 has been eliminated.

Although the biasing arrangements presented in this chapter were developed with reference to the parameters and static characteristics of the grounded emitter circuit, they are equally applicable to the other two connections of the junction transistor, and in fact, to any circuit in which the quiescent point is to be located in the linear range of the collector characteristics. Certain nonlinear circuits, such as Class B amplifiers, require special biasing circuits, which will be discussed under the particular applications. Class A complementary symmetry circuits may be stabilized satisfactorily by the methods of this chapter, as will be seen later.

PROBLEMS

4-1. Given an *n-p-n* transistor with the following characteristics: $\alpha_{cb} = 60$, $r_d = 20{,}000$ ohms, $I'_{CO} = 0.004$ ma, a battery supply voltage of 16 v, and a desired operating point of 6 v, 2 ma, find the following: (a) the circuit resistances for fixed-bias operation; (b) the operating point for this circuit if I'_{CO} increases to 0.010 ma; (c) the operating point if I'_{CO} remains at 0.004 ma, and α_{cb} increases by $33\frac{1}{3}$%.

4-2. Repeat Problem 4.1 for the case of self-bias supplied as shown in Fig. 4.7.

4-3. Repeat Problem 1 for the circuit shown in Fig. 4-11 if a bias supply of -10 v is available, and a resistor of 200,000 ohms is used between this battery and the base.

4-4. A circuit is to be designed in which the collector current does not vary from its original value by more than 0.5 ma for an increase in I_{CO} of 50 μa. The circuit of Fig. 4-11 is to be used, and a collector supply source of 10 v is available. The original operating point is to be 5 v, 5 ma. What should be the values of R_L and R_F in this circuit, and what is the value of the reverse bias current to be fed from the separate source? The transistor has an α_{cb} of 50, the initial value of I_{CO} is 0.010 ma, the output impedance may be assumed to be very large, and the base to emitter voltage is zero.

4-5. Design a circuit for operation at 5 ma, 5 v with a transistor having $\alpha_{cb} = 50$, $I_{CO} = 0.000$ ma, and an effectively infinite r_d, such that the collector current will not exceed 6 ma when a transistor with $\alpha_{cb} = 75$ and $I_{CO} = 0.030$ ma is inserted in the circuit. Use the circuit of Fig. 4-11, assuming a reverse bias battery of 1.5 v, and a collector supply of 10 v.

4-6. A transistor is to be used in the power output circuit shown in the accompanying diagram. The transistor characteristics are: $\alpha_{cb} = 30$, $I_{CO} = 0.00$, and r_d is very high. The supply voltage is 12 v, and the transistor is to be operated at 10 v, 10 ma. The transformer primary resistance is 100 ohms.

(a) Find the values of R_A, R_B, and R_E if the collector current is not to exceed 12 ma when I_{CO} increases to 0.050 ma, and α_{cb} increases to 40. (b) Recompute the above values if the supply voltage is increased to 13.5 v. (c) What is the power consumed in the stabilization resistor in each case (for the initial condition)?

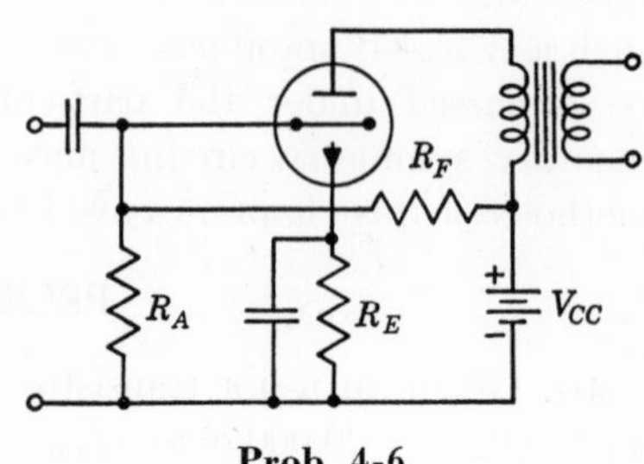

Prob. 4-6.

4-7. Repeat Problem 4.5, using the combination stabilization method of Fig. 4-16. Use a collector supply of 11.5 v, and let 1.5 v appear across the emitter resistor in the initial condition. Find the values of R_F, R_A, R_E, and R_L.

Chapter 5

LOW-FREQUENCY AMPLIFIERS

5.1 Classification of low-frequency amplifiers

Transistor amplifiers may be classified according to the mode of operation of the transistor, as in the case of tube amplifiers. Thus a *Class A* amplifier is one in which the transistor is always operated in the linear region of the collector characteristics, the bias currents and the signal being of proper magnitude to achieve this condition.

A *Class B* amplifier is one in which the transistor is biased at the boundary of the linear region of the characteristics, so that amplifier action takes place only during one-half of the input signal cycle. This definition is a broadening of the usual definition of Class B operation for tube amplifiers, since it not only includes quiescent operation at collector current cutoff, but may also include quiescent operation at zero collector voltage with high current flowing through the transistor. Either quiescent point features low collector dissipation in the transistor itself, so that we may generalize the definition, and say that Class B operation is that in which the idling or quiescent power dissipation in the transistor is low compared with the power dissipation under signal conditions.

Class AB operation is intermediate between Class A and Class B operation, so that this type of operation is characterized by either the collector voltage or current being zero for part, but less than half of the electrical cycle.

A *Class C* amplifier is one in which the collector current or voltage is zero for more than 180° of the electrical cycle. This mode of operation is rarely used in low-frequency amplifiers.

An amplifier may be classified also according to its application. Because of the low-impedance characteristic of the input circuit of most transistors, and because we find it convenient to deal with input currents rather than voltages, the term *voltage amplifier* used in relation to tube circuits is not very meaningful. The corresponding type of low-level amplifier used with transistors is the *current amplifier*.

A series of cascaded RC coupled amplifier stages, for instance, would be made up of current amplifiers.

A power amplifier is one in which the signal excursion in the collector circuit usually traverses the area bounded by the maximum allowable values of collector voltage, current, and power dissipation.

5.2 Basic circuits of transistor amplifiers

Some of the more common transistor amplifier circuits are shown in Fig. 5-1. Part (a) of Fig. 5-1 shows a basic common emitter amplifier stage. Energizing current is applied to the collector of this transistor by means of a potential source and a load resistor. Base current bias is derived by connection of a resistor between the collector supply battery and the base of the transistor. Signal is applied to the base and emitter terminals, and appears in amplified form across the load resistor R_L. In general, both the voltage and current gains will be greater than unity in the common emitter connection.

Isolation of the signal from the d-c component often is desired, so that capacitive coupling may be used as shown in Fig. 5-1b. The base bias current for this circuit is derived by connecting a resistor between collector and base, thereby stabilizing the d-c operating point as shown in the previous chapter. The circuit of Fig. 5-1b is a practical embodiment of the common emitter stage. Again, both voltage and current gains of greater than unity are realized. This circuit is widely used as an amplifier at moderate frequencies.

Figure 5-1c shows a common-base circuit in which separate batteries are used to bias the emitter and collector. This circuit is characterized by a current gain of less than unity and a high ratio of output to input impedance. Power gain is realized by virtue of this impedance transformation. While this circuit is shown capacitively coupled, it is possible in this circuit as well as any other of the circuits of Fig. 5-1 to use transformer coupling.

One method of transformer coupling for the input circuit of a common-base stage is shown in Fig. 5-1d. The bias provisions for this circuit are the same as those for the grounded emitter circuit of Fig. 5-1b. Note, however, that in this case the collector to base bias resistor is in shunt with the output signal and is not a feedback element. One application of this circuit might be to couple a low-impedance device to the grid of a vacuum tube.

In the circuit of Fig. 5-1e, the collector is common to both input and output circuits. The input impedance of this circuit is high and the output impedance is low relative to the common-emitter stage. The voltage gain is less than unity and the available power gain of the stage is considerably lower than either the common-emitter or

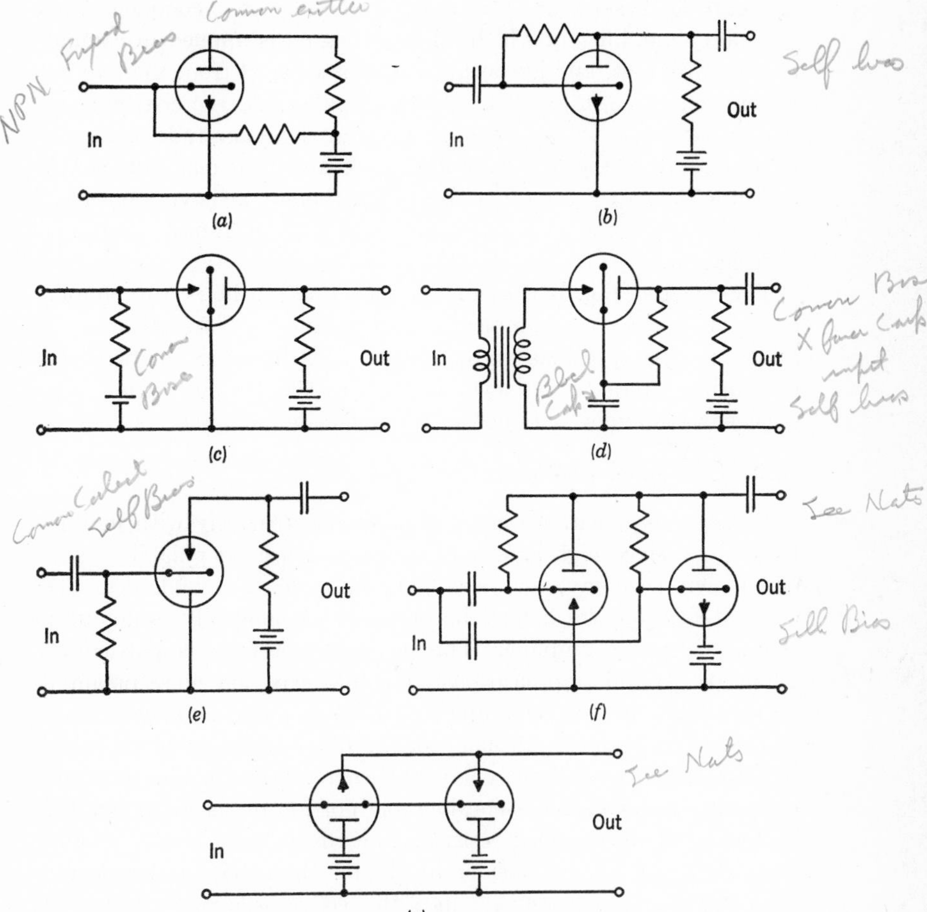

Fig. 5-1. Basic transistor amplifier circuits.

the common-base stages. It may be useful, however, as an impedance transformation device, and may also be useful in power stages where bias provisions may be simplified.

The availability of transistors of opposite conductivity types gives rise to a class of circuits utilizing the principle known as *complementary symmetry*, which is studied in detail in a later section. Parts (f) and (g) of Fig. 5-1 show two amplifier circuits utilizing this principle.

Figure 5-1f shows a Class A common-emitter complementary symmetry amplifier in which an input signal is applied in common to the two bases, and an output signal is derived from the two collectors connected in parallel. In this amplifier, a given change in the base input signal will cause an increase in the magnitude of the collector current of one transistor and a decrease in the magnitude of the collector current of the other transistor, thereby achieving push-pull operation with the attendant advantages of even-order harmonic cancellation.

The circuit of Fig. 5-1g is similar except that it utilizes two common-collector stages in a complementary symmetry Class B amplifier. Slight reverse base bias current flows in each transistor, biasing it off during alternate half cycles of a sinusoidal input signal. High efficiency is thereby obtained in a single-ended amplifier.

5.3 RC coupled amplifiers

Resistance-capacitance coupling is used extensively with junction transistors, since high gain is obtainable with good reliability, good component economy, and small over-all size. The high degree of d-c stabilization which may be obtained economically is unique in the *RC* coupled amplifier. This type of coupling is particularly adaptable to audio applications from low-level, low-noise preamplifiers to high-level driver amplifiers for power output stages.

The over-all power efficiency of an *RC* coupled amplifier which receives its output circuit energizing current from a low resistance d-c source is low, since a considerable portion of the total power is dissipated in the d-c load resistor. The efficiency of an *RC* coupled transistor amplifier is considerably better than that of the vacuum tube counterpart, however, since the collector characteristics are linear even at very low values of current and voltage.

The cascaded *RC* coupled transistor amplifier differs in at least one important respect from the vacuum tube amplifier in that the input impedance of the following stage is low, and considerable current must be supplied to it. The peak-to-peak output signal current of an *RC* coupled amplifier may approach a value which is double the quiescent collector current, as may be seen by inspection of the a-c and d-c load lines on the transistor collector characteristics of Fig. 5-2. In this respect, RC coupling is more suitable for use with transistors than with tubes.

Two transistor stages may be cascaded as shown in Fig. 5-3. In each stage, a battery supplies energizing currents to the collectors through the d-c load resistors R_D. The capacitors C_i, C_1, and C_2 block unwanted direct currents from flowing into the base electrodes of the transistors and the load. Fixed bias current is applied to each base by means of a resistor connected to the collector supply voltage source. This type of operation may cause excessive variations in the d-c operating point compared with the self-bias methods described in the previous chapter, but is used initially for the sake of simplicity. The analysis and design of the self-biased amplifier will be treated in detail in later sections.

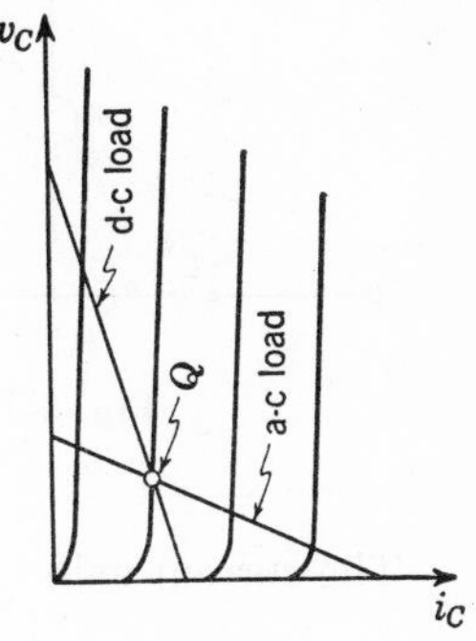

Fig. 5-2. A-c and d-c load lines for an RC coupled amplifier.

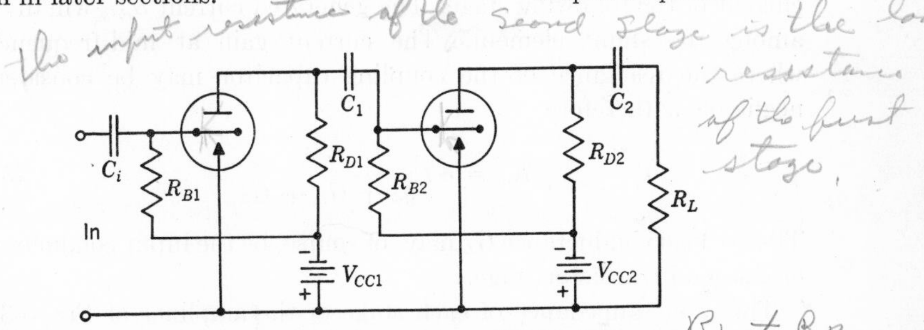

Fig. 5-3. RC coupled amplifier with fixed-bias.

An equivalent circuit representation of the two-stage amplifier of Fig. 5-3 is shown in Fig. 5-4, in which the two-generator h circuit is used to represent the transistor. The resistors R_{B1} and R_{B2} are normally large enough that their loading effect upon the input circuit may be neglected. The current gain and the input and output impedances for this amplifier may be derived by analysis of the equivalent circuit. Because of the many shunt elements in the collector circuit, it is convenient to use conductances rather than resistances in the analysis; accordingly, conductances (having the same identifying subscript as the resistances they replace) will be used in the following sections.

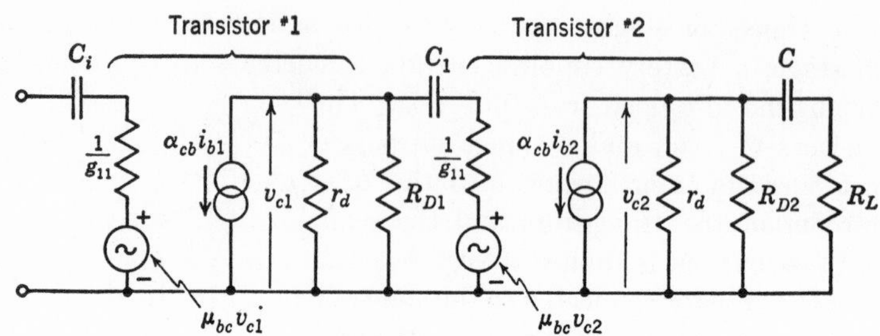

Fig. 5-4. Equivalent circuit for the two-stage amplifier of Fig. 5-3.

The current gain of the RC coupled stage will be given by

$$K_i = i_L/i_b \tag{5-1}$$

where i_L is the current through the a-c load resistance, or the base current of the following stage. The generated current $\alpha_{cb}i_b$ will divide among the shunt elements. The current gain at mid-frequencies where the reactance of the coupling capacitor may be considered negligible is therefore

$$K_i = \alpha_{cb} \frac{G_L}{g_d + G_D + G_L} \tag{5-2}$$

The a-c load conductance G_L may, of course, be the input conductance of a second transistor stage.

The input impedance of each stage of the amplifier of Fig. 5-3 is therefore of interest. In general, from consideration of the equivalent circuit,

$$R_{in} = \frac{1}{g_{11}} + \mu_{bc} \frac{v_c}{i_b} \tag{5-3}$$

But

$$v_c = - \frac{\alpha_{cb} i_b}{g_d + G_D + G_L} \tag{5-4}$$

where the negative sign indicates a phase reversal. Therefore

$$R_{in} = \frac{1}{g_{11}} - \frac{\mu_{bc} \alpha_{cb}}{g_d + G_D + G_L} \tag{5-5}$$

For the RC coupled amplifier operating into a succeeding transistor stage, the second term in Eq. (5-5) is small compared with the first. The reason for this is the very small value of the feedback factor μ_{bc}, which may be of the order of 10^{-4}. Normally, considerably less than 5 per cent error will be introduced if the second term of Eq. (5-5) is neglected. This will be true also for the second stage if G_L is not too small. Hence

$$R_{in} \approx 1/g_{11} \tag{5-6}$$

In accordance with this approximation, the input circuit of the transistor RC coupled amplifier stage is passive. For high values of d-c and a-c load resistance, which occur only rarely in the RC coupled amplifier, Eq. (5-5) must be used to determine the input resistance.

The value of the output resistance or conductance was determined in Chapter 3 for the common-emitter stage. The output conductance

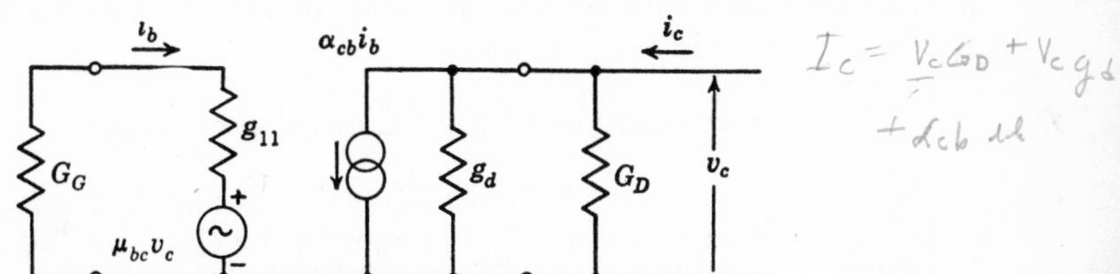

Fig. 5-5. Equivalent circuit for the determination of output impedance.

of the RC coupled amplifier includes in addition to that value the d-c load conductance, which is normally considerably larger than the output conductance of the transistor itself.

If a signal voltage is applied to the collector of the RC coupled stage shown in Fig. 5-5, the current i_c which flows will be given by

$$i_c = v_c\,(G_D + g_d) + \alpha_{cb}i_b \tag{5-7}$$

The base current generated by the feedback generator in the input circuit in response to the applied collector voltage is

$$i_b = -\frac{\mu_{bc}\,v_c}{(1/g_{11}) + (1/G_G)} \tag{5-8}$$

The output conductance is then found by substituting Eq. (5-8) in (5-7) and dividing the resulting expression by v_c. Therefore

$$G_o = G_D + g_d - \mu_{bc}\,\alpha_{cb}\,\frac{G_G\,g_{11}}{G_G + g_{11}} \tag{5-9}$$

The third term in (5-9) may become appreciable relative to g_d if the source conductance G_G is high. This term, however, relative to G_D, is rarely appreciable in common *RC* coupled amplifiers.

Equations (5-2) for the current gain, (5-5) or (5-6) for the input impedance, and (5-9) for the output impedance may be used to analyze the small signal or a-c properties of an *RC* coupled amplifier of any number of stages in cascade. There is some degree of interdependence in the characteristics of cascaded stages because of the internal feedback in the transistor. As a practical matter, this interdependence is normally negligibly small in the middle range of frequencies, and will have considerably less effect upon the a-c characteristics than will the normal tolerances on the values of transistor parameters and circuit resistors.

Large signal and d-c considerations in the *RC* coupled amplifier will be treated in Secs. 5.6 and 5.7.

5.4 Frequency response of the RC coupled amplifier

The low-frequency response of the two-stage amplifier is determined by the value of the coupling capacitors in the circuit of Fig. 5-3, and by the total series resistance with which they are associated. This series resistance amounts to the sum of the source and load resistances on either side of the capacitor. In the case of C_1, for instance, the frequency f_1 at which the response is 3 db down from its mid-frequency value is

$$f_1 = \frac{1}{2\pi C_1(R_{o1} + R_{in2})} \tag{5-10}$$

where R_{o1} is the output resistance of the first stage, and R_{in2} is the input resistance of the second stage. Note that the response is determined primarily by the output impedance of the transistor stage, since R_{o1} is usually larger than R_{in2}.

The high-frequency response is determined by frequency dependence of the transistor parameters, a subject which will be treated extensively in Chapter 7. For the *RC* coupled amplifier, the high-frequency response is related simply to the measurable parameters, as discussed in Sec. 2.12. The frequency dependence of the current gain may be determined by replacing the conductances in (5-2) by admittances, and by introducing the measured frequency dependence of α_{cb}. The current gain expression of Eq. (5-2) becomes

$$K_i = \alpha_{cb} \frac{Y_L}{y_d + G_D + Y_L} \tag{5-11}$$

in which all terms may be functions of frequency.

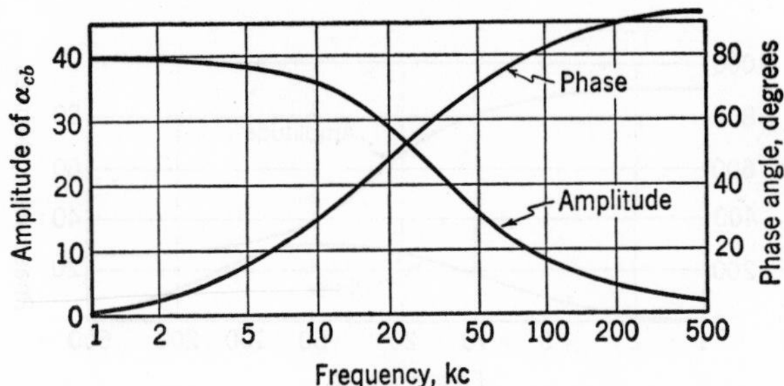

Fig. 5-6. Frequency dependence of α_{cb} for a typical audio transistor.

The variation of α_{cb} with frequency is shown for a typical transistor in Fig. 5-6 in terms of magnitude and phase shift. These curves are seen to closely resemble those for a single reactive element, i.e.,

$$\alpha_{cb} \doteq \frac{\alpha_{cbo}}{1 + jf/f_c} \tag{5-12}$$

where α_{cbo} is the low-frequency value of α_{cb}, f_c is the cutoff frequency or the frequency at which α_{cb} is 3 db down from its low-frequency value, and f is the frequency at which α_{cb} is to be evaluated. The cutoff frequency of α_{cb} for a typical general purpose junction transistor is approximately at the top of the audio range.

The open-circuit output conductance y_d of the transistor itself is reactive in nature because a shunt capacitance appears between collector and emitter of the transistor. The d-c load conductance normally is much higher in value than y_d, so that frequency dependence of the amplifier output admittance is usually of importance only at very high frequencies.

If the amplifier stage is coupled to a second transistor stage, Y_L of (5-11) becomes the input admittance of this second stage, which is nearly equal to y_{11}. The frequency dependence of y_{11} for a typical transistor is shown in Fig. 5-7. This frequency dependence is such to partially compensate for the reduction in α_{cb} with frequency in Eq. (5-11), and is shown qualitatively in the vector diagram of Fig. 5-8. Study of this diagram shows that the frequency response will be improved by use of a low value of d-c load resistance, since the frequency dependence of the input admittance of the following stage is allowed to correct for variation of α_{cb} with frequency.

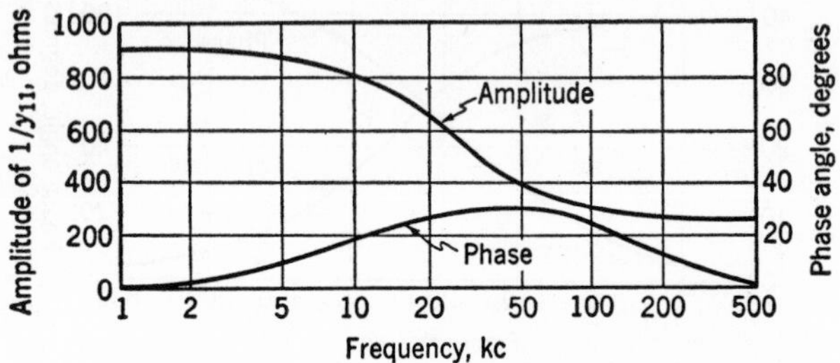

Fig. 5-7. Frequency dependence of the short-circuit input resistance $1/y_{11}$, for a typical audio transistor.

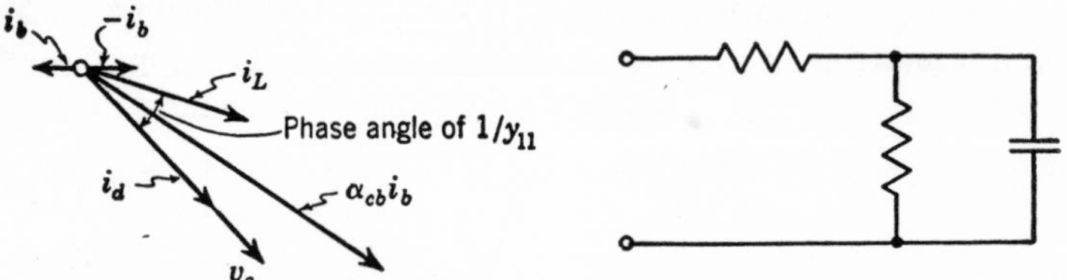

Fig. 5-8. Vector relations in an *RC* coupled amplifier at high frequencies.

Fig. 5-9. Equivalent network for the short-circuit input admittance of a transistor.

An equivalent network which closely represents the input admittance of the transistor stage is shown in Fig. 5-9. This network will have a frequency characteristic similar to that shown in Fig. 5-7. The series resistance is related to the base resistance of the transistor, and imposes a limit upon the amount of frequency correction which may be obtained by use of low values of d-c load resistance.

From the foregoing considerations, it is apparent that the frequency dependence of α_{cb} is of prime importance in determining the high-frequency response of the *RC* coupled amplifier. The frequency dependence of y_{11} of the following stage is of less importance, and is in a direction to improve the response of the amplifier. The frequency dependencies of y_d and μ_{bc} are important only at very high frequencies, or under unusual circuit operating conditions. A conservative rough estimate of the current-gain frequency response may therefore be derived by noting the frequency dependence of α_{cb} .

5.5 Self-bias in the RC coupled amplifier

Practical embodiments of the RC coupled amplifier will require some form of d-c operating point stabilization in order to realize reliable operation. This requirement is met adequately and economically by the method described in Chapter 4 for deriving the base current bias by means of a resistor connected between collector and base.

This feedback connection will result in reduced gain, output resistance, and input resistance, unless means are provided for reducing or eliminating the degenerative current at signal frequencies. If the input impedance of the following stage (i.e., the a-c load) is low, relatively little signal voltage will appear on the collector, and the degeneration will not be excessive. In a typical RC coupled amplifier designed for high output current capability and high d-c stabilization, degeneration may reduce the current gain by one-half. If it is found desirable to reduce the amount of degeneration, the feedback bias resistor may be split into two parts, the junction between them being returned to ground through a capacitor.

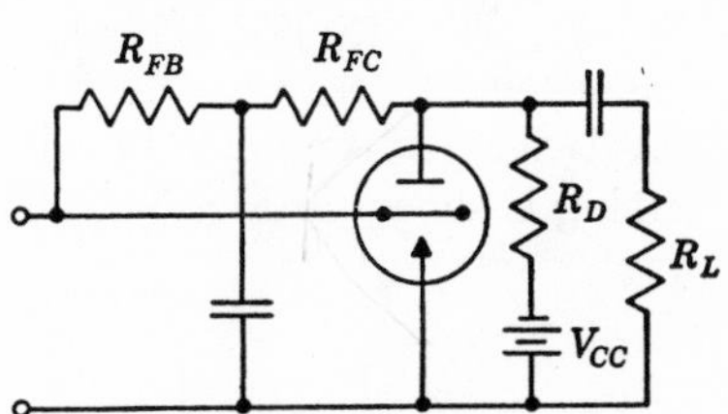

Fig. 5-10. Self-bias RC coupled amplifier stage.

In the case where the degenerative currents are eliminated by means of a capacitor, as shown in Fig. 5-10, the effect of the use of self-bias is to load both the input and output circuits by a section of the feedback resistor. In general, these effects will be small, but may be included in the expressions for gain and input and output impedances developed in Sec. 5.3 by adding these conductive elements in parallel in the appropriate places. The best point at which to break the feedback resistor into two parts for by-passing will depend upon loading, source and load impedances for the amplifier, and cost of available components; generally, a satisfactory arrangement is to make the two parts equal.

With by-passing, the expressions for current gain and input and output resistances given by Eqs. (5-2), (5-5), and (5-9) become, respectively,

$$K_i = \alpha_{cb} \frac{G_L}{g_d + G_D + G_L + G_{FC}} \tag{5-13a}$$

$$R_{in} = \frac{1}{g_{11} + G_{FB}} \tag{5-13b}$$

$$G_o = G_D + g_d + G_{FC} - \mu_{bc}\alpha_{cb} \frac{(G_G + G_{FB})\, g_{11}}{G_G + G_{FB} + g_{11}} \tag{5-13c}$$

in which G_{FC} is the collector portion and G_{FB} is the base portion of the self-bias resistor, as shown in Fig. 5-10.

The by-pass capacitor must be large enough in value to by-pass the degenerative currents to ground at the lowest frequency of interest. At very low frequencies, the response is reduced by degeneration.

A two-stage amplifier in which self-bias is utilized without by-passing is shown in Fig. 5-11. This amplifier is quite practical, since

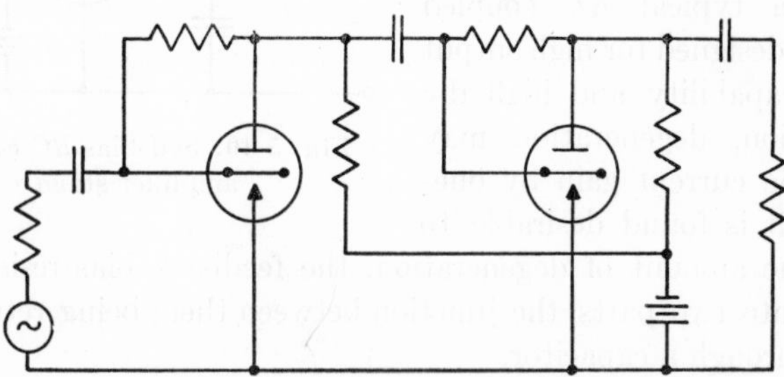

Fig. 5-11. Practical two-stage *RC* coupled amplifier.

it may be designed to afford both a good degree of d-c stabilization and reasonable gain with a minimum number of components. The supply voltage may be made common to the two stages, since the degenerative bias connection will render the amplifier stable.

The effect of the feedback resistor upon the a-c characteristics of the amplifier stage is the reduction of gain and input and output impedances.

The equivalent circuit for an amplifier stage with self-bias feedback is shown in Fig. 5-12. If it is assumed that the signal voltage at the base is negligible compared with that at the collector, the feedback current gain K_i' will be

$$K_i' \approx -\frac{v_c G_L}{i_b + i_f} = \frac{\dfrac{\alpha_{cb}\, i_b\, G_L}{g_d + G_D + G_F + G_L}}{i_b + \dfrac{\alpha_{cb}\, i_b\, G_F}{g_d + G_D + G_F + G_L}} \tag{5-14}$$

Hence

$$K_i' \approx \alpha_{cb} \frac{G_L}{g_d + G_D + G_L + G_F(1 + \alpha_{cb})} \tag{5-15}$$

If v_b is not considered to be negligible, analysis of the equivalent circuit of Fig. 5-12 shows that the current gain with feedback is very closely

$$K_i' = \alpha_{cb} \frac{G_L}{g_d + G_D + G_L + G_F[1 + \alpha_{cb} + (g_d + G_D + G_L)/g_{11}]} \tag{5-16}$$

The input impedance is reduced by the feedback, since the feedback current adds to the base current for a given base signal voltage.

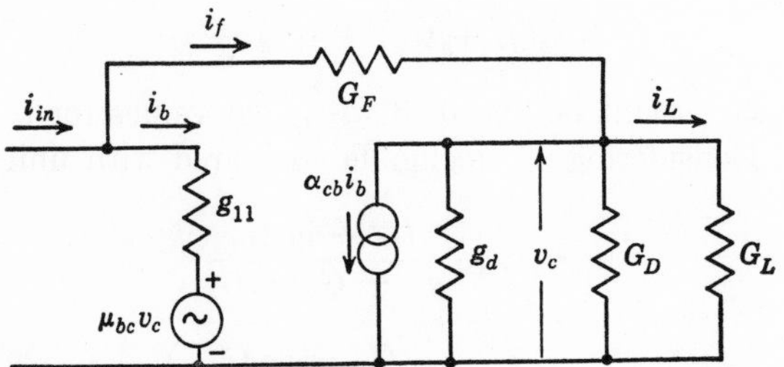

Fig. 5-12. Equivalent circuit for the determination of feedback current gain.

Assuming the input resistance without feedback to be simply $1/g_{11}$, as given in Eq. (5-6), the input resistance with feedback becomes

$$R_{in}' = \frac{1}{g_{11}} \frac{i_b}{i_{in} + i_f} \tag{5-17}$$

If v_b is again considered small compared with v_c,

$$i_f = \alpha_{cb}\, i_b \frac{G_F}{g_d + G_D + G_L + G_F} \tag{5-18}$$

Substituting Eq. (5-18) in Eq. (5-17),

$$R_{in} = \frac{1}{g_{11}} \left(\frac{g_d + G_D + G_L + G_F}{g_d + G_D + G_L + G_F(1 + \alpha_{cb})} \right) \tag{5-19a}$$

or

$$G_{in} = g_{11} \left(1 + \frac{\alpha_{cb} G_F}{g_d + G_D + G_L + G_F} \right) \tag{5-19b}$$

The output resistance is reduced by the application of self-bias from collector to base. If a voltage is applied between the collector

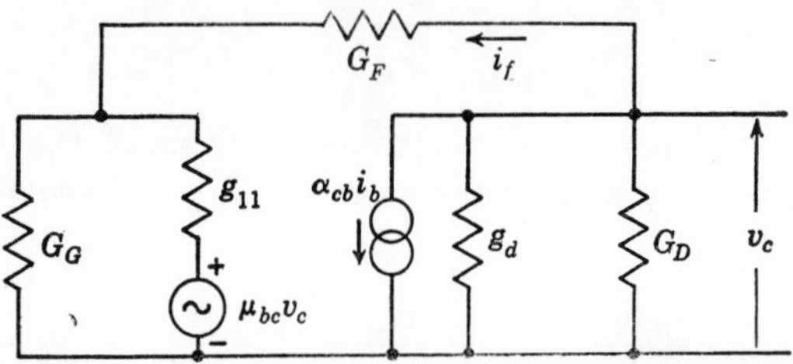

Fig. 5-13. Determination of the output impedance.

and emitter of the feedback amplifier, as shown in the equivalent circuit of Fig. 5-13, the current which flows is given by

$$i_c = v_c(g_d + G_D) + \alpha_{cb} i_b + i_f \tag{5-20}$$

Analysis of the circuit of Fig. 5-13 will yield values for i_b and i_f in terms of v_c. Considering μ_{bc} negligible compared with unity,

$$i_b = v_c \, g_{11} \frac{G_F - \mu_{bc} G_G}{g_{11} + G_G + G_F} \tag{5-21}$$

and

$$i_f = v_c \left(1 - \frac{G_F - \mu_{bc} G_G}{g_{11} + G_G + G_f} \right) \tag{5-22}$$

The output conductance with feedback, G_o', will be obtained by dividing Eq. (5-20) by v_c, having substituted Eqs. (5-21) and (5-22) in it.

Assuming that $\alpha_{cb} \gg G_F/g_{11}$,

$$G_o' = G_D + g_d - \frac{\mu_{bc}\, \alpha_{cb}\, g_{11} G_G}{G_G + g_{11} + G_F} + G_f \left(1 + \alpha_{cb} \frac{g_{11}}{g_{11} + G_G + G_f} \right) \tag{5-23}$$

Comparison of Eqs. (5-23) and (5-9) shows that the output conductance with feedback is given by

$$G_o' \approx G_o + G_f\left(1 + \alpha_{cb}\frac{g_{11}}{g_{11} + G_G + G_f}\right) \tag{5-24}$$

Static characteristics may be measured for the combination of the transistor with self-bias, by connecting the transistor, with self-bias resistor in place, in standard characteristic curve measuring apparatus. This is shown schematically in Fig. 5-14a, and the output

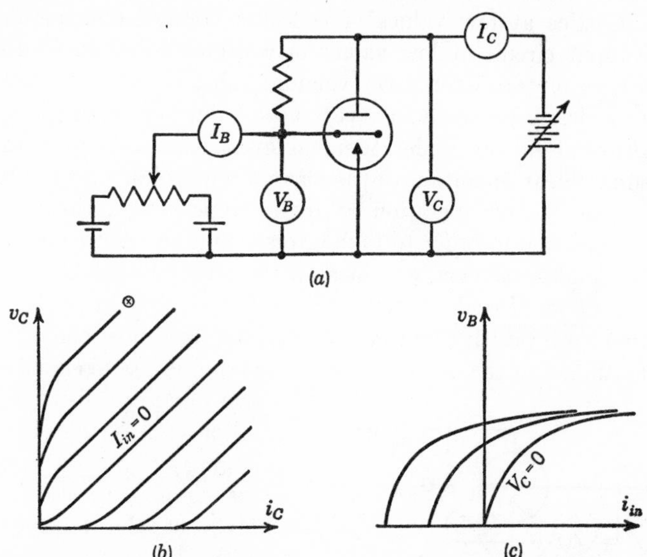

Fig. 5-14. Characteristics of a transistor with self-bias and circuit arrangement for the measurement of these characteristics.

and input characteristics so derived are shown in Figs. 5-14b and 5-14c. The effect of feedback on the characteristics of the transistor is thereby shown graphically. The line of zero input current is the bias curve discussed in Chapter 4.

5.6 Design of RC coupled amplifiers

The design of the *RC* coupled amplifier will depend, of course, upon the parameters and boundary conditions which are given and upon the results desired. Among the initially specified data we usually find the a-c load impedance R_L (often the input impedance of a following stage), the peak signal output current I_o or voltage V_o required, and the characteristics of the transistor to be used. In addition, the direct supply voltage V_{CC} is often specified initially; for instance, it may be desirable to utilize the same source of supply voltage for the RC coupled amplifier as is used for a power output stage.

For a Class A amplifier circuit, limits will be imposed upon the signal level which may be accommodated because of curvature of the characteristics at low values of collector voltage, and nonlinearity of the input circuit at low values of collector currents. One of the advantages of transistors over vacuum tubes is the fact that these limits occur, respectively, at very low values of collector voltage and current. For even moderate signal levels, it is a fair approximation to assume linear operation to the current and voltage axes. For low-level operation, or operation at high temperatures, the equations may be modified in order to take into account curvature of the characteristics; alternatively, graphical analysis may be used.

The nonlinearities discussed above will cause clipping of the output signal on both positive and negative peaks. The most efficient mode of operation, and the one which yields maximum useful signal output for a given transistor collector dissipation, is that in which clipping of the a-c signal begins simultaneously on both halves of the output signal wave. In order to achieve this mode of operation, the d-c operating point must lie midway between the current and voltage axes on the a-c or total load line. It must also lie, of course, on the d-c load line.

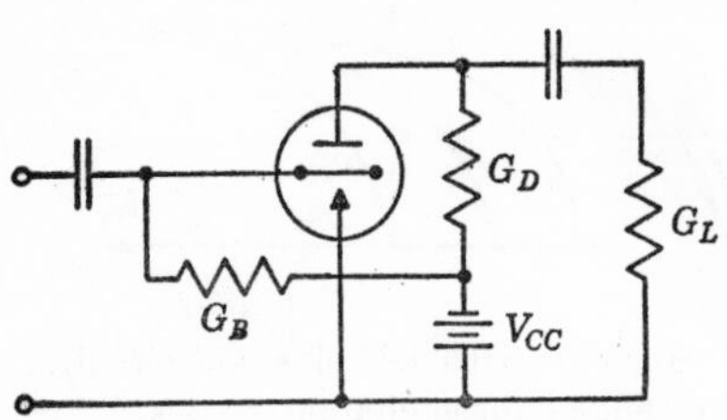

Fig. 5-15. Fixed-bias RC coupled stage.

For the fixed-bias amplifier shown in Fig. 5-15, the d-c load line is given by

$$I_C = (V_{CC} - V_C)G_D \tag{5-25}$$

where G_D is the d-c load conductance. In accordance with the foregoing discussion, the optimum operating point must lie at the mid-point of the a-c load line, which has a slope of $-1/(G_D + G_L)$. It must therefore lie on a line which is the locus of all a-c load line mid-points having this slope. Assuming operation to extend to zero collector voltage and current, this locus must be given by

$$I_C = V_C(G_D + G_L) \tag{5-26}$$

The quiescent voltage is found by equating Eqs. (5-25) and (5-26).

$$V_C = V_{CC} \frac{G_D}{2G_D + G_L} \tag{5-27}$$

The quiescent voltage must be large enough to accommodate the required peak output signal voltage, V_o.

$$V_C = V_o = \frac{I_o}{G_L} \tag{5-28}$$

The d-c load resistance may then be found in terms of the given quantities by combining Eqs. (5-27) and (5-28).

$$G_D = G_L \frac{V_o}{V_{CC} - 2V_o} \tag{5-29a}$$

or

$$R_D = R_L \left(\frac{V_{CC}}{V_o} - 2 \right) \tag{5-29b}$$

The quiescent current is given by substituting Eq. (5-29) in (5-26).

$$I_C = V_o G_L \frac{V_{CC} - V_o}{V_{CC} - 2V_o} \tag{5-30}$$

The value of base bias current required to give this operating point may be obtained from the given transistor characteristics. A resistor of appropriate value is then connected between the collector supply potential source and the base to provide a fixed bias current. Stabilized self-bias operation may be obtained instead by connecting a bias resistor between collector and base, as discussed in Chapter 4. Since the base bias current then flows through the d-c load resistance, the above equations will be somewhat inaccurate; this current, however, is normally quite small relative to the direct collector current, so that the inaccuracy is not large. The design of the self-bias *RC* coupled amplifier is treated in the following section.

These equations provide what may be termed an optimum design for an *RC* coupled amplifier, given the direct supply voltage, the a-c load resistance, the signal output voltage (or current), and assuming "idealized" transistor characteristics. Since a definite relationship exists between the d-c and the a-c load resistances, the approximate current gain for this optimum design may be derived in terms of the given quantities. From Eq. (5-2),

$$K_i = \alpha_{cb} \frac{G_L}{G_D + g_d + G_L} \tag{5-31}$$

$$K_i = \alpha_{cb} \frac{1}{1 + \dfrac{V_o}{V_{CC} - 2V_o} + \dfrac{g_d}{G_L}} \tag{5-32}$$

If $g_d/G_L \ll 1$, as usually will be the case,

$$K_i = \alpha_{cb} \frac{V_{CC} - 2V_o}{V_{CC} - V_o}. \tag{5-33}$$

As the supply voltage is made larger, the d-c load resistance for optimum operation is also increased, so that the current gain increases. The variation of current gain with supply voltage is shown in Fig. 5-16 for the RC coupled amplifier stage of optimum design.

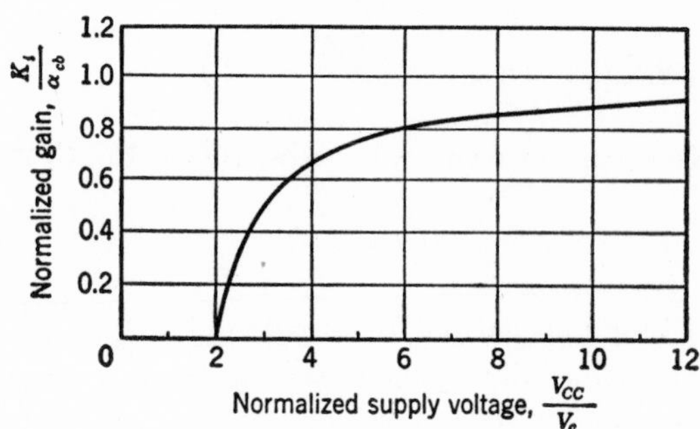

Fig. 5-16. Current gain as a function of the supply voltage for an RC coupled amplifier of optimum design.

The foregoing paragraphs will be more clearly understood by means of the following example.

Example. An rms signal current of 3.5 ma is to be applied to a transistor output stage having an input impedance of 500 ohms from an RC coupled driver transistor with $\alpha_{cb} = 30$ and $r_d = 50{,}000$ ohms. The direct supply voltage is 22.5 volts. Assuming the transistor characteristics to be linear, find for the driver stage the optimum d-c load resistance and operating point for minimum collector dissipation, and determine the current gain.

The peak output signal voltage is

$$V_C = 3.5\sqrt{2} \times 10^{-3} \times 500 = 2.5 \text{ volts}$$

By Eq. (5-29),

$$R_D = 500\left(\frac{22.5}{2.5} - 2\right) = 3500 \text{ ohms}$$

By Eq. (5-30),

$$I_C = \frac{2.5}{0.50}\frac{20}{17.5} = 5.71 \text{ milliamperes}$$

from Eq. (5-2), the current gain is

$$K_i = 30\frac{1/500}{1/20{,}000 + 1/3500 + 1/500} = 25.6$$

Where the assumption may not be made that the characteristics are linear to zero values of current and voltage, as in the case of a very low-level amplifier, Eq. (5-26) must be modified. One method by which the nonlinearities at low voltages and currents may be accommodated is to assume minimum values of voltage V_m and current I_m for the signal excursion. The effect of this assumption would be to move the locus of a-c load line midpoints of Eq. (5-36) so that

$$I_C - I_m = (V_C - V_m)(G_D + G_L) \tag{5-34}$$

Also, the direct collector voltage would be given by

$$V_C = V_o + V_m \tag{5-35}$$

instead of by Eq. (5-28). The d-c load resistance is obtained from Eqs. (5-34) and (5-35).

$$R_D = R_L\frac{V_{CC} - 2V_C + V_m}{V_C - V_m + I_mR_L} \tag{5-36}$$

or

$$R_D = R_L\frac{V_{CC} - 2V_o - V_m}{V_o + I_mR_L} \tag{5-37}$$

5.7 Practical design of a stabilized RC coupled amplifier

Stability considerations dictate the use of self-bias in the *RC* coupled amplifier. Component economy considerations may demand that no by-passing to ground of the degenerative currents be used. In this case, the design will proceed differently from that given in the previous section.

The d-c load line for the amplifier shown in Fig. 5-17 is given by

$$I_C = V_{CC}G_D - (G_D + G_F)V_c \tag{5-38}$$

where G_F is the feedback conductance. The direct base voltage is considered negligible compared with the collector voltage in this

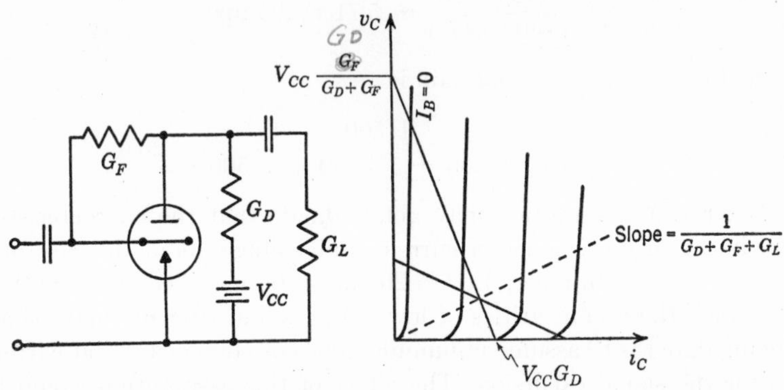

Fig. 5-17. Self-bias stage and characteristics showing a-c and d-c load lines. The dashed line passes through the midpoint of all a-c lo°d lines having the slope $-1/(G_D + G_F + G_L)$.

equation. The operating point will again lie at the mid-point of the a-c or total load line, and hence will lie on the line given by

$$I_C = (G_D + G_F + G_L)V_C \tag{5-39}$$

The quiescent direct collector voltage is determined as in Eq. (5-28) by the signal output voltage required. By equating (5-38) and (5-39), we may obtain the value of the d-c load resistance in terms of the given quantities and the self-bias resistance:

$$G_D = \frac{V_o(2G_F + G_L)}{V_{CC} - 2V_o} \tag{5-40a}$$

or

$$R_D = R_L \frac{V_{CC} - 2V_o}{V_o(1 + 2R_L/R_F)} \tag{5-40b}$$

If $2G_F$ is negligible compared with G_L, Eq. (5-40a) reduces to the expression of (5-29a).

A useful guide to the design of the degenerative self-bias *RC* coupled amplifier may be obtained if the assumption is made that

$$I_B = I_C/\alpha_{cb} \tag{5-41}$$

As may be seen by the comparison of Eq. (5-41) with Eq. (4-8), this assumes that $(1 + \alpha_{cb})I_{co}$ and $V_C g_d$ form a negligible portion of the collector current. This is a reasonable approximation for high-current, low-voltage operation, as is often encountered in RC coupled amplifiers. In accordance with Eq. (5-41),

$$G_F = I_B/V_C = I_C/\alpha_{cb}V_C \tag{5-42}$$

Combining Eqs. (5-39) and (5-42), we obtain the interesting result[1] that

$$G_F = \frac{G_D + G_L}{\alpha_{cb} - 1} \tag{5-43}$$

or that the feedback resistance for optimum operation is approximately α_{cb} times the parallel resistance of the a-c and d-c load resistances. Using Eq. (5-43) in (5-40a) we obtain

$$G_D = \frac{G_L V_o(\alpha_{cb} + 1)/(\alpha_{cb} - 1)}{V_{CC} - 2V_o\alpha_{cb}/(\alpha_{cb} - 1)} \tag{5-44}$$

Although (5-41) is a fairly rough approximation, (5-44) is quite accurate, since G_F is but a small factor in (5-40a). The d-c load resistance is thereby expressed in terms of the given quantities.

Inserting the value for G_F given by Eq. (5-43) in the equation for the current gain of the degenerative self-bias amplifier given by Eq. (5-15), the gain for the amplifier of optimum design becomes

$$K_i = \frac{\alpha_{cb} G_L}{G_D + g_d + G_L + [(1 + \alpha_{cb})/(\alpha_{cb} - 1)](G_D + G_L)} \tag{5-45}$$

If g_d is small relative to $G_D + G_L$, and α_{cb} is large relative to unity, an approximate expression for the gain may be written

$$K_i = \alpha_{cb} \frac{G_L}{2(G_D + g_d + G_L)} \tag{5-46}$$

in which the error introduced by the two assumptions tends to cancel. Comparison of this equation with Eq. (5-2) shows that

[1] In cases where I_{CO} is high, it may be shown that

$$G_F = \frac{G_D + G_L}{\alpha_{cb} - 1} - \frac{I_{CO}}{V_o}$$

$$K_i' = K_i/2 \tag{5-47}$$

or that the a-c degeneration due to self-bias in the amplifier of optimum design is approximately 6 db. The input impedance is also approximately halved, and the output impedance is effectively reduced by the additional shunting of approximately $G_D + G_L$ across the output.

A measure of the d-c operating point stabilization afforded by the self-bias connection is the d-c gain reduction introduced by the feedback. If the collector current tends to change for any reason, for instance because of a change in I_{CO}, the tendency for change will be reduced by an amount equal to the d-c gain reduction. The gain reduction is therefore a measure of the improvement in stability of the self-bias over the fixed-bias amplifier.

The d-c current gain without feedback is given by

$$K_{dc} = \alpha_{cb} \frac{G_D}{g_d + G_D}. \tag{5-48}$$

The d-c current gain with feedback is to a good degree of approximation

$$K_{dc}' = \alpha_{cb} \frac{G_D}{g_d + G_D + G_F(1 + \alpha_{cb})} \tag{5-49}$$

The gain reduction ratio S will be given by

$$S = \frac{K_{dc}}{K_{dc}'} = \frac{g_d + G_D + G_F(1 + \alpha_{cb})}{g_d + G_D} \tag{5-50}$$

For a self-bias stage of optimum design, the approximate relationship of Eq. (5-43) applies, and

$$S = \frac{g_d + G_D + (G_D + G_L)(\alpha_{cb} + 1)/(\alpha_{cb} - 1)}{g_d + G_D} \tag{5-51}$$

The relationship between G_D and G_L is given in Eq. (5-44). Inserting this value in Eq. (5-51), the following simple relationship is found:

$$S = \frac{g_d + G_D(V_{CC}/V_o)}{g_d + G_D} \tag{5-52}$$

For an amplifier of optimum design, the stabilization therefore depends upon the direct supply voltage relative to the desired output voltage. As the supply voltage is increased, the d-c load conductance must be reduced, thereby providing increased d-c feedback and stability.

Thus, for the RC coupled amplifier, the relationship existing between the a-c signal requirements and the d-c circuit characteristics has been explored for the most common design criteria. There will be many design problems with special requirements and different design criteria; these problems will be treated in similar fashion to those treated above.

The design equations for the stabilized RC coupled amplifier are developed by assuming fairly ideal transistor characteristics. The design will not deviate greatly with the use of less than ideal transistors. Optimum final design is normally based upon experimental verification. To this end, the above analysis should provide a useful guide.

5.8 Efficiency of RC coupled amplifiers

Battery operation of transistor amplifiers may cause the efficiency of the amplifier, defined as the ratio of a-c signal load power to battery supply power, to be of importance. It is therefore desirable to determine the battery voltage and load resistance which should be used in order to obtain maximum efficiency.

The d-c battery power supplied to an RC coupled amplifier stage will be

$$P_B = V_C I_C + \frac{I_C^2}{G_D} \tag{5-53}$$

The signal power output will be given by

$$P_L = \frac{V_C^2 G_L}{2} \tag{5-54}$$

assuming that the signal swing is to zero voltage (i.e., ignoring curvature of the characteristics at low values of collector voltage).

The efficiency is therefore given by the ratio of Eq. (5-54) to Eq. (5-53), which may be written

$$\eta = \frac{P_L}{P_B} = \frac{G_L G_D}{(G_D \ast I_C/V_C + I_C/V_C^2)2} \tag{5-55}$$

If the operating point is set at the mid-point of the a-c or total load line,

$$\eta = \frac{G_L G_D}{\left(\frac{G_D I_C}{V_C} + \frac{I_C^2}{V_C^2}\right) 2}$$

$$\frac{I_C}{V_C} = G_D + G_L \tag{5-56}$$

Substituting Eq. (5-56) into Eq. (5-55) the efficiency becomes

$$\eta = \frac{G_L G_D}{2(2G_D^2 + 3G_L G_D + G_L^2)} \tag{5-57}$$

If Eq. (5-57) is differentiated with respect to G_D, and the result is set equal to zero, the value of G_D for maximum efficiency may be found.

$$G_D = \frac{\sqrt{2}}{2} G_L \tag{5-58a}$$

or

$$R_D = \sqrt{2}\, R_L \tag{5-58b}$$

The numerical value of the efficiency, found by substituting Eq. (5-58) into Eq. (5-57), is

$$\eta = 8.59 \text{ per cent} \tag{5-59}$$

The maximum efficiency of the RC coupled amplifier operated from a constant voltage supply source is therefore quite low.

The battery voltage required for operation at maximum efficiency is dependent upon the required output voltage.

$$V_{CC} = V_C + \frac{I_C}{G_D} \tag{5-60}$$

and from (5-56),

$$I_C = V_C(G_D + G_L) \tag{5-61}$$

Combining Eqs. (5-60), (5-61), and (5-58a),

$$V_{CC} = V_C(2 + \sqrt{2}) \tag{5-62}$$

5.9 Transformer coupling

Maximum available power gain may be derived from a transistor amplifier if the input and output circuits are matched to the source and load circuits, respectively. Transformer coupling may be used to achieve this condition, although the use of transformer coupling is not restricted to the establishment of the matched condition; the maximum collector voltage rating on the transistor normally restricts matching to amplifiers of low-level signals, since the output impedance of the transistor is quite high. Transformer coupling, however, allows the freedom of selecting the a-c load impedance for efficient utilization of the amplification properties of the transistor.

A d-c stabilized transformer coupled amplifier stage is shown in Fig. 5-18, in which a tapped battery and series emitter resistor serve to keep the emitter current constant. Direct current flows to the collector through the output transformer primary winding. A capacitor by-passes the emitter resistor in order to avoid degeneration. The reactance of this capacitor must be low compared with the dynamic emitter impedance down to the lowest frequency of interest. The input signal is coupled to the base by means of the input transformer.

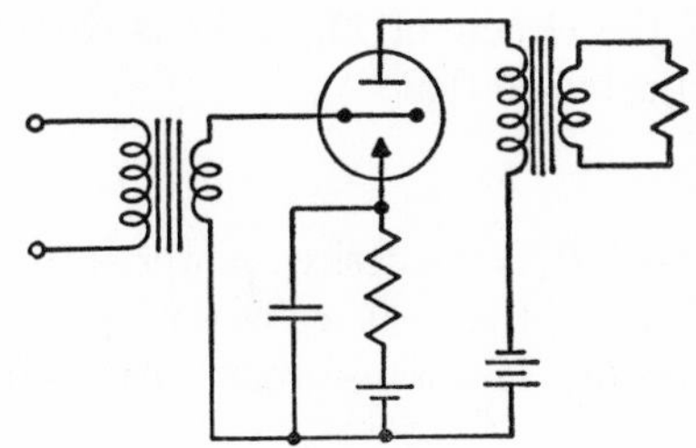

Fig. 5-18. Transformer-coupled amplifier.

When matched operation is desired, the turns ratios of the two transistors are adjusted to give the matched condition. The input transformer secondary is made to present an effective generator resistance of

$$R_G = \frac{\sqrt{1 - \alpha_{cb}\,\mu_{bc}\,g_{11}\,r_d}}{g_{11}} \tag{5-63}$$

and the output transformer primary is made to present a collector load of

$$R_L = \frac{r_d}{\sqrt{1 - \alpha_{cb}\,\mu_{bc}\,g_{11}\,r_d}} \tag{5-64}$$

The value of load impedance dictated by Eq. (5-64) is excessively high for most low-frequency amplifiers. Very little current output may be obtained in such an arrangement because of the limitation imposed by the maximum collector voltage rating. The matched condition is therefore of little importance in low-frequency amplifiers.

High efficiency, approaching the theoretical maximum of 50 per cent, may be achieved by use of transformer coupling, aside from the power consumed by the d-c stabilizing networks. This fact makes the transformer coupled stage attractive for amplifiers in which battery power is used, such as hearing aid devices and the like.

In the design of a transformer coupled stage, the output signal power, current, or voltage, and the load resistance, are specified initially. The d-c collector supply voltage may also be determined initially by the supply voltage requirements elsewhere in the circuit. It will be assumed that curvature of the characteristics is negligible at low values of current and voltage. The quiescent collector voltage of the circuit of Fig. 5-18 is closely V_{CC}. The quiescent current is adjusted so that

$$V_{CC} I_C = 2P_o \tag{5-65}$$

where P_o is the desired power output, since V_{CC} will be approximately equal to the peak collector signal voltage, and I_C, the peak signal current. The transformer turns ratio is adjusted so that

$$\frac{N_1}{N_2} = \sqrt{\frac{V_{CC}}{I_C R_L}} \tag{5-66}$$

The current gain of the amplifier in the middle range of frequencies will be

$$K_i = \alpha_{cb} \frac{N_1}{N_2} \frac{r_d}{r_d + (N_1/N_2)^2 R_L} \tag{5-67a}$$

or, in terms of the design parameters,

$$K_i = \alpha_{cb} \sqrt{\frac{V_{CC}}{I_C R_L}} \left(\frac{r_d}{r_d + V_{CC}/I_{CC}} \right) \tag{5-67b}$$

At low frequencies, the shunt reactance of the transformer will decrease, causing the low-frequency response to fall off The frequency at which the response is down 3 db is given by

$$f_1 = \frac{1}{2\pi L_p[(N_2/N_1)^2 G_L + G_o]} \tag{5-68}$$

where $[(N_2/N_1)^2 G_L + G_o]$ is the total shunt conductance referred to the primary, and L_p is the primary inductance of the output transformer.

The high-frequency response is dependent upon the transistor as in the case of the RC coupled amplifier, and also upon the leakage reactance between primary and secondary of the transformer. The effect upon the response of the latter is to give 3 db attenuation at a frequency f_2 at which

$$f_2 = \frac{R_o + (N_1/N_2)^2 R_L}{2\pi L_S} \tag{5-69}$$

in which R_o is the transistor output resistance, $(N_1/N_2)^2R_L$ is the load resistance referred to the primary, and L_S is the leakage reactance between primary and secondary referred to the primary. In addition to this effect, the transistor output capacitance may resonate with the leakage, giving a peak in the high-frequency response. The response of the transformer coupled amplifier is generally poorer than that of the RC coupled amplifier.

In general, the higher cost, poorer frequency response, and greater circuit complexity for a given amount of d-c stabilization of the transformer coupled amplifier point to the use of other types of coupling, as is the case with amplifiers employing vacuum tubes. Two exceptions are cases where (1) high circuit efficiency, and (2) high output power are required.

5.10 Impedance coupled amplifiers

The impedance coupled amplifier as shown in Fig. 5-19 has in common with the transformer coupled amplifier the advantage of high circuit efficiency when used in conjunction with a constant voltage energizing source. Although the a-c load may not be varied at will as in the transformer coupled amplifier, its high-frequency response is not limited by leakage reactance. The output voltage may be high relative to the supply direct voltage. Since the d-c resistance in the collector circuit is low, d-c feedback must be utilized to stabilize the operating point.

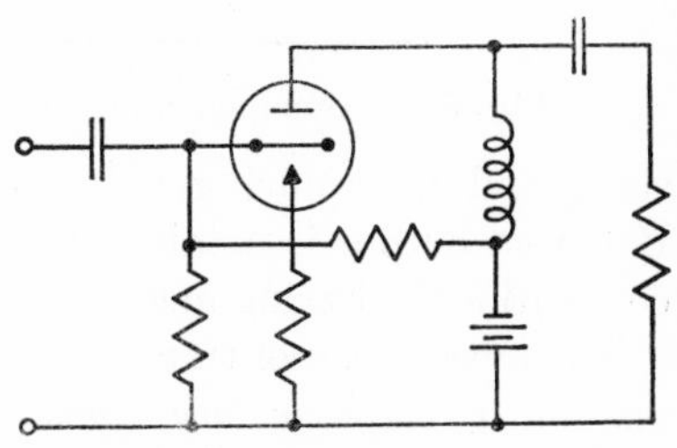

Fig. 5-19. Impedance-coupled amplifier.

The mid-frequency current gain of the impedance coupled amplifier is high because of lack of a-c signal currents in the d-c path.

$$K_i = \alpha_{cb} \frac{r_d}{r_d + R_L}. \tag{5-70}$$

The frequency response is limited at low frequencies by the shunting reactance of the inductor. In addition the coupling capacitance and shunt inductance will resonate at some low frequency to give a rise in response. This effect is particularly severe if the a-c load impedance is relatively low and if the resonance occurs at a frequency at which the Q of the inductor is relatively high.

At high frequencies, the transistor limits the frequency response in much the same way as in the RC coupled amplifier. Distributed capacitances in the inductor will also have an effect at high frequencies.

5.11 The complementary symmetry amplifier

In the foregoing sections, amplification stages utilizing a single transistor have been discussed. Push-pull amplification may be obtained by utilizing two substantially identical transistors in each

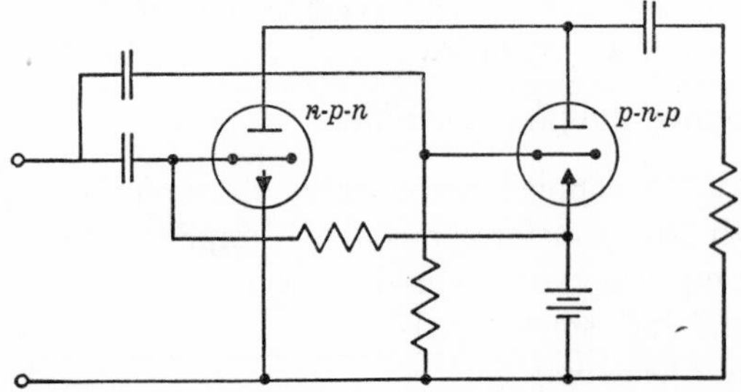

Fig. 5-20. Complementary symmetry push-pull amplifier stage.

stage and by applying a balanced signal to the input terminals. Balanced output is obtained from the two transistors by any of the conventional coupling methods treated in the foregoing sections.

The availability of transistors of opposite conductivity type makes possible a *complementary symmetry* push-pull amplifier having many features to recommend it over the conventional push-pull amplifier utilizing transistors of only one conductivity type. An example of a circuit which uses a *p-n-p* and an *n-p-n* transistor in the grounded emitter configuration is shown in Fig. 5-20. The energizing current for the output circuit is derived from the battery, and flows through the two transistors in series, thereby eliminating the need for a passive d-c load element. Fixed bias current is supplied to the base of each transistor through a resistor connected with the battery.

Input signal is applied in parallel to the two bases through coupling capacitors. Output signal is derived from the collectors, which are also in parallel. Coupling capacitors are used to block direct current from the a-c load and to secure the proper d-c operating conditions for the transistors.

Since the d-c load element is eliminated in the complementary symmetry amplifier, signal which would normally be shunted through the d-c load flows into the a-c load as useful output signal. For this reason, the gain and the signal output capability of this amplifier are high compared with RC coupled amplifier. Since no battery power is dissipated in a d-c load element, the efficiency is also high and may approach the theoretical maximum of 50 per cent. In addition, the usual advantages of even-order harmonic cancellation are obtained for this push-pull amplifier, without the inconveniences associated with balanced operation.

The direct voltage across the n-p-n or first transistor of Fig. 5-20 is given by

$$V_{C1} = V_{CC} - V_{C2} \tag{5-71}$$

where the collector voltages of each transistor are functions of the common collector current and the respective base bias currents. These functions are given by the static characteristics of the two transistors, so that the relationship of Eq. (5–71) may be expressed graphically as given in Fig. 5-21, in which the second transistor is shown as providing a d-c load for the first. The operating point will be established by selection of the base bias current for the two transistors, and will lie at the intersection of the appropriate lines of constant base current.

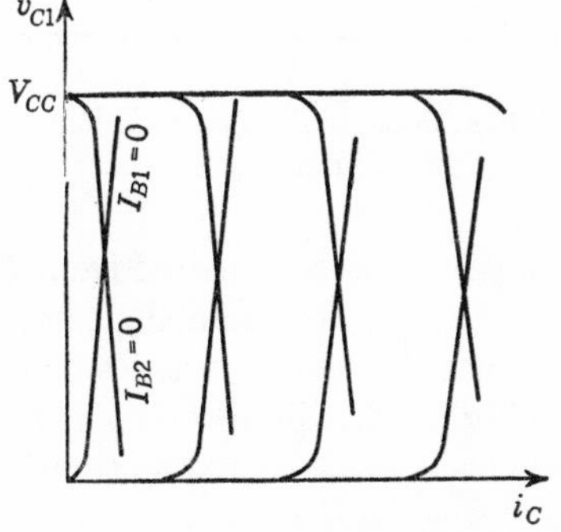

Fig. 5-21. D-c circuit analysis of complementary symmetry stage with capacitive coupling to the load.

The maximum peak signal output voltage which can be obtained from the amplifier (ignoring curvature of the characteristics) will be equal to the lower of the collector voltages across the transistors, and is consequently maximized when the collector voltage across each transistor is equal to half the supply voltage.

For Class A amplification, the common collector energizing current must be set at one-half the peak signal current required, since each transistor should supply half the output signal. In practice, the energizing current must be set somewhat higher to allow for differences in the characteristics of the two transistors.

The curves of Fig. 5-21 show that the lines of constant base current intersect at a very small angle, and that a slight shift in the characteristics of one of the two transistors, caused, for instance, by a change in I_{CO}, will change the collector voltage by a large amount. The operating point will therefore be highly variable with changes in the transistor characteristics. The operating point stability may be greatly improved by the use of collector to base feedback on each

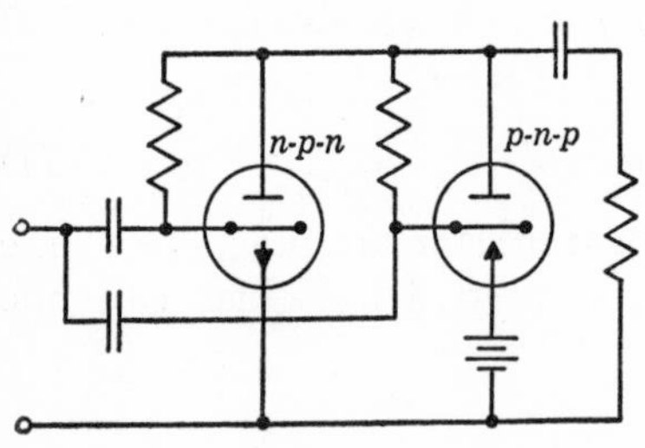

Fig. 5-22. Stabilized complementary symmetry amplifier.

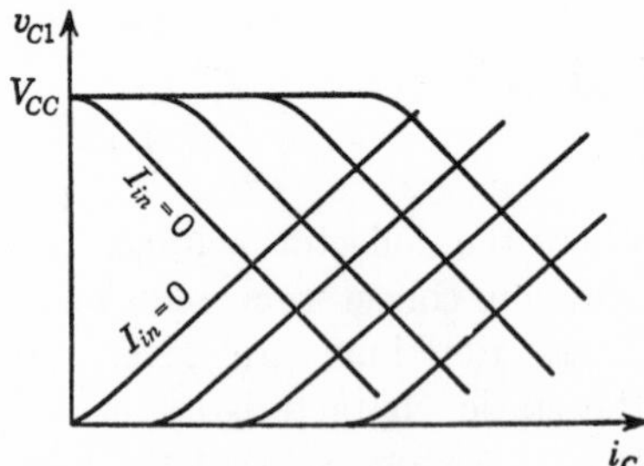

Fig. 5-23. Characteristics with feedback stabilization.

transistor as shown in Fig. 5-22. The effect of this feedback is to lower the output impedance of the transistors, as noted in Sec. 5.5, so that the characteristics intersect at a less acute angle, as seen in Fig. 5-23. The feedback resistors have the correct value to supply the necessary bias to the transistors.

If a greater amount of stabilization is required, the feedback resistors may have a lower value than required for correct bias, so that reverse bias must be applied by the use of the emitter resistors as shown in Fig. 5-24.

Direct coupling to the signal load may be employed if the signal return is made to a center tap on the supply voltage source as shown in Fig. 5-25. In this case, depending upon the d-c resistance of the load, the collector energizing currents of the two transistors will not necessarily be equal, since an unbalance current may flow in the load.

By the same token, the collector voltage unbalance between the two transistors is reduced. With a low-resistance d-c load, stabilization of the collector voltage is no longer necessary, but a method for equalizing the currents in the two transistors is desirable. One such method, employing current feedback, is given in Fig. 5-25.

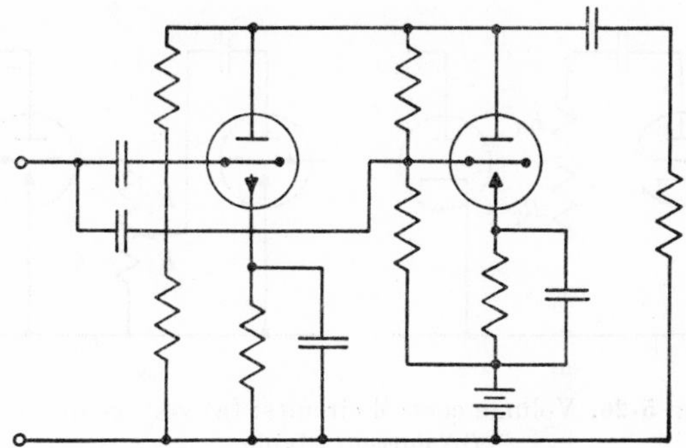

Fig. 5-24. Highly stabilized complementary symmetry amplifier.

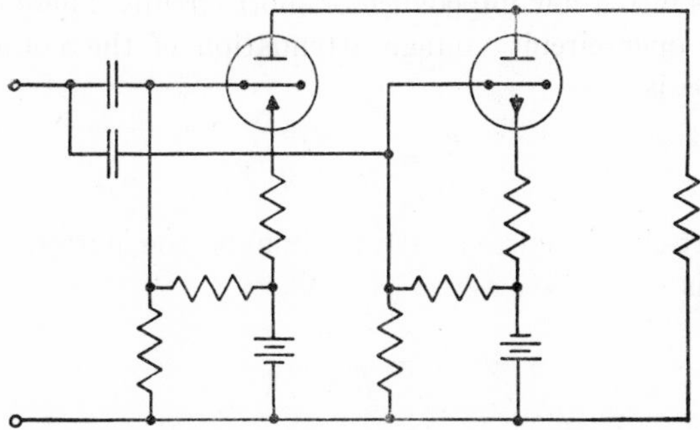

Fig. 5-25. Complementary symmetry amplifier direct-coupled to load.

Further aspects of the complementary symmetry amplifier will be treated in the following chapter on power amplifiers.

5.12 Amplifier controls

Audio volume and tone controls for transistor amplifiers are basically similar to those used in vacuum tube circuits, in that the applied signal is divided in a manually controllable manner. In a tone control, the division of signal is frequency selective; in a volume control, the division is independent of frequency. The major difference between vacuum tube controls and transistor controls is that in the former, signal voltages are divided, while in the latter, signal currents must be divided.

Voltage and current divider circuits, for use with vacuum tubes and transistors, respectively, are shown in Fig. 5-26. The voltage

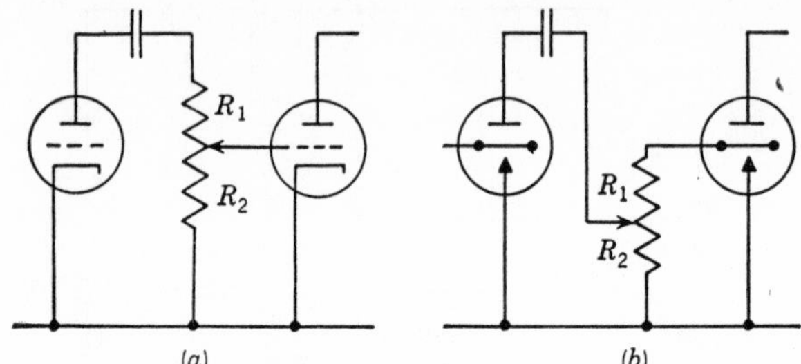

Fig. 5-26. Volume control circuits: (a) voltage divider; (b) current divider.

divider works into a high impedance or open circuit; the current divider works into a low impedance or short circuit. These circuits are duals. The open-circuit voltage attenuation of the voltage divider of Fig. 5-26a is

$$\frac{e_o}{e_i} = \frac{R_2}{R_1 + R_2}. \tag{5-72a}$$

The short-circuit current attenuation of the current divider of Fig. 5-20b is

$$\frac{i_o}{i_i} = \frac{R_2}{R_1 + R_2} \tag{5-72b}$$

Thus a given potentiometer will have similar voltage and current attentuation characteristics. The taper of the potentiometer (the relationship between R_2 and angle of rotation) will therefore be the same for both voltage and current division. Departure from the unloaded condition (i.e., open circuit for the voltage divider or short circuit for the current divider) will cause the taper characteristics to be modified. Hence the current divider works best from a high-impedance source to a low-impedance load. The total resistance of the potentiometer should have a value between the impedance of the source and load.

Tone control circuits and equalizers for transistor amplifiers utilize reactive elements to divide the current in a frequency selective manner. Inductors are not ordinarily used because of high cost and the possibility of hum pickup. Resistance-capacitance networks ordinarily employed may be used in either a frequency selective feedback arrangement, or in simple loss networks, for which characteristics will be similar but inverse. The latter type will be considered here.

Four functions of bass and treble boost and attentuate and combinations of these are commonly provided in audio tone control circuits. A circuit employing variable current division only at low frequencies and thereby providing both increase and decrease in bass response is shown in Fig. 5-27. The first transistor stage utilizes

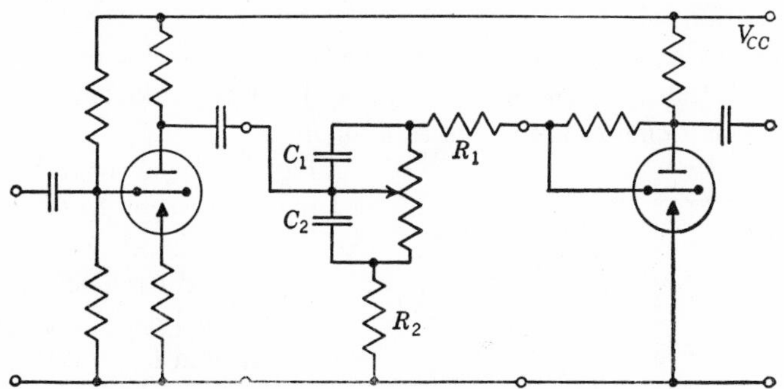

Fig. 5-27. Low-frequency tone control.

current feedback stabilization and a d-c load resistor of high value in order to provide a source of high impedance for the tone control circuit. The signal current from this stage is divided at mid-frequencies by the resistors R_1 and R_2, the capacitors having negligible reactance in this range. The total resistance of the potentiometer is large relative to R_1.

At mid-frequencies, most of the signal current is shunted to ground through R_2, the remainder flowing through R_1 to the input circuit of the following stage. At low frequencies, however, the division of current is changed, depending upon the setting of the potentiometer arm, so that low-frequency signals are either increased or attenuated relative to mid-band signals.

With the variable tap set near R_1, the combination of C_2 and R_2

causes the current flowing to the input of the following stage to increase as the frequency is lowered. The frequency at which the response is 3 db above its mid-band value is the frequency at which the reactance of C_2 is equal to R_2. The response will continue to rise until the gain has attained the value which it would have attained with C_2 open-circuited.

With the variable tap set near R_2 the bass boost capacitor C_2 is short-circuited and the combination of C_1 and R_1 comes into play. The bass response is attenuated and will be 3 db down when the reactance of C_1 is equal to R_1, the impedance of the following stage being considered negligible. At intermediate points between the two ends of the potentiometer the net response will include the effect of the boost and the attentuation networks. In order to secure a potentiometer position which yields a relatively flat response, the time constants R_1C_1 and R_2C_2 should be made equal. The flat position will then be attained when the resistances of the top and bottom parts of the potentiometer are in the ratio of R_1/R_2.

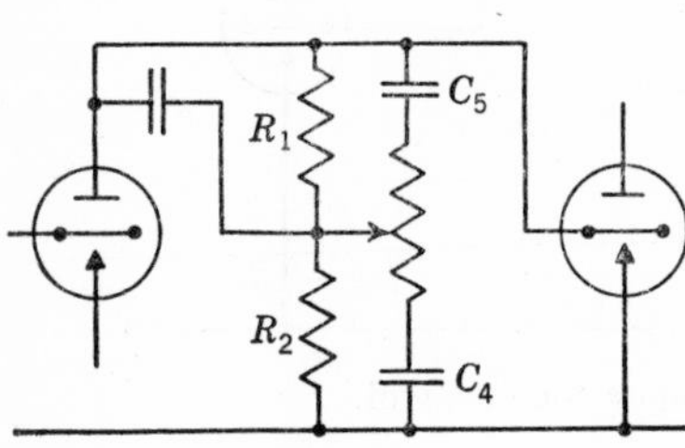

Fig. 5-28. High-frequency tone control.

A high-frequency or treble control of similar type to the above bass control is shown in Fig. 5-28. The mid-band signal current is divided as before by the resistors R_1 and R_2, but these resistors may be shunted at high frequencies by the capacitors C_3 and C_4, depending upon the position of the variable tap on the potentiometer.

At the maximum treble position the combination of C_3 and R_1 produces a rise in frequency response which starts at the frequency at which the reactance of C_3 is equal to R_1. With the control in the minimum treble position, the response will start to fall off at the frequency at which the reactance of C_4 is equal to R_2. A flat position may be obtained as before by making the time constants R_1C_3 and R_2C_4 equal.

Since both the bass and treble controls introduce a mid-frequency loss as determined by the resistors R_1 and R_2, it will often be desirable from the standpoint of economy of gain to combine the low-frequency and high-frequency controls. Such a circuit is shown in Fig. 5-29, in which the single set of resistors R_1 and R_2 provides the mid-frequency current division for both controls. There is little interaction between these controls, since the frequency range covered by each is separate.

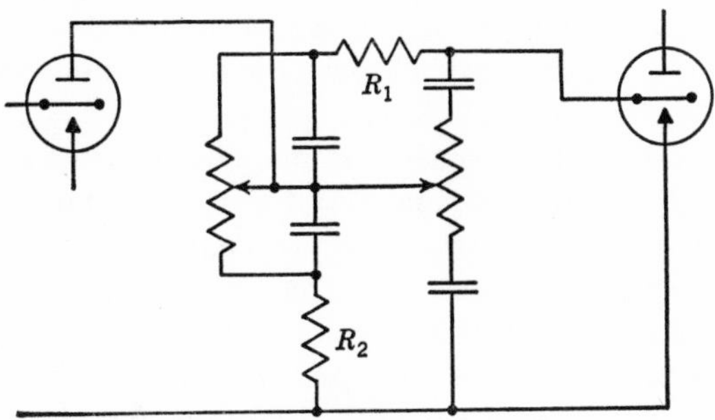

Fig. 5-29. Dual tone control.

5.13 Terminal circuits

Previous sections of this chapter have described the operation of transistors working in conjunction with other transistors, as in cascaded amplifiers. Performance of a useful function by the transistor circuit requires that it be coupled to an external driving force. It is the purpose of this section to show, in a few typical low-frequency applications, the manner in which this problem is treated.

It must be kept in mind that the input circuit of the transistor is current operated. In some cases, the source can be arranged to provide a signal at an optimum impedance level. Other cases demand that the transistor circuit be adapated to the source.

A common signal source for an audio amplifier is the second detector of a radio receiver. Detectors will be treated in detail in Chapter 11, but as an example of the adaptation of the source to the characteristics of the transistor input circuit, consider the detector of Fig. 5-30. In this circuit, a shunt diode, fed from a source of relatively high impedance, causes a current to flow through the volume control network and the input circuit of the transistor. The inductor, which is chosen to have a reactance which is relatively large at the incoming signal frequency, but relatively small at audio frequencies, causes the

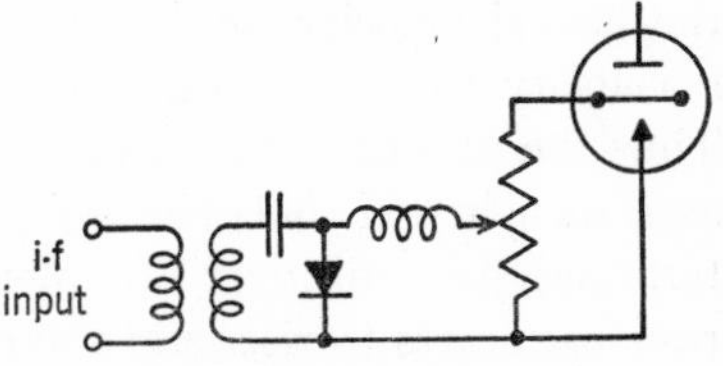

Fig. 5-30. Diode detector.

low-frequency output current to approach the peak value of the high-frequency input current. The operation is analogous, in dual fashion, to the operation of a diode detector with capacitive filtering, as used in most radio receivers.[2] Use of a dual circuit is required in order to adapt the linear diode detector to the input circuit of a transistor.

Another common signal source for an audio amplifier is the phonograph pickup. There are several types in use, the most common of which are the piezoelectric or crystal pickup, the moving iron pickup, and the moving coil pickup. The latter two types, termed magnetic pickups, will have similar characteristics except that the moving iron type will usually be of higher impedance than the moving coil pickup. Other pickup types, such as the FM pickup and the variable resistance pickup may also be used with transistors, but for purpose of illustration only the crystal and magnetic types will be considered.

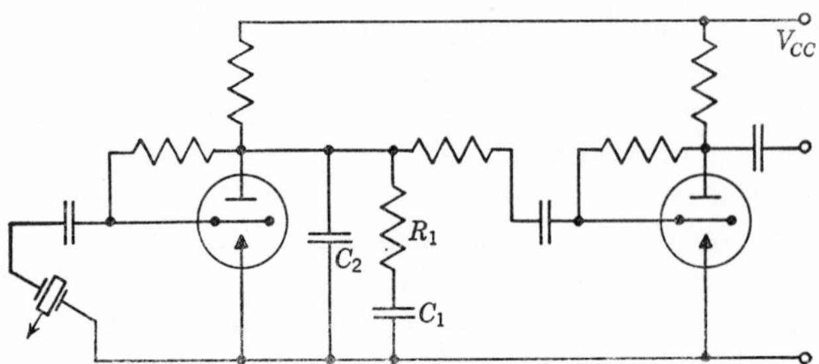

Fig. 5-31. Preamplifier equalizer for crystal pickup.

The crystal pickup may be directly connected to the base of a common emitter amplifier as shown in Fig. 5-31. The short-circuit current output of this type of pickup is essentially proportional to the lateral velocity of the pickup stylus. Present-day records have a velocity frequency response substantially as shown in Fig. 5-32a. Thus the output of the common emitter amplifier must be equalized as shown in Fig. 5-31, in which the combination of R_1 and C_1 determines the "turnover" frequency, or frequency at which the bass response starts to rise, and the combination of C_2 and R_1 effectively determines the "roll-off" frequency, or frequency at which the treble response begins to fall.

[2] See F. Terman, *Radio Engineering*, McGraw-Hill Book Co., Inc., New York, p. 502 ff.

The magnetic pickup may also be connected to the base of the common emitter transistor as shown in Fig. 5-33. The pickup output current will be proportional to the lateral amplitude of the stylus motion as long as the inductive reactance of the pickup remains high relative to the series combination of the pickup resistance and the

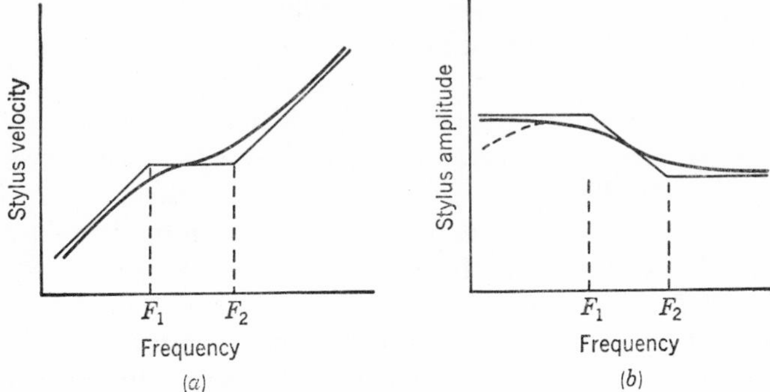

Fig. 5-32. Frequency response of phonograph records in terms of lateral stylus motion.

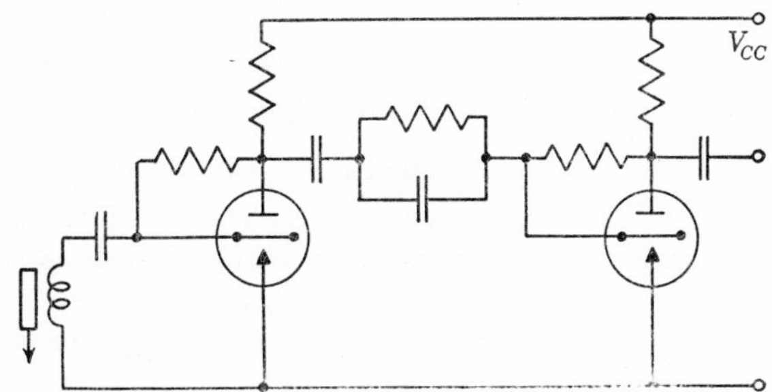

Fig. 5-33. Amplifier and equalizer for magnetic phonograph pickups.

transistor input resistance. The amplitude-frequency response curve of a typical record, corresponding to the velocity response curve of Fig. 5-32a, is shown in Fig. 5-32b.

At low frequencies, the inductive reactance of the pickup becomes small relative to the series input circuit resistance, and the bass response is thereby reduced. The dotted curve of Fig. 5-27b shows the frequency response of a typical magnetic cartridge operated directly into the input circuit of a transistor. In order to reduce the transistor input resistance, and thereby to extend the bass response, a common base stage may be used.

It is noted that considerably less equalization is required when operating the magnetic pickup with a transistor amplifier than with a vacuum tube amplifier. In certain noncritical applications, the magnetic pickup output may be used without equalization. The frequency response so obtained is generally similar to that obtained from an unequalized crystal cartridge connected to a vacuum tube amplifier.

Similar considerations apply to the combination of a magnetic tape playback head and a transistor amplifier, except that noise from the transistor will be an additional problem. Excluding high-frequency effects, the tape is recorded by feeding a current to the record head which is constant with frequency, thereby creating an essentially constant flux vs. frequency condition on the tape. The short-circuit current output from the playback head is proportional to the flux on the tape, so that the output current is essentially flat with frequency. This should be compared with the open-circuit output voltage from the playback head, which is proportional to the rate-of-change of flux, and which therefore increases in direct proportion to the frequency.

5.14 Feedback in transistor amplifiers

The principle of negative feedback is covered extensively in the literature, particularly as it relates to amplifiers employing vacuum tubes. The improvement obtainable in stability of gain, linearity, and frequency response at the expense of a reduction in gain is well known. It will suffice here to point out a few of the specific circuit features which apply directly to transistor circuits.

Local feedback, or feedback over a single stage of amplification, has been discussed in connection with stabilization of the d-c operating point. The common base and common collector circuits, as discussed in Chapter 3, offer, respectively, the maximum amount of current and voltage feedback which may be applied to a single transistor stage without the use of a transformer.

Feedback may be applied to a multistage amplifier in order to secure the advantages cited above or to fulfill predetermined input or output impedance requirements. A two-stage amplifier employing voltage feedback is shown in Fig. 5-34. The feedback signal is capacitively coupled between the output stage collector to the input stage emitter. Feedback currents flowing in the emitter circuit cause

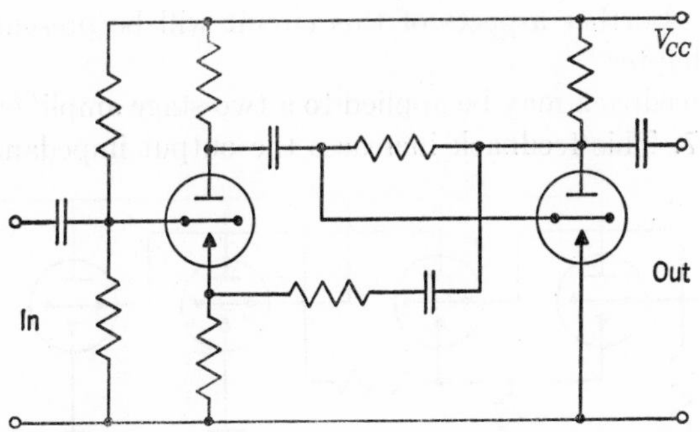

Fig. 5-34. Two-stage amplifier with voltage feedback.

the input impedance of the stage to be raised. The output impedance is reduced. This type of feedback tends to make the output voltage a close replica of the input voltage, and is generally similar in its effect to that of plate-to-previous-cathode feedback in a two-stage vacuum tube amplifier. It should be noted, however, that the relatively high input impedance of this amplifier may cause it to be difficult to drive.

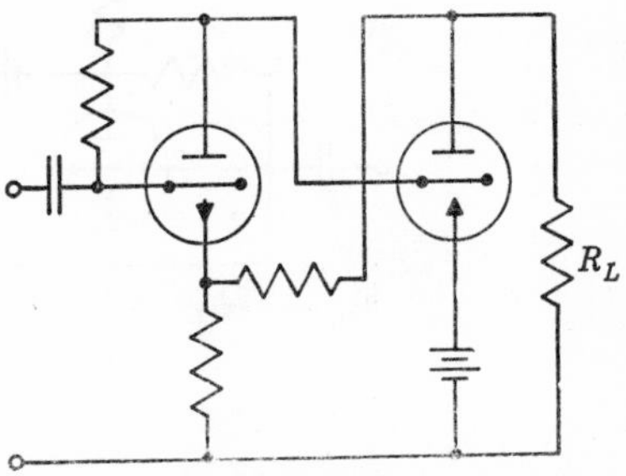

Fig. 5-35. Two-stage direct-coupled feedback amplifier.

The amplifier of Fig. 5-34 is capacitively coupled. Direct coupling is facilitated, however, by the use of a transistor of opposite conductivity type, as shown in Fig. 5-35. The direct coupling, aside from being economical of components and allowing d-c signals to be amplified, is capable of higher efficiency, and more fully stabilizes the d-c operating point than the *RC* coupled amplifier of Fig. 5-34.

The direct load current may be balanced out in this amplifier by the use of the push-pull complementary symmetry coupling, as shown in Fig. 5-36. In this circuit, the emitters of the two transistors are connected together so that no net voltage appears between the emitter and ground. A d-c return path is provided between the bases and ground, so that both transistors operate at zero bias, or essentially in Class B. Further aspects of this circuit will be presented in the following chapter.

Current feedback may be applied to a two-stage amplifier as shown in Fig. 5-37. This feedback increases the output impedance and re-

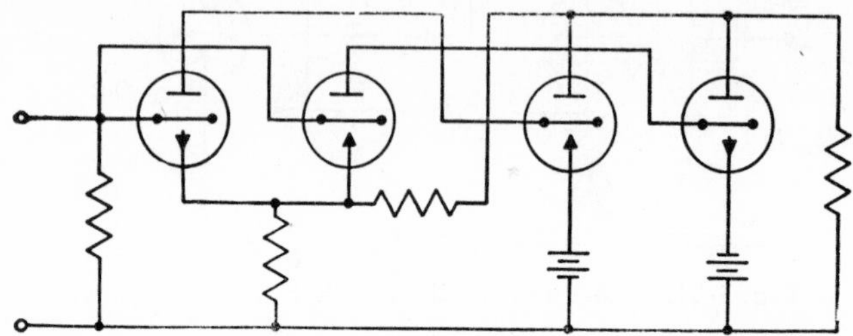

Fig. 5-36. Two-stage push-pull Class B amplifier employing complementary symmetry.

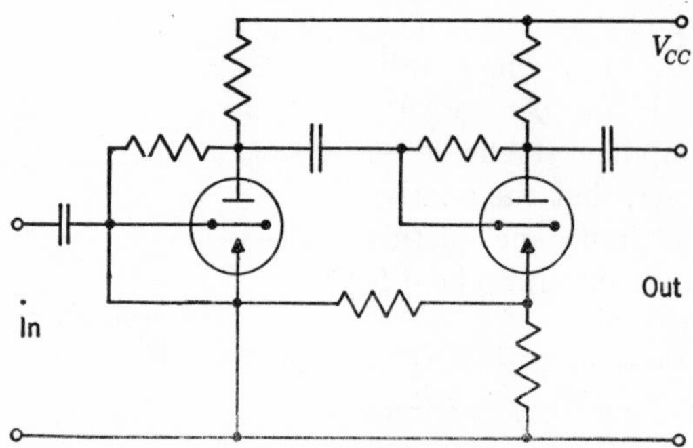

Fig. 5-37. Two-stage current-feedback amplifier.

duces the input impedance. The emitter current of the second stage transistor tends to be a replica of the input current to the first stage.

Negative current or voltage feedback over two phase-reversing stages, or any even number of such stages, has the effect of linearizing the current or the voltage gain, respectively.

Negative current or voltage feedback over an odd number of phase-reversing stages, on the other hand, will tend to linearize the forward transfer admittance or impedance, respectively. It may be desirable, for instance, to make the output voltage waveform of a transistor amplifier an exact replica of the input current waveform. In this case, negative voltage feedback would be applied over an odd number of stages.

In an amplifier of more than two stages, excessive phase shifts at extreme frequencies may cause instability and oscillation. This may be avoided by introducing a step in the gain-frequency curve, for instance by making one of the stages have a more limited bandwidth than the other two. If a power transistor is utilized in the last stage, the difference in frequency response between it and the other transistors will tend to supply the required step in the gain-frequency curve.

Negative feedback will receive further treatment in the following chapter on power amplifiers.

PROBLEMS

5-1. An RC coupled amplifier consists of two identical junction transistor stages with fixed bias. A 10 v battery is used as the common voltage supply. The d-c load resistance for each stage is 10,000 ohms. The transistors may be assumed to be linear and to have the following characteristics: $\alpha_{cb} = 50$, $r_d = 40{,}000$ ohms, $g_{11} = 10^{-3}$ mho, $\mu_{bc} = 10^{-4}$. (a) Compute the current gain of this amplifier. (b) Compute the input conductance of the first stage. (c) Compute the output impedance of the amplifier with the a-c load disconnected.

5-2. What should be the operating point of the transistor of the second stage of the amplifier circuit of Problem 1 if maximum current is to be delivered to be a-c load? What should be the value of the fixed-bias resistor to be connected between the base and the supply voltage? Assume I_{co} to be negligible.

5-3. Compute the value of the interstage coupling capacitor in the amplifier circuit of Problem 1 for a loss in low frequency response of 1 db at 20 cps.

5-4. An RC coupled amplifier stage is to supply a maximum signal level of 0 dbm (i.e., 1 milliwatt) into a 600 ohn load. A battery supply of 22½ v is available. (a) Design an RC coupled amplifier stage having minimum current drain, using a transistor having the characteristics given in Problem 1. Use a fixed bias circuit. (b) Find the current gain of the amplifier. (c) What power level, in dbm, must be supplied to the base of this amplifier circuit for 0 dbm output level? (d) What is the collector circuit efficiency?

5-5. Repeat Problem 4 for a self-biased amplifier stage which uses no bypassing. What is the stability factor S for this amplifier?

5-6. An RC coupled amplifier stage utilizing self-bias and delivering 5 milliwatts to an a-c load of 2000 ohms is to be designed. What supply voltage should be utilized in order to realize maximum collector circuit efficiency? Find the values of d-c load resistance and self-bias resistance which must be used, assuming the transistor to be linear, to have negligible I_{co}, and to have $\alpha_{cb} = 30$, $r_d = 50{,}000$ ohms. Assume μ_{bc} to be negligible, and $g_{11} = 2 \times 10^{-3}$ mho.

Chapter 6

POWER AMPLIFIERS

6.1 Introduction

Transistor power amplifiers differ from those amplifiers discussed in Chapter 5 in that power output to a load is the primary consideration. Efficient coupling means are used between the transistor or transistors and the load. Power gain is a secondary consideration, and is determined by the interrelation between the transistor maximum ratings and small signal parameters, as will be shown.

Home entertainment systems, including television and radio receivers, provide the most widespread use of audio power amplifiers. Amplifiers for use in these applications generally have power output ratings ranging from a fraction of a watt to approximately 20 watts. These power levels are in the range which present power transistors can accommodate. Emphasis will be placed upon audio frequency power amplifiers in this chapter.

Transistor power amplifiers may be operated in Class A or Class B, or the operating condition may be adjusted to a point between these to afford Class AB operation. For linear operation, a single transistor must be operated in Class A. If two transistors are used, the push-pull connection may be employed, allowing the use of the more efficient classes of operation. Various push-pull arrangements, including those using a pair of transistors having complementary symmetrical characteristics, will be discussed.

Basic causes of nonlinearity in the transistor will receive special attention. In an amplifier which is to be of good quality, a predetermined performance specification is usually met most easily with the use of negative feedback. It is desirable, therefore, to consider negative feedback as a part of the original design in such amplifiers. Various feedback methods for use with transistor amplifiers will be presented.

6.2 Junction power transistor characteristics

Transistors are generally limited by the maximum temperature at which the semiconductor material utilized operates satisfactorily. Since there are unavoidable power losses in the transistor, heat will be generated, tending to cause the temperature of the transistor to rise. This heat must be transferred to the surroundings. The heat transfer problem is difficult because of the relatively small temperature difference which may be allowed to exist beteeen the transistor and its surroundings. These factors limit the maximum power which may be dissipated.

The maximum voltage which may be applied to the collector junction of a transistor is determined in practice by one of three factors.[1] The first is the maximum electric field which the semiconductor can withstand without breakdown. The maximum field has been found to be dependent upon the purity of the semiconductor material in the base region. High-voltage transistors will thus have to utilize relatively pure (high-resistivity) base material, which may have an adverse effect upon the frequency response of the transistor. Presently, two theories are considered applicable to explain electrical breakdown in the semiconductor material. The first of these, proposed by Zener,[2] states that under a condition of high electric field, there occurs internal field emission of electrons from the filled band to the conduction band. More recently, it has been proposed that internal ionization similar to the Townsend avalanche in gaseous discharge devices may be responsible for semiconductor breakdown.[3]

The second factor which limits the maximum voltage which may be applied to the collector junction of a transistor is the effect of the widening of the depletion region as the junction voltage is increased. At some high voltage, the depletion region will widen sufficiently to reach the emitter junction, thereby causing break-through between the collector and emitter junctions. This factor may be the limiting one on maximum voltage if the break-through voltage is less than that

[1] This discussion of maximum current and voltage ratings is adapted from W. M. Webster, "A Comparison of Analogous Gaseous and Semiconductor Electronic Devices," *Ph.D. thesis*, Princeton University, 1953.

[2] C. Zener, "A Theory of the Electrical Breakdown of Solid Dielectrics," *Proc. Royal Soc.* (London), Vol. 145, p. 523, 1934.

[3] K. G. McKay, and K. B. McAfee "Electron Multiplication in Silicon and Germanium," *Phys. Rev.*, Vol. 91, pp. 1079–1084.

required to cause electrical breakdown. Break-through is chiefly of importance in alloy junction transistors wherein the depletion region must widen into the base region. In this type of transistor, the collector junction is formed by alloying an impurity material into a semiconductor base wafer. The collector region is therefore of very low purity, and the depletion region can form effectively only in the base material. If the base region is made thin in order to secure good current amplification and good frequency response, the break-through voltage will be relatively low. A high voltage rating is therefore obtained at the expense of current gain and frequency response of the alloy junction transistor. In the grown junction transistor, where the purity of the collector region may be controlled and may be very high, the depletion region widens into the collector region, thereby reducing the break-through problem.

The third factor which limits the maximum voltage of the transistor is a practical one. There is always some reverse current, caused by thermal generation, which flows past the collector junction. At high collector voltages, this current may cause an excessive amount of power to be generated, which in turn raises the temperature of the transistor and increases the thermal generation and the collector current. Thermal instability, a factor of great importance in germanium transistors, may result.

The maximum collector current rating of a transistor is determined in part by the practical consideration that the current amplification factor α_{cb} varies approximately inversely with emitter current at high values of emitter current density. A maximum current rating therefore may be established by the amount of reduction in α_{cb} which can be tolerated.

In the original theory of the junction transistor, no variation in α_{cb} with emitter current was predicted. It was assumed in the derivation of this theory that the minority carrier density due to emitter injection was at all times negligible. A modified theory by Webster[4] shows that the minority carrier density in the base region is not negligible even for relatively low values of emitter current. The result is to raise the conductivity of the base region, which in turn reduces the emitter efficiency and raises the rate of volume recombination in the base region. Both of these results cause an increase in base

[4] W. M. Webster, "The Variation of Junction Transistor Current Amplification Factor with Emitter Current," *Proc. I.R.E.*, Vol. 42, p. 914, June 1954.

signal current, and therefore a reduction in α_{cb}. These factors are discussed in greater detail in Sec. 6.4 with respect to nonlinearities in the transistor.

6.3 Single-transistor power amplifiers

Relatively low output requirements may be accommodated with the use of a single transistor. Class A operation must be used to obtain linear operation. A transformer is usually used as the load coupling element in order to isolate the direct energizing currents from the load with high efficiency. Any one of the three transistor configurations may be utilized as a power amplifier, the choice being made on the basis of linearity and power gain (i.e., relative ease of input drive). The relative merits of the three configurations will be discussed subsequently.

The first problem confronting the designer of a power amplifier is the load resistance which must be presented to the transistor output circuit. Maximum power output will be determined by the current, voltage, and power dissipation ratings on the transistor. The optimum output load resistance is not affected appreciably by the configuration used. The common-emitter, common-base, and common-collector arrangements all include the collector junction in series with the output circuits. The ratings on this junction determine the optimum load resistance, since the voltage across the emitter junction is relatively very small.

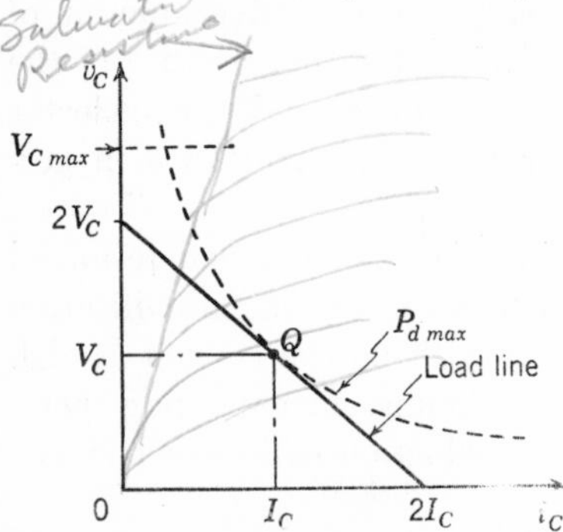

Fig. 6-1. Determination of load resistance by the transistor ratings.

In order to obtain maximum power output for a Class A amplifier, the operating point should lie upon the rectangular hyperbola[5] of maximum collector dissipation as shown in Fig. 6-1. The position

[5] It is assumed, for simplicity, that the maximum collector dissipation is not a function of collector voltage. It is on this basis that Eqs. (6-1) and (6-2) are developed. Actually, maximum allowable collector dissipation is reduced as the collector voltage is increased, because of thermal generation, as noted above.

of the operating point on this hyperbola and the value of the load resistance must be adjusted to that the maximum voltage rating on the transistor is not exceeded under any conditions of signal input. The relationship between the load resistance R_L and the power dissipation P_d in terms of the collector voltage V_C is given by

$$R_L = \frac{V_C^2}{P_d} \tag{6-1}$$

It is often desirable to use the highest value of load resistance as given by (6-1) for two reasons. First, the ratings of most available transistors impose a load resistance upon the output circuit of the transistor which is much lower than the output impedance of the transistor. This causes a large mismatch between the transistor and load, which in turn causes the power gain of the transistor to be relatively low. This mismatch is minimized when the highest possible value of load resistance is utilized. The second reason for using a high value of load resistance is that by so doing the collector current is reduced. This has the advantage of reducing the effects of α_{cb} reduction at high emitter currents, as will be discussed in the following section. Distortion thereby may be reduced, and the power gain is increased because of the relatively high value of α_{cb} at low emitter currents.

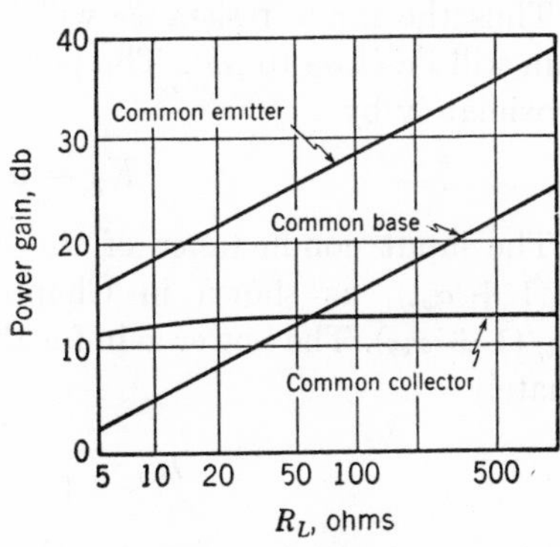

Fig. 6-2. Power gain as a function of load resistance for the three configurations of a transistor having $\alpha_{cb} = 20$, $1/g_{11} = 50$ ohms.

The highest permissible value of R_L is that which is used when the operating point voltage is made equal to half the collector voltage rating. Substituting this value in (6-1) we have

$$R_L = \frac{V_{C\,max}^2}{P_{d\,max}} \tag{6-2}$$

There may be certain cases in which it is desirable that R_L be lower than the value given in (6-2), as the case in which the supply voltage has been previously established, or in which the transistor circuit must be designed to supply signals to an existing load.

The load resistance determined in accordance with the preceding considerations may be used for a transistor amplifier in any of the three configurations. Either the common-emitter stage or one of the two feedback configurations (i.e., the common-base circuit or the common-collector circuit) may be used. The feedback configurations have lower gain but better linearity than the common-emitter stage. On the other hand, the common-emitter circuit will be considerably easier to drive than either of the other two connections. In order to improve linearity in this configuration, feedback signals may be applied to an earlier stage of amplification while still retaining the advantage of easy output circuit drive.

The power gain for the common-emitter circuit may be approximated by a simple expression if it is assumed that the load resistance is small compared with the transistor output resistance, as will be the case with available transistors.

Thus the input resistance will be close to $1/g_{11}$, and the current gain will be close to α_{cb}. The power gain will therefore be given approximately by

$$K_p = \alpha_{cb}^2 R_L g_{11} \tag{6-3}$$

The input conductance of the common-base circuit will become $g_{11}(1 + \alpha_{cb})$, as shown in Chapter 3. The current gain will be $\alpha_{cb}/(1 + \alpha_{cb})$. The power gain for this connection is therefore approximately

$$K_p = \frac{\alpha_{cb}^2}{1 + \alpha_{cb}} R_L g_{11} \tag{6-4}$$

subject to the assumption that the load resistance is small compared with the output impedance.

In the case of the common-collector circuit, the voltage gain will be close to unity, as shown in Chapter 3. The power gain is therefore equal approximately to the current gain. If it is again assumed that R_L is small relative to r_d,

$$K_p = (1 + \alpha_{cb})^2 \frac{R_L}{1/g_{11} + (1 + \alpha_{cb})R_L} \tag{6-5}$$

If it is further assumed that $(1 + \alpha_{cb})R_L$ is large relative to $1/g_{11}$

$$K_p = 1 + \alpha_{cb} \tag{6-6}$$

The above equations utilize the small-signal parameters of the transistor and are therefore subject to some error because of curvature of the characteristics. They, may be used however, to compare the power gain under matched input conditions for the three transistor configurations. This comparison is made for a typical transistor in Fig. 6-2. Since the value of load resistance is determined primarily by the collector ratings regardless of the configuration used, power gains may be compared directly at a given load resistance.

The common-emitter circuit is thus seen to have considerably higher gain than either of the other two connections. For amplifier circuits in which the optimum load resistance is higher than approximately $1/g_{11}$, the common-base stage will have higher power gain than the common-collector circuit. The reverse is true for load resistances below approximagely $1/g_{11}$.

The comparison of the power gain of the three configurations given above applies to the case of an output stage operating under matched input conditions. Unless an input transformer is used, this condition may be impossible to obtain. For maximum over-all power gain, the equivalent generator output impedance of the driver stage should be equal to the input impedance of the following stage. The input impedance of the transistor of Fig. 6-2 is shown for the three configurations in Fig. 6-3.

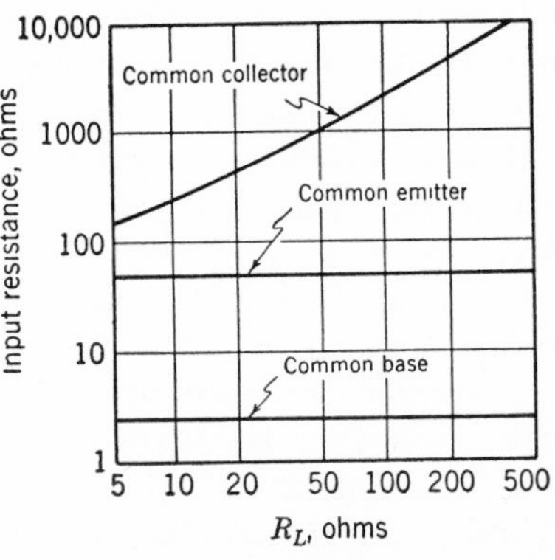

Fig. 6-3. Input resistance as a function of load resistance for the three configurations of a transistor having $\alpha_{cb} = 20$, $1/g_{11} = 50$ ohms.

It should be apparent that transformer coupling is almost mandatory for the common-base power output stage because of the large input current requirement. The other two configurations may utilize *RC* coupled or direct-coupled driver stages. The common-collector circuit will generally afford the closest match to a previous transistor driver stage. This tends to compensate for the relatively low power gain of the common-collector connection.

The driving circuit for the output stage may be an *RC* coupled amplifier as described in the previous chapter. The other types of coupling shown in Chapter 5 may also be used. A particularly successful arrangement is the use of a driving transistor of opposite conductivity type, directly coupled to the output stage as shown in Sec. 5.14.

The collector efficiency of a single-stage Class A amplifier approaches 50 per cent, since the area of operation includes substantially the entire quadrant of the collector characteristics. Losses which subtract from the over-all efficiency occur in the bias circuit and in unavoidable transformer resistances.

6.4 Nonlinearity in power amplifiers

It is desirable in amplifier applications that the relationship between the output signal and the input signal be linear. In so far as this relationship is not completely achieved in practical amplifiers, it is desirable to study the causes of nonlinearity and to determine methods for reducing it. Nonlinearity may be expressed in various ways. Initially, we shall relate amplifier distortion to nonlinearities in a consistent set of transistor parameters.

The parameters which are most useful in the analysis of distortion should be those which lead to the desired result most simply. For the reasons cited in Chapter 2, the hybrid parameters are quite suitable for analysis of transistor characteristics. Nonlinearity of the common-emitter connection will be studied, the other two connections of the transistor being treated as feedback connections. Thus the effect on amplifier distortion of nonlinearities in the common-emitter hybrid parameters will be investigated.

As stated in the previous section, the load impedance which must be used to obtain maximum power output from a transistor is normally considerably lower than the output impedance of the transistor. In normal use, therefore, the input impedance to the transistor will be close to the short-circuit input impedance as given by the hybrid parameters. The feedback parameter μ_{bc} may usually be neglected because of the low load impedance, and the open-circuit output impedance will normally be considerably higher than the load impedance. Nonlinearities in the feedback and output impedance will therefore contribute a negligible amount to the total transistor distortion. Nonlinearities in the short-circuit input resistance $1/g_{11}$ and in the current amplification factor α_{cb} will contribute essentially all the distortion generated by the transistor. Nonlinearities of these two parameters will therefore be studied in some detail.

6.5 Variation of the current amplification factor with emitter current

The current amplification factor is a function of the emitter current as shown in Fig. 6-4 for a typical low-power *p-n-p* alloy junction transistor. The variation of α_{cb} with emitter current is characterized by a peak in the value of α_{cb} at relatively low emitter current, followed by reduction in α_{cb}, in which α_{cb} is approximately inversely proportional to emitter current. The terms varying with emitter current which affect α_{cb} are the surface recombination, the volume recombination, and the emitter efficiency. Webster[6] has shown the mechanism through which these factors depend upon emitter current.

At low values of emitter current, surface recombination of holes and electrons is the chief contributor to base current, and consequently limits the value of α_{cb}. As the emitter current is increased (i.e., more minority carriers are injected into the base region) the minority carrier density gradient between the junctions increases. Since there is always a tendency in the base region for space charge neutrality to be maintained, a majority carrier density gradient is also set up, the majority carriers tending to concentrate near the emitter junction to balance the charge of the minority carriers. Under the influence of this majority carrier density gradient, the majority carriers tend to diffuse toward the collector, from which they cannot escape. Space charge neutrality is therefore not strictly maintained at these higher values of emitter current, and a restoring force in the form of a small electric field is set up in the base region. This field is in a direction to speed minority carrier flow between emitter and collector junctions, thereby reducing the opportunity for surface recombination in the base region. This explains the initial rise of α_{cb} with emitter current as depicted in Fig. 6-4.

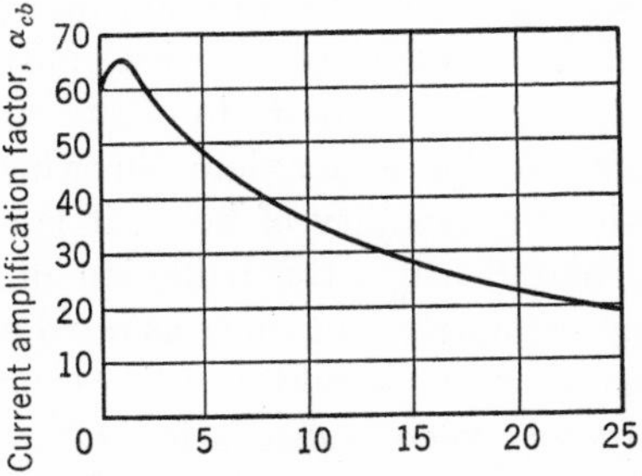

Fig. 6-4. Variation of current amplification factor with emitter current for a typical *p-n-p* alloy junction transistor.

As the emitter current is further increased, the minority carrier

[6] W. M. Webster, *op. cit.*

concentration becomes high enough to increase the base region conductivity to a marked degree. As the concentration of minority carriers in the base region is increased, the portion of the emitter current due to base region majority carriers flowing into the emitter increases. Furthermore, it becomes increasingly difficult for a minority carrier to diffuse across the emitter junction into the base region. The emitter efficiency, which is proportional to the ratio of minority carrier current to total emitter junction current, thereby is reduced, and α_{cb} decreases with increasing emitter current.

A further effect of the increased base region conductivity is to increase the volume recombination of holes and electrons in the base region. Volume recombination causes additional base current and an additional reduction in α_{cb} at high values of emitter current density.

The reduction of α_{cb} with emitter current has been found to be proportional to the ratio of the mobilities of majority and minority carriers. For germanium, in which electrons have approximately twice the mobility of holes, it is apparent that for a given emitter current density, the reduction in α_{cb} of a *p-n-p* transistor will be approximately four times as rapid as that of an *n-p-n* transistor. This factor is of importance in complementary symmetry push-pull circuits, where cancellation of even-order harmonics may not be effective for two transistors of opposite conductivity type which are otherwise closely matched.

6.6 Effect of nonlinearity of α_{cb} on amplifier distortion

The effect of the variation of α_{cb} with emitter current on the linearity of amplification of a power amplifier may be shown in a transfer characteristic of i_C as a function of i_B. Since the load impedance is small compared with the output impedance in most power amplifiers, the dynamic transfer characteristic for the output circuit (i.e., the curve of i_C vs i_B including the load impedance) is essentially the same as the static forward transfer characteristic shown in Chapter 2 for the hybrid parameters. Other forward dynamic transfer characteristics of course may be used; the one in which collector current is plotted as a function of base-to-emitter voltage has particular merit as a somewhat different approach to the problem of power amplifier nonlinearity.[7]

[7] L. J. Giacolletto, "Power Transistors for Audio Output Circuits," *Electronics*, Vol. 27, No. 1, p. 144, Jan. 1954.

The hybrid transfer characteristic for a typical junction transistor is shown in Fig. 6-5. It has been shown[8] that this curve may be approximated by the relationship

$$i_B = \frac{1}{\alpha_{cb}}\left(i_C + \frac{1}{\beta}\,i_C^2\right) \tag{6-7}$$

where α_{cb} corresponds to the short-circuit current gain at relatively low values of i_C, and β corresponds to that value of i_C at which the ratio i_C/i_B has dropped to $\alpha_{cb}/2$. The nonlinearity of the current transfer characteristic at low values of collector current is neglected.

High-quality amplification demands that an approximately sinusoidal output signal be derived in response to a sinusoidal signal applied to the input terminals of the amplifier. To achieve this, a distorted signal must be applied to the base of the output stage. This corrective "predistortion" is usually obtained by means of negative feedback applied over several stages of amplification. The relative amplitude of the harmonic distortion components which must be applied to the base is a measure of the nonlinearity of the output stage. This percentage will be computed for a single-transistor Class A amplifier in accordance with Eq. (6-7).

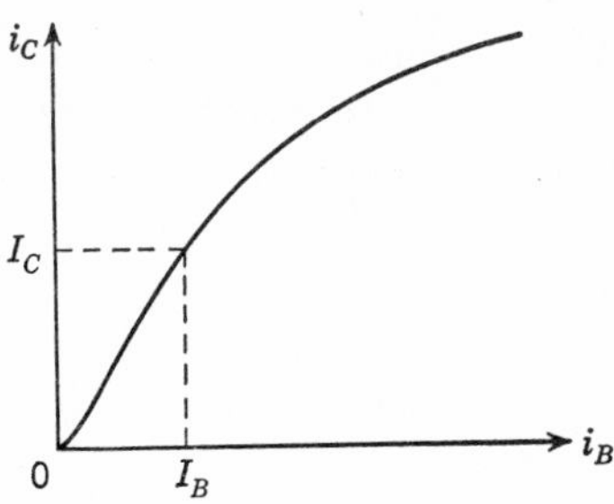

Fig. 6-5. Transfer characteristic for a typical transistor.

Assume that the collector current may be expressed

$$i_C = I_C + I_{C_{max}} \cos \omega t \tag{6-8}$$

where I_C is the direct energizing current, and $I_{C\,max}$ is the peak value of the signal current. Then Eq. (6-7) becomes

$$i_B = \frac{1}{\alpha_{cb}}\left(I_C + I_{C_{max}} \cos \omega t + \frac{I_C^2 + I_{C_{max}}^2 \cos^2 \omega t + 2I_C I_{C_{max}} \cos \omega t}{\beta}\right) \tag{6-9}$$

[8] Equation (6-7) and much of the following discussion are derived from the work of W. M. Webster and T. O. Stanley, private communication.

which by trigonometric identity becomes

$$i_B = \frac{1}{\alpha_{cb}}\left[I_C + I_{C\,max}\cos\omega t + \frac{1}{\beta}\left(I_C^2 + \frac{I_{C\,max}{}^2}{2} + \frac{I_{C\,max}{}^2}{2}\cos 2\omega t + 2I_C I_{C\,max}\cos\omega t\right)\right] \quad (6\text{-}10)$$

Only the a-c terms of the above expression are of interest for computation of distortion. Consequently, we may write

$$i_b = \frac{1}{\alpha_{cb}}\left[\left(1 + \frac{2I_C}{\beta}\right) I_{C\,max}\cos\omega t + \frac{1}{\beta}\frac{I_{C\,max}{}^2}{2}\cos 2\omega t\right] \quad (6\text{-}11)$$

where i_b designates the alternating signal current. The percentage distortion is simply the ratio of the amplitudes of the second harmonic term and the fundamental term.

$$\text{distortion} = \frac{I_{C\,max}}{2\beta + 4I_C} \quad (6\text{-}12)$$

At maximum output, $I_c = I_{C\,max}$, so that

$$\text{distortion} = \frac{1}{2\beta/I_C + 4} \quad (6\text{-}13)$$

When the collector current (and consequently the emitter current) is considerably higher than the value of β, the distortion is thus seen to approach 25 per cent. This represents the limiting value of distortion without clipping for a common-emitter stage operated under conditions of severe α_{cb} reduction resulting from high emitter current. Practical operation of transistor output stages is normally restricted to lower values of emitter current with better distortion characteristics.

6.7 The effect of nonlinear input impedance

The foregoing analysis applies to nonlinearity in the transfer of current from input to output. The computed distortion would be in evidence if the base of the transistor were fed from a source of infinite impedance. In practice, the driver may have an internal impedance which is very high compared with the transistor input impedance over essentially the full cycle of signal input current. In such a case, the distortion of the output stage will be that computed above. If the internal impedance of the driver stage is comparable with the input impedance of the output stage (essentially $1/g_{11}$), the variation of $1/g_{11}$ with emitter current must be considered.

At the high operating currents used in Class A operation of a power transistor, the impedance of the emitter junction is very low. The input impedance is therefore made up largely of the base lead resistance, or the resistance of the germanium path between the base connection and the active base region. The base lead resistance decreases somewhat as the emitter current is increased, thereby tending to reduce the distortion resulting from reduction of α_{cb} with emitter current. At very low values of emitter current the input impedance rises sharply, as shown in Fig. 6-6. In a Class A amplifier, this causes a rounding of signal peaks, which may approach clipping for very low-impedance driving sources. The sudden rise in input impedance at low emitter current is particularly troublesome in Class B amplifiers, and will be further considered in the appropriate section later in this chapter.

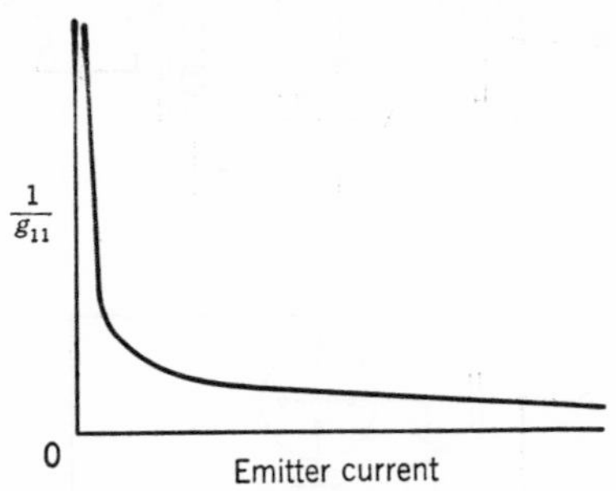

Fig. 6-6. Variation of short circuit input resistance with emitter current.

6.8 Push-pull amplification

Utilization of two transistors in a push-pull connection offers numerous advantages in the operation of transistor amplifiers. Direct energizing currents and even-order harmonics are eliminated from the output circuit provided that the two transistor devices are identical or symmetrical in characteristics. Furthermore, the high-efficiency classes of operation such as Class B may be used. There are basically four push-pull transistor circuit arrangements; two utilize transistors of the same conductivity type, and the other two utilize transistors of opposite conductivity types (i.e., transistors having complementary symmetrical characteristics). These four basic arrangements are shown in Fig. 6-7. Input circuit biasing will depend upon the class of operation, and is not included in the figure.

The circuit of Fig. 6-7a is the familiar balanced push-pull arrangement in which direct energizing currents are fed to the two transistors in parallel, while signals are developed across the transistors in series. This circuit, which requires transistors of the same conductivity type, further requires phase inverting means for applying oppositely phased signals to the input circuits of the two transistors. Figure 6-7b illustrates the push-pull single-ended circuit in which energizing

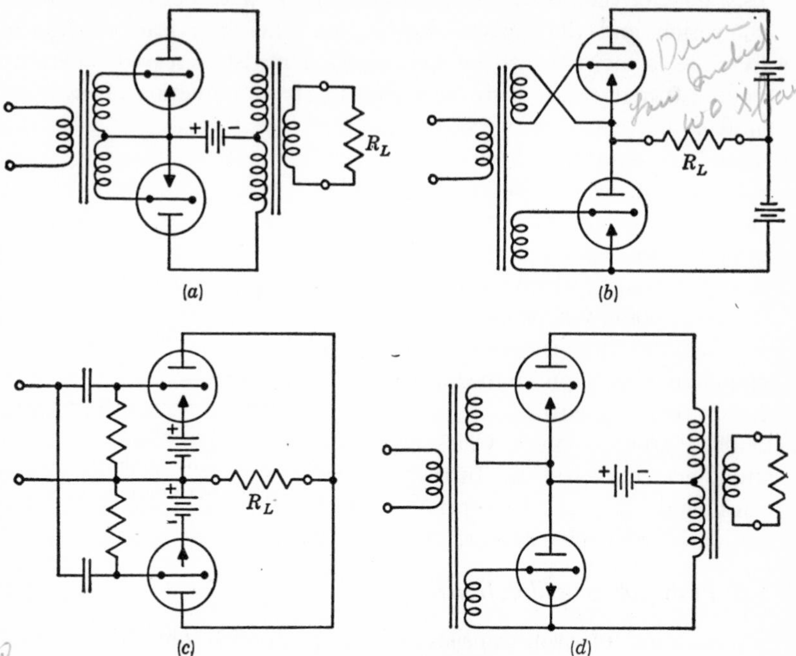

Fig. 6-7. Push-pull circuit arrangements for the common-emitter connection.

currents flow in series through the two transistors and the output signal is derived from the two transistors in parallel. Two transistors of the same conductivity type are used. Input signals to the two transistors must be applied between the respective base and emitter electrodes, in 180° phase relation. Note that the full load voltage appears between the two input circuits. An input transformer may be arranged to supply these input signals as shown; phase inverter circuits may also be adapted for use with the push-pull single-ended circuit. The load impedance for this circuit will be one-quarter that of the balanced push-pull arrangement shown in Fig. 6-7a. This may be a worth-while advantage for the single-ended circuit, since the output transformer can often be eliminated, a loud-speaker being connected directly to the output terminals.

Push-pull circuits utilizing transistors of opposite conductivity type require input signals which are in phase, so that no phase inverter is required in such circuits. Figure 6-7c illustrates a single-ended push-pull amplifier in which currents are fed to the input circuits of the transistor in phase. The output circuit load receives signal current from the two transistors connected in parallel. Although circuits utilizing the principle of complementary symmetry may often be simpler than those using transistors of the same conductivity type, there is sometimes more difficulty in obtaining transistors having exactly symmetrical characteristics.

The circuit of Fig. 6-7d is rarely used in amplifier work, but is included here for completeness. It is a push-pull balanced amplifier utilizing transistors of opposite conductivity type.

Push-pull circuits are relatively more important in transistor amplifiers than they have been in cases of amplifiers utilizing vacuum tubes. One reason is that Class B circuits utilizing transistors require relatively simpler bias provisions. Thus Class B circuits may be utilized to enjoy advantages of greater efficiency and high power output for a given transistor capability. Another reason for the greater relative importance of push-pull transistor amplifiers is the availability of the complementary symmetry connection of a pair of transistors of opposite conductivity type. Since a phase inverter is not required, push-pull circuits need be little more complicated than corresponding nonpush-pull circuits.

6.9 Phase inverters

Push-pull operation of a pair of transistors of the same conductivity type requires the use of a phase inverter circuit. It will be assumed that the power transistors are matched in current amplification, so that the requirement for a phase inverter circuit is that equal currents, in 180° phase relation, be fed to the output transistors.

The most direct method of obtaining phase inversion is by use of a split-load arrangement as shown in Fig. 6-8. Here the signal current flowing through the collector-emitter path of a driver transistor is applied to the base electrodes of the output transistors. The resistors

R_1 and R_2, which provide energizing current for the collector-emitter path of the transistor, should preferably have high resistance in order that most of the signal current shall flow to the output transistors.

The output impedances of the collector and emitter circuits of the two transistors are unequal, so that unbalanced operation of the output transistors will result. The output transistor which is fed from the collector of the driver will be subject to more flattening of

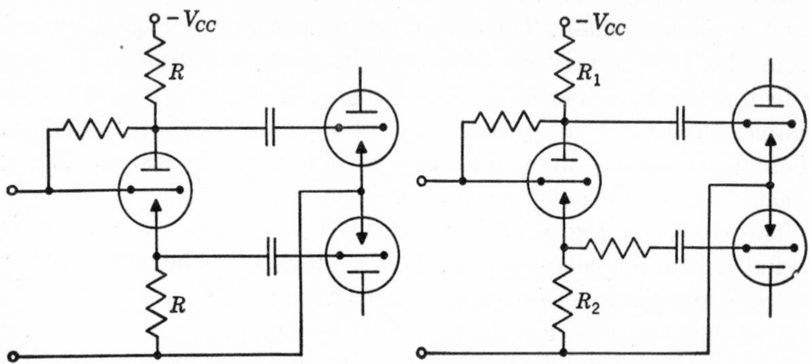

Fig. 6-8. Split-load phase inverter.

Fig. 6-9. Split-load phase inverter modified to present equal source resistances for each output transistor.

the output wave due to α_{cb} fall-off than will the other transistor, which is fed from the low-impedance emitter circuit of the driver. This difficulty may be obviated by use of an impedance equalizing resistor connected between the driver stage emitter and the output stage base, as shown in Fig. 6-9. In a practical circuit, the supply voltage will limit the values of R_1 and R_2, which will therefore absorb some of the signal current. In order to correct for the unbalance in output current caused by the series resistors, the emitter load resistance R_2 is made larger than the collector load resistance R_1. Simultaneous balance of both the current and the output impedance of the phase inverter is thereby obtained.

The input impedance of the two phase inverter circuits described is high because of the relatively high resistance in the emitter circuit. It may therefore be somewhat difficult to drive.

A phase inverter circuit which eliminates this difficulty is shown in Fig. 6-10. This circuit is similar to the cathode-coupled vacuum tube phase inverter, but is particularly adaptable to transistor circuits since it is basically an inverter of currents. The input impedance is relatively low (approximately double that of a similar common-emitter stage) and the output currents are automatically balanced to any prescribed degree.

In this circuit, input signal current is fed to the base of transistor $T1$. The collector current of this transistor is coupled to one input of the power output stage. The emitter current of transistor $T1$ is fed to the emitter of transistor $T2$, the base of which is grounded for a-c signals. The collector current of $T2$ is slightly less than the emitter current and is out of phase with the collector current of $T1$. The coupling resistor R_1 provides a d-c return between the emitter electrodes and ground. It also shunts a portion of the emitter signal current of $T1$ to ground. The emitter input impedance of $T2$ is very low, however, so that R_1 does not have to be excessively high to equalize the two emitter currents. A further effect of the emitter input resistance of $T2$ is the increase of base input impedance of transistor $T1$, which for balanced transistors is seen to be slightly less than double that for the grounded emitter input impedance of transistor $T1$.

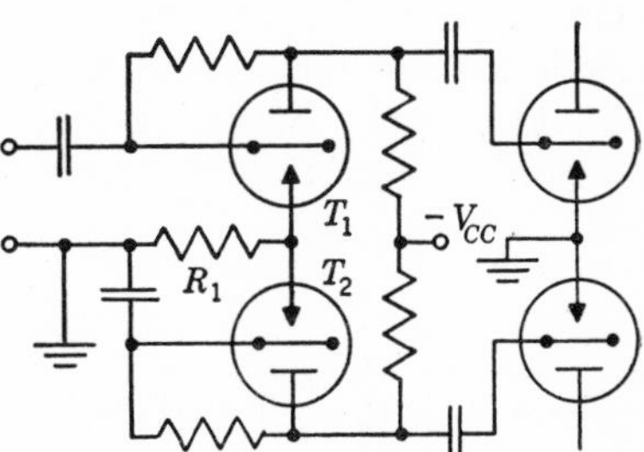

Fig. 6-10. Emitter-coupled phase inverter.

6.10 Class B amplifiers

Use of Class B operation offers two main advantages over the less efficient modes of operation. First, the output circuit efficiency under the maximum signal condition is higher, so that for a transistor of given power dissipation rating, the maximum obtainable power output is increased. Second, the power supply drain during periods of small signal or no signal is substantially reduced, so that signals in which the duty cycle is low, such as speech and music, can be amplified more efficiently.

Class B operation is characterized by low power supply drain under the zero signal or idling condition. The pair of transistors may be operated under idling conditions near either the voltage or the current axis of the output characteristics. Operation at the voltage axis is used when the power supply is of the constant voltage type, such as battery or conventional rectifier supplies. Operation at the current axis may be used if a power supply of the constant current type is available. The discussion below is restricted to the former type of operation, since efficient, practical constant current sources are not presently available.

Any one of the four push-pull arrangements shown in Sec. 6.5 may be used in Class B by application of appropriate bias to the input circuit, and by proper design of the driver circuit.

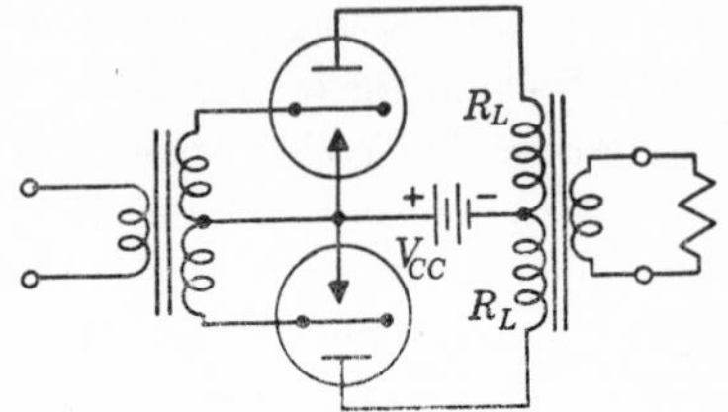

Fig. 6-11. Simplified Class B circuit.

A simplified Class B amplifier circuit in which input bias provisions are not included is shown in Fig. 6-11. Assuming linear operation down to zero collector current, the power output will be

$$P = \frac{V_{CC}^2}{2R_L} \tag{6-14}$$

where R_L is the reflected load resistance to one-half the primary. The load resistance must be so chosen that with a given supply voltage and signal duty cycle, the maximum power dissipation rating of the transistor is not exceeded. A further limitation upon R_L is imposed by the requirement that the α_{cb} reduction at high currents shall not be too severe. A still further limitation upon R_L is imposed by the fact that the power gain will vary approximately directly with load resistance, as shown by Eq. (6-3). These three limitations upon R_L each set a minimum value for R_L, and consequently a maximum limit for the output power at a given value of supply voltage. It is desirable, therefore, to use the maximum value of supply voltage which the transistor will withstand in order to obtain maximum power output, minimum distortion (due to reduction in α_{cb} at high current), and maximum power gain. The maximum voltage ratings for the transistor, as discussed in Sec. 6.2, are therefore of major importance in Class B amplifiers.

At low emitter current $1/g_{11}$ rises sharply, as shown in Fig. 6-6. Inspection of Eqs. (6-3), (6-4), and (6-5) shows that the power gain decreases as $1/g_{11}$ increases. There is therefore a region of operation, at low emitter currents, in which the gain falls sharply. Note that in accordance with (6-5) the common-collector stage is the least affected of the three configurations in this regard.

The drop in power gain at low emitter currents is particularly important in Class B amplifiers, where it is desirable from the standpoint of economy to bias each transistor to the lowest emitter current consistent with proper circuit operation. A type of distortion known as crossover distortion is thereby introduced, particularly in the common-emitter and common-base circuits. Figure 6-12 shows the output waveform of a Class B amplifier having this type of distortion.

Note that the distortion introduced by the rapid rise in input impedance could be reduced by use of a driver stage having a very high generator resistance, which would force current into the high-resistance input circuit. This method is not very satisfactory, however, since there would thus be introduced a large mismatch between the driver and output stages, thereby causing the over-all power gain to be reduced.

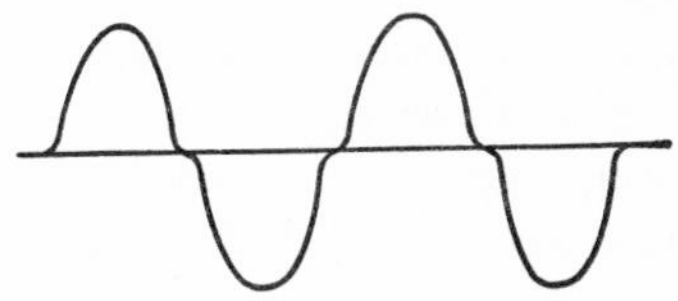

Fig. 6-12. Output waveform of the amplifier circuit of Fig. 6-9.

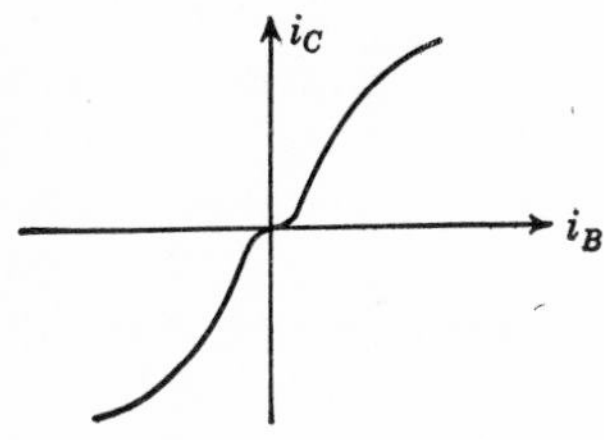

Fig. 6-13. Transfer characteristic with zero voltage bias.

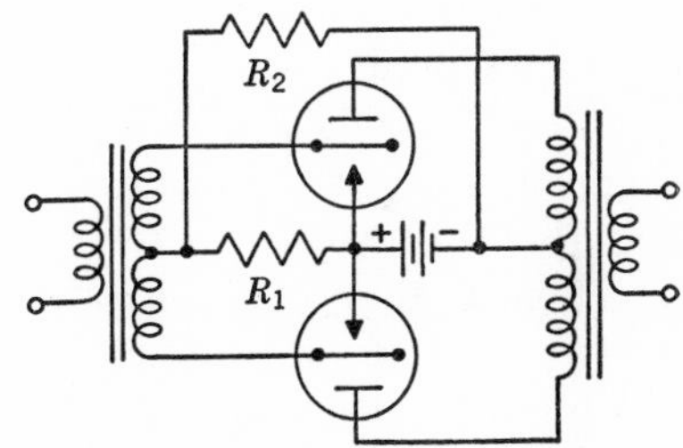

Fig. 6-14. Forward bias applied to a Class B output stage.

Another factor which increases the crossover distortion is the variation of α_{cb} at low emitter currents, as shown in Fig. 6-4. The base current to collector current transfer characteristic is consequently nonlinear, as shown in Fig. 6-13 for the case of zero voltage bias.

In order to eliminate crossover distortion, forward bias may be applied to the transistor, as shown in Fig. 6-14. The resistance R_1 in the base circuit must be kept to a low value in order to avoid signal power loss in the input circuit. (The input signal current to the transistor which is conducting must flow through this resistance, since the base-to-emitter path of the nonconducting transistor is of very high impedance.) Capacitive by-passing of R_1 is unsatisfactory, since the input signal rectification under signal conditions will cause a reverse bias to appear between the base and emitter of the output transistors, thereby introducing further crossover distortion.

It is necessary to maintain a low-resistance d-c path between base and ground as well as to provide a small amount of forward bias in order to minimize crossover distortion. The transformer coupling shown in Fig. 6-14 is one method of accomplishing this. It is often desirable however, to eliminate the input transformer.

Resistance-capacitance coupling to a Class B output stage may be employed if means are provided for maintaining the proper bias under signal conditions. The circuit of Fig. 6-15 employs a pair of semiconductor diodes for this purpose. Without the diodes, positive signals would cause the coupling capacitors to charge in a direction which would bias the transistors in a reverse direction, because of the rectification characteristic of the base-to-emitter path of the transistors. Addition of the diodes in the circuit prevents such a charge being built up, and linearizes the input circuit. A small amount of forward bias must be applied to both the diodes and the transistor input circuit to avoid crossover distortion, as stated above. This is provided, as in the circuit of Fig. 6-14, by a voltage divider connected across the collector voltage supply. The resistance of R_1 must be low in order to avoid input signal loss, as in the case of the circuit of Fig. 6-14. This circuit may be driven directly from one of the phase inverter circuits as shown in Sec. 6.6.

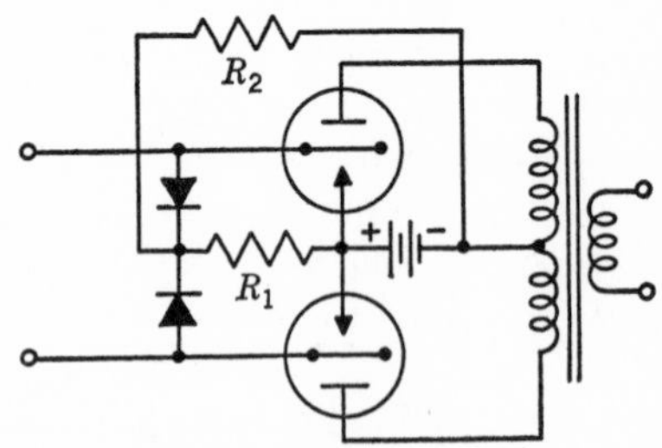

Fig. 6-15. *RC* coupling to a Class B output stage.

As mentioned in Sec. 6.4, linearity is somewhat improved by use of a low-impedance driving source. As shown above, it is also desirable to provide a low-resistance d-c path between the base and emitter of a transistor. A driver circuit which provides both features is shown in Fig. 6-16. This circuit utilizes a pair of transistors connected in the common-collector configuration to drive the common-emitter Class B output circuit. The common-collector driver stage may also be operated in Class B. Bias is provided for the output stage by virtue of the direct coupling to the emitters of the driver stage. The bias may be established at any desired voltage level by choice of the emitter resistors and the bias battery V_{EE}. The internal d-c re-

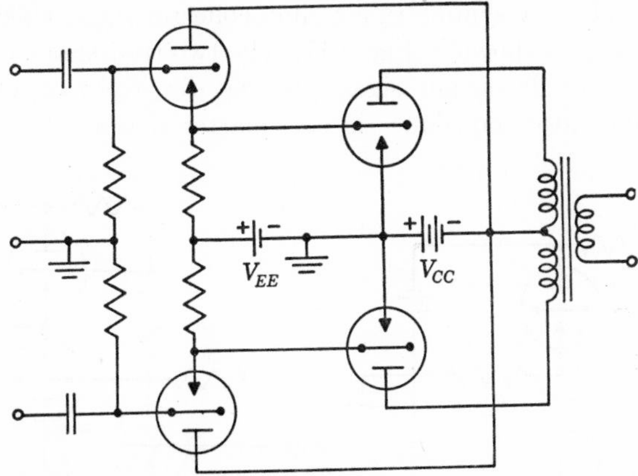

Fig. 6-16. Low impedance driver for a Class B output stage.

sistance of the bias source is low, as is the a-c driver impedance, since the output resistance of a grounded collector stage is low. This circuit is easily adaptable for high-temperature operation, as we shall see in a later section.

6.11 Class B complementary symmetry circuits

The provisions for operating-point establishment and signal drive for each individual transistor of a complementary symmetry amplifier are similar to those for the balanced amplifier employing transistors of but one conductivity type. Biasing provisions may be quite simple if the common-collector arrangement is used. Common-emitter circuits require more complicated bias provisions or the use of a transformer, as will be shown subsequently.

One of the chief advantages of the complementary symmetry connection is the relative ease with which direct (transformerless) output coupling may be used. If the signal load is to be a loud-speaker, it is usually desirable that the amplifier have a low internal output impedance, in order to provide adequate loud-speaker damping. The common-collector arrangement provides a convenient method for achieving this goal, in addition to its low distortion characteristics. The common-collector arrangement is therefore relatively more popular in complementary symmetry applications than in balanced amplifiers employing transistors of the same conductivity type.

A complementary symmetry common-collector stage which utilizes no transformers is shown in Fig. 6-17. The two transistors, connected in parallel, provide output signals to the directly connected load. The optimum load impedance is one-quarter that for the balanced amplifier.

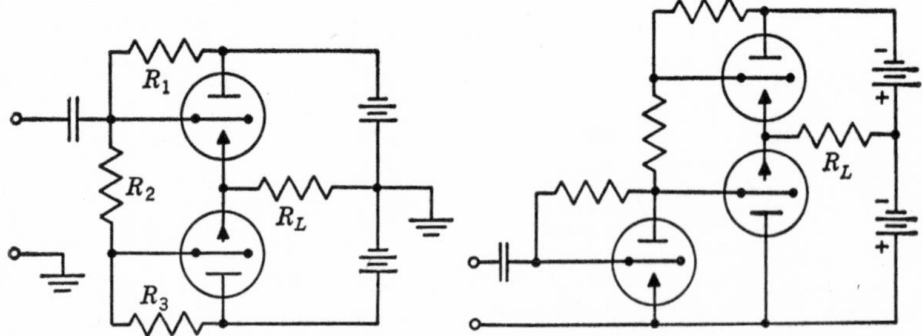

Fig. 6-17. Common-collector complementary symmetry Class B stage.

Fig. 6-18. Direct-coupling of driver stage providing bias for a common-collector output stage.

A small amount of forward bias is provided by R_1, R_2, and R_3. The resistance of R_2 is low enough to provide a low-resistance d-c path in accordance with the requirements set forth in the previous section. This resistance is small enough to cause negligible signal unbalance between the two transistors. Note that capacitive input coupling may be employed without utilizing diodes as in the case of the amplifier of Fig. 6-15, since the input circuits of the two transistors are complementary, thereby providing a symmetrical input impedance for both positive and negative input signals.

Alternatively, a direct-coupled driver circuit may be employed as shown in Fig. 6-18, in which the driver stage energizing current flowing through R_1 provides bias voltage for the input circuits of the output stage.

If higher power gain is desired than is available in the common-collector configuration, one of the somewhat more complicated common-emitter circuits may be utilized. In this configuration, the input signal must be applied directly between the base and emitter of each transistor. A requirement of practical circuits is that one terminal of the voltage supply source should be at ground potential, particularly with supplies operating from the power line. Two common-emitter circuit arrangements which satisfy these requirements are shown in Fig. 6-19.

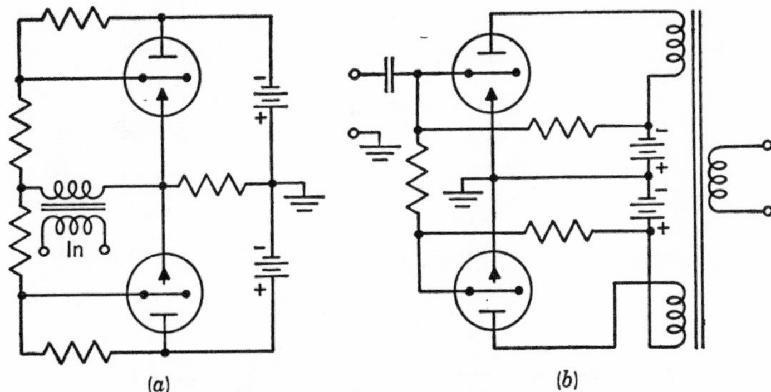

Fig. 6-19. Common-emitter complementary symmetry Class B circuits.

The circuit of Fig. 6-19a is similar to that of Fig. 6-17 except that an input transformer is used in order to apply signals directly between base and emitter of each transistor. The input circuit is biased as in the case of Fig. 6-17; the resistors from collector to base are degenerative in this circuit, however, so that the full gain of the common emitter current is not realized.

The circuit of Fig. 6-19b utilizes an output transformer with two separate primary windings. The biasing in this circuit is not degenerative. Capacitive input coupling may be used, since the symmetrical input circuit prevents the coupling capacitor from charging under signal conditions.

By use of a direct-coupled push-pull driver circuit, as shown in Fig. 6-20, transformerless operation is made possible. In this circuit, energizing currents for the driver transistors are used to bias the output stage transistors. Note that each driver transistor is of opposite conductivity type to the output transistor which it drives. The driver stage may also be operated in Class B for greater amplifier efficiency.

The linearity of the arrangement of Fig. 6-20 may not be good enough for many applications, consisting as it does of two Class B

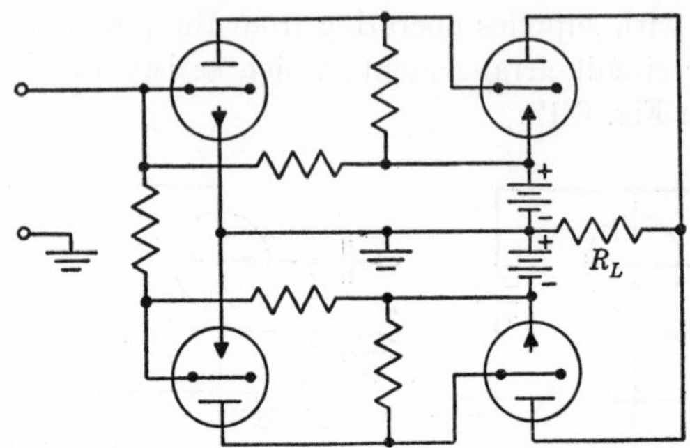

Fig. 6-20. Common-emitter Class B driver and output stage.

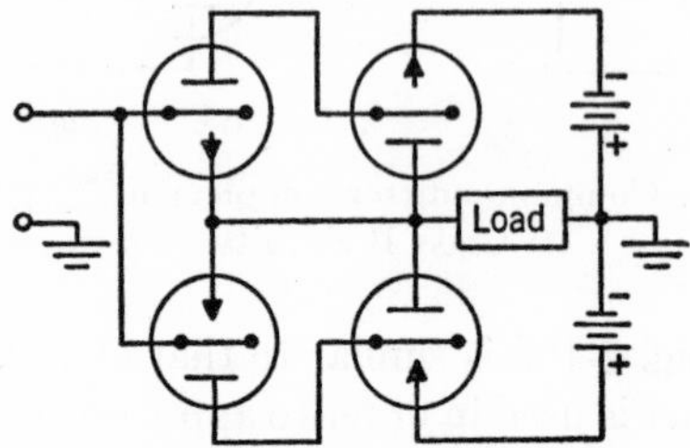

Fig. 6-21. Class B driver and output stage with 100 per cent voltage feedback.

common-emitter stages in cascade. Feedback in this circuit is easily applied, however, by coupling output signals back to the emitters of the driver stage.

The maximum amount of feedback is obtained if the output stage collectors are directly connected to the driver stage emitters. The voltage gain falls to slightly below unity with this connection, but the current gain remains at approximately the product of α_{cb} of each stage. Thus the power gain is given by

$$K_p \doteq \alpha_{cb_1}\alpha_{cb_2} \tag{6-15}$$

where α_{cb_1} and α_{cb_2} are the current amplification factors of the driver and output stage transistors, respectively. The input impedance must therefore be given approximately by

$$R_{in} \doteq \alpha_{cb_1}\alpha_{cb_2}R_L \tag{6-16}$$

The negative feedback in this circuit is quite high, affording good circuit linearity. In fact, the linearizing effect of the feedback is so high that it may be permissible to dispense with the bias provisions shown in Fig. 6-20. Figure 6-21 shows this novel circuit[9], in which no components other than the transistors and the d-c supply are used.

6.12 High-temperature operation of Class B amplifiers

Operation at high ambient temperatures is often a requirement for electronic equipment. Miniaturization of heat-producing equipment compounds the problem. We have seen in Chapter 4 the manner in which linear d-c feedback methods may be used to stablize the operation of a Class A amplifier over a wide range of temperatures. The problem in a Class B amplifier is to establish the zero-signal operating condition at an optimum value, the value being a function of temperature. Linear feedback methods are not applicable to Class B systems, since neither the direct output circuit voltage nor current is uniquely related to the input circuit bias condition under operating conditions. The direct output circuit voltage is generally fixed by the voltage supply, while the direct output circuit current is primarily a function of the signal level, and depends to a smaller degree upon the zero-signal bias condition. Linear feedback means as used in Class A circuits are of little use, therefore, since there is generally no component of output circuit voltage or current to feed back.

The optimum value of zero-signal collector current for Class B operation is the minimum current for which the crossover distortion is acceptably low. This optimum collector current has been found to be fairly constant with temperature, provided that I_{CO} is not too high. Stabilization of the operating point by means of a resistance inserted in the emitter lead of the power transistor would tend to keep the collector current at this optimum value. This method is not satisfactory, however, since there would be excessive signal power loss in

[9] R. D. Lohman, "Complementary Symmetry Transistor Circuits," *Electronics*, Vol. 26, p. 140, Sept. 1953.

this emitter resistance, and elimination of this power loss by capacitive by-passing would result in a reverse bias being applied to the transistor, dependent upon signal level.

It has been shown above that it is desirable to maintain a low-resistance d-c path between base and emitter of the transistor for Class B operation. A bias supply which is to provide the optimum value of collector current therefore should ideally be a voltage source having a low internal impedance connected between the base and emitter. The voltage bias which must be applied between base and emitter to achieve the optimum condition will vary with temperature approximately as shown in curve A of Fig. 6-22, for a typical germanium transistor. Optimum voltage bias is thus seen to decrease with temperature at a rate of approximately 2.5 mv per degree centigrade.

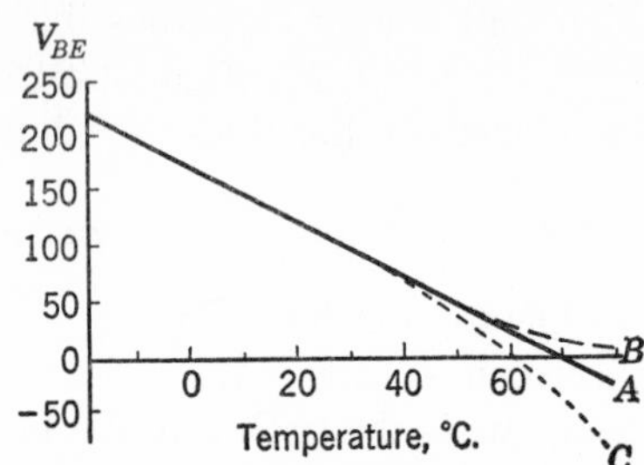

Fig. 6-22. Optimum bias for Class B operation of various germanium transistors.

This optimum bias will vary, particularly at the higher temperatures, between various transistors. The reason for this is most easily explained by the fact that the actual transistor may be considered as composed of an intrinsic transistor and some extrinsic base-lead resistance in series with the base of the intrinsic transistor. The intrinsic transistor requires a forward voltage bias between its base and emitter electrodes which does not vary appreciably among transistors constructed of the same material, but which varies with temperature as shown in curve B of Fig. 6-22. The base-lead resistance may be thought of as the resistance of the germanium between the base connection of the actual transistor and the active base region between the collector and emitter junctions.

Thermally generated current I_{CO} from the collector will flow through this base-lead resistance and through the base terminal of the transistor. The voltage drop across the base-lead resistance and any further resistance in the external base circuit will be applied as a voltage bias which is in a direction to tend to bias the emitter junction in the forward direction. Since I_{CO} increases greatly with temperatures, the forward bias applied to the transistor by this voltage drop will also increase with temperature. The voltage bias which must be applied to the external terminals of the actual transistor will therefore decrease as the temperature is increased; in extreme cases of high base-lead resistance or I_{co}, the voltage bias will sometime have to be reversed in polarity in order to provide the optimum bias condition as shown in curve C of Fig. 6-22.

One practical method for applying optimum bias to a Class B amplifier utilizes a temperature-sensitive resistance element to approximate the appropriate optimum bias curve of Fig. 6-22. Figure 6-23 illustrates the use of a thermistor in a voltage divider bias circuit

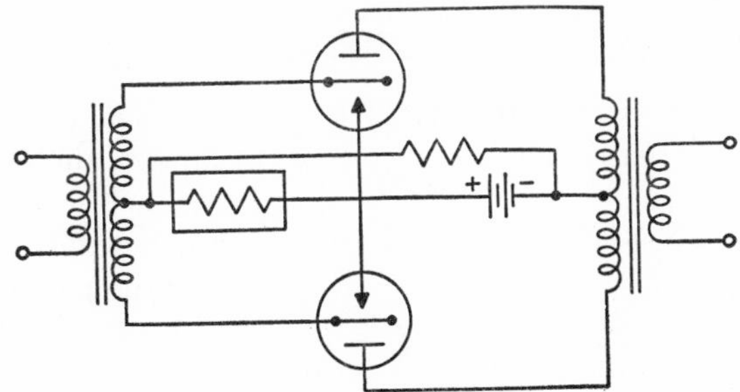

Fig. 6-23. Use of a thermistor for applying temperature-varying bias.

connected across the collector voltage supply. As the temperature rises, the resistance of the thermistor decreases, affording less forward bias. The resistance of the thermistor must be kept low for the reasons stated above. The resistance vs. temperature curve for the thermistor may usually be matched more accurately to the direct characteristic by use of series and parallel resistive padding.

It should be noted that the temperature of the thermistor is not necessarily that of the collector junction of the transistor, since the latter may be heated by internal dissipation under signal conditions. This condition may be rectified by incorporating the temperature-sensitive bias element in the transistor embediment.

Most types of Class B amplifiers discussed in the previous sections can be stablized by use of temperature-sensitive resistive elements connected to reduce the bias with temperature in accordance with the curves of Fig. 6-22. In addition to thermistors, some semiconductor diodes have been found to have satisfactory temperature dependence of resistance for this application.

The temperature problem will be a continuing one in transistor power amplifiers, even as transistors made from material which will withstand higher temperatures become available. Generally, transistors will have current and voltage ratings which are quite high considering the amount of power which can be dissipated safely in them. In other words, the ratio of the power dissipation rating to the product of the current and voltage ratings will be characteristically smaller compared with this ratio for most vacuum tubes. This leads directly to the use of the more efficient classes of operation. Class B operation will therefore be relatively more important in transistor circuits than in vacuum tube circuits.

PROBLEMS

6-1. If the maximum voltage which may be applied to the collector junction of a transistor is 25 v, and the maximum allowable power dissipation is 1 w: (a) what is the maximum value of load resistance which may be used to obtain maximum output power from a transformer-coupled Class A amplifier? (b) Compute the power gain of a common emitter amplifier, using the value of load resistance found in (a). Assume the transistor to be linear and to have $\alpha_{cb} = 20$, $r_d = 10{,}000$ ohms, $1/g_{11} = 100$ ohms; I_{co} and μ_{bc} may be considered to be negligible.

6-2. Compute the power gain of a common-base power-amplifier stage utilizing the same transistor as that of Problem 1 and having a load resistance for obtaining maximum signal-power output. What is the input resistance of this amplifier?

6-3. Repeat Problem 2 for a common-collector power-amplifier stage.

6-4. If it is assumed that the base and collector currents are related by Eq. (6-7) for a transistor having $\alpha_{cb} = 20$ at low values of collector current, and $\beta = 100$ ma, what percentage of "predistortion" is required at 0.5 w output into a load impedance of 400 ohms, if the base is driven from a generator having a high internal impedance?

Chapter 7

HIGH-FREQUENCY OPERATION

7.1 Introduction

The static characteristics of a device, together with the equivalent circuit and analytical expression which may be obtained from them, serve to describe the device at very low frequencies. However, if the response of the device is found to change as the frequency is increased, it is an indication that reactive effects are present, and in order to identify these reactances additional information is required.

In vacuum tubes the reactances mostly consist of the interelectrode capacitances. At extremely high frequencies cathode lead inductance and the transit time of the electrons become important, and these are responsible for two additional reactances. In transistors the interelectrode capacitances are of minor importance compared with the other reactances which are present by virtue of the mechanism by which charges are transported.

In order to obtain (a) the magnitude of the reactances in terms of the physical dimensions of the transistor and the materials used, and (b) the manner in which these reactances are interconnected, it is essential to know the mechanism of transistor action. Sections 7.2 to 7.6 treat this subject for the case of junction transistors in a general descriptive manner. Chapter 8 provides more rigorous treatment of the derivation of the various circuit elements from physical data.

For an understanding of the high-frequency operation of a transistor, the circuit engineer may find it sufficient if only an equivalent circuit for it is given, without explanation of the actual mechanism from which it was derived, and thus he may commence at Sec. 7.7.

In connection with equivalent circuits the following should be borne in mind. Any circuit may be transformed into any other arbitrary circuit configuration such as a T, π, etc. (see Chapter 3). At low frequencies where all impedances are substantially resistive, the choice of an equivalent circuit for a practical problem is not quite so important. However, at higher frequencies it is desirable that the equivalent circuit contain no frequency-dependent components, as these require preliminary calculations before the circuit can be applied to the solution of a particular problem. Furthermore, if possible, no negative R, L, or C should be present, since such elements are not common in nature. Also, the active part of the circuit should preferably be simply in cascade with the passive, and should not be of the feedback type, since this often obscures the impedance levels of the network as seen at the terminals.

In this chapter an equivalent circuit for junction transistors is derived which is basic in that it is synthesized from elements *each* of which is the circuit analogy of *a particular* phenomenon in transistor action. (The four-pole impedances are rigorously derived in Chapter 8.) This circuit[1, 2] is found to have the desirable circuit properties mentioned above, particularly for common-base operation. Rearrangements of the basic elements for common-emitter and common-collector operation are also discussed.

7.2 Flow of charges in junction transistors

In Sec. 1.11 the mechanism of transistor action in an *n-p-n* transistor was briefly discussed. The action for a *p-n-p* transistor is analogous to that of an *n-p-n* with the role of holes and electrons interchanged.

Consider a *p-n-p* transistor as shown in Fig. 7-1a, having plane-parallel sides of unit cross section. Metallurgically the transistor consists of three regions; one n and two p regions, i.e., the regions are here distinguished by the type of impurity atoms present. However, electrically we divide the transistor into five regions: emitter, base, and collector regions, separated by two *transition* regions which are situated in the vicinity of the metallurgical junctions. For reference purposes we insert an x coordinate, with the origin coinciding with the edge of the base region.

In Fig. 7-1a, ohmic contacts are made to the emitter, base, and collector. Furthermore, the emitter battery V_{EE} has its positive and negative leads connected to the p and n regions, respectively. The emitter is now said to have a *forward bias*. The collector battery V_{CC},

[1] J. Zawels, "Physical Theory of a New Circuit Representation for Junction Transistors," *J. Appl. Phys.*, Vol. 28, Aug. 1954.

[2] J. Zawels, "The Natural Equivalent Circuit for Junction Transistors" *RCA Review*, Vol. 16, Sept. 1955.

on the other hand, has its positive and negative leads connected to the n and p regions, respectively, so that it has *reverse bias*. It is noted, however, that both batteries will encourage the flow in the

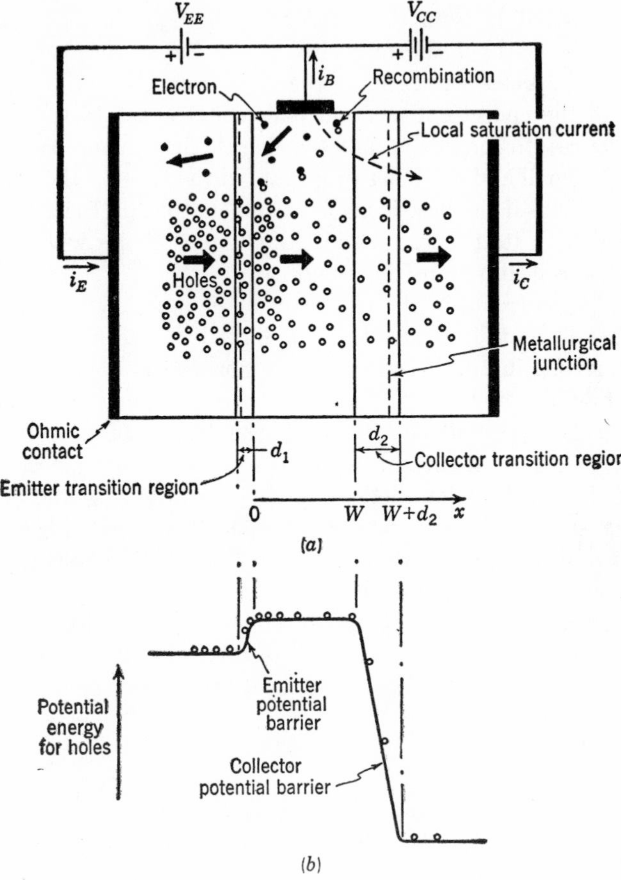

Fig. 7-1. (a) Flow of charges in p-n-p transistor; (b) potential energy diagram for holes.

positive x direction of any positive charges which may be present in the transition regions.

There are various paths followed by the free holes and electrons in the bulk of the transistor. For example, the emitter battery V_{EE} causes a hole current to flow from emitter to base, and an electron current in the reverse direction. By deliberately choosing a high ratio for the resistivity of the base material to the resistivity of the emitter material, say 100 to 1, we can insure that the hole current will be very much larger than the electron current. The path of this electron current is from the base lead, through the base into the emitter. The path of the majority of the holes, however, is quite different; the holes which enter the base from the emitter proceed mainly to the collector transition region and hence to the collector lead. The reason for this is that the electric field in the base is comparatively small and the holes propagate in the base by the process of diffusion. Thus if the base is made extremely thin (in the x direction) compared with its transverse dimensions, most holes will reach the edge of the collector transition region at $x = W$.

The other currents in the transistor arise as follows. Some of the holes that leave the emitter are annihilated by the process of hole-electron recombination, both in the interior and on the surface of the base. The finite lifetimes of the holes therefore give rise to an additional electron current flowing from the base lead into the base. Finally, a small local current, which is akin to the reverse saturation current of a p-n junction diode, flows between the base and collector leads across the collector transition region. This current is made up of holes and electrons flowing in opposite directions because of the reverse bias which is placed by V_{CC} across the collector junction.

The direct voltage-current relationships at the terminals E, C, and B are derived in Chapter 8, and are given by Eqs. (8-27a) to (8-27c), viz.

$$I_E = (\epsilon^{\Lambda(V_E - I_B r_{bb'})} - 1)\frac{G_{11}}{\Lambda} + (\epsilon^{\Lambda(V_C - I_B r_{bb'})} - 1)\frac{G_{12}}{\Lambda} \tag{7-1a}$$

$$I_C = (\epsilon^{\Lambda(V_E - I_B r_{bb'})} - 1)\frac{G_{21}}{\Lambda} + (\epsilon^{\Lambda(V_C - I_B r_{bb'})} - 1)\frac{G_{22}}{\Lambda} \tag{7-1b}$$

also

$$\begin{aligned} -I_B = (\epsilon^{\Lambda(V_E - I_B r_{bb'})} - 1)\left(\frac{G_{11} + G_{21}}{\Lambda}\right) \\ + (\epsilon^{\Lambda(V_C - I_B r_{bb'})} - 1)\left(\frac{G_{12} + G_{22}}{\Lambda}\right) \end{aligned} \tag{7-1c}$$

where G_{11}, G_{12}, G_{21}, and G_{22} are conductances which are determined by the dimensions of the transistor and the physical properties of the material; $1/\Lambda \doteq 0.026$ volt at room temperature, and $r_{bb'}$ is the *base spreading resistance* (see Sec. 7.4d). Leakage conductances which are due to extraneous matter are here neglected. The sign convention used is shown in Fig. 8-3. Thus V_C in the equations above is normally a negative number, and hence the exponential term containing V_C may be neglected in practice for collector voltage greater than about 0.5 volt.

Figure 7-1b shows an approximate potential energy diagram for holes in the transistor. It is seen that there are two potential barriers, the heights of which are dependent on the voltages of the two supply batteries. The potential barriers define the location of the transition region, while the plateaux occur in the emitter, base, and collector regions. This means that while the voltage drops and electric fields in the plateaux are very small indeed, the electric field in the transition regions, especially in the collector transition region, is very large.

When small alternating voltages are superimposed on the two battery voltages, the heights of the potential barriers in Fig. 7-1b are varied. Because the emitter barrier is so much smaller than that at the collector, it is clear that a given voltage increment across the emitter transition region will cause a greater increment in current than if the same voltage increment were applied across the collector transition region. Circuitwise, this means that the a-c resistance of the transistor as viewed from the *emitter* battery terminals is much smaller than that viewed from the *collector* battery terminals.

7.3 Reactive effects

Reactive effects are discernible in transistors for frequencies often as low as 1 kc. We now examine these effects.

The electric field in the transition regions is a manifestation of a space charge which exists there. Conversely, the electric field strips some of the donor and acceptor atoms on each side of the metallurgical junction of their free electrons and holes, respectively, resulting in a region where the stripped atoms constitute fixed charges of opposite sign imbedded in a quasi-dielectric medium (which is the intrinsic germanium). The width of this space charge region depends on the magnitude of the electric field in this region, and hence on the voltage across this region.

Application now of a small alternating voltage in series with the d-c battery will result in a periodic partial neutralization of the space charge region by free electrons and holes. In fact, the resulting alternating charge flow is similar to the charging and discharging of a capacitor except that here a considerable direct current also flows, whereas in a conventional capacitor we usually assume that no conduction current exists. Thus two reactive effects are present in transistors in the form of the emitter and the collector *transition capacitances*, which we associate with the two transition regions. In the common type of junction transistors, the magnitude of the collector transition capacitances varies from about 7 to 50 $\mu\mu$f, whereas the emitter transition capacitance is around 100 to 150 $\mu\mu$f. In spite of the emitter transition capacitance being larger, however, it is often neglected on account of the small resistance with which it appears in parallel. These capacitances are derived in Sec. 8.13, where it is shown that

$$C_T = AV^{-n} \tag{7-2}$$

where A is a constant dependent on the dimensions and the properties of the material, V is the applied voltage, and n is a fraction such as $\frac{1}{2}$ or $\frac{1}{3}$ depending on the distribution of the impurity atoms.

Another important reactive effect is a result of the base being capable of storing *minority charge carriers*.[3] In fact, the carrier density differs from point to point causing *diffusion*, i.e., a net flow of carriers due to thermal agitation, proportional to the *density gradient*. In the equivalent circuit we may represent the charge-storing ability of the base (which also determines the transit time of the carriers) by a distributed capacitance termed *diffusion* capacitance. This capacitance when viewed from the base and emitter terminals appears to be nonlinear, by virtue of the emitter potential barrier which is present. It is derived in Sec. 8.10, where it can be shown from Eqs. (8-45f) and (8-44b) that

$$C'_D \doteq BI_E \tag{7-3}$$

where B is a constant dependent on the dimensions and properties of the material, and I_E is the emitter bias direct current.

Unlike the case for vacuum tubes, the interelectrode capacitances are usually of lesser importance in transistors, on account of the

[3] In a *p-n-p* transistor the minority charge carriers are holes.

magnitude of the other capacitances which are present. Occasionally, however, a small capacitance between the collector and base leads of about 0.25 to 5 $\mu\mu$f may be of some importance, especially if the base spreading resistance is high. This capacitance, however, probably arises from the fact that the collector transition capacitance is in direct proximity to the material which is responsible for the base spreading resistance, rather than from the geometrical capacitance of the base and emitter leads.

7.4 Generalized equivalent circuit

In Sec. 7.3 some of the elements of the equivalent circuit of a junction transistor were mentioned, such as the emitter and collector transition capacitances, diffusion capacitance, and the collector to base interelectrode capacitance. In addition to these, elements such as the base spreading resistance, collector leakage resistance, and surface recombination admittances are present, as discussed below,

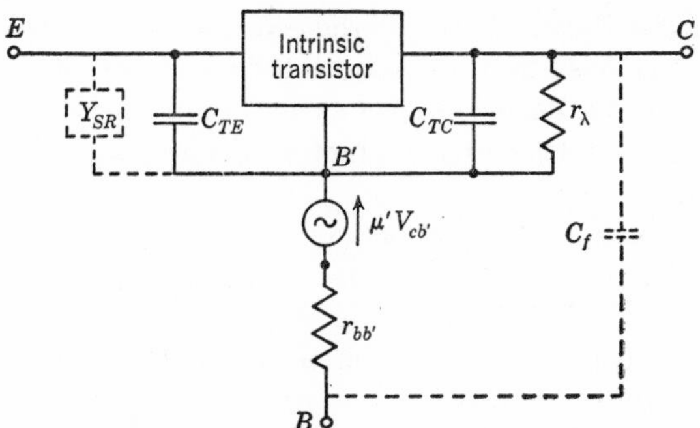

Fig. 7-2. Generalized equivalent circuit.

whose importance largely depends on the particular transistor under consideration. The generalized equivalent circuit containing all these elements is shown in Fig. 7-2. Although the interconnections of these elements is achieved through intuitive reasoning, the placing of the most important elements has been checked experimentally for the common type of junction transistors.

In Fig. 7-2, the block marked "intrinsic transistor" represents elements which arise purely as a result of the *diffusion* process of the minority and majority carriers. Thus for example, the diffusion capacitance is included in the intrinsic transistor but the transition capacitances are excluded. The distinction between the "intrinsic transistor" and the rest of the circuit is made quite arbitrarily for reference purposes only. The equivalent circuit for the intrinsic transistor is discussed in detail in Secs. 7.5 and 7.6.

The other elements appearing in Fig. 7-2 arise as follows:

1. As mentioned in Sec. 7.3, the *collector and emitter transition capacitances* appear between the collector and base, and the emitter and base, respectively. These are shown as C_{TC} and C_{TE}.

2. Extraneous matter is often found to shunt the two junctions. Obviously the shunting of the collector junction is more serious than the shunting of the emitter junction, since the impedance of the former may be as high as several megohms. We account for the effect of this extraneous matter by inserting a *collector leakage resistance* r_λ $(\equiv 1/g_\lambda)$ in the equivalent circuit.

3. The effect of hole-electron recombination in the interior of the base is considered to be a property of the intrinsic transistor, and is dealt with elsewhere. However, the effect of recombination on the surface of the base may or may not be included in the intrinsic transistor. In Fig. 7-2 it is shown as a separate *surface recombination admittance* Y_{SR}. Surface recombination is dealt with quantitatively in Sec. 8.11.

4. *The base spreading resistance* $r_{bb'}$ represents the resistance of the bulk material from which the base is made, and appears in series with the base lead. Its magnitude depends on the thickness of the base (which is usually small compared with its transverse dimensions) and the resistivity of the base material which, as mentioned in Sec. 7.2, is deliberately made much larger than the emitter material resistivity. This explains why the base spreading resistance is so much larger than the emitter spreading resistance. The emitter and collector spreading resistances are usually negligible compared with the impedance with which they appear in series.

The base spreading resistance has a drastic effect on the gain of the transistor, especially at high frequencies. The reason is that in the complete equivalent circuit of the transistor, it appears in series with an RC parallel network, thereby comprising a low-pass filter. The base spreading resistance is discussed in greater detail in Sec. 8.14.

5. In series with the base spreading resistance $r_{bb'}$ is the feedback

generator $\mu' V_{cb'}$.[4] This generator is a result of the dependence of a portion of $r_{bb'}$ on the effective base width, which in turn is dependent on the collector voltage. As an alternative to this feedback generator, the magnitude of $r_{bb'}$, and possibly of other elements, can be altered to account to some extent for this nonlinear behavior of the base spreading resistance.

In practice this phenomenon is often not distinguishable as a separate effect if the portion of $r_{bb'}$ which is outside of the active transistor region is large, and is therefore neglected in the equivalent circuit. This is more fully discussed in Sec. 8.14.

6. Capacitance C_f is the collector-to-base "interelectrode" capacitance.

With reference to the importance of the various elements we summarize the previous as follows: For the common junction transistors the most important external elements are C_{TC} and $r_{bb'}$. Next in importance is r_λ. The effect of Y_{SR} is often incorporated in the intrinsic transistor. C_f is usually perceptible only at very high frequencies where the useful gain of the transistor is quite small. Capacitance C_{TE} is usually swamped by the capacitance of the intrinsic transistor which appears in parallel with it. The importance of the generator $\mu' V_{cb'}$ is determined by the dependance of $r_{bb'}$ on collector voltage, and is most often small.

7.5 Intrinsic-transistor equivalent circuit

The equivalent circuit of the intrinsic transistor, as mentioned in Sec. 7.4, is defined as that portion of the complete equivalent circuit of a transistor which arises mainly out of the diffusion process of the minority and majority carriers. The short-circuit admittances of a plane-parallel intrinsic transistor are derived in Sec. 8.10 and are given by Eqs. (8-43a) to (8-43d).

$$y_{11} = G\theta \coth \theta + Y_n \tag{7-4a}$$

$$y_{21} = -G\theta \operatorname{cosech} \theta \tag{7-4b}$$

$$y_{12} = \frac{-G\theta \operatorname{cosech} \theta}{K} \tag{7-4c}$$

[4] J. M. Early, "Effect of Space-Charge Layer Widening in Junction Transistors," *Proc. I.R.E.*, Vol. 40, p. 1401, Nov. 1952.

$$y_{22} = \frac{G\theta \coth \theta}{K} \tag{7-4d}$$

where G is a conductance and K is a number, both of which are dependent on the dimension and the properties of the material; Y_n represents the flow of majority carriers from the base across the emitter junctions, and θ contains a frequency-sensitive factor $(1 + j\omega\tau_p)^{1/2}$.

In Appendix 1 it is shown rigorously that the above admittances may be represented by a transmission line[5] in cascade with a "K amplifier" having Y_n in parallel. In this and the following section this circuit will be obtained qualitatively.

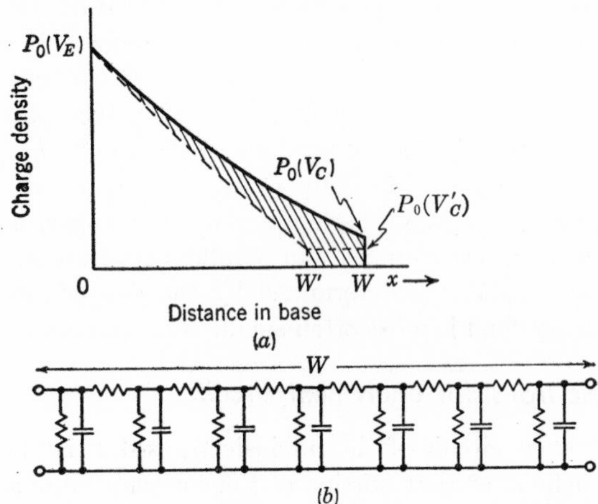

Fig. 7-3. (a) Charge density distribution in base; (b) *RC* transmission line.

The Transmission Line

Figure 7-3a shows the distribution of minority carriers in the base of a transistor when a steady direct current is flowing through it. If hole-electron recombination is neglected, the rate of propagation of

[5] The constants of this transmission line, for a plane-parallel intrinsic transistor are: characteristic impedance, $Z_o = 1/G\theta$ ohms; propagation constant, $\gamma = \theta/W$ per unit length, where W is the length of the line. The resistance, conductance, and capacitance per unit length are given by Eqs. (8-45d) to (8-45f).

the minority carriers at a given point will be directly proportional to the density gradient at that point. Such a process is termed diffusion, and the constant of proportionality is the diffusion constant D. Circuitwise we may represent the process of diffusion by a transmission line having series resistance and shunt capacitance. Such a line permits a variable charge density to exist along the length of the line, and it is easily shown that the current flowing at a given point is proportional to the charge density gradient at that point. The constant of proportionality here is the inverse time constant of the line ($1/rC$) and is analogous to the diffusion constant D.

The fact that not all of the minority carriers which leave the emitter reach the collector (mostly because of hole-electron recombination) is represented in the transmission line of Fig. 7-3b by the shunt resistance. It is also clear that the transmission line will be uniform only if the diffusion constant and the rate of recombination are uniform everywhere in the base.

K Amplifier and Its Properties

Figure 7-1a shows that a potential barrier exists in the transition region on each side of the base. Circuitwise the potential barrier may be represented by an amplifier. The properties of this amplifier should represent the fact that if hole-electron recombination in the transition region is neglected, the number of carriers which enter a transition region in a given time interval equals the number that leave the region in a similar time interval, and that only their potential energy changes. In other words, the input current of the amplifier should equal the output current, while the input and output voltages differ.

We define therefore a K amplifier as a device where for all termination

$$\frac{\text{output current}}{\text{input current}} = 1 \tag{7-5a}$$

and

$$\frac{\text{output voltage}}{\text{input voltage}} = K \tag{7-5b}$$

where K is a constant which is a function of the voltage across the transition region.

The above definition describes the K amplifier completely. However, in order to become familiar with its uses, we examine the implication of the above definition more closely.

Consider a grounded-grid vacuum tube triode at low frequencies as seen in Fig. 7-4b. Let the amplification factor of the tube be μ. It is clear that $I_{in} = I_{out}$ and $V_{out}/V_{in} = (\mu + 1)$ for all terminations provided the plate resistance of the tube is very low or zero.

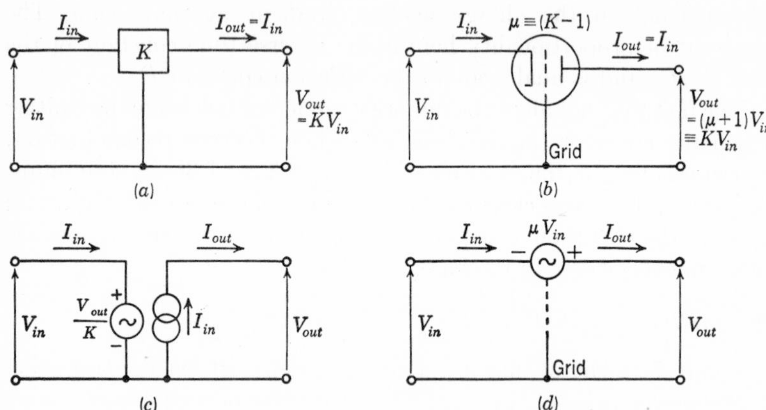

Fig. 7-4. Four equivalent representations of a K amplifier: (a) block diagram; (b) vacuum tube triode with zero plate resistance; (c) two-generator representation; (d) conventional single-generator representation used for tubes.

A K *amplifier is therefore equivalent to a grounded-grid vacuum tube with extremely low or zero plate resistance and an amplification factor* $\mu = K - 1$.

A conventional method for representing a vacuum tube triode consists of a voltage generator μV_{in} in series with a resistance representing the plate resistance of the tube. Thus for the tube shown in Fig. 7-4b we represent it by the circuit shown in Fig. 7-4d, since we have assumed the plate resistance to be virtually zero. Another alternative for representing a K amplifier using one current and one voltage generator is shown in Fig. 7-4c. However, it is often simpler to consider the K amplifier a single circuit component, as follows, without resorting to generators.

A K amplifier has simple impedance-transforming properties. For example, if a load Z_L is connected to the output, then obviously

$$Z_L = \frac{V_{out}}{I_{out}} = \frac{V_{in}K}{I_{out}} = \frac{V_{in}K}{I_{in}} = Z_{in}K$$

Hence the input impedance $Z_{in} = Z_L/K$. Alternatively if a resistance Z_g is connected to the input, the output impedance is Z_gK. Thus as far as the impedance-transforming properties are concerned, the K amplifier acts like a conventional ideal transformer with a turns ratio of $K^{1/2}$. As a result of this property, an impedance which is connected to one side may be transferred to the other side by simply multiplying it by K (or $1/K$, as the case may be) without changing the impedance levels as viewed from the terminals.

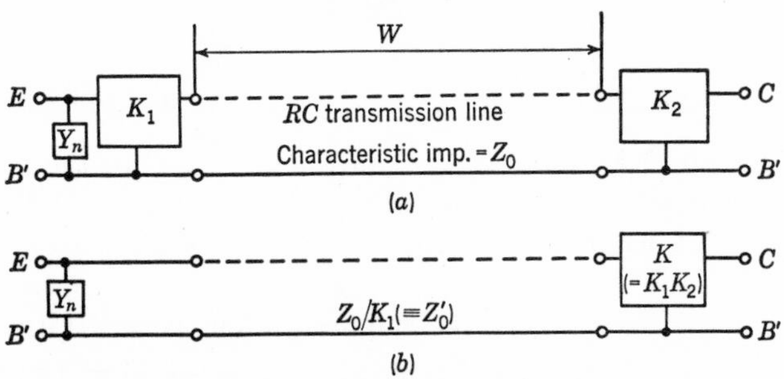

Fig. 7-5. Equivalent circuit of intrinsic transistor: (a) two K amplifiers; (b) combination of K amplifiers.

Figure 7-5a shows the transmission line representing the base, terminated by the two K amplifiers which represent the two potential barriers. The K amplifiers are considered to be independent of frequency, since the transit time of the charge carriers across the transition region, where an electric field is present, is negligible compared with the transit time in the base. The two K amplifiers may now be combined into a single K amplifier with an amplification factor $K = K_1K_2$, as seen in Fig. 7-5b. This is achieved by transferring the transmission line of Fig. 7-5a to the left of the K_1 amplifier, simply by dividing its characteristic impedance Z_o by K_1. The concept of the K amplifier therefore leads to an equivalent circuit consisting of two cascaded sections, one passive and one active, with the active part being independent of frequency.

Majority Carrier Admittance

As mentioned earlier, a majority carrier current flows by virtue of the voltage across the emitter junction. In a *p-n-p* transistor this current consists of electrons which flow from the base to the emitter as indicated in Sec. 7.2. This is responsible for an impedance Y_n which is placed between E and B' as seen in Fig. 7-5b. For a good transistor, where this majority carrier current is very small compared with the minority carrier current, it follows that Y_n is small compared with the admittance of the transmission line.

It can also be shown that the corresponding impedance between terminals C and B' by virtue of the voltage across the collector junction is entirely negligible, if the collector bias voltage is greater than about 0.5 volt.

7.6 Base width modulation[6]

Consider Fig. 7-5a showing the equivalent circuit for the intrinsic transistor consisting of the transmission line terminated by two K amplifiers. The length of the transmission line corresponds to the effective width W of the base region, as indicated in Fig. 7-1a.

In a *p-n* junction where the impurity atom concentrations are uniform in the p and n regions, and change abruptly at the metallurgical junction, it can be shown (see Sec. 8.13) that the width of the transition region is (from Eq. 8-70)

$$d = A\sqrt{V\left(\frac{b}{\sigma_n} + \frac{1}{\sigma_p}\right)} \qquad (7\text{-}6)$$

where V = direct voltage across the junction; σ_n = conductivity of n region; σ_p = conductivity of p region; A and b = constants. From the above formula it is obvious that the transition regions extend mostly into the region where the conductivity is lowest. This can also be understood intuitively from the fact that the electric lines of force which start on an ionized donor atom on one side of the metallurgical junction in the transition region must end on the ionized acceptor atom on the other side. Thus in the region of small con-

[6] Base width modulation was first investigated by J. M. Early (*op. cit.*) with reference to the resistances of the T equivalent circuit. Base width modulation is here also referred to as the "Early effect."

ductivity, i.e., where the density of the impurity atoms is small, the lines of force have to extend deeper into the interior.

This explains why the transition regions in a transistor having highly doped emitter and collector regions mostly extend into the base region, thereby reducing the effective base width W.

The number of ionized impurity atoms, and hence the width of the transition regions, depend on the voltage across the junction as indicated by Eq. (7-6). Hence the collector transition region, which normally has a much larger bias voltage across it than the emitter transition region, is by far the larger of the two. In fact it is the collector bias voltage which largely determines the effective base width W.

Consider now the effect of an alternating voltage across the collector junction on the equivalent circuit of Fig. 7-5a. This voltage will modulate the base width, which is equivalent to changing continuously the length of the transmission line of Fig. 7-5a. This results in the introduction of a nonlinear characteristic into the equivalent circuit, which complicates it considerably. Our aim is now to modify the equivalent circuit so that the effect of this base width modulation is largely incorporated without introducing nonlinear elements. It should be realized that this can be done only to an approximate extent, since a circuit having a nonlinear characteristic cannot be constructed by using only linear elements.

Let the distribution of the minority carriers in the base under d-c conditions, i.e., for a fixed emitter and collector voltage, be as shown by the solid line in Fig. 7-3a. It is easily shown that this distribution of charge will also be found in the RC transmission line of Fig. 7-3b (or Fig. 7-5a) when a direct current is flowing through it. As explained above, a change in the collector voltage from V_C to V'_C will now not only change the charge carrier density at point $x = W$ from $P_o(V_C)$ to $P_o(V'_C)$, but will also change the length of the line from W to W'. The shaded area in Fig. 7-3a now represents the excess charge, which will cause an incremental current to flow out of the collector lead, and which is obviously greater than if the effective base width had remained constant at $x = W$. Hence the ratio of the resultant increment of collector current to the increment of collector voltage is greater, i.e., the impedance is smaller, than if base width modulation were ignored.

Summarizing: the net effect of base width modulation is to decrease the small-signal output impedance of the transistor. To achieve this effect in the circuit of Fig. 7-5a it is readily seen that we can simply lower the value of K_2 of the collector K amplifier. This results in a lower value for K in Fig. 7-5b.

Similarly, when considering the *input* impedance of a common-base transistor amplifier for a given load connected to the output, it can be shown that in actual practice it is larger than it would be if the Early effect[7] were absent. Also in this case, therefore, lowering the value of K_2 in Fig. 7-5a, and hence the value of K in Fig. 7-5b, achieves the desired correction to the equivalent circuit.[8]

The value of K for the K amplifier in terms of physical quantities is approximately given at room temperature by

$$K \doteq \frac{38}{n}\frac{W}{d} V_C \tag{7-7}$$

where V_C is the collector bias voltage in volts, W and d are the base and the effective transition region widths, respectively, and $n = \frac{1}{2}$ for a Schottky or "step" junction, and $n = \frac{1}{3}$ for a uniform impurity concentration gradient junction (see Eq. 8-44e and Problem 8.8b of Chapter 8).

7.7 Practical equivalent circuit

The complete equivalent circuit of a junction transistor may be constructed by combining the generalized equivalent circuit shown

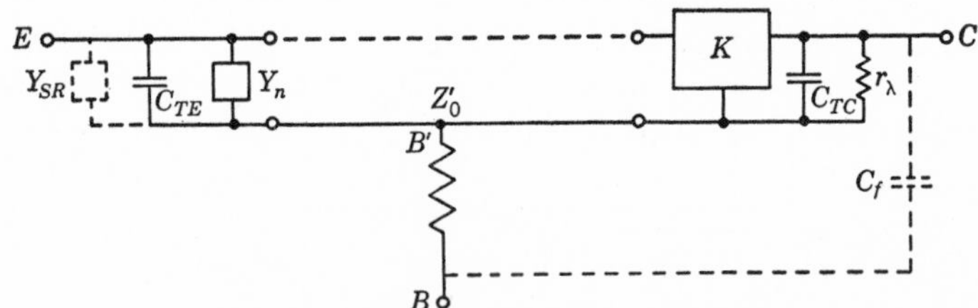

Fig. 7-6. Equivalent circuit of transistor.

in Fig. 7-2 with the equivalent circuit of the intrinsic transistor given in Fig. 7-5b, as shown in Fig. 7-6. The $\mu' V_{cb'}$ generator of Fig. 7-2 is considered to be negligible here.

[7] See footnote 6.

[8] Lowering the value of K implies here that the load impedance is divided by a smaller number; hence the input impedance is larger.

Figure 7-6 is normally too complicated for practical circuit applications because the transmission line is present, and we therefore endeavour to replace the line by a lumped parameter network. It can be shown that for a parallel-sided transistor with uniform volume recombination, the lumped parameters are substantially independent of frequency over the useful frequency range if a π network representation is used such as that shown in Fig. 7-7 (see Problem 8.6). Figure 7-6 is thus simplified by the use of a π network and by the combination of elements appearing in parallel with it, as shown in Fig. 7-8. The elements of this circuit are as follows:

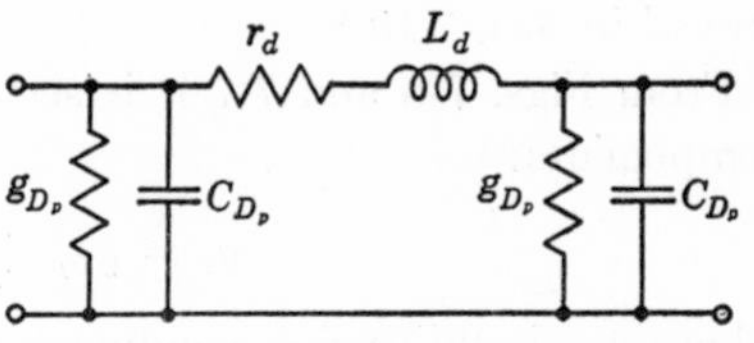

Fig. 7-7. Approximation to *RC* transmission line.

Emitter series resistance, r_d is approximately given at room temperature by[9]

$$r_d \doteq \frac{26}{I_E} \text{ ohm} \tag{7-8}$$

for not too small values of emitter bias direct current I_E, which is here in milliamperes. Resistance r_d arises from the approximation of the transmission line.

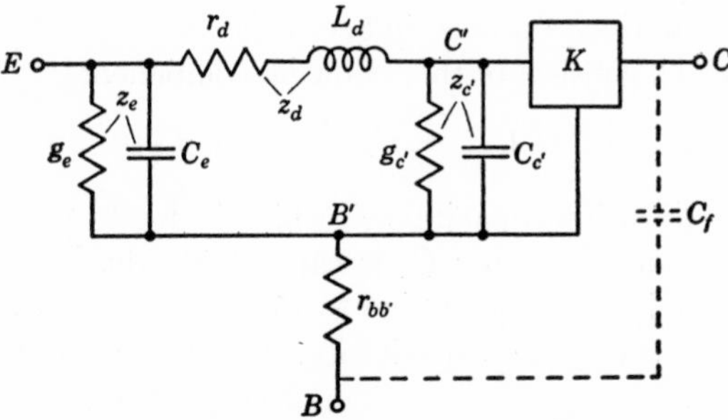

Fig. 7-8. Practical high-frequency equivalent circuit.

Emitter shunt conductance, g_e. This element may have a conductance in the order of 0.002 to 0.001 mho. An important practical

[9] See Eqs. (8-44b) and (8-46d) for the origin of this equation.

relation between g_e and r_d is

$$g_e = \frac{1}{\alpha_{cbo} r_d} \tag{7-9}$$

where α_{cbo} is the short-circuit current amplification factor for the common-emitter connection at low frequency. (This equation is proved in Sec. 7.10.)

From Figs. 7-6 and 7-7 it is seen that g_e consists of the following components:[10]

$$g_e = g_{Dp} + g_n + g_{SR} \tag{7-10}$$

where g_{Dp} is "diffusion conductance," which is due to the approximation of the transmission line, g_n is conductance due to the real part of Y_n, and g_{SR} is conductance due to the real part of Y_{SR}.

Emitter shunt capacitance, C_e may be of the order of 0.01 μf, and is primarily responsible for the dependence of the common-emitter and common-base short-circuit current amplification factors, α_{cb} and α_{ce}, on frequency. An important relationship between C_e and g_e is to a very good approximation

$$\omega_{cb} = \frac{g_e}{C_e} \tag{7-11}$$

where ω_{cb} is the cutoff (angular) frequency, i.e., the angular frequency at which the magnitude of α_{cb} is 3 db lower than its low-frequency value. (This equation is proved in Sec. 7.10.)

Capacitance C_e consists of the following components.[11]

$$C_e = C_{Dp} + C_n + C_{SR} + C_{TE} \tag{7-12}$$

where C_{Dp} is "diffusion capacitance" which is due to the approximation of the transmission line; C_n is capacitance due to the reactive part of Y_n; C_{SR} is capacitance due to the reactive part of Y_{SR}, and C_{TE} is emitter transition capacitance. This component is usually very small.

Emitter series inductance, L_d may be of the order of 5 μh, and is negligible at all except very high frequencies. From physical considerations it can be shown that[12]

[10] These components are derived in terms of the physical properties of the material in Secs. 8.10, 8.11, and 8.13.

[11] See footnote 10.

[12] See Problem 8.6(b).

$$L_d = \frac{r_d}{n'\alpha_{cbo}\omega_{cb}} \tag{7-13}$$

where n' is a number in the order of 3.

Thus L_d has a reactance of only (r_d/n') ohm when the angular frequency is as high as $(\alpha_{cbo}\omega_{cb})$ where very little power gain is usually possible.

Transferred collector capacitance,[13] $C_{c'}$ may be of the order of 0.1 μf; $C_{c'}$ consists of the following components:

$$C_{c'} = C_{Dp} + KC_{TC} \tag{7-14}$$

where C_{Dp} is "diffusion capacitance" which is due to the approximation of the transmission line, and C_{TC} is collector transition capacitance. The product KC_{TC}, which is usually the dominating term in Eq. (7-14), results from the transfer of C_{TC} to the left of the K amplifier in Fig. 7-6.

Transferred collector conductance, $g_{c'}$. The value of this component is often of the same order as g_e; conductance $g_{c'}$ consists of the following components:

$$g_{c'} = g'_{Dp} + \frac{K}{r_\lambda} \tag{7-15}$$

where r_λ is leakage conductance (which is transferred to the left of the K amplifier in Fig. 7-6) and g'_{Dp} is diffusion conductance which is due to the approximation of the transmission line. For a uniform transmission line (i.e., for uniform volume recombination) $g'_{Dp} = g_{Dp}$, where g_{Dp} is the corresponding component of g_e.

Base spreading resistance, $r_{bb'}$ may be of the order of 50 to 500 ohms.

Collector-to-base interelectrode capacitance, C_f is in the order of 1 $\mu\mu$f.

K amplifier is defined in Sec. 7-5b. Practical values for K vary from about 500 to 10,000.

Note that the names given above for the different elements are quite general in order to avoid any association with any particular physical phenomenon. Also, single subscripts are used for simplicity; however, if differentiation between the elements of this circuit and that of any other equivalent circuit is required, double subscripts may be used to indicate the nodes between which they are connected. For example, $C_{eb'}$ may be used for C_e; $C_{c'b'}$ for $C_{c'}$, etc.

[13] In contrast, *collector capacitance* refers to $C_c \equiv C_{c'}/K$.

7.8 Frequency ranges of operation

The importance of a particular element in a circuit depends on the frequency of operation. Thus we define three frequency ranges and simplify Fig. 7-8 by eliminating various elements depending on the frequency range under consideration. Let

$$\omega_c(\equiv 2\pi f_c) \equiv \frac{g_{c'}}{C_{c'}}$$

Also from Eq. (7-11), and Eq. (7-9),

$$\omega_{cb}\,(\equiv 2\pi f_{cb}) = \frac{g_e}{C_e}; \qquad \alpha_{cbo} = \frac{1}{r_d g_e}$$

Thus approximately,

$$\frac{\alpha_{cbo} f_{cb}}{3} \doteq \frac{1}{20 r_d C_e}; \quad \frac{f_{cb}}{3} \doteq \frac{g_e}{20C_e}; \quad \frac{f_c}{3} \doteq \frac{g_{c'}}{20C_{c'}}$$

The three frequency ranges are now defined as follows: The *high-frequency range* extends above the frequency $\alpha_{cbo}f_{cb}/3$. When working in this range the complete high-frequency equivalent circuit shown in Fig. 7-8 should be used. The *medium-frequency range* extends between $\alpha_{cbo}f_{cb}/3$ and $f_{cb}/3$ or $f_c/3$, whichever is the lower. In this range L_d and C_f may be neglected as seen in Fig. 7-9. The *low-frequency range* extends up to the lower limit of the medium-frequency range. Here all reactances are ignored.

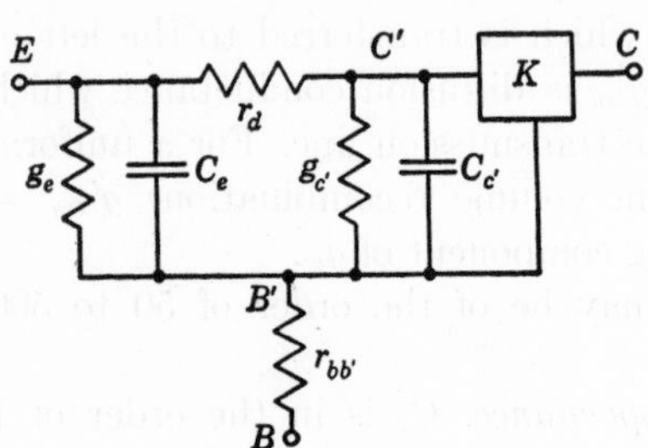

Fig. 7-9. Equivalent circuit for medium-frequency range.

The above limits of the frequency ranges are naturally only a rough indication, and the recommended circuits for the particular frequency range are thought to be sufficiently accurate for most problems. If greater accuracy is required, the high-frequency equivalent circuit can be used at all frequencies.

The circuit of Fig. 7-8 (or Fig. 7-9) consists simply of a passive network in cascade with an active element, and contains no *active* feedback elements. This commends its application for the solution of practical problems. For example, suppose that the current gain is required in a common-base amplifier when a load Z_L is present as shown in Fig. 7-10. Here

$$z_e = \frac{1}{g_e + j\omega C_e} \tag{7-16a}$$

$$z_{c'} = \frac{1}{g_{c'} + j\omega C_{c'}} \tag{7-16b}$$

and

$$z_d = r_d + j\omega L_d \tag{7-16c}$$

(The respective reactive parts of these impedances may be placed equal to zero depending on the frequency range of operation.)

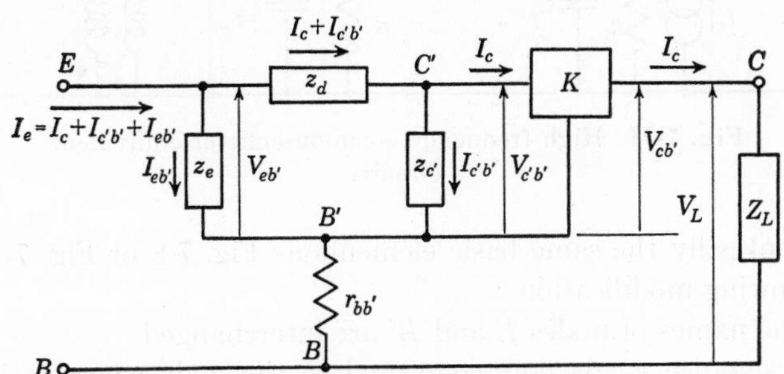

Fig. 7-10. Common-base amplifier with load, showing branch currents and voltages.

Thus in Fig. 7-10, if the load current is I_c, then

$$V_L = I_c Z_L \approx V_{cb'} = KV_{c'b'} = KI_{c'b'}z_{c'} \tag{7-17a}$$

(The approximation arises from the fact that in practical applications $r_{bb'} \ll Z_L$ if a gain is expected.) Also, the current through z_d is $(I_c + I_{c'b'})$ and hence

$$V_{eb'} = (I_c + I_{c'b'})z_d + V_{c'b'} \quad (= z_e I_{eb'}) \tag{7-17b}$$

From Eqs. (7-17a) and (7-17b),

$$\begin{aligned} I_e &= I_c + I_{c'b'} + I_{eb'} \\ &= I_c + \frac{I_c Z_L}{Kz_{c'}} + \frac{(I_c + I_c Z_L/Kz_{c'})z_d + I_c Z_L/K}{z_e} \end{aligned}$$

i.e., the current gain is

$$K_i = \frac{I_c}{I_e} = \frac{1}{(1 + Z_L/Kz_{c'})(1 + z_d/z_e) + Z_L/Kz_e} \tag{7-17c}$$

7.9 Common-emitter and common collector equivalent circuits

The equivalent circuit shown in Fig. 7-8 or Fig. 7-9 is particularly useful in calculations where the transistor is connected with the base common. However, when operating with the emitter common it is advantageous to modify the circuit, e.g. as in Fig. 7-11. This circuit

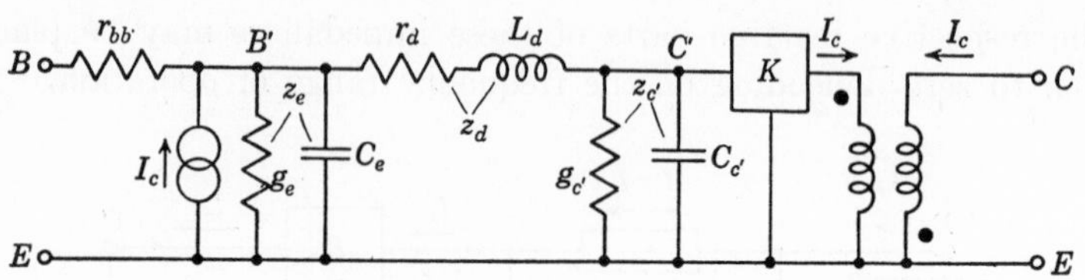

Fig. 7-11. High-frequency common-emitter equivalent circuit.

uses identically the same basic elements as Fig. 7-8 or Fig. 7-9 with the following modifications:

1. The names of nodes E and B' are interchanged.
2. Resistance $r_{bb'}$ is now connected to the node where resistance r_d and conductance g_e join.
3. A phase-reversing transformer is added in cascade.
4. A current generator is added, whose current is equal to the current in the collector lead.

The conversion from the common base to the common emitter is proved in Appendix 2.[14]

An alternative common-emitter circuit[15] is shown in Fig. 7-12b. (See also Sec. 7-13.) The circuit is seen to have a topological resemblance to the high frequency equivalent circuit of a vacuum tube triode, if elements $r_{bb'}$ and $g_{c'}/K$ (as well as the differing impedance levels) are ignored. A practical advantage which can be claimed for Fig. 7-11 over Fig. 7-12b is that the generator in Fig. 7-11 is dependent on the current at a terminal, viz. I_c, which in practical problems may

[14] The conversion is premised on the fact that generally $y_{11} \gg y_{12}$; $y_{21} \gg y_{22}$ where y_{11}, y_{12}, etc. are the four-pole admittances.

[15] Figure 7-12b can be derived from Fig. 7-8 as follows: First the K amplifier is shifted to the left as shown in Fig. 7-12a; this necessitates multiplying the resistances and inductance by K and dividing the capacitance by K. Next, the K amplifier is replaced by the voltage generator μV_{in}, as shown in Fig. 7-4d. (Here $\mu = (K - 1)$, and $V_{in} = V_{b'e}$.) Finally this circuit is simply redrawn in the more convenient form seen in Fig. 7-12b.

be known, whereas the generator of Fig. 7-12b is a function of a voltage $V_{b'e}$ at the internal point of the circuit, which is quite difficult to determine.

In a very similar manner to that used in the derivation of the common-emitter circuit of Fig. 7-12b, a common-collector circuit may be derived. In fact, the two circuits show a marked topological resem-

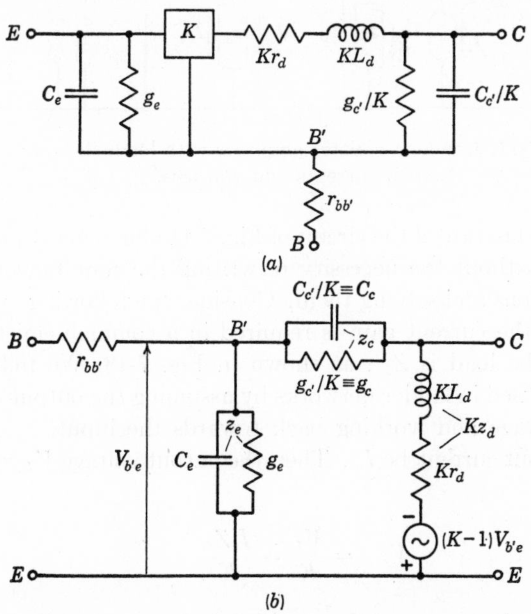

Fig. 7-12. Derivation of an alternate circuit to Fig. 7-11: (a) K amplifier shifted to left in Fig. 7-10; (b) circuit of Fig. 7-12(a) redrawn with a feedback generator replacing the K amplifier.

blance. (See Prob. 7-5.) It can be shown that the voltage generator is here $(K - 1)/KV_{b'c} \doteq V_{b'c}$ since $K \gg 1$, whereas in Fig. 7-12b it is $(K - 1)V_{b'e} \doteq KV_{b'e}$.

Note that the circuits of Figs. 7-11 and 7-12b use the same basic equivalent circuit elements as Fig. 7-8, except for the factor K. This means that (a) the expressions for power gain, impedance levels, etc., are simultaneously applicable to all these circuits; (b) the expressions can be more easily directly related to the physical properties of the transistor; and (c) the dependence of each of the expressions on the d-c bias parameters can be more easily established, since each basic element is to a first order approximation either independent of bias parameters or a function of only one bias parameter.

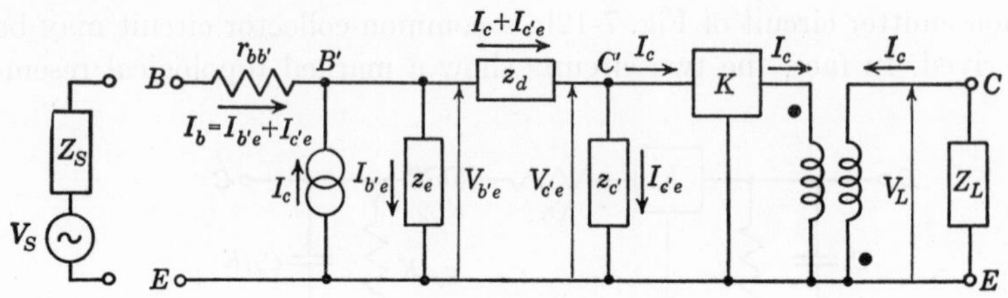

Fig. 7-13. Common-emitter amplifier with load, showing branch currents and voltages.

The cascaded nature of the circuit of Fig. 7-11 allows many problems to be solved without the necessity of writing the simultaneous loop or node equations and solving them. Consider the following example: Suppose that the current gain is required in a common-emitter amplifier when the load is Z_L, as shown in Fig. 7-13. We follow the method often used in ladder networks by assuming the output current or output voltage and working back towards the input.

Let the output current be I_c. Then the output voltage $V_L = I_c Z_L$; hence

$$V_{c'e} = \frac{V_L}{K} = \frac{I_c Z_L}{K}$$

and
$$I_{c'e} = \frac{V_{c'e}}{z_{c'}} = \left(\frac{I_c Z_L}{K}\right)\frac{1}{z_{c'}}$$

Furthermore,
$$V_{b'e} = V_{c'e} + (I_{c'e} + I_c)z_d$$

Summing the currents at node B',

$$I_b = I_{b'e} + I_{c'e} = \frac{V_{b'e}}{z_e} + I_{c'e}$$

Substituting from above,

$$I_b = I_c\left(\frac{Z_L}{Kz_{c'}} + \frac{z_d}{z_e} + \frac{Z_L}{Kz_e} + \frac{Z_L z_d}{Kz_{c'}z_e}\right)$$

Thus the current gain is

$$K_i = \frac{I_c}{I_b} = \frac{1}{Z_L/Kz_{c'} + z_d/z_e + Z_L/Kz_e + Z_Lz_d/Kz_{c'}z_e} \tag{7-18}$$

7.10 High-frequency properties of junction transistors

It is apparent that the high-frequency equivalent circuit of transistors is somewhat more complicated than that normally used for a vacuum tube triode. This is due to the more complex behavior of the charge carriers and the more complex distribution of voltage in transistors.

From the point of view of simplicity it is often desirable that no feedback generator should appear in a circuit. A feedback generator is defined as a generator whose current or voltage is either equal to or proportional to the current or voltage in another part of the circuit. Thus, for example, whereas the open-circuit output impedance of a circuit such as that in Fig. 7-8 may be written by inspection:

$$z_{22b} = r_{bb'} + \frac{K}{1/z_{c'} + 1/(z_d + z_e)} \tag{7-19}$$

this cannot be done so simply if a feedback generator is present, as the case is, for example, with the circuit of Fig. 7-11.[16] Nevertheless this circuit has various merits as mentioned in Sec. 7.9. We next use it to study the common emitter properties of a transistor.

The open-circuit input impedance z_{11e} (defined as the input impedance for an a-c open circuit at the output) is found from Fig. 7-11 by placing $I_c = 0$. Hence the K amplifier, transformer, and current generator can be ignored as shown in Fig. 7-14a. Now, by inspection

$$z_{11e} = r_{bb'} + \frac{1}{1/z_e + 1/(z_d + z_{c'})} \tag{7-20}$$

The short-circuit input impedance $1/y_{11e}$ is defined as the input impedance for an a-c short circuit at the output. A plot of the magnitude and phase angle of $1/y_{11e}$ as a function of frequency is shown in Fig.

[16] The same difficulty is encountered with the π circuit (Fig. 7-12b) or the T circuit (e.g., Fig. 7-26) when the latter is connected with the emitter common.

7-15 for a particular transistor.[17] The expression for $1/y_{11e}$ may be found from Fig. 7-11 as follows. A short circuit on the transformer

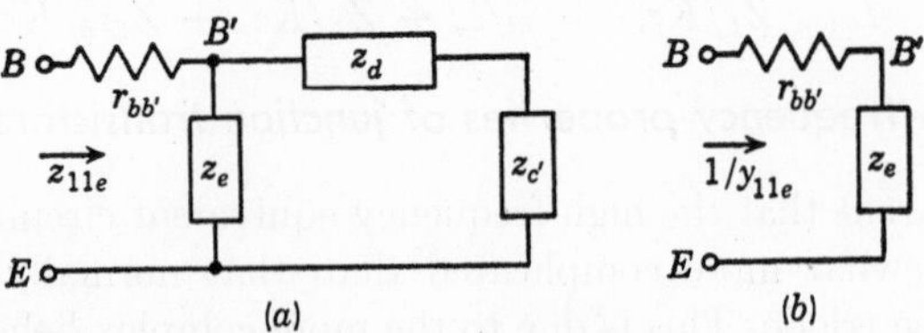

Fig. 7-14. (a) Open-circuit input impedance for common-emitter operation; (b) short-circuit input impedance for common-emitter operation.

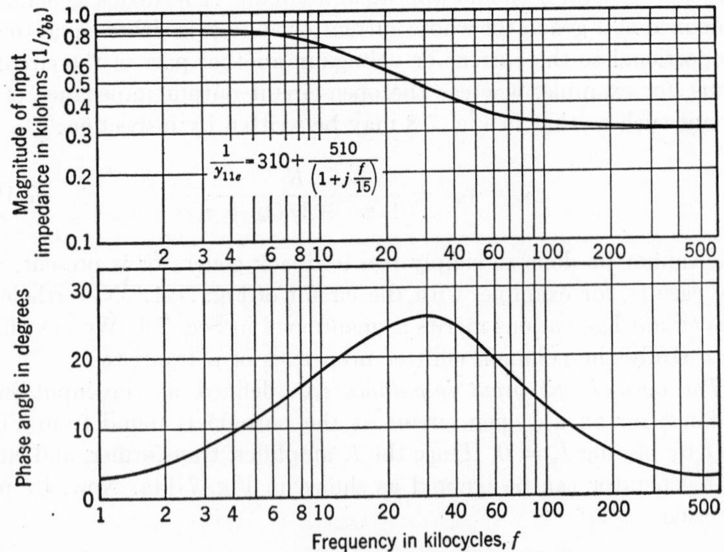

Fig. 7-15. Frequency dependence of short-circuit input impedance $1/y_{11e}$.

implies that the K amplifier is short-circuited and that the node C' is virtually connected to ground, as shown in Fig. 7-16a. It is thus obvious that the total collector current flows through z_d, which by

[17] The values for the elements of this transistor are approximately as follows: $r_{bb'} = 310$ ohms; $1/g_e = 510$ ohms; $C_e = 0.02\ \mu f$; $r_d = 15$ ohms; $1/g_{c'} = 430$ ohms; $C_{c'} = 0.43\ \mu f$; $K = 8500$; $L_d = 1.56\ \mu h$; $C_f = 4.4\ \mu\mu f$.

inspection of Fig. 7-16a, means that no current flows in link x-y. Hence Fig. 7-16a may be split into two sections as seen in Fig. 7-16b. Now by inspection,

$$\frac{1}{y_{11e}} = r_{bb'} + z_e \tag{7-21}$$

This impedance is shown in Fig. 7-14b.

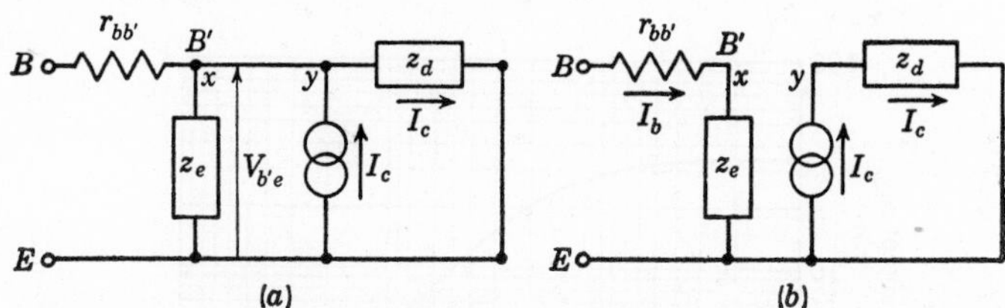

Fig. 7-16. Derivation of short-circuit input impedance and current amplification factor for common-emitter operation: (a) circuit derived from Fig. 7-11; (b) circuit of Fig. 7-15(a) split into two circuits.

The short-circuit current amplification factor α_{cb} is defined as the ratio of collector to base current for a short circuit at the collector. A plot of the magnitude and phase angle of α_{cb} as a function of frequency is shown in Fig. 7-17, for the transistor referred in footnote 17. The expression for α_{cb} follows directly from Fig. 7-16b. Thus, although Fig. 7-16a was split into two parts, actually x and y are at the same potential, $V_{b'e}$, and the current I_c flowing through z_d is therefore $V_{b'e}/z_d$. By inspection,

$$\alpha_{cb} \equiv \frac{I_c}{I_b} = \frac{z_e}{z_d} \tag{7-22}$$

The importance of the quantity α_{cb} in transistors is equivalent to that of the amplification factor μ in tubes. We examine it therefore more closely by substituting for z_e and z_d in Eq. (7-22) their full expressions.

$$\alpha_{cb} = \frac{1}{(g_e + j\omega C_e)(r_d + j\omega L_d)} \tag{7-23a}$$

$$= \frac{1/g_e r_d}{(1 + j\omega C_e/g_e)(1 + j\omega L_d/r_d)} \tag{7-23b}$$

which we define as

$$\alpha_{cb} \equiv \frac{\alpha_{cbo}}{(1 + j\omega/\omega_e)(1 + j\omega/\omega_d)} \tag{7-23c}$$

The low-frequency value of α_{cb} is therefore

$$\alpha_{cbo} = \frac{1}{g_e r_d} \tag{7-24a}$$

where α_{cbo} may be of the order of 50 and is often as high as 100 or more.

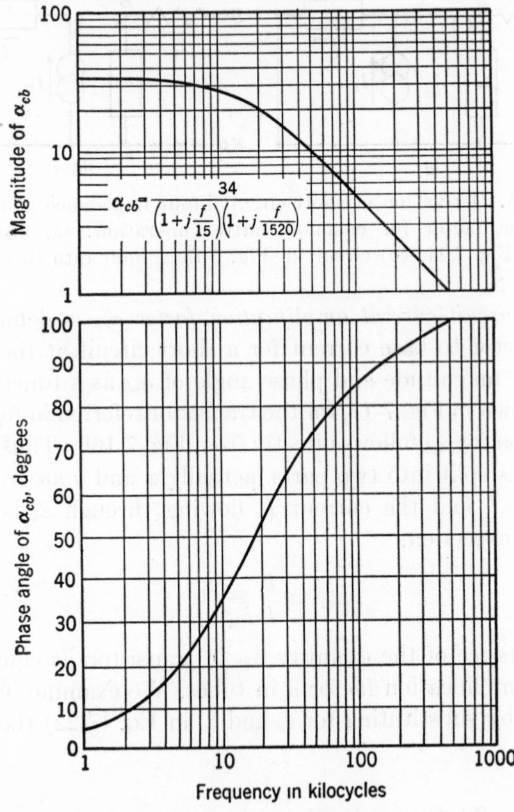

Fig. 7-17. Frequency dependence of short-circuit current amplification factor α_{cb}.

It is found experimentally that the time constant C_e/g_e ($\equiv 1/\omega_e$) is very much greater than L_d/r_d ($\equiv 1/\omega_d$). In fact[18] $\omega_e/\omega_d = 1/n'\alpha_{cbo}$,

[18] This follows from Eqs. (7-13) and (7-24a).

where n' is a number in the order of 3. Hence the frequency $\omega_{cb}/2\pi$ at which $|\alpha_{cb}|$ has decreased from its low-frequency value by 3 db, is virtually determined only by the time constant C_e/g_e; i.e., the angular cutoff frequency ω_{cb} may be written

$$\omega_{cb} \doteq \omega_e \equiv \frac{g_e}{C_e} \tag{7-24b}$$

Thus the expression for α_{cb} is now

$$\alpha_{cb} = \frac{\alpha_{cbo}}{(1 + j\omega/\omega_{cb})(1 + j\omega/n'\alpha_{cbo}\omega_{cb})} \tag{7-25}$$

Equations (7-24a) and (7-24b) give two useful relationships between r_d, g_e, and C_e; α_{cb} is discussed further in Sec. 7.11.

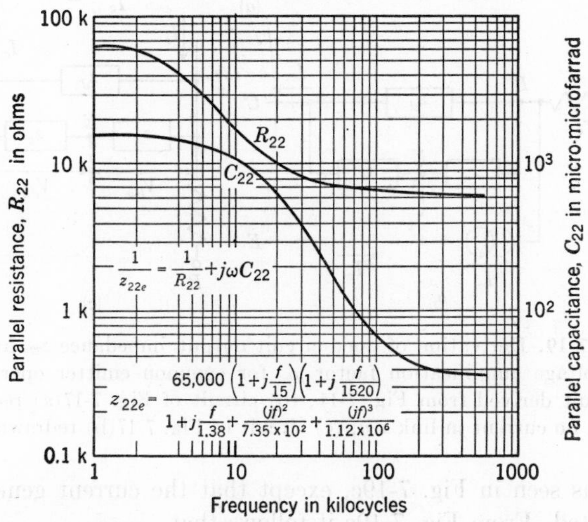

Fig. 7-18. Frequency dependence of equivalent parallel resistance and capacitance of open-circuit output impedance z_{22e}.

The open-circuit output impedance z_{22e} is defined as the output impedance for an a-c open circuit at the input. A plot of the equivalent parallel resistance and capacitance of z_{22e} as a function of frequency is shown in Fig. 7-18 for the transistor referred to earlier. Now z_{22e} is found from Fig. 7-11 by noting that if the output voltage is V_{ce}, then the voltage at the input of the K amplifier is $V_{ce}/K \equiv V_{c'e}$. Also, neglecting the K amplifier and the phase-reversing transformer in Fig. 7-11, we obtain Fig. 7–19a, where the output impedance is obviously

$$\frac{z_{22e}}{K} = \frac{V_{c'e}}{I_c} \tag{7-26}$$

Figure 7-19a is now redrawn as seen in Fig. 7-19b, where it is apparent that no current flows in link x-y. Thus Fig. 7-19b may next be simply

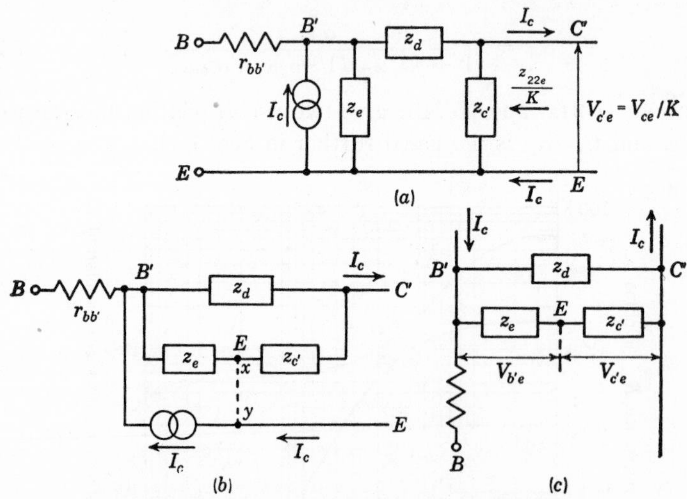

Fig. 7-19. Derivation of open-circuit output impedance z_{22e} and reverse-voltage amplification factor μ_{bc} for common emitter operation: (a) circuit derived from Fig. 7-11; (b) circuit of Fig. 7-17(a) redrawn showing no current in link x-y; (c) circuit of Fig. 7-17(b) redrawn.

redrawn as seen in Fig. 7-19c, except that the current generator is here omitted. From Fig. 7-19c it follows that

$$V_{c'e} = z_{c'} \frac{z_d I_c}{(z_d + z_e + z_{c'})} \tag{7-27}$$

which, from Eqs. (7-26) and (7-27), yields

$$z_{22e} = K \frac{z_{c'} z_d}{(z_d + z_e + z_{c'})} \tag{7-28}$$

The short-circuit output impedance, $1/y_{22e}$ (defined as the output impedance for an a-c short circuit at the input) is found from Fig.

7-11 by connecting B to ground. This simply places $r_{bb'}$ in parallel with g_e, which means that the expression for $1/y_{22e}$ is obviously identical to Eq. (7-28), except that for z_e we write

$$\frac{1}{1/z_e + 1/r_{bb'}}$$

Thus
$$\frac{1}{y_{22e}} = K \frac{z_{c'} z_d}{z_d + 1/(1/z_e + 1/r_{bb'}) + z_{c'}} \tag{7-29}$$

The reverse-voltage amplification factor μ_{bc} is defined as the ratio of voltage at the input to that at the output when a voltage is applied at the output and the input is open-circuited. A plot of the magnitude and phase angle of μ_{bc} as a function of frequency is shown in Fig. 7-20 for the particular transistor referred in footnote 17. The expression for μ_{bc} follows directly from Figs. 7-19a and 7-19c.

$$\mu_{bc} = \frac{V_{be}}{V_{ce}} = \frac{V_{be}}{KV_{c'e}} = \frac{z_e}{Kz_{c'}} \tag{7-30}$$

The above expression assumes that the collector-to-base interelectrode capacitance C_f is negligible. However, when it is not neglected, its effect on the expression for μ_{bc} is to add a term $r_{bb'}/X_f$ to Eq. (7-30), where $X_f = 1/j\omega C_f$, and it is assumed that $r_{bb'} \ll 1/\omega C_f$. The solid line in Fig. 7-20 shows the effect of this capacitance, while the dotted line neglects it.

It should be pointed out, however, that because C_f is much smaller than C_c ($\equiv C_{c'}/K$) it may be considered to be lumped with C_c in the other expressions derived in this section.

Loaded conditions. Consider a load Z_L, together with a signal generator having an internal impedance Z_s and an open-circuit voltage V_s, to be connected to a common-emitter amplifier as seen in Fig. 7-13. Suppose that the input impedance, the voltage gain, and the output impedance of this amplifier are to be determined. One way of finding these is to assume an output voltage, and utilizing Ohm's and Kirchhoff's laws, work systematically back toward the input.

Thus if the output voltage is V_L, then

$$V_{c'e} = I_{c'e} z_{c'} = \frac{V_L}{K} = \frac{I_c Z_L}{K}$$

Furthermore

$$V_{b'e} = I_{b'e}z_e = V_{c'e} + (I_c + I_{c'e})z_d$$

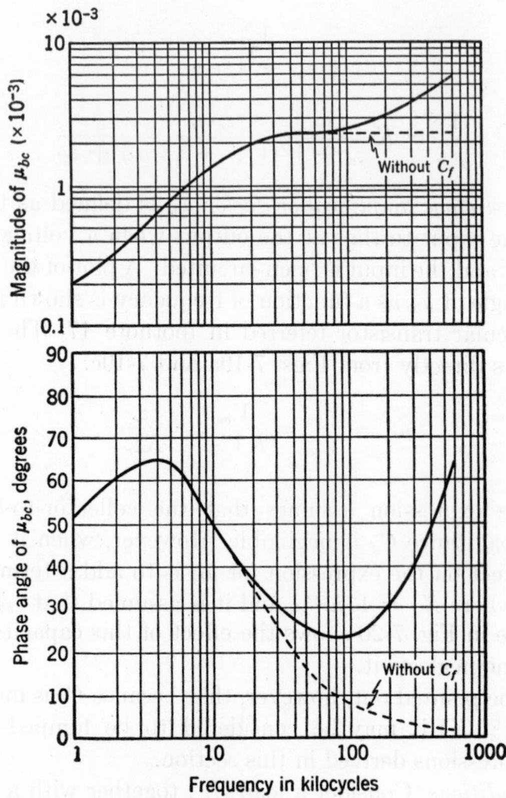

Fig. 7-20. Frequency dependence of reverse-voltage amplification factor μ_{bc}.

which from the above may be written

$$V_{b'e} = \frac{V_L}{K} + \left(\frac{V_L}{Z_L} + \frac{V_L}{Kz_{c'}}\right) z_d$$

Also the base current

$$\begin{aligned} I_b &= I_{b'e} + I_{c'e} \\ &= \frac{1}{z_e}\left[\frac{V_L}{K} + \left(\frac{V_L}{Z_L} + \frac{V_L}{Kz_{c'}}\right) z_d\right] + \frac{V_L}{Kz_{c'}} \end{aligned}$$

Thus the input impedance is

$$z_{in} = r_{bb'} + \frac{V_{b'e}}{I_b} = r_{bb'} + \frac{1}{1/z_e + 1/(z_{c'} + Kz_{c'}z_d/Z_L + z_d)} \qquad (7\text{-}31)$$

The voltage gain is

$$\frac{V_L}{V_s} = \frac{V_L}{V_{b'e} + I_b(r_{bb'} + Z_s)}$$

$$= \frac{1}{[1/K + (1/Z_L + 1/Kz_{c'})z_d] \cdot [1 + (r_{bb'} + Z_s)/z_e] + (r_{bb'} + Z_s)/Kz_{c'}} \qquad (7\text{-}32)$$

Finally, the output impedance z_{out} is found by short-circuiting the signal generator V_s in Fig. 7-13, which places $(r_{bb'} + Z_s)$ in parallel with z_e. Hence the expression for the output impedance is identical to that for z_{22e} given in Eq. (7-28), except that z_e is replaced by an impedance consisting of $(r_{bb'} + Z_s)$ in parallel with z_e; i.e.,

$$Z_{out} = K \frac{z_{c'}z_d}{z_d + 1/[1/z_e + 1/(r_{bb'} + Z_s)] + z_{c'}} \qquad (7\text{-}33)$$

7.11 Discussion of short-circuit current amplification factors

The short-circuit current amplification factor is one of the most important parameters in transistors and is likely to vary greatly from one transistor to another. The common-emitter short-circuit current amplification factor is defined by

$$\alpha_{cb} \equiv \left.\frac{I_c}{I_b}\right|_{V_{ce}=0} \qquad (7\text{-}34)$$

By convention we shall consider all currents flowing into a device as positive. Thus the common-emitter short-circuit current amplification factor α_{cb} is a positive number at low frequency. Similarly we can also define a common-base short-circuit amplification factor α which is a positive number at low frequency. Thus we write

$$\alpha \equiv -\alpha_{ce} \equiv -\left.\frac{I_c}{I_e}\right|_{V_{cb}=0} \qquad (7\text{-}35)$$

It is now easily shown that α_{cb} and α are related as follows.

$$\alpha_{cb} = \frac{\alpha}{1 - \alpha} \qquad (7\text{-}36a)$$

or

$$\alpha = \frac{\alpha_{cb}}{1 + \alpha_{cb}} \tag{7-36b}$$

The *exact* theoretical expression for α_{cb} (i.e., when the transmission line of Fig. 7-6 is used instead of the lumped parameters) may be viewed as containing an infinite number of terms in the denominator.

$$\alpha_{cb} = \frac{\alpha_{cbo}}{(1 + j\omega/\omega_1)(1 + j\omega/\omega_2)(1 + j\omega/\omega_3) \ldots} \tag{7-37a}$$

However, up to the highest frequency where a power gain may be expected, only the first two factors in the denominator are of any significance. Thus, as stated in Eq. (7-25) of Sec. 7.10, we may write

$$\alpha_{cb} = \frac{\alpha_{cbo}}{(1 + j\omega/\omega_{cb})(1 + j\omega/n'\alpha_{cbo}\omega_{cb})} \tag{7-37b}$$

In the medium-frequency range, Eq. (7-37b) simplifies to

$$\alpha_{cb} = \frac{\alpha_{cbo}}{(1 + j\omega/\omega_{cb})} \tag{7-37c}$$

Note that if Eq. (7-37c) is used, α_{cb} cannot exceed a phase shift of 90°. This is seen vectorially from Fig. 7-21a, where I_b is the base

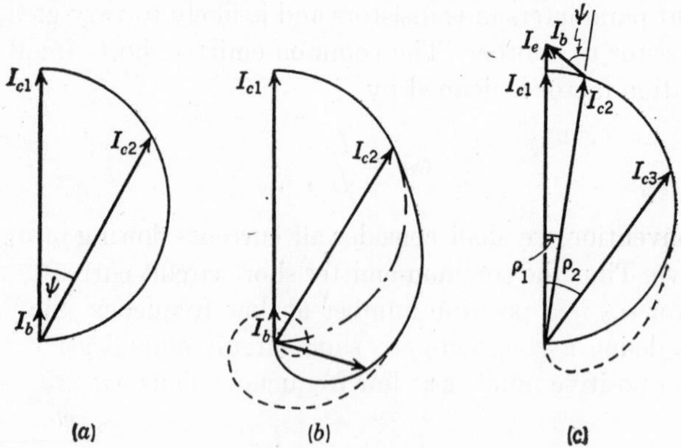

Fig. 7-21. Vector representation of α_{cb} and α_{oe}.

current, which is kept constant, and I_c is the collector current at various frequencies. Thus at very low frequencies I_c and I_b are in phase (or 180° out of phase, depending on the sign convention), as shown by I_{c1}. At higher frequencies the collector current lags by an angle ψ, as shown by I_{c2}. It is seen that I_c cannot shift more than 90° from its low-frequency value, since the locus of I_c is a semicircle.

Figure 7-21b shows the locus of I_c when two denominator terms are used as in Eq. (7-37b). Now ψ may exceed 90° but not 180°. If more terms are included as indicated by Eq. (7-37a), for example, the locus is a spiral as indicated by the dotted curve in Fig. 7-21b.

Note that irrespective of whether we use Eq. (7-37a), (7-37b), or (7-37c), $|\alpha_{cb}|$ has a value which is 3 db lower than its low-frequency value when the real and imaginary parts of the denominator are equal. Hence, at the cutoff frequency $(\omega_{cb}/2\pi)$, $\psi = 45°$.

The expression for the short-circuit current amplification factor α may be found from Eqs. (7-36b) and (7-37b).

$$\alpha = \alpha_{ce} \doteq \frac{\alpha_o}{1 + j\omega/\alpha_{cbo}\omega_{cb} + (j\omega/\alpha_{cbo}\omega_{cb})^2(1/n')} \tag{7-38}$$

for $\alpha_{cbo} \gg 1$, where $\alpha_o = \alpha_{cbo}/(1 + \alpha_{cbo})$

To represent the relation of I_e to I_c vectorially, we may either utilize Fig. 7-21 by noting that I_e is the vector sum of I_b and I_c, or we may keep I_e constant and trace the locus of I_c by utilizing Eq. (7-38) as shown in Fig. 7-21c. Thus in the medium-frequency range where the third term in the denominator of Eq. (7-38) may be neglected, the locus of I_c is a semicircle. If the third term is not neglected, α is able to attain a phase angle greater than 90°, as shown by the dotted curve.

It is instructive to note in Fig. 7-21c that at a frequency where α_{ce} has a small phase angle ρ_1, the phase angle ψ for α_{cb} is comparatively very large. Also, at this frequency α_{ce} has hardly changed in magnitude from its low-frequency value, while α_{cb} has changed considerably. It is also obvious from the vector diagram that if $\rho_2 = 45°$, then $|\alpha_{ce}|$ has decreased by 3 db; α_{cb} falls approximately to unity, and ψ will be approximately 90°.

7.12 Determination of circuit elements from h-parameters

The equivalent circuit shown in Fig. 7-8 or Fig. 7-11 contains in the medium-frequency range seven independent parameters: $r_{bb'}$, g_e, C_e, r_d, $g_{c'}$, $C_{c'}$, and K. Thus seven independent measurements will specify it completely. For the high-frequency range, two more elements should be considered, L_d and C_f. It is important to realize, however, that the number of elements is not a result of the particular equivalent circuit chosen, but that the elements represent independent physical phenomena which influence the characteristics of the transistor in different ways. Hence a circuit with fewer elements implies less accuracy.

In deciding on the required measurements from which the elements of a particular equivalent circuit could be determined, it is well to note that a transistor has a low impedance on the input side and a relatively high impedance on the output side, both for common-base and common-emitter operation. This means that on the input side it is easier to measure the open-circuit voltage than the short-circuit current, while on the output side the reverse is true. It is for this reason that the so-called *h-parameter* measurements are often made.

The h parameters[19] are: h_{11} = short-circuit input impedance $1/y_{11}$; h_{21} = short-circuit forward current amplification factor α_{21}; h_{12} = open-circuit reverse voltage amplification factor μ_{12}; h_{22} = open-circuit output admittance $1/z_{22}$. These measurements need not necessarily be made all with one type of connection, i.e., $1/y_{11}$ and α_{21} may be measured with the emitter common, while $1/z_{22}$ and μ_{12} may be measured with the base common.

Suppose that all h-parameter measurements are made with the emitter common. From Sec. 7.10 the h parameters are

$$\frac{1}{y_{11e}} = r_{bb'} + z_e \tag{7-39a}$$

$$\alpha_{cb} = \frac{z_e}{z_d} \tag{7-39b}$$

$$\mu_{bc} = \frac{z_e}{Kz_{c'}} \tag{7-39c}$$

$$\frac{1}{z_{22e}} = \frac{1}{K}\left(\frac{1}{z_{c'}} + \frac{1}{z_d} + \frac{z_e}{z_{c'}z_d}\right) \tag{7-39d}$$

where $z_e = 1/(g_e + j\omega C_e)$; $z_d = r_d + j\omega L_d \doteq r_d$ at medium frequencies; $z_{c'} = 1/(g_{c'} + j\omega C_{c'})$; and K is a number. The actual measurements may be either of a phase angle, or of the absolute magnitude of an h parameter, at a particular frequency, or of the frequency at which the magnitude of a particular h parameter increases or decreases by,

[19] See Chapter 3, Sec. 3.8.

say, 3 db from its low-frequency value. For example, from Eq. (7-39c),

$$\mu_{bc} = \frac{g_{c'} + j\omega C_{c'}}{K(g_e + j\omega C_e)} = \frac{g_{c'}(1 + j\omega/\omega_c)}{Kg_e(1 + j\omega/\omega_{cb})} \tag{7-40}$$

where $\omega_c \equiv g_{c'}/C_{c'}$ and $\omega_{cb} = g_e/C_e$. Very often $\omega_c \ll \omega_{cb}$; hence $|\mu_{bc}|$ is approximately 3 db higher than its low-frequency value at the angular frequency ω_c, which permits its determination directly from an oscillogram of μ_{bc}.

The h parameters are experimentally not only easiest to determine, but also lead to simple formulas when the elements of the equivalent circuit of Fig. 7-8 or 7-10 are expressed in terms of the actual experimental readings. Thus let the actual common emitter measurements be as follows:

r_{10} = low-frequency value of $|1/y_{11e}|$

r_{1h} = high-frequency value of $|1/y_{11e}|$

α_{cbo} = low-frequency value of $|\alpha_{cb}|$

ω_{cb} = angular frequency at which $|\alpha_{cb}|$ is 3 db lower than α_{cbo}

r_{20} = low-frequency value of $|z_{22e}|$

μ_o = low frequency value of $|\mu_{bc}|$

ω_c = angular frequency at which $|\mu_{bc}|$ is 3 db higher than μ_o.

It is assumed that $\omega_c \ll \omega_{cb}$; see Eq. (7-40). The seven elements which are most important in the medium-frequency range are now found from Eqs. (7-39a) to (7-39d) in terms of the above seven measurements as follows:

$$r_{bb'} \doteq r_{1h} \tag{7-41a}$$

$$\frac{1}{g_e} = r_{10} - r_{bb'} \tag{7-41b}$$

$$r_d = \frac{1}{g_e\alpha_{cbo}} \tag{7-41c}$$

$$C_e = \frac{g_e}{\omega_{cb}} \tag{7-41d}$$

$$K = \frac{1}{\mu_o(r_d/\mu_o r_{20} - 1)} \tag{7-41e}$$

$$g_{c'} = K\mu_o g_e \tag{7-41f}$$

$$C_{c'} = \frac{g_{c'}}{\omega_c} \tag{7-41g}$$

Note that r_{1h} is the only measurement which is made here at an angular frequency which exceeds ω_{cb}. As an alternative, therefore, the magnitude of y_{11e} may be determined at the angular frequency ω_{cb}. Let this measurement be designated $|y_{13}|$. It can now be shown by using Eq. (7-39a) that

$$\frac{1}{g_e} = r_{10}\left(1 - \sqrt{2\frac{|y_{13}|}{r_{10}} - 1}\right) \tag{7-42a}$$

and therefore

$$r_{bb'} = r_{10} - \frac{1}{g_e} \tag{7-42b}$$

The other parameters are found as above. The value of $r_{bb'}$ in Eq. (7-42b) is more exact than that from Eq. (7-41a), but as can be seen, it involves a somewhat more complicated calculation.

7.13 π circuits

In Sec. 7.7 it is shown that the equivalent circuit of Fig. 7-8 is distinctly correlated with the physical mechanism on which transistor action is based. Hence this circuit may be regarded as basic. Before the development of this circuit several circuits of an arbitrary construction were proposed, such as a π or a T circuit. We shall now transform the basic equivalent circuit of Fig. 7-8 into two *modified* π circuits, one for common-base and one for common-emitter operation.[20]

In general, any four-terminal network may be transformed into a π circuit such as shown in Fig. 7-22. However, in order to limit the complexity of the branches when transforming Fig. 7-8, we first neglect $r_{bb'}$ and evaluate the admittances $(y_{11} + y_{12})$, $(-y_{12})$, $(y_{22} + y_{12})$, and $(y_{21} - y_{12})$ as required by Fig. 7-22. Next $r_{bb'}$ is added to obtain the modified π circuit shown in Fig. 7-23.

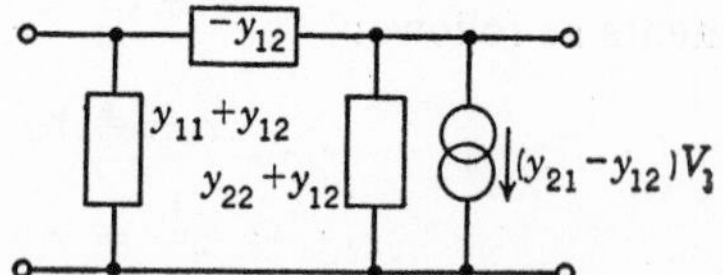

Fig. 7-22. Generalized π circuit.

[20] H. Johnson, "Diffusion Reactances in Junction Transistors," Paper read at the Transistor Research Conference, Pennsylvania State College in July 1953.

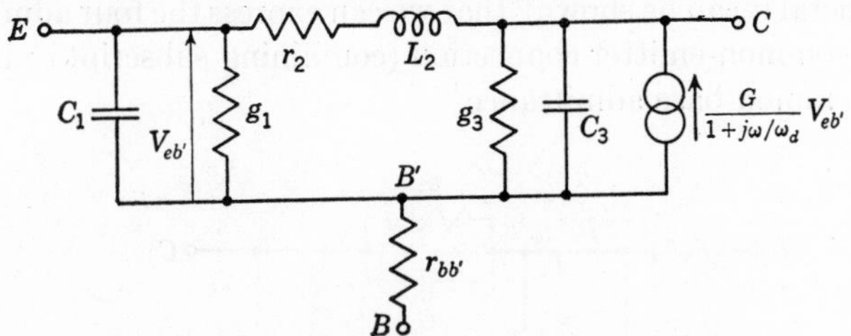

Fig. 7-23. Common-base modified π circuit.

For the circuit of Fig. 7-8, neglecting $r_{bb'}$, the four-pole admittances are

$$y_{11} = g_e + j\omega C_e + \frac{1}{r_d + j\omega L_d} \tag{7-43a}$$

$$-y_{21} = \frac{1}{r_d + j\omega L_d} \tag{7-43b}$$

$$-y_{12} = \frac{y_{21}}{K} \tag{7-43c}$$

$$y_{22} = \frac{1}{K}\left(g_{c'} + j\omega C_{c'} + \frac{1}{r_d + j\omega L_d}\right) \tag{7-43d}$$

The admittances required for Fig. 7-22, and hence the elements for Fig. 7-23, are now as follows.[21]

$$(y_{11} + y_{12}) \doteq y_{11} \equiv g_1 + j\omega C_1 \tag{7-44a}$$

$$-y_{12} = \frac{1}{K(r_d + j\omega L_d)} \equiv \frac{1}{r_2 + j\omega L_2} \tag{7-44b}$$

$$(y_{22} + y_{12}) = \frac{1}{K}(g_{c'} + j\omega C_{c'}) \equiv g_3 + j\omega C_3 \tag{7-44c}$$

$$(y_{21} - y_{12}) \doteq y_{21} = \frac{-1/r_d}{1 + j\omega L_d/r_d} \equiv \frac{-G}{1 + j\omega/\omega_d} \tag{7-44d}$$

For common-emitter operation it is advantageous to use a different circuit from that of Fig. 7-23. This circuit is shown in Fig. 7-24 and is derived as follows:

[21] Note that if the full transmission line equivalent circuit of Fig. 7-6 is used to determine y_{11}, it can be shown that for Eq. (7-44a) we may write

$$y_{11} + y_{12} \doteq y_{11} \doteq \frac{1}{r_d} + j\omega \tfrac{2}{3} C_e = g_1 + j\omega C_1$$

In general it can be shown[22] that we can express the four admittances for the common-emitter connection (containing subscript e) in terms of the common-base admittance.

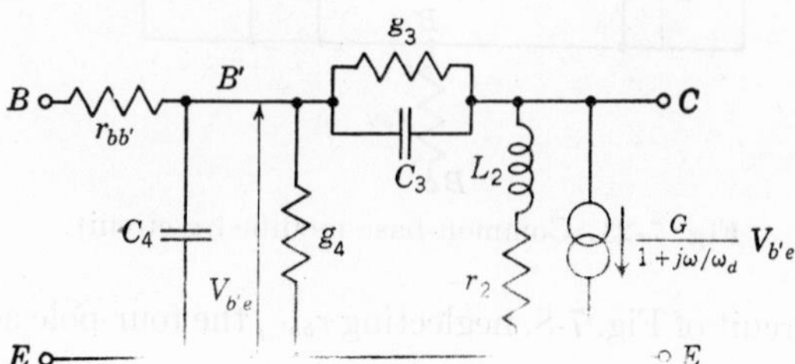

Fig. 7-24. Common-emitter modified π circuit.

$$y_{11e} = y_{11} + y_{12} + y_{21} + y_{22} \tag{7-45a}$$

$$y_{21e} = -(y_{22} + y_{21}) \tag{7-45b}$$

$$y_{12e} = -(y_{22} + y_{12}) \tag{7-45c}$$

$$y_{22e} = y_{22} \tag{7-45d}$$

Thus from Eqs. (7-44a) to (7-44c) the admittances required for a π circuit (Fig. 7-22) are

$$y_{11e} + y_{12e} = g_e + j\omega C_e \equiv g_4 + j\omega C_4 \tag{7-46a}$$

$$-y_{12e} = \frac{1}{K}(g_{c'} + j\omega C_{c'}) \equiv g_3 + j\omega C_3 \tag{7-46b}$$

$$(y_{22e} + y_{12e}) = \frac{1}{K(r_d + j\omega L_d)} \equiv \frac{1}{r_2 + j\omega L_2} \tag{7-46c}$$

$$(y_{21e} - y_{12e}) \doteq \frac{1/r_d}{1 + j\omega L_d/r_d} \equiv \frac{G}{1 + j\omega/\omega_d} \tag{7-46d}$$

From these equations, the common-emitter modified π circuit shown in Fig. 7-24 is constructed. This circuit becomes identical to Fig. 7-12b if the current generator is transformed to a voltage generator.

With reference to the modified π circuits derived in Figs. 7-23 and 7-24, the following should be noted.

1. Both circuits employ eight independent elements (as does the original circuit from which they were derived). However, only six of

[22] L. J. Giacoletto, "Terminology and Equations for Linear Active Four-Terminal Networks Including Transistors," *RCA Rev.*, Vol. 14, Mar. 1953.

the elements are the same in both circuits; the two elements C_1 and g_1 of Fig. 7-23 are not present in Fig. 7-24; i.e., two new elements C_4 and g_4 have to be calculated in order to convert the common-base circuit to the common-emitter circuit.

2. The current generator in both circuits is of the feedback type and its current is proportional to the voltage between an internal node B' and a terminal E. As stated earlier this constitutes a disadvantage in practical problems, since such a voltage has no immediate significance in contrast to the voltages at the terminals.

7.14 T circuits

In a manner similar to the derivation of the π circuit, a T circuit can be obtained. Indeed any circuit may be developed into a T circuit such as shown in Fig. 7-25. Thus, by determining the open-circuit

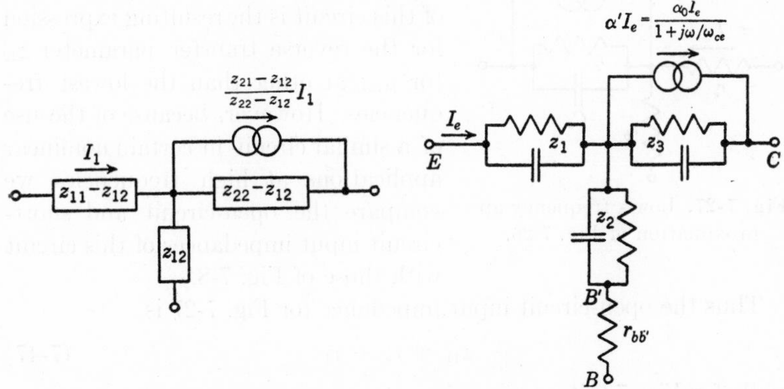

Fig. 7-25. Generalized T circuit.

Fig. 7-26. T circuit derived by an approximate conversion of Fig. 7-9.

impedances z_{11}, z_{12}, z_{21}, and z_{22} from Fig. 7-8 and utilizing Fig. 7-25, the equivalent circuit shown in Fig. 7-26 is obtained.

The following is noted:

1. The circuit employs eight independent elements. It is found that considerable approximations must be made when determining these elements and hence it is less accurate at high frequencies (see Problem 8.3b). As an alternative, additional elements could be used in order to obtain the same degree of accuracy as Fig. 7-8. However, this would further complicate the circuit.

2. The current generator is of the feedback type, and its current is proportional to the current in the emitter lead; the constant of proportionality is approximately equal to the common-base short-circuit current amplication factor α, which is frequency dependent.

3. When using the transistor in the common-emitter connection, the current generator is no longer a direct function of the current in the input lead, which now is the base lead. This complicates its use in practical problems. As an alternative, the T circuit may be converted into a common-emitter T circuit utilizing an $\alpha_{cb}I_b$ generator. However, in this case more passive elements are required if one is to avoid frequency-dependent resistances and capacitances.

A rough approximation to the circuit of Fig. 7-26 is shown in Fig. 7-27. This is the conventional T circuit used in early publications.[23] It is easily shown that the main inaccuracy of this circuit is the resulting expression for the reverse transfer parameter z_{12} (or μ_{12}) at other than the lowest frequencies. However, because of the use of a similar circuit in certain nonlinear applications at high frequencies we compare the open-circuit and short-circuit input impedances of this circuit with those of Fig. 7-8.

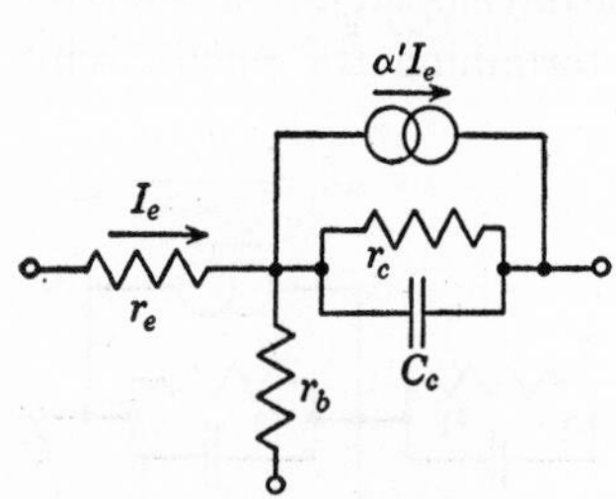

Fig. 7-27. Low - frequency approximation of Fig. 7-26.

Thus the open-circuit input impedance for Fig. 7-27 is

$$z_{11}' = r_e + r_b \tag{7-47}$$

while for Fig. 7-8 it is

$$z_{11} = \frac{1}{1/z_e + 1/(z_d + z_{c'})} + r_{bb'} \tag{7-48}$$

It is seen that Eq. (7-47) entirely neglects all reactive effects, although this defect could be remedied somewhat by placing a capacitance C_e' in parallel with r_e in Fig. 7-27. Also, the common-base short-circuit input impedance for Fig. 7-27 is

$$\frac{1}{y_{11}'} = r_e + \frac{r_b}{1 + \alpha_{cb}} \tag{7-49}$$

[23] R. L. Wallace and W. J. Pietenpol, "Some Circuit Properties and Applications of *n-p-n* Transistors," *Proc. IRE*, Vol. 39, p. 765, July 1951.

while for Fig. 7-8 it is

$$\frac{1}{y_{11}} = \alpha z_d + \frac{r_{bb'}}{1 + \alpha_{cb}} \tag{7-50}$$

where $\alpha_{cb} = z_e/z_d$. In both Eqs. (7-49) and (7-50) use is made of the relation $\alpha = \alpha_{cb}/(1 + \alpha_{cb})$ as given in Eq. (7-36). Thus in the frequency range where αz_d is substantially resistive (or alternatively, if some capacitance C_e' is placed in parallel with r_e in Fig. 7-27), the two equations (7-49) and (7-50) are somewhat similar provided that $r_{bb'}$ is identified with r_b, and r_d with r_e (and also C_e with C_e').

As stated earlier, although the general use of the above circuit is limited (unless it is used at very low frequencies) it does commend itself for many nonlinear applications which are shown in later chapters. There the "emitter resistance" (and if necessary the "collector resistance") is usually replaced by a nonlinear element, thereby resulting in a nonlinear circuit which is not too difficult to analyze. Corrections are then applied to the final solution to account for some of the reactive effects which are neglected in Fig. 7-27.

APPENDIX 1

The equivalent circuit given in Fig. 7-5b may be rigorously derived as follows:

The node equations of a four-terminal network are written in matrix form.

$$\begin{Vmatrix} I_e \\ I_c \end{Vmatrix} = \begin{Vmatrix} y_{11} & y_{12} \\ y_{21} & y_{22} \end{Vmatrix} \begin{Vmatrix} V_e \\ V_c \end{Vmatrix} \tag{7-51}$$

Consider a network having the following admittances. These apply for an intrinsic transistor having plane-parallel sides, and uniform volume recombination. See Eqs. (7-4a) to (7-4d).

$$y_{11} = G\theta \coth \theta + Y_n \tag{7-52}$$

$$y_{21} = -G\theta \operatorname{cosech} \theta \tag{7-53}$$

$$y_{12} = -\frac{G\theta \operatorname{cosech} \theta}{K} \tag{7-54}$$

$$y_{22} = \frac{G\theta \coth \theta}{K} \tag{7-55}$$

Neglecting the term Y_n for the present, it is seen that $y_{11}/K = y_{22}$ and $y_{21}/K = y_{12}$. Thus Eq. (7-51) is rewritten

$$\begin{Vmatrix} I_e \\ I_c \end{Vmatrix} = \begin{Vmatrix} y_{11} & \dfrac{y_{21}}{K} \\ y_{21} & \dfrac{y_{11}}{K} \end{Vmatrix} \begin{Vmatrix} V_e \\ V_c \end{Vmatrix} = \begin{Vmatrix} y_{11} & y_{21} \\ y_{21} & y_{11} \end{Vmatrix} \begin{Vmatrix} V_e \\ \dfrac{V_c}{K} \end{Vmatrix} \tag{7-56}$$

The y matrix in Eq. (7-56) is seen to be symmetrical about both diagonals. This indicates a passive symmetrical network. On closer examination it is also seen that this network is a transmission line of length W with characteristic impedance

$$Z_o = \frac{1}{G\theta} \tag{7-57}$$

and propagation constant

$$\gamma = \frac{\theta}{W} \tag{7-58}$$

It is also seen that the V matrix contains the voltages V_e and V_c/K, while the I matrix is unchanged. This means that the transmission line is terminated by a device which multiplies the voltage in one direction by a factor K, but leaves the current unchanged. We define this device as a K amplifier as described in Sec. 7.5b.

The effects of the admittance Y_n is to add an admittance in parallel with the input, as indicated in Fig. 7-5b.

APPENDIX 2

We prove below that the circuit of Fig. 7-11 and the circuit of Fig. 7-8 both represent the same transistor.

Consider a four-terminal network such as shown in Fig. 7-28a (lead 3 is common). The node equations are in matrix form.

$$\begin{Vmatrix} I_1 \\ I_2 \end{Vmatrix} = \begin{Vmatrix} y_{11} & y_{12} \\ y_{21} & y_{22} \end{Vmatrix} \begin{Vmatrix} V_{13} \\ V_{23} \end{Vmatrix} \tag{7-59}$$

Now we use this network in two different ways: In Fig. 7-28b we cross leads 1 and 3, place it in a box (shown dotted) and label the leads brought out as X, Y, and Z. In Fig. 7-28c we connect a one-to-one phase reversing transformer to leads 2 and 3 and place a current generator I_y across the input (I_y is also the current flowing in lead Y). Again we place this network in a box (shown dotted) and label the leads X, Y, and Z. We now show that the characteristics

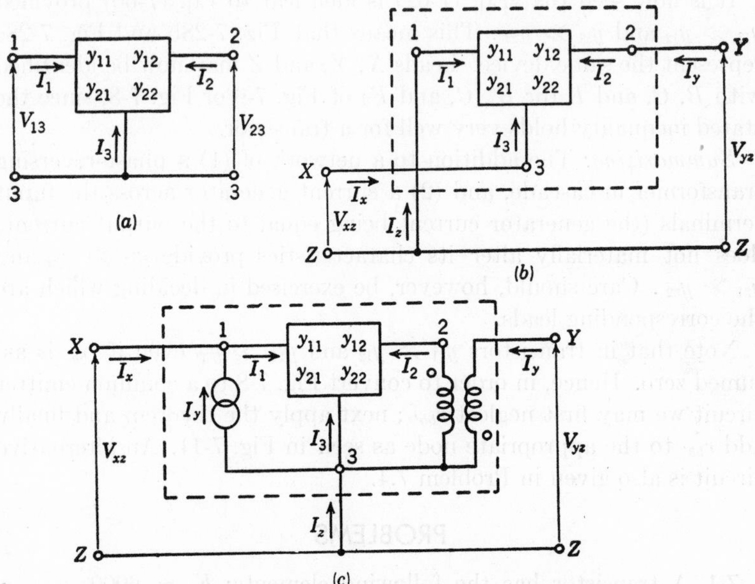

Fig. 7-28. Same device represented by circuits which are equivalent provided $y_{11} \gg y_{12}$ and $y_{21} \gg y_{22}$.

of Fig. 7-28b and 7-28c, as viewed from terminals X, Y, and Z, are virtually identical provided $y_{11} \gg y_{12}$ and $y_{21} \gg y_{22}$.

Consider Fig. 7-28b. Here $I_1 \equiv I_z$; $I_2 \equiv I_y$; $I_3 \equiv I_x$; $V_{13} \equiv V_{zx} = -V_{xz}$ and $V_{23} \equiv V_{yx} = (V_{yz} - V_{xz})$. Substituting in Eq. (7-59),

$$\begin{Vmatrix} I_z \\ I_y \end{Vmatrix} = \begin{Vmatrix} y_{11} & y_{12} \\ y_{21} & y_{22} \end{Vmatrix} \begin{Vmatrix} -V_{xz} \\ V_{yz} - V_{xz} \end{Vmatrix} \tag{7-60}$$

Now consider Fig. 7-28c. Here $I_1 \equiv I_x + I_y = -I_z$; $I_2 = -I_y$; $I_3 \equiv I_z$; $V_{13} \equiv V_{xz}$ and $V_{23} \equiv -V_{yz}$. Substituting in Eq. (7-59),

$$\begin{Vmatrix} -I_z \\ -I_y \end{Vmatrix} = \begin{Vmatrix} y_{11} & y_{12} \\ y_{21} & y_{22} \end{Vmatrix} \begin{Vmatrix} V_{xz} \\ -V_{yz} \end{Vmatrix} \tag{7-61}$$

Regrouping this equation,

$$\begin{Vmatrix} I_z \\ I_y \end{Vmatrix} = \begin{Vmatrix} y_{11} + y_{12} & y_{12} \\ y_{21} + y_{22} & y_{22} \end{Vmatrix} \begin{Vmatrix} -V_{xz} \\ V_{yz} - V_{xz} \end{Vmatrix} \tag{7-62}$$

It is now seen that Eq. (7-62) is identical to Eq. (7-60) provided $y_{11} \gg y_{12}$ and $y_{21} \gg y_{22}$. This means that Fig. 7-28b and Fig. 7-28c represent the same device. Leads X, Y, and Z may now be identified with B, C, and E (or B', C, and E) of Fig. 7-6 or Fig. 7-8, since the stated inequality holds very well for a transistor.

Summarizing: The addition to a network of (1) a phase-reversing transformer in cascade, and (2) a current generator across the input terminals (the generator current being equal to the output current) does not materially alter its characteristics provide $y_{11} \gg y_{12}$ and $y_{21} \gg y_{22}$. Care should, however, be exercised in deciding which are the corresponding leads.

Note that in transistors $y_{11} \gg y_{12}$ and $y_{21} \gg y_{22}$ even if $r_{bb'}$ is assumed zero. Hence, in order to convert Fig. 7-8 to a common-emitter circuit we may first neglect $r_{bb'}$; next apply the theorem and finally add $r_{bb'}$ to the appropriate node as seen in Fig. 7-11. An alternative circuit is also given in Problem 7.4.

PROBLEMS

7-1. A transistor has the following elements: $K = 6000$; $r_{bb'} = 300$ ohms; $1/g_e = 500$ ohms; $C_e = 0.02\ \mu$f; $r_d = 10$ ohms; $1/g_{c'} = 500$ ohms; $C_{c'} = 0.15\ \mu$f. Calculate the insertion power gain at 5 kc for a common-emitter amplifier if the load is 20,000 ohms and the generator impedance is 300 ohms.

7-2. Starting with the load current, sketch a vector diagram for the complete circuit of Problem 7.1, finishing with the input voltage and current.

7-3. (a) Derive expressions for the z parameters for the common-base circuit (Fig. 7-8) in terms of K, z_e, z_d, $z_{c'}$, and $r_{bb'}$ and show that $\alpha \doteq z_e/(z_d + z_e)$. (b) Write z_e and z_d in terms of α_{cbo}, r_d, ω_{cb}, and L_d and compare α as derived in (a) with Eq. (7-38).

7-4. In transforming the circuit of Fig. 7-8 to a common-emitter circuit, the following procedure may be adopted: (1) Neglecting $r_{bb'}$ and $C_{c'}$, it is obvious that the inequalities $y_{11} \gg y_{12}$ and $y_{21} \gg y_{22}$

still hold. Hence we add the current generator and the phase reversing transformer and rename nodes B', E, and C, as shown in Appendix 2. (2) We next connect $r_{bb'}$ to B', and $C_{c'}$ between C and B' (as the case is in Fig. 7-8) to obtain Fig. 7-29. Derive now the h parameters

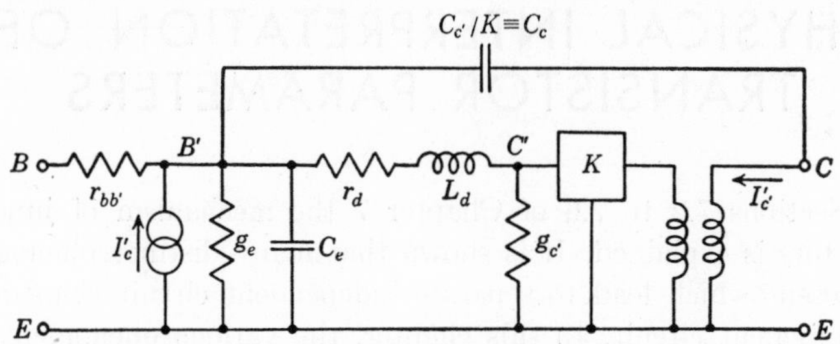

Fig. 7-29. Common-emitter equivalent circuit showing alternate location of $C_{c'}$.

of Fig. 7-29 and compare them with those of Fig. 7-11. Estimate any difference on a percentage basis for a transistor such as that described in Problem 7-1.

7-5. By a method similar to that used to derive Fig. 7-12b, derive a common-collector equivalent circuit from Fig. 7-8. Note the resemblance of this circuit to Fig. 7-12b and compare the polarities of the generators. (Hint: The elements of this circuit are $r_{bb'}$, g_e, C_e, $g_{c'}/K$, $C_{c'}/K$, r_d, L_d and a voltage generator $(K - 1)/KV_{b'c} \doteq V_{b'c}$.)

7-6. Using Fig. 7-12b, derive the common-emitter h parameters given in Eq. (7-39), while noting that $K \gg 1$.

Chapter 8

PHYSICAL INTERPRETATION OF TRANSISTOR PARAMETERS

In Sections 7.2 to 7.6 of Chapter 7 the mechanism of junction transistors is explained. It is shown that many distinct phenomena are present which lead to separate independent circuit elements in the equivalent circuit. In this chapter, the various phenomena are treated quantitatively, the d-c and a-c characteristics are derived, and the elements of the equivalent circuit are evaluated from physical considerations.

8.1 A problem in diffusion

In order to illustrate the concept of diffusion, consider the following example.[1] A slab of porous material of thickness W is permeated by a liquid. The one broad surface is in contact with the liquid, while the other is being dried by evaporation as shown in Fig. 8-1. The areas of the edges of the slab are comparatively small, so that the amount of evaporation which occurs from them is small. The concentration of the liquid at both broad surfaces will be constant after a given lapse of time when the "steady state" is reached.

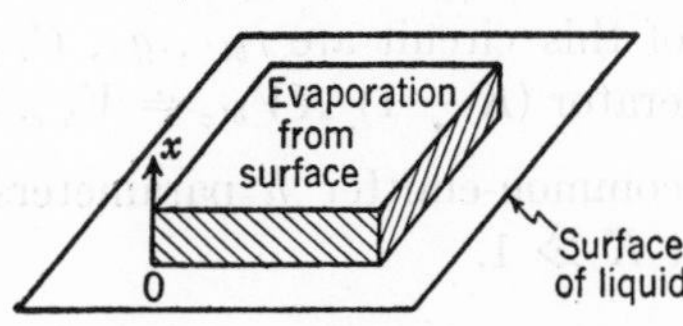

Fig. 8-1. Drying of porous slate.

The liquid molecules move in a random fashion in the slab because of thermal agitation. There is, however, a net movement from the region of high molecular density of the liquid to one of lower molecular density. This process is termed *diffusion*. The law states that *the rate of diffusion of a substance is proportional to the cross-sectional area through which it moves, and to the concentration gradient of the*

[1] For related problems see H. W. Reddick and F. H. Miller, *Advanced Mathematics for Engineers,* John Wiley & Sons, Inc., 1938.

substance. The constant of proportionality which characterizes diffusion, D, has the dimension (length)^2/time.

Let the concentration of the liquid near the bottom surface be C_o (gram per cubic centimeter). Near the top surface the concentration will approach zero. Noting the x coordinate in Fig. 8-1, let the concentration at a point x along the coordinate be $c(x, t)$. Also let Q (gram) be the amount of liquid in the slab between $x = 0$ and $x = x$ at time t. Thus if the slab has unit area, the rate of evaporation of the liquid is by the law of diffusion

$$\frac{\partial Q}{\partial t} = D\frac{\partial c}{\partial x} \tag{8-1}$$

where gravity and end effects are neglected. By definition,

$$Q = \int_0^x c\,dx$$

or

$$\frac{\partial Q}{\partial x} = c \tag{8-2}$$

Q can be eliminated from Eqs. (8-1) and (8-2) by differentiating Eq. (8-1) with respect to x and Eq. (8-2) with respect to t and subtracting. Thus

$$\frac{\partial c}{\partial t} = D\frac{\partial^2 c}{\partial x^2} \tag{8-3a}$$

Analogous to Eq. (8-3a), the diffusion equation for the three-dimensional case is

$$\frac{\partial c}{\partial t} = D\left(\frac{\partial^2 c}{\partial x^2} + \frac{\partial^2 c}{\partial y^2} + \frac{\partial^2 c}{\partial z^2}\right) \tag{8-3b}$$

The general solution to Eq. (8-3b) can be obtained either in the form of exponential or hyperbolic functions. The constants for the general solution are found from the stated boundary conditions.

8.2 The diffusion equation

Referring to Fig. 7-1, which represents a plane parallel p-n-p junction transistor with a base width W, consider the passage of holes which enter at $x = 0$ and diffuse mainly in the positive x direction. End effects are for the present neglected. Let the concentration of holes at x, at time t, be p. Then analogous to Eq. (8-3a) we write

$$\frac{\partial p}{\partial t} = D_p \frac{\partial^2 p}{\partial x^2} \tag{8-4}$$

where D_p is the diffusion constant for holes.

An assumption made in Eq. (8-4) is that no electric field exists in the base due either to the bias batteries or to the presence of the minority carriers themselves. In other words, it is assumed that the charge density of the injected minority carriers is small compared with the density of the ionized impurity atoms which are present in the base.

Equation (8-4) ignores the fact that the holes have a finite lifetime, and that is next considered. The lifetime obviously influences the concentration of minority carriers at any point. Let p_n be the thermal equilibrium value of the concentration of holes in the base. Let the concentration of holes in a given region be increased at time $t = 0$ by p_1'. Experimentally it is found that the number of holes will decay exponentially with time due to hole-electron recombination. The instantaneous number of holes in the region is then

$$p = p_n + p_1' \exp\left(-\frac{t}{\tau_p}\right) \tag{8-5}$$

where τ_p is defined as the lifetime and is the time at which the number of injected holes have declined to $1/\epsilon$ of their original number.

Differentiating Eq. (8-5),

$$\frac{\partial p}{\partial t} = -\frac{1}{\tau_p} p_1' \exp\left(-\frac{t}{\tau_p}\right) \tag{8-6}$$

Combining Eqs. (8-5) and (8-6),

$$\frac{\partial p}{\partial t} = -\frac{1}{\tau_p}(p - p_n) \tag{8-7}$$

We may now combine the effect of diffusion given by Eq. (8-4) with that of lifetime given by Eq. (8-7) to obtain[2]

$$\frac{\partial p}{\partial t} = D_p \frac{\partial^2 p}{\partial x^2} + \frac{p_n - p}{\tau_p} \tag{8-8}$$

[2] W. Shockley, "Theory of p-n Junction in Semiconductors and p-n Junction Transistors," *Bell System Tech. J.*, Vol. 28, p. 459, 1949.

Equation (8-8) is a second-order linear differential equation. To obtain the d-c and a-c solutions we assume a solution:

$$p = P_o(x) + p_1(x)e^{j\omega t} \tag{8-9}$$

Substitute Eq. (8-9) into Eq. (8-8) and rearrange to obtain the time-independent d-c equation

$$\frac{\partial^2 P_o}{\partial x^2} = \frac{P_o - p_n}{L_p^2} \tag{8-10}$$

and the a-c equation,

$$\frac{\partial^2 p_1}{\partial x^2} = \frac{p_1}{L_p^2}(1 + j\omega\tau_p) \tag{8-11}$$

where

$$L_p = (D_p\tau_p)^{1/2} \tag{8-12}$$

Here L_p is termed the *diffusion length for holes* in the base region. The physical meaning of L_p will be evident from the solution of the differential equations (Sec. 8.4).

8.3 Direct current boundary conditions

By the use of Boltzmann statistics it can be shown that the number of charge carriers which surmount a potential barrier, such as that at the emitter or collector as shown in Fig. 7-1b, is related to the height of the barrier, say ϕ', by the expression

$$p_n = p_p \exp\left(-\frac{q\phi'}{kT}\right) \tag{8-13}$$

where q = electronic charge; k = Boltzmann's constant; T = temperature in degrees Kelvin; p_p = equilibrium density of holes in p region; p_n = equilibrium density of holes in n region. In other words, when the potential energy of the system is increased by a thermal unit of energy kT, the number of charges which cross the barriers is either increased or decreased by a factor ϵ, depending on the polarities involved.

If the potential barrier across, say, the emitter region is now decreased by the application of an external direct voltage,[3] V_E, and if P_o is the new value of the concentration of holes in the base, then from Eq. (8-13) at $x = 0$ (Fig. 7-1a),

[3] For the present we assume that the *base spreading resistance* is zero and hence there is no voltage drop due to this resistance.

$$P_o(0) = p_p \exp\left[-\frac{q(\phi' - V_E)}{kT}\right] = p_n e^{\Lambda V_E} \tag{8-14}$$

where[4] $\Lambda \equiv q/kT$. By similar reasoning at $x = W$, where the potential barrier is *increased* by the application of voltage V'_C,

$$P_o(W) = p_n e^{-\Lambda V'_C} \tag{8-15}$$

8.4 Direct current solution

Hole Current

A general solution to the differential Eq. (8-10) is

$$P_o(x) = A \sinh \frac{x}{L_p} + B \cosh \frac{x}{L_p} + p_n \tag{8-16}$$

If the hyperbolic functions are written in terms of exponentials, it is seen that the diffusion length may be interpreted as the linear distance in which the concentration of the charge carriers falls (due to recombination) to $1/\epsilon$ of its original value.

The constants A and B in Eq. (8-16) can be evaluated by using the boundary conditions (8-14) and (8-15). Thus the hole density at a point x is

$$\begin{aligned} P_o(x) &= \frac{(e^{-\Lambda V'_C} - e^{\Lambda V_E})}{2 \sinh (W/2L_p)} p_n \sinh \frac{(x - W/2)}{L_p} \\ &\quad + \frac{(e^{-\Lambda V'_C} + e^{\Lambda V_E} - 2)}{2 \cosh (W/2L_p)} p_n \cosh \frac{(x - W/2)}{L_p} + p_n \end{aligned} \tag{8-17}$$

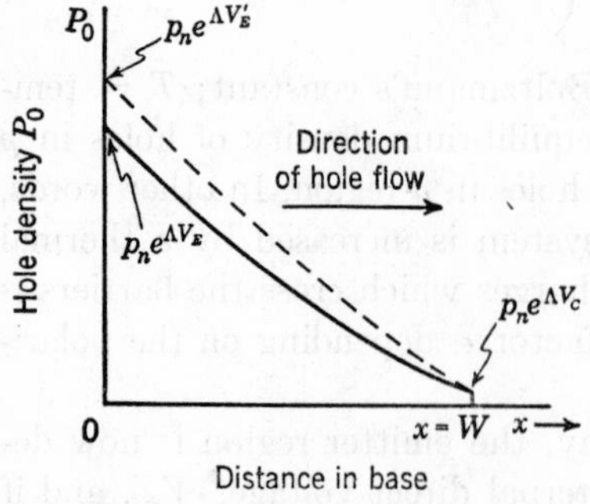

Fig. 8-2. D-c hole density in base of *p-n-p* transistor for two values of emitter voltage.

Figure 8-2 shows a plot of Eq. (8-17) for two values of V_E. The term $\exp(-\Lambda V'_C)$ is virtually negligible for greater than about 0.5 volt, and hence the concentration of holes at $x = W$ is shown to be nearly zero. The plot is virtually a straight line for $W/L_p \leq 0.1$. The concentration gradient as seen in Fig. 8-2 will cause a steady d-c flow of holes to occur in the positive x direction.

[4] Here Λ has the dimension of $(\text{volts})^{-1}$. At room temperature, $1/\Lambda = 0.026$ volt.

From the definition of the diffusion constant, the current due to holes is

$$I_p(x) = -qD_p \frac{\partial P_o}{\partial x} \tag{8-18}$$

where q is the charge of an electron and $\partial P_o/\partial x$ is the concentration gradient of holes. In other words, the current (in amperes) at any point x in Fig. 8-2 is proportional to the slope of curve at that point. Thus the emitter hole current I_{E_p} is from Eqs. (8-17) and (8-18) (setting $x = 0$),

$$I_{E_p} = \left[(e^{\Lambda V_E} - 1)\coth\frac{W}{L_p} - (e^{-\Lambda V'_C} - 1)\operatorname{cosech}\frac{W}{L_p}\right]\frac{qD_p p_n}{L_p} \tag{8-19a}$$

Similarly the collector hole current I_{C_p} is (setting $x = W$)

$$I_{C_p} = \left[(e^{\Lambda V_E} - 1)\operatorname{cosech}\frac{W}{L_p} - (e^{-\Lambda V'_C} - 1)\coth\frac{W}{L_p}\right]\frac{qD_p p_n}{L_p} \tag{8-19b}$$

Electron Current

The current due to electrons flowing from the base to the emitter in a *p-n-p* transistor as a result of the voltage across the emitter junction, may be found by inspection from Eq. (8-19a). Thus, assuming that the distance from the emitter junction to the external boundary is large compared with L_n (the diffusion length of electrons in the emitter p region), the emitter electron current is

$$I_{E_n} = (e^{\Lambda V_E} - 1)\frac{qD_n n_p}{L_n} \tag{8-20a}$$

since $\coth x \to 1$ as $x \to \infty$, and $\tanh x \to 1$ as $x \to \infty$. Similarly the collector electron current is

$$I_{C_n} = -(e^{-\Lambda V'_C} - 1)\frac{qD_n n'_p}{L'_n} \tag{8-20b}$$

where n'_p is the thermal equilibrium value and L'_n is the diffusion length of electrons in the collector p region.

Total Current

The total emitter current I_E is obtained by adding the hole and electron currents from Eqs. (8-19a) and (8-20a).

$$I_E = \left[(e^{\Lambda V_E} - 1)\left(\coth \frac{W}{L_p} + \frac{D_n n_p L_p}{D_p p_n L_n}\right) - (e^{-\Lambda V'_C} - 1) \operatorname{cosech} \frac{W}{L_p}\right] \frac{qD_p p_n}{L_p} \tag{8-21a}$$

Similarly the collector current I'_C is

$$I'_C = \left[(e^{\Lambda V_E} - 1) \operatorname{cosech} \frac{W}{L_p} - (e^{-\Lambda V_C} - 1) \cdot \left(\coth \frac{W}{L_p} + \frac{D_n n'_p L_p}{D_p p_n L'_n}\right)\right] \frac{qD_p p_n}{L_p} \tag{8-21b}$$

8.5 Direct current characteristics

Assume a sign convention where all currents flowing into a device are considered positive as shown in Fig. 8-3. Since the hole current in Fig. 7-1a flows in the positive x direction, it follows from the sign convention, that

$$I'_C = -I_C$$

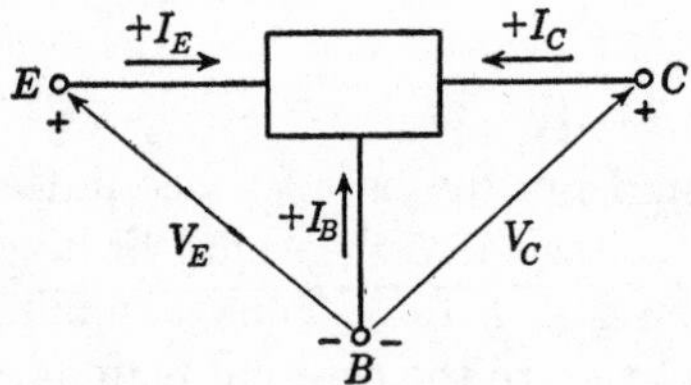

Fig. 8-3. Sign convention.

Similarly, the polarity of the voltages in Fig. 7-1a is such that we may write for the collector to base voltage,

$$V'_C = -V_C$$

Now, Eqs. (8-21a) and (8-21b) which describe the d-c characteristics of the intrinsic transistor may be rewritten:

$$I_E = (e^{\Lambda V_E} - 1)\frac{G_{11}}{\Lambda} + (e^{\Lambda V_C} - 1)\frac{G_{12}}{\Lambda} \tag{8-22a}$$

$$I_C = (e^{\Lambda V_E} - 1)\frac{G_{21}}{\Lambda} + (e^{\Lambda V_C} - 1)\frac{G_{22}}{\Lambda} \tag{8-22b}$$

where

$$G_{11} \equiv \frac{q\mu_p p_n}{L_p}\left(\coth \frac{W}{L_p} + \frac{D_n n_p L_p}{D_p p_n L_n}\right) \tag{8-23a}$$

$$G_{21} \equiv -\frac{q\mu_p p_n}{L_p} \operatorname{cosech} \frac{W}{L_p} \tag{8-23b}$$

$$G_{12} \equiv -\frac{q\mu_p p_n}{L_p} \operatorname{cosech} \frac{W}{L_p} \tag{8-23c}$$

$$G_{22} \equiv \frac{q\mu_p p_n}{L_p}\left(\coth\frac{W}{L_p} + \frac{D_n n'_p L_p}{D_p p_n L'_n}\right) \tag{8-23d}$$

and[5]

$$\frac{D_p}{\mu_p} = \frac{1}{\Lambda} \tag{8-24}$$

where μ_p is the mobility constant for holes.

Expressions (8-23a) to (8-23d) apply to a transistor of unit cross-sectional area. These conductances may be expressed in terms of the conductivities of the material of the emitter, base, and collector regions by noting that (from Appendix 1)

$$q\mu_p p_n = \frac{b\sigma_i^2}{(1+b)^2\sigma_n} \tag{8-25a}$$

and

$$q\mu_n n_p = \frac{b\sigma_i^2}{(1+b)^2\sigma_p} \tag{8-25b}$$

where n_p is the thermal equilibrium concentration of electrons in p regions; μ_n = mobility of electrons; $b = \mu_n/\mu_p = D_n/D_p \doteq 2.1$ for germanium, and σ_p, σ_n, σ_i are the conductivities of the p type, n type, and intrinsic germanium, respectively. Thus the conductances for a p-n-p transistor may be written

$$G_{11} = \frac{b\sigma_i^2}{(1+b)^2\sigma_n L_p}\left(\coth\frac{W}{L_p} + \frac{\sigma_n L_p}{\sigma_p L_n}\right) \tag{8-26a}$$

$$G_{21} = -\frac{b\sigma_i^2}{(1+b)^2\sigma_n L_p}\operatorname{cosech}\frac{W}{L_p} \tag{8-26b}$$

$$G_{12} = -\frac{b\sigma_i^2}{(1+b)^2\sigma_n L_p}\operatorname{cosech}\frac{W}{L_p} \tag{8-26c}$$

$$G_{22} = \frac{b\sigma_i^2}{(1+b)^2\sigma_n L_p}\left(\coth\frac{W}{L_p} + \frac{\sigma_n L_p}{\sigma'_p L'_n}\right) \tag{8-26d}$$

As stated earlier, Eqs. (8-22a) and (8-22b) apply to the intrinsic transistor; i.e., they ignore the voltage drop due to the base spreading resistance $r_{bb'}$, and any leakage resistance which might exist. If the voltage drop across $r_{bb'}$ is included, the equations are modified as follows:

$$I_E = (e^{\Lambda(V_E + I_B r_{bb'})} - 1)\frac{G_{11}}{\Lambda} + (e^{\Lambda(V_C + I_B r_{bb'})} - 1)\frac{G_{12}}{\Lambda} \tag{8-27a}$$

[5] The relationship $D/\mu = kT/q$, which links the diffusion constant to the mobility of a particle, is known as the Einstein relationship.

$$I_C = (e^{\Lambda(V_E + I_B r_{bb'})} - 1)\frac{G_{21}}{\Lambda} + (e^{\Lambda(V_C + I_B r_{bb'})} - 1)\frac{G_{22}}{\Lambda} \qquad \text{(8-27b)}$$

Also, the base current I_B is given by

$$\begin{aligned} I_B &= -(I_E + I_C) \\ &= -\left[(e^{\Lambda(V_E + I_B r_{bb'})} - 1)\frac{G_{11} + G_{21}}{\Lambda} \right. \\ &\qquad \left. + (e^{\Lambda(V_C + I_B r_{bb'})} - 1)\frac{G_{12} + G_{22}}{\Lambda}\right] \end{aligned} \qquad \text{(8-27c)}$$

In practice V_C, which represents a negative or reverse bias voltage, is so large that the exponentials which are functions of V_C in Eqs. (8-22) and (8-27) are nearly equal to zero. Furthermore, for the special case where a large reverse bias is also placed across the emitter junction, all exponential terms in the above equations are negligible, and hence the emitter current is

$$I_{ES} = -\frac{G_{11} + G_{12}}{\Lambda} \qquad \text{(8-28a)}$$

the collector current is

$$I_{CS} = -\frac{G_{22} + G_{21}}{\Lambda} \qquad \text{(8-28b)}$$

and the base current is

$$I_{BS} = -(I_{ES} + I_{CS}) = \frac{G_{11} + G_{12} + G_{21} + G_{22}}{\Lambda} \qquad \text{(8-28c)}$$

Currents I_{ES}, I_{CS}, and I_{BS} are often termed *saturation* currents because they resemble the maximum reverse current of a *p-n* junction diode. In addition to these, we define two other saturation currents I_{CO} and I_{CBO}, which are particularly important in circuit design.

Current I_{CO} is defined as the current flowing in the collector and base leads when the emitter current is zero. It can be obtained from Eqs. (8-22) or (8-27) by placing $I_E = 0$ and solving these equations. Thus we obtain

$$I_{CO} = (e^{\Lambda V_C} - 1)\left(\frac{1}{\sigma_c L_n'} + \frac{\tanh \frac{W}{L_p}}{\sigma_b L_p}\right)\frac{b\sigma_i^2}{(1+b)^2\Lambda} \qquad \text{(8-29)}$$

where use is made of Eqs. (8-26a) to (8-26d) and the voltage drop across $r_{bb'}$ is considered negligible compared with V_C.

Current I_{CBO} is defined as the current flowing in the collector and emitter leads when the base current is zero. This may be obtained from Eqs. (8-22) or (8-27) by a method similar to that used in Eq. (8-29), except that now $I_B = 0$ and therefore $I_E = I_C$ (see Problem 8.1).

8.6 Small-signal conductances

The d-c characteristics of a junction transistor given by Eq. (8-22) or Eq. (8-23) may be utilized to find the small-signal conductances (or resistances) at a given d-c operating point simply by observing the slope of the curves at that point. Thus the a-c short-circuit input conductance for the intrinsic transistor is, from Eq. (8-22a),

$$g_{11} \equiv \left.\frac{\partial I_E}{\partial V_E}\right|_{V_C=\text{const.}} = G_{11}e^{\Lambda V_E} \tag{8-30a}$$

while the a-c short-circuit forward transfer conductance is, from Eq. (8-22b),

$$g_{21} \equiv \left.\frac{\partial I_C}{\partial V_E}\right|_{V_C=\text{const.}} = G_{21}e^{\Lambda V_E} \tag{8-30b}$$

If W, and therefore G_{12} and G_{22}, were independent of collector voltage, the a-c short-circuit reverse-transfer conductance would be

$$g'_{12} \equiv \left.\frac{\partial I_E}{\partial V_C}\right|_{\substack{V_E=\text{const.}\\ W=\text{const.}}} = G_{12}e^{\Lambda V_C} \tag{8-31a}$$

and the a-c short-circuit output conductance would be

$$g'_{22} \equiv \left.\frac{\partial I_C}{\partial V_C}\right|_{\substack{V_E=\text{const.}\\ W=\text{const.}}} = G_{22}e^{\Lambda V_C} \tag{8-31b}$$

It is noted that both g'_{12} and g'_{22} are functions of exp (ΛV_C) which for collector voltage greater than 0.5 volt yield smaller values than those measured experimentally. This discrepancy is accounted for by the dependence of the effective base width, W, primarily on the collector voltage V_C, as discussed in Sec. 8.7.

Thus if W is considered to be a function of V_C, the a-c short-circuit reverse-transfer conductance is, from Eq. (8-22a),

$$g_{12} \equiv \left.\frac{\partial I_E}{\partial V_C}\right|_{V_E=\text{const.}}$$
$$= -\frac{q\mu_p p_n}{L_p} \operatorname{cosech} \frac{W}{L_p} e^{\Lambda V_E} \left(\frac{1}{\Lambda L_p} \frac{\partial W}{\partial V_C} \operatorname{cosech} \frac{W}{L_p} \right) \tag{8-32a}$$

and the a-c short-circuit output conductance is, from Eq. (8-22b),

$$g_{22} \equiv \left.\frac{\partial I_C}{\partial V_C}\right|_{V_E=\text{const.}}$$
$$= \frac{q\mu_p p_n}{L_p} \coth \frac{W}{L_p} e^{\Lambda V_E} \left(\frac{1}{\Lambda L_p} \frac{\partial W}{\partial V_C} \operatorname{cosech} \frac{W}{L_p} \right) \tag{8-32b}$$

where use is made of Eqs. (8-23a) to (8-23d), where all terms containing exp (ΛV_C) have been neglected, and where it is assumed that $(W/L_p)^2 \ll 1$.

8.7 Base width modulation

The dependence of the width of the transition region of a *p-n* junction on the voltage across it has been described by various writers.[6, 7] In a junction transistor the change in the width of the two transition regions, due to an alternating voltage being present, obviously influences the effective base width. However, only the collector transition region need be considered, since it is much wider than the emitter transition region on account of the larger voltage across the former.

The variation of base width with the collector voltage is bound to effect all electrical parameters that are functions of the base width. This fact was used by Early[8] to derive a value for "collector resistance" which was much more in agreement with experimental results than that calculated on the basis of a normal diode inverse resistance (following the exponential law exp (ΛV_C))[9]. We shall refer to this modulation of the base width by the collector voltage as the *Early effect.*

The Early effect can be taken into account when calculating the

[6] N. F. Mott, *Proc. Roy. Soc.*, Vol. 171A, p. 27, 1949.

[7] W. Schottky, *Z. Physik*, Vol. 113, p. 367, 1939.

[8] J. M. Early, "Effect of Space-Charge Layer Widening in Junction Transistors." *Proc. I.R.E.*, Vol. 40, pp. 1401, Nov. 1952.

[9] The term *collector resistance* as used here refers to the T equivalent circuit element.

small-signal short-circuit conductances g_{12} and g_{22} by noting that W is a function of V_C as in Eqs. (8-32a) and (8-32b). Alternatively, the complete short-circuit admittances of the transistor may be obtained by including the Early effect in the boundary conditions for the a-c diffusion Eq. (8–11), as shown in Sec. 8.8.

8.8 Alternating current boundary conditions

Consider Eq. (8-17) which describes the distribution of holes in the base as a function of V_E and V_C.

Let the emitter voltage change by an incremental amount $\Delta V_E \equiv v_e$ while V_C is kept constant. The change in hole density at the emitter at $x = 0$ will be $\Delta P_o(0) \equiv p_1(0)$. Thus, from Eq. (8-17), at $x = 0$,

$$p_1(0) = \frac{\partial P_O(0)}{\partial V_E} v_e \equiv p_n \Lambda e^{\Lambda V_E} v_e \tag{8-33a}$$

When obtaining the incremental change in hole density at $x = W$, due to an incremental change in collector voltage $\Delta V_C \equiv v_c$, it should be borne in mind that W is itself a function of V_C as explained in Sec. 8.7. Hence, the small-signal boundary condition at some average value $x = W$ is written in two parts,[10]

$$p_1(W) = \left.\frac{\partial P_O(x)}{\partial x}\right|_{x=W} \frac{\partial W}{\partial V_C} v_C + \frac{\partial P_O(W)}{\partial V_C} v_c \tag{8-33b}$$

$$= p_n \frac{\Lambda e^{\Lambda V_E}}{K} v_c \tag{8-33c}$$

where

$$\frac{1}{K} = \frac{1}{\Lambda L_p} \frac{\partial W}{\partial V_C} \operatorname{cosech} \frac{W}{L_p} + \frac{e^{\Lambda V_C}}{e^{\Lambda V_E}} \tag{8-33d}$$

From Eqs. (8-33a) and (8-33c) it is seen that K is simply the ratio of the incremental change in hole density at the emitter to that at the collector for the same increment of voltage. From Eq. (8-33b) it consists of two terms; the first is a result of the Early effect, and the second ignores it.

A physical interpretation of the first term can be obtained from Fig. 8-4, which shows a plot of the d-c (steady state) hole density

[10] J. Zawels, "Physical Theory for a New Circuit Representation of Junction Transistor". *J. Appl. Phys.*, Vol. 28, Aug. 1954.

as a function of distance through the base.[11] It is assumed that the hole concentration at the collector $P_o(W)$ is virtually zero, since it is a function of exp (ΛV_C) which is normally very small. By holding

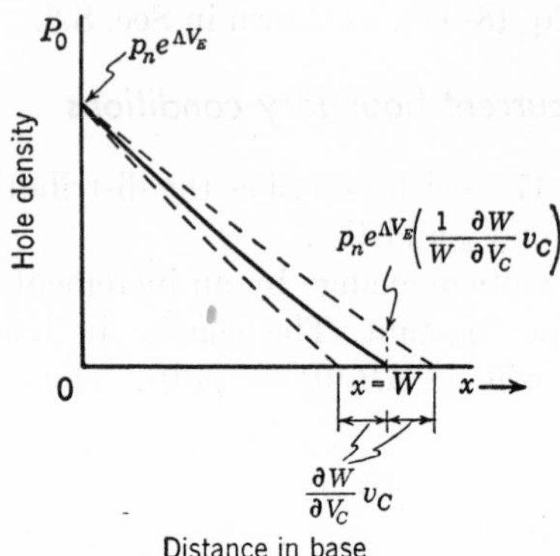

Fig. 8-4. D-c hole density in base of p-n-p transistor for two values of collector voltage ($V_c \gg 0$).

the concentration of the holes at the emitter constant (i.e., the emitter voltage is kept constant) and changing the collector voltage by the incremental amount v_c, the change in base width will be $v_c\partial W/\partial V_C$. Assuming the graph to be a straight line, then from the property of similar triangles, the change in hole density at the point $x = W$ is

$$p_1(W) = \frac{v_c(\partial W/\partial V_C)}{W} p_n e^{\Lambda V_E} = p_n \Lambda e^{\Lambda V_E} v_c \left(\frac{1}{\Lambda W}\frac{\partial W}{\partial V_C}\right) \quad (8\text{-}33e)$$

Comparing Eq. (8-33e) with Eq. (8-33c), it is seen that the parenthetical factor for Eq. (8-33e) is the same as the first term of K provided $W/L_p \ll 1$.

Assume that a sinusoidal voltage of peak amplitude V_e is applied at the emitter; i.e., $v_e = V_e$ exp $(j\omega t)$. Thus at $x = 0$, the incremental hole density is, from Eq. (8-33a),

$$p_1(o, t) = p_n \Lambda e^{\Lambda V_E} V_e e^{j\omega t} \quad (8\text{-}34a)$$

Similarly, for a sinusoidal voltage of peak amplitude V_c, the incremental hole density at $x = W$ is

[11] This is in accordance with H. Johnson, "Diffusion Reactances in Junction Transistors," Paper read at the Transistor Research Conference, Pennsylvania State College in July 1953.

$$p_1(W, t) = p_n \frac{\Lambda e^{\Lambda V_E}}{K} V_c e^{j\omega t} \tag{8-34b}$$

Equations (8-34a) and (8-34b) are the boundary conditions for the a-c diffusion Eq. (8-11).

8.9 Alternating current solution

The Hole Alternating Current

From the boundary conditions, Eqs. (8-34a) and (8-34b), the solution of the a-c diffusion Eq. (8-11) may be written

$$p_1(x, t) = e^{j\omega t} e^{\Lambda V_E} p_n \Lambda \left[\frac{V_c/K - V_e}{2 \sinh (W/2L_p)(1 + j\omega\tau_p)^{1/2}} \sinh \frac{(x - (W/2))}{L_p} (1 + j\omega\tau_p)^{1/2} + \frac{V_c/K + V_e}{2 \cosh (W/2L_p)(1 + j\omega\tau_p)^{1/2}} \cdot \cosh \frac{(x - (W/2))}{L_p} (1 + j\omega\tau_p)^{1/2} \right] \tag{8-35}$$

From the definition of the diffusion constant, the current due to holes is

$$I_p(x) = -qD_p \frac{\partial p}{\partial x} \tag{8-36}$$

Hence from Eqs. (8-35) and (8-36), the alternating current due to holes at the emitter ($x = 0$) is

$$I_{ep} = \frac{q\mu_p p_n}{L_p} e^{\Lambda V_E}(1 + j\omega\tau_p)^{1/2} \left[V_e \coth \frac{W}{L_p} (1 + j\omega\tau_p)^{1/2} - \frac{V_c}{K} \operatorname{cosech} \frac{W}{L_p} (1 + j\omega\tau_p)^{1/2} \right] \tag{8-37a}$$

and the collector ($x = W$),

$$I_{cp} = \frac{q\mu_p p_n}{L_p} e^{\Lambda V_E} (1 + j\omega\tau_p)^{1/2} \left[V_e \operatorname{cosech} \frac{W}{L_p} (1 + j\omega\tau_p)^{1/2} - \frac{V_c}{K} \coth \frac{W}{L_p} (1 + j\omega\tau_p)^{1/2} \right] \tag{8-37b}$$

where use is made of the Einstein relationship given in Eq. (8-24).

The Electron Alternating Current

Simultaneously with the hole current there is the electron current which flows in a *p-n-p* transistor from the base to emitter by virtue of the voltage across the emitter junction. This electron current is found by inspection from Eq. (8-37a) by a reasoning similar to that in Sec. 8.4b.

$$I_{en} = \frac{q\mu_n n_n}{L_n} e^{\Lambda V_E} (1 + j\omega\tau_n)^{1/2} V_e \tag{8-38a}$$

Similarly the electron current across the collector is

$$I_{cn} = \frac{q\mu_n n_p'}{L_n'} e^{\Lambda V_C} (1 + j\omega\tau_n')^{1/2} V_c \tag{8-38b}$$

where the primed quantities refer to the collector p region.

Total Alternating Current

The total emitter current is the sum of the hole and electron currents.

$$I_e = I_{ep} + I_{en} \tag{8-39}$$

where I_{ep} and I_{en} are obtained from Eqs. (8-37a) and (8-38a), respectively. Similarly the total collector current is

$$I_c' = I_{cp} + I_{cn} \tag{8-40}$$

Since Eq. (8-38b) is a function of exp (ΛV_C) it is usually negligible at all but very low collector voltages, and the collector alternating current is to a first approximation assumed to be composed entirely of holes, i.e., $I_c' = I_{cp}$.

8.10 The short-circuit admittances of the intrinsic transistor

Generally the node equations for a four-terminal network may be written

$$I_e = y_{11}V_e + y_{12}V_c \tag{8-41a}$$

$$I_c = y_{21}V_e + y_{22}V_c \tag{8-41b}$$

where the sign convention is as indicated in Fig. 8-3. Comparing the coefficients of V_e and V_c in Eqs. (8-41a) and (8-41b) with that of the Eqs. (8-39) and (8-40) when fully developed, we obtain the short-circuit admittances of the intrinsic transistor.

$$y_{11} = \frac{q\mu_p p_n}{W} e^{\Lambda V_E} \left[\frac{W}{L_p}(1 + j\omega\tau_p)^{1/2} \coth \frac{W}{L_p}(1 + j\omega\tau_p)^{1/2} + \frac{D_n n_p W}{D_p p_n L_n}(1 + j\omega\tau_n)^{1/2}\right] \tag{8-42a}$$

$$y_{21} = -\frac{q\mu_p p_n}{W} e^{\Lambda V_E} \left[\frac{W}{L_p} (1 + j\omega\tau_p)^{1/2} \operatorname{cosech} \frac{W}{L_p} (1 + j\omega\tau_p)^{1/2} \right] \tag{8-42b}$$

$$y_{12} = -\frac{q\mu_p p_n}{W} e^{\Lambda V_E} \left[\frac{W}{L_p} (1 + j\omega\tau_p)^{1/2} \operatorname{cosech} \frac{W}{L_p} (1 + j\omega\tau_p)^{1/2} \right] \frac{1}{K} \tag{8-42c}$$

$$y_{22} = \frac{q\mu_p p_n}{W} e^{\Lambda V_E} \left[\frac{W}{L_p} (1 + j\omega\tau_p)^{1/2} \coth \frac{W}{L_p} (1 + j\omega\tau_p)^{1/2} \right] \frac{1}{K} \tag{8-42d}$$

It is easily seen that these admittances reduce to the conductances derived in Eqs. (8-30a), (8-30b), (8-32a), and (8-32b) for $\omega = 0$.

Equations (8-42a) to (8-42d) may be rewritten in more compact form as follows:

$$y_{11} = G\theta \coth \theta + Y_n \tag{8-43a}$$

$$y_{21} = -G\theta \operatorname{cosech} \theta \tag{8-43b}$$

$$y_{12} = \frac{-G\theta \operatorname{cosech} \theta}{K} \tag{8-43c}$$

$$y_{22} = \frac{G\theta \coth \theta}{K} \tag{8-43d}$$

where

$$G \equiv \frac{q}{W} \mu_p p_n e^{\Lambda V_E} = \frac{b\sigma_i^2 e^{\Lambda V_E}}{(1 + b)^2 \sigma_n W} \tag{8-44a}$$

or[12]

$$\doteq \frac{I_E}{26} \text{ mhos} \tag{8-44b}$$

where I_E is in milliamperes. Also

$$\theta = \frac{W}{L_p} (1 + j\omega\tau_p)^{1/2} \tag{8-44c}$$

$$Y_n/G = \frac{D_n n_p W}{D_p p_n L_n} (1 + j\omega\tau_n)^{1/2} = \frac{\sigma_b W}{\sigma_e L_n} (1 + j\omega\tau_n)^{1/2} \tag{8-44d}$$

and

$$1/K = \frac{1}{\Lambda L_p} \frac{\partial W}{\partial V_C} \operatorname{cosech} \frac{W}{L_p} + \frac{e^{\Lambda V_C}}{e^{\Lambda V_E}} \tag{8-44e}$$

[12] This follows from Eqs. (8-22a), (8-26a), and (8-28a) where it can be shown that $G \doteq \Lambda(I_E - I_{ES})$. Alternatively $G = \Lambda(I_C - I_{CS})$. Thus if I_{ES} or I_{CS} is small compared with I_E and I_C, respectively, then $G = I_E\Lambda$, or $G = I_C\Lambda$, where $1/\Lambda = 0.026$ volt at room temperature.

In Eqs. (8-44a) and (8-44d) use is made of Eqs. (8-82) and (8-83) of Appendix 1. An expression for $\partial W/\partial V_C$ is given in Sec. 8.13 by Eq. (8-71b).

In Appendix 1 of Chapter 7 it is shown that the above admittances may be represented by a network consisting of a transmission line in cascade with a K amplifier, as shown in Fig. 7-5b. The transmission line whose length is W has a characteristic impedance

$$Z_o = \frac{1}{G\theta} \tag{8-45a}$$

and a propagation constant $\gamma = \theta$. This implies that the total distributed series impedance

$$zW = \frac{1}{G} \tag{8-45b}$$

while the total distributed parallel admittance

$$yW = G\theta^2 \tag{8-45c}$$

Thus if r'_D, g'_D, and C'_D are the series resistance, the parallel conductance, and the parallel capacitance per unit length, respectively, the total values are as follows:

$$r'_D W = \frac{1}{G} \tag{8-45d}$$

$$g'_D W = G\left(\frac{W}{L_p}\right)^2 \tag{8-45e}$$

$$C'_D W = G\left(\frac{W}{L_p}\right)^2 \tau_p \tag{8-45f}$$

The transmission line may be approximated in a given frequency range by lumped parameters which are virtually independent of frequency. It is found that if a π configuration is chosen, such as shown in Fig. 7-7, the elements are substantially independent of frequency for the complete frequency range where a power gain is expected from the transistor. (See Problem 8.6.)

Thus, neglecting the term Y_n in Eq. (8-43a), it is easily shown that since for a good transistor $(W/L_p)^2 \ll 1$ the shunt admittances of Fig. 7-7 are

$$y_{11} + y_{21} \doteq \frac{1}{g_{D_p} + j\omega C_{D_p}} \tag{8-46a}$$

where

$$g_{D_p} = \frac{G}{2}\left(\frac{W}{L_p}\right)^2 \tag{8-46b}$$

$$C_{D_p} = \tau_p g_{D_p} \tag{8-46c}$$

and G is defined in Eq. (8-44a). Similarly, the series impedance of the π circuit can be shown to be

$$-y_{21} \doteq \frac{1}{r_d + j\omega L_d} \tag{8-46d}$$

where

$$r_d = \frac{1}{G} \tag{8-46e}$$

and

$$L_d = \frac{W^2 \tau_p}{6L_p^2 G} \tag{8-46f}$$

As shown in Appendix 1 of Chapter 7 the effect of the term Y_n in Eq. (8-43a) is to add an admittance in parallel with the input terminals. Thus, since Y_n appears in parallel with the shunt branch of the π circuit, we endeavour to resolve it into a parallel capacitance and conductance as follows:

$$Y_n = g_n + j\omega C_n \tag{8-47}$$

However, here g_n and C_n are not quite so independent of frequency in the useful frequency range as are the elements g_{Dp}, C_{Dp}, r_d, and L_d. Nevertheless, since for a good transistor Y_n is small compared with the admittance with which it appears in parallel, the elements of the complete lumped parameter equivalent circuit may be considered to be substantially independent of frequency.

8.11 Surface recombination

In the derivation of the transistor characteristics as given by the d-c and a-c equations in Secs. 8.5 and 8.10, it is assumed that the surfaces of the transistor are perfectly plane, parallel, and infinite. In practice this is not true, and the effect of its geometry is that some carriers are able to reach the surface of the base region. Since the rate of recombination (or lifetime) of the carriers on the surface of the base region differs substantially from that in the interior, it is bound to modify the expressions for the characteristics.

As a rough approximation, a composite lifetime $\tau_{comp.}$ may be simply used instead of the normal volume recombination lifetime in the solution of the diffusion Eqs. (8-10) and (8-11). Thus[13]

$$\frac{1}{\tau_{comp.}} = \frac{1}{\tau_v} + \frac{1}{\tau_s}$$

where τ_v = volume recombination lifetime and τ_s = surface recombination lifetime. A different approach, taking the geometry of the transistor into account, is as follows:

We first endeavour to obtain a plot of the paths of the minority carriers in the base. This may be found from a solution of the diffusion equation in three dimensions. Thus,[14] analogous to Eq. (8-10),

$$\nabla^2 P_o = \frac{P_o - p_n}{L_p^2} \equiv \frac{P_o - p_n}{\tau_p D_p} \tag{8-48a}$$

where τ_p is the volume recombination lifetime. If τ_p is large, i.e., all holes are lost by surface recombination,

$$\nabla^2 P_o = 0 \tag{8-48b}$$

or

$$\nabla^2 p' = 0 \tag{8-48c}$$

where $p' = P_o - p_n$ = excess hole density, and p_n = thermal equilibrium density for holes in the n region.

Equation (8-48c) is Laplace's equation. To solve it we may consider p' as analogous to electric potential in an electrical analog solution. In this sense, the emitter and collector junctions are equipotential surfaces. The boundary conditions may be found as follows:

Writing Eq. (8-18) for the three-dimensional case, the current at any point is

$$\mathrm{J} = -qD_p \nabla p' \tag{8-49a}$$

[13] E. Conwell, "Properties of Silicon and Germanium," *Proc. I.R.E.*, Vol. 40, pp. 1335, Nov. 1952.

[14] A. R. Moore and J. I. Pankove, "The Effect of Junction Shape and Surface Recombination on Transistor Current Gain," *Proc. I.R.E.*, Vol. 42, p. 907, June 1954.

We define now the concept of the *surface recombination velocity* s, which describes the rate of hole-electron recombination at the surface of a material:

$$s = \frac{\text{number recombining per second per unit surface area}}{\text{excess density over thermal equilibrium value just below surface}}$$

The effect of surface recombination manifests itself in the form of a current flowing into the surface.

$$J = qp's \tag{8-49b}$$

Now from Eqs. (8-49a) and (8-49b) it follows that at the boundary,

$$\frac{\nabla p'}{p'} = \frac{-s}{D_p} \tag{8-50}$$

Using this boundary condition, the solution to Eq. (8-48c) in the form of a field plot for a particular fused alloy transistor is shown[14] in Figs. 8-5a and 8-5b. In Fig. 8-5a where the emitter area is made much

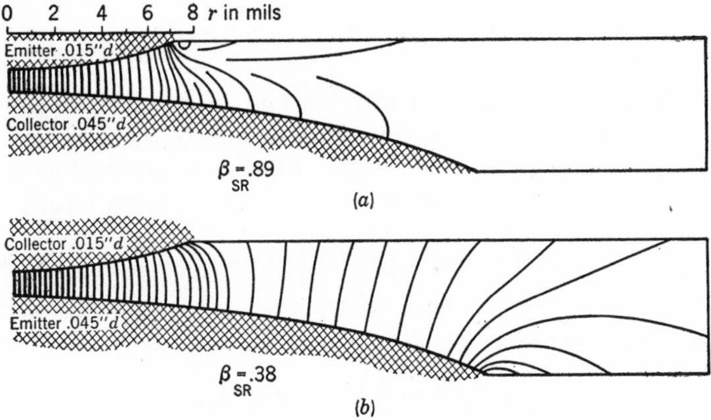

Fig. 8-5. Hole flow maps for fused alloy junction transistor. (From A. R. Moore, loc. cit.)

smaller than that of the collector, the ratio of the number of holes which leave the emitter to that which arrive at the collector is about 0.9. This ratio (in the absence of volume recombination) may be considered as a *surface recombination transport* factor β_{SR}. In Fig. 8-5b, $\beta_{SR} = 0.38$.

The circuit implication of the fact that some holes leave the emitter and proceed towards the surface of the base is that an additional admittance must be added to the expression for the input admittance y_{11} which is given by Eq. (8-42a) or Eq. (8-43a). This admittance we define as the *surface recombination admittance* Y_{SR} ; it can be derived as follows.

Let the effective area on the base surface over which recombination takes place be A_s'.[15] Then from Eq. (8-49b) the surface recombination current is

$$I_{SR} = qp'sA_s' \tag{8-51}$$

Since recombination is bound to take place nearer the emitter (at $x = 0$), the excess hole density p' is, from Eq. (8-14),

$$p' = P_o(0) - p_n = p_n e^{\Lambda V_E} - p_n \tag{8-52}$$

From Eqs. (8-51) and (8-52) the small-signal surface recombination conductance is

$$g_{SR} = \frac{dI_{SR}}{dV_E} = qp_n \Lambda s A_s' e^{\Lambda V_E} \tag{8-53a}$$

The surface recombination admittances may be expected to have a frequency dependence of the same form as that of the electron current given by Eq. (8-38), if the length of the path traversed by holes flowing to the surface is comparable with the diffusion length L_p.

$$Y_{SR} = qp_n s A_s' \Lambda e^{\Lambda V_E}(1 + j\omega\tau_p)^{1/2} \tag{8-53b}$$

Thus the short-circuit input admittance y_{11} given by Eq. (8-43a) may now be modified as follows.

$$y_{11} = G\theta \coth \theta + Y_n + Y_{SR} \tag{8-54}$$

8.12 The short-circuit current amplification factor and its variation with current

From the node equation of a four-terminal network, it follows that the short-circuit amplification factor is

[15] In this chapter the emitter is assumed to have a cross-sectional area of unity. Hence A_s' is here normalized, i.e., $A_s' = A_s/A$, where A_s is the area in, say, square centimeters over which recombination takes place, and A is the area of the emitter, in the same units.

$$\alpha_{21} = \left.\frac{I_2}{I_1}\right|_{V_2=0} = \frac{y_{21}}{y_{11}}$$

Thus in accordance with Eq. (7-35), and utilizing Eqs. (8-54) and (8-43b),

$$\alpha = \frac{G\theta \operatorname{cosech} \theta}{G\theta \coth \theta + Y_n + Y_{SR}} \tag{8-55}$$

Also from Eq. (7-36a),

$$\alpha_{cb} = \frac{G\theta \operatorname{cosech} \theta}{G\theta(\coth \theta - \operatorname{cosech} \theta) + Y_n + Y_{SR}} \tag{8-56}$$

The low-frequency values of these factors are[16]

$$\alpha_o \doteq \frac{1}{1 + \frac{1}{2}(W/L_p)^2 + \sigma_b W/\sigma_e L_n + sA_s W/D_p A} \tag{8-57}$$

$$\alpha_{cbo} \doteq \frac{1}{\frac{1}{2}(W/L_p)^2 + \sigma_b W/\sigma_e L_n + sA_s W/D_p A} \tag{8-58}$$

where it is assumed that $(W/L_p)^2 \ll 1$.

The terms in the denominators of Eqs. (8-57) and (8-58) describe different phenomena of transistor action. Thus α_o may be written as

$$\alpha_o \doteq \beta_{VR}\beta_{SR}\gamma$$

where

$$\gamma = \frac{1}{1 + \sigma_b W/\sigma_e L_n} \tag{8-59a}$$

$$\beta_{VR} = \frac{1}{1 + \frac{1}{2}(W/L_p)^2} \tag{8-59b}$$

$$\beta_{SR} = \frac{1}{1 + sA_s W/D_p A} \tag{8-59c}$$

where γ is the injection efficiency and is the fraction of the current flowing across the emitter junction which consists only of minority carriers (holes in *p-n-p* transistor); β_{VR} is the *volume recombination transport factor* and is the fraction of the minority carriers which reach the collector after leaving the emitter, if surface recombination is negligible; β_{SR} is the *surface recombination transport factor* and is the

[16] W. M. Webster, "On the Variation of Junction Transistor Current Amplification Factor with Emitter Current"; *Proc. I.R.E.*, Vol. 42, p. 914, June 1954.

fraction of the minority carriers which reach the collector after leaving the emitter, if *volume* recombination is negligible.

From the equations above it appears that α_o and α_{cbo} are independent of current. In actual fact this is not the case, as seen from Fig. 8-6, which shows an experimental plot of α_{cbo} as a function of emitter current. This is explained on the basis of the variation of β_{SR}, β_{VR}, and γ with current, when the density of the injected minority carriers in the base is high.

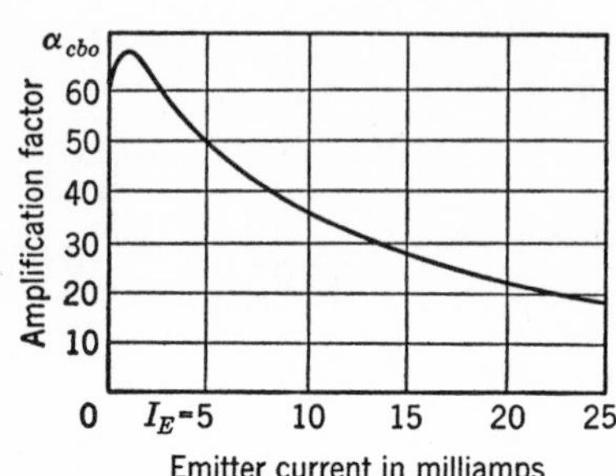

Fig. 8-6. Current dependence of common-emitter short-circuit current amplification factor.

In the first-order theory on which Eqs. (8-57) and (8-58) are based, it was assumed (Sec. 8.2) that no electric field exists in the base region; and that the density of the injected minority carriers is small compared with the ionized impurity atoms in the base region. However, according to Webster's theory[16] this is not the case. Thus the number of injected minority carriers present, in combination with the majority carriers in the base, set up an electric field. This in turn tends to reduce the transit time, or causes a virtual increase in the diffusion constant of the minority carriers, thereby *decreasing* the surface recombination term in Eq. (8-57) or (8-58). Also, the other two terms representing injection efficiency and volume recombination are *increased* with an increase of current. These opposite effects give rise to a maximum in the α_{cbo} vs. emitter current curve, as seen in Fig. 8-6.

Consider a *p-n-p* transistor such as shown in Fig. 7-1a, having plane-parallel sides. Equation (8-18) is now modified to include the effects of any electric fields which may exist in the base. Thus the current (per unit area) due to holes in the base is

$$I_p(x) = -qD_p \frac{\partial p}{\partial x} - pq\mu_p \frac{\partial V}{\partial x} \tag{8-60a}$$

where V is the electric potential. Similarly the electron current, which for a good transistor is very small, may be written

$$I_n(x) = qD_n \frac{\partial n}{\partial x} - nq\mu_n \frac{\partial V}{\partial x} \doteq 0 \tag{8-60b}$$

Since the net charge density in the base region must be zero, and the number of ionized acceptor atoms N_a in the base is assumed to be negligible, we write

$$p + N_d = n + N_a \doteq n \tag{8-61}$$

Assuming the density of donor ions N_d to be uniformly distributed, and differentiating Eq. (8-61),

$$\frac{\partial p}{\partial x} = \frac{\partial n}{\partial x} \tag{8-62}$$

Eliminating $\partial V/\partial x$ between Eqs. (8-60a) and (8-60b) and substituting Eq. (8-61) and Eq. (8-62) into the result, we obtain

$$I_p(x) = -qD_p \frac{\partial p}{\partial x}\left(1 + \frac{p}{N_d + p}\right) \tag{8-63}$$

Comparing Eq. (8-63) with Eq. (8-60a), it is seen that the effect of assuming a field in the base region is equivalent to increasing the diffusion constant D_p by a factor $1 + p/(N_d + p)$.

By inspection of Eq. (8-58) it is now clear that this effective increase in D_p causes α_{cbo} to rise. However, as seen from Fig. 8-6, the rise in α_{cbo} occurs only for relatively small emitter currents before the effects make themselves felt which cause α_{cbo} to fall. There are two such effects which modify the emitter efficiency and volume recombination terms $\sigma_b W/\sigma_e L_e$ and $\frac{1}{2}(W/L_p)^2$ of Eq. (8-58), respectively, as follows.

1. Consider the base conductivity σ_b, which from Eq. (8-79), Appendix 1, is

$$\sigma_b \doteq q\mu_n n_n$$

where n_n is the concentration of electrons in the conduction band in the base. From Eq. (8-61) it is seen that the concentration of electrons in the base is modified by the injection of holes to the extent that the base conductivity is effectively multiplied by a factor $(p + N_d)/n$. Now by integrating Eq. (8-63) and noting that p varies across the width of the base, falling to zero at the collector junction, it can be shown that for large values of p the factor p/N_d is proportional to emitter current. Hence when the emitter efficiency term is the dominating one in Eq. (8-58), α_{bco} falls as the current rises.

2. The term $\frac{1}{2}(W/L_p)^2$ also increases with emitter current, mainly

due to the increase in n_n, which is explained above. This follows from Eq. (8-12), viz., $L_p = (\tau_p D_p)^{1/2}$ since τ_p decreases as the number of electrons in the base region, n_n, increases because the probability of electron-hole recombination is greater.

8.13 Transition region

The collector transition region is responsible for a major portion of the capacitative effects which are present in transistors. The properties of this region also determine the magnitude of the effective base width, the magnitude of the amplification factor K of the K amplifier (in Fig. 7-6, etc.), and the maximum collector bias voltage which may be used.

Consider a *p-n* junction with an abrupt change in impurity concentration[17] such that for $x > 0$ there are only donor atoms, while for $x < 0$ there are only acceptor atoms. (See Fig. 8-7a.) The reverse bias voltage causes a depletion region at $-d_2 < x < d_1$, but outside of these limits all impurity atoms are neutralized by the free (excess) charges. (The impurity atoms are shown arranged in straight lines in Fig. 8-7a for reason of clarity.)

Figure 8-7b shows the resulting charge density distribution ρ. The electrostatic potential ψ, which is caused by (or is the cause of) the charge distribution, is shown in Fig. 8-7d. Poisson's equation links ψ and ρ by the expression[18]

$$\frac{\partial^2 \psi}{\partial x^2} = -\frac{4\pi\rho}{\epsilon} \tag{8-64a}$$

where ϵ is the permittivity of the medium. Also the electric field intensity, E is related to ψ by the expression

$$E = -\frac{\partial \psi}{\partial x} \tag{8-64b}$$

Thus ψ, E, and ρ may be obtained graphically from each other by differentiation or integration, as the case may be.

Because of the abrupt change in charge at $x = 0$, the electrostatic potential in the transition region, and hence the width of this region as a function of the voltage across it may be obtained from Eq.

[17] This is often referred to as a Schottky type junction.

[18] For a derivation of Eq. (8-64a) from Gauss' theorem, see for example, M.I.T. Staff, *Applied Electronics*, John Wiley & Sons, Inc., 1943, p. 117.

(8-64a) by solving it in two parts, i.e., for $x > 0$ and for $x < 0$. Thus for $x > 0$ the charge density is

$$\rho = qN_d \tag{8-65}$$

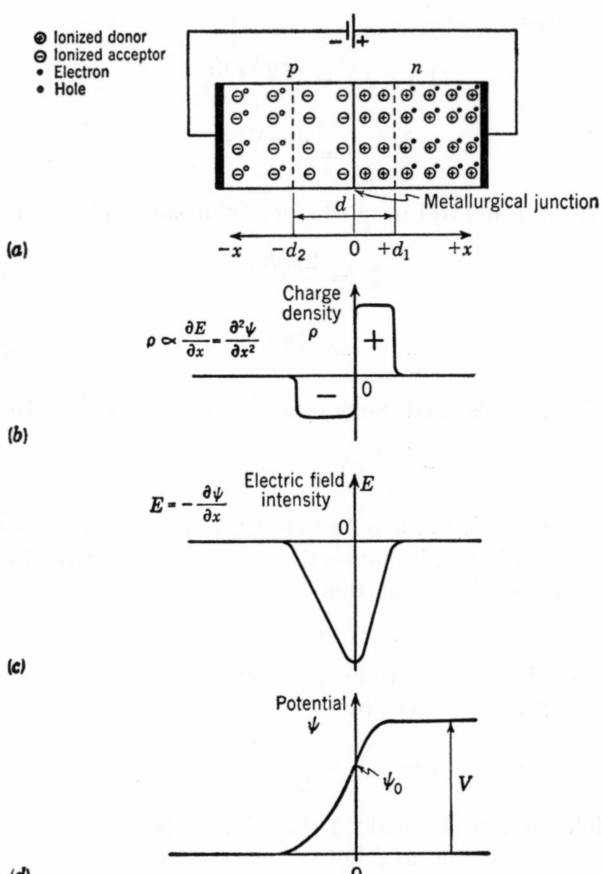

Fig. 8-7. Space charge in the transition region of a *p-n* junction.

where N_d is the density of donor atoms and is assumed to be uniformly distributed. Furthermore, the boundary conditions are at $x = 0$,

$$\psi = \psi_o$$

and at $x = d_1$,

$$\psi = V, \quad \text{and} \quad \frac{\partial \psi}{\partial x} = 0$$

By solving Eq. (8-64) and using these boundary conditions it is easily shown that

$$(V - \psi_o) = \frac{2\pi q N_d\, d_1^2}{\epsilon} \tag{8-66a}$$

$$\left.\frac{\partial \psi}{\partial x}\right|_{x=0} = \frac{4\pi q N_d\, d_1}{\epsilon} \tag{8-66b}$$

Similarly, the solution to Eq. (8-64) for $x < 0$ can be obtained.

$$\psi_o = \frac{2\pi q N_a\, d_2^2}{\epsilon} \tag{8-66c}$$

$$\left.\frac{\partial \psi}{\partial x}\right|_{x=0} = \frac{4\pi q N_a\, d_2}{\epsilon} \tag{8-66d}$$

Now from Eqs. (8-66a) and (8-66c) the potential V in Fig. 8-7d is

$$V = \frac{2\pi q}{\epsilon}(N_d\, d_1^2 + N_a\, d_2^2) \tag{8-67}$$

where N_a is the density of acceptor atoms, which also is assumed to be uniformly distributed. Equating the slopes at $x = 0$ given by Eqs. (8-66b) and (8-66d), it follows that

$$N_d d_1 = N_a d_2 \tag{8-68}$$

The effective width of the transition regions d is found from Eqs. (8-67) and (8-68), and is given by

$$d^2 \equiv (d_1 + d_2)^2 = \frac{V\epsilon}{2\pi q}\left(\frac{1}{N_d} + \frac{1}{N_a}\right) \tag{8-69}$$

It now follows from Appendix 1 that Eq. (8-69) may be rewritten in terms of conductivities as follows:

$$d^2 = \frac{V\epsilon\mu_p}{2\pi}\left(\frac{b}{\sigma_n} + \frac{1}{\sigma_p}\right) \tag{8-70}$$

where σ_n and σ_p are the conductivities of the n and p regions, respectively, provided that all impurity atoms are ionized, i.e., $N_d = n_n$ and $N_a = p_p$.

The following important conclusions may now be drawn for a transistor with Schottky type barriers.

1. From Eq. (8-68) it follows that the space charge region extends mostly into the direction where the impurity concentration, or conductivity, is smallest. Thus in a transistor the collector space charge extends mostly into the base region if the conductivity of the collector region is much larger than that of the base, i.e., if $\sigma_c \gg \sigma_b$. Also for such transistors it follows from Eq. (8-70) that the collector transition width can be expressed as

$$d \propto \left(\frac{V_C}{\sigma_b}\right)^{1/2}$$

where V_C is the collector voltage.

2. The factor $\partial W/\partial V_C$, which occurs in the expression for K given by Eqs. (8-44e), and is important when base width modulation is considered, may be found by noting that

$$W \doteq W' - d \tag{8-71a}$$

where W' is the base width measured between the metallurgical junctions (see Fig. 7-1a); W is the base width measured between edges of transition regions; d is the width of collector transition region. (It is assumed here that $\sigma_c \gg \sigma_b$, and that the width of the emitter transition region is negligible as a result of the comparatively low voltage across it.) Thus from Eq. (8-70),

$$\left|\frac{\partial W}{\partial V_C}\right| = \frac{\partial d}{\partial V_C} = \sqrt{\frac{\epsilon\mu_p}{4\pi}\left(\frac{b}{\sigma_b}\right)\frac{1}{V_C}} \tag{8-71b}$$

3. The *transition capacitance*, or effective capacitance of the transition region, is

$$C_T = \frac{dQ}{dV}$$

where $Q = qN_d d_1 = qN_a d_2$ = total negative, or total positive charge in the region. Thus utilizing Eq. (8-69) or Eq. (8-70),

$$C_T = \frac{1}{2}\sqrt{\frac{\epsilon}{2\pi\mu_p(b/\sigma_n + 1/\sigma_p)V}} \tag{8-72}$$

4. The *breakdown voltage* is the reverse voltage at which an appreciable increase in the reverse current occurs, possibly as a result of the strong electric field pulling electrons directly out of the valence band.[19] Such action is analogous to field emission in metals.

[19] The breakdown voltage is sometimes referred to as the *Zener* voltage. However, it has not been conclusively shown that the effect which is observed

The maximum electric field occurs at $x = 0$. Thus from Eqs. (8-66b) and (8-66d),

$$E_{max} = \left.\frac{\partial\psi}{\partial x}\right|_{x=0} = \frac{4\pi d}{\epsilon\mu_p(b/\sigma_n + 1/\sigma_p)} \tag{8-73}$$

where the conductivities are obtained as in Eq. (8-70). This electric field intensity should be below a value E_Z at which breakdown occurs. A reported value for E_Z for germanium is 2×10^5 volts/cm.[20] The breakdown voltage may be obtained from Eqs. (8-73) and (8-70), and is

$$V_Z = \frac{\epsilon\mu_p}{8\pi}\left(\frac{b}{\sigma_n} + \frac{1}{\sigma_p}\right) E_Z^2 \tag{8-74}$$

As stated earlier, the above results are applicable to a junction transistor where a Schottky type potential barrier exists. This type of junction is often found in alloy junction transistors. For the grown junction transistor the transition from n to p material is more gradual, and hence the junction width may be found to vary according to the law $d \propto V^{1/3}$.

8.14 The base spreading resistance

The spreading resistance is the resistance of the bulk material from which the transistor is made. In the equivalent circuit it obviously should appear in series with the three leads. However, it is usually found that only the base spreading resistance is sufficiently large to be of any consequence.

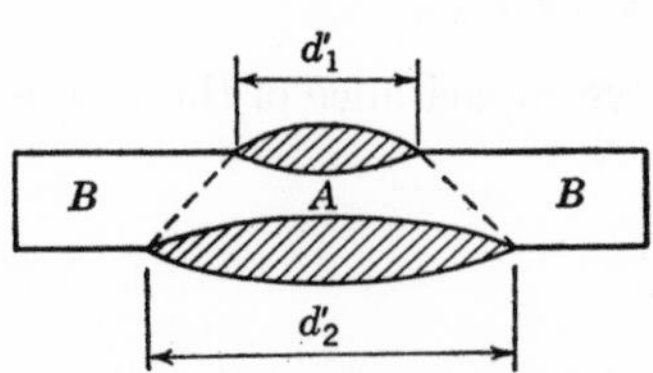

Fig. 8-8. Regions constituting base spreading resistance in a fused alloy junction transistor.

Figure 8-8 shows a cross section of a fused alloy junction transistor. The germanium wafer which constitutes the base is divided into two regions. Region A is the active region across which the minority carriers diffuse, while region B is an inactive region. From the point of

---

in the case of the collector junction of a transistor is the same as described for a p-n junction diode.

[20] K. B. McAfee, E. J. Ryder, W. Shockley, and M. Sparks, "Observations of Zener Current in Germanium p-n Junctions," *Phys. Rev.*, Vol. 83, pp. 650–651, 1951.

view of wishing to reduce the base spreading resistance it is obviously desirable to make the base lead contact as close as possible to region A, in which case region A would alone be responsible for the observed base spreading resistance. However, in practice, the placing of a contact too close to the emitter may have an adverse effect on the effective lifetime of the minority carriers by providing a recombination surface (Sec. 8.11).

It is easily seen that the base spreading resistance is not quite constant, since region A depends on the effective base width, which is a function of the collector voltage, as shown in Sec. 8.13. This nonlinearity may be taken into account, for example, by inserting a feedback generator in series with the base spreading resistance (see Fig. 7-2). In many common type transistors, however, this effect has not been found to be significant.

In order to judge the order of magnitude of base spreading resistance, consider a concentric cylinder of germanium with 0.01 in. inside and 0.05 in. outside diameters. (This may be the order of magnitude of the emitter and collector diameters.) Let the height of the cylinder be 0.002 in. If the resistivity of the germanium is, say, 30 ohm-cm, then the resistance of the cylinder between the inside and outside surfaces is

$$R = \frac{\rho}{2\pi L} \ln\left(\frac{d_2'}{d_1'}\right) = 150 \text{ ohms}$$

Most junction transistors have a base spreading resistance which varies from about one-quarter to about four times this value.

It is obvious that reduction of resistivity of the material constituting the base will reduce the base spreading resistance. However, a reduction in the resistivity of the base region also reduces the emitter efficiency (see Eq. 8-59a), increases the collector barrier capacitance (see Eq. 8-72), increases the factor K (see Eqs. 8-44e and 8-71b), and decreases the breakdown voltage (see Eq. 8-74). It is thus seen that design compromises must be made.

8.15 The junction tetrode[21]

The theory of the operation of the junction transistor triode may serve to explain the mechanism of operation of the junction tetrode.

[21] R. L. Wallace, L. G. Schimpf, and E. Dickten, "A Junction Transistor Tetrode for High Frequency Use," *Proc. I.R.E.*, Vol. 40, p. 1395, Nov. 1952.

Figures 8-9a and 8-9b show an *n-p-n* junction transistor with two base leads connected at opposite ends of the base section. The biasing of this tetrode is the same as that for the conventional triode except that an additional bias battery V'_{BB} is connected to the second base lead through a bias resistance.

Suppose that the collector and emitter bias batteries cause a voltage of 12 v and −0.1 v to appear from collector to ground and from emitter to ground, respectively. The result of the current I'_{BB}, which flows through the base, is that a voltage drop appears across the base section. Let this voltage drop be 0.6 v as indicated in Fig. 8-9a.

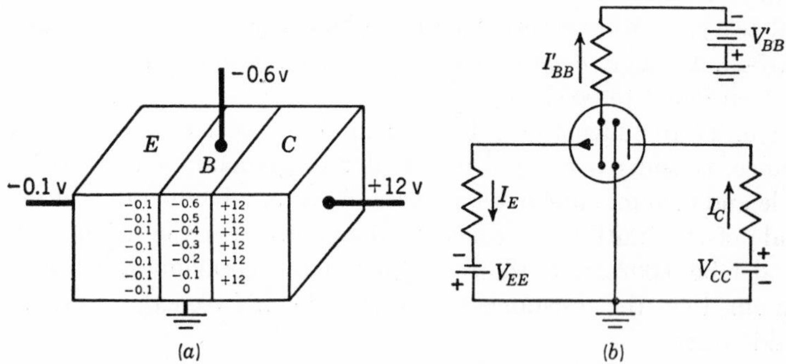

Fig. 8-9. Junction tetrode.

In order for transistor action to occur, the emitter must be biased negatively with respect to the base, and this is seen to occur only at the bottom end of the base. This confines transistor action to a small region in the immediate vicinity of the base lead, which results in a decrease of the effective base spreading resistance, and also in a smaller collector transition capacitance, on account of the increase in collector to base voltage at the top of the junction. The net result is a larger gain at the higher frequencies.

An accompanying factor is a drop in α_o or α_{cbo}. This is partly due to transistor action now occurring closer to the surface, which results in an increase in surface recombination.

8.16 Temperature dependence of transistor parameters

The dependence of the transistor parameters on temperature is generally greater than the temperature dependence of vacuum tube parameters. Consider the variation of the resistivity of *n*- and *p*-type

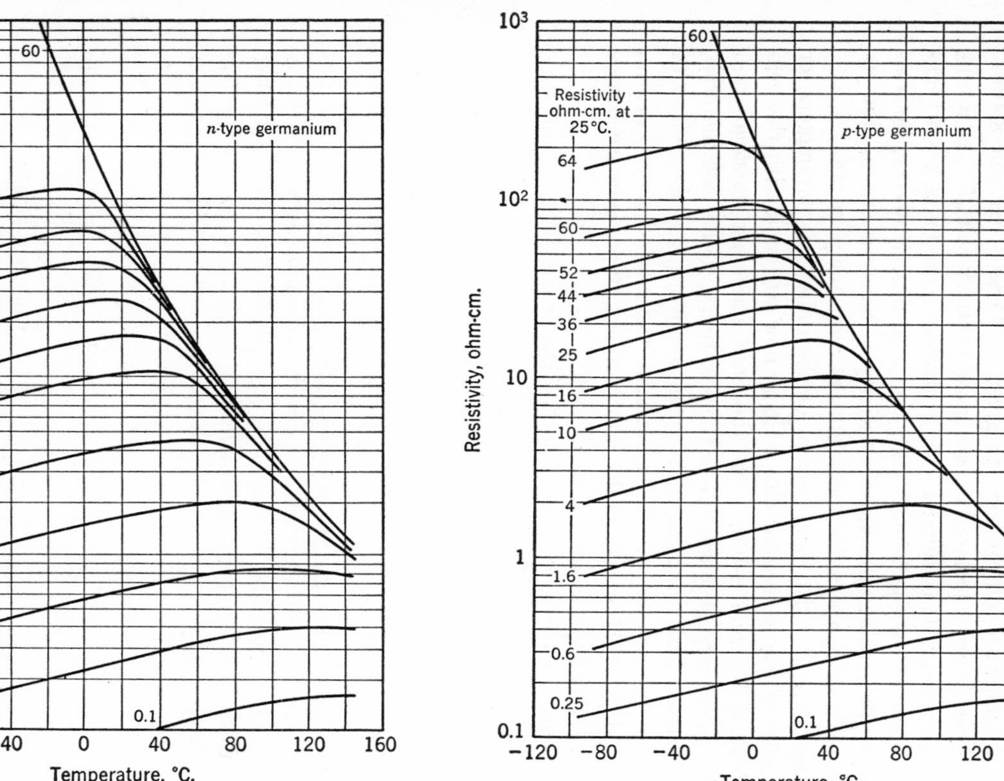

Fig. 8-10. (a) Resistivity of n-type germanium as a function of temperature; (b) resistivity of p-type germanium as a function of temperature.

germanium with temperature as given in Figs. 8-10a and 8-10b.[22] These curves are calculated by using the resistivity at 25°C as a running parameter. It is apparent that intrinsic germanium has a negative temperature coefficient at all temperatures. However, both *n*- and *p*-type germanium whose resistivity is below about 16 ohm-cm have positive temperature coefficients at room temperature.

The variation with temperature of the individual parameters, or elements of the equivalent circuit, may now be found with the help of Figs. 8-10a and 8-10b. Thus the base spreading *resistance* $r_{bb'}$, which is directly proportional to the resistivity of the base material, will increase with temperature at room temperature if the resistivity is below 16 ohm-cm. At the same time the *conductances* G_{11}, G_{12}, G_{21}, and G_{22} will increase at the rate of about 10 per cent per degree Kelvin. This may be proved as follows.[23]

Let the temperature dependence of the conductivity of intrinsic germanium given by

$$\sigma_i^2 \propto e^{-Eg/kT} \tag{8-75a}$$

and for impure germanium, near room temperature, let

$$\sigma_n \quad \text{or} \quad \sigma_p \propto T^{-3/2} \tag{8-75b}$$

where E_g is the energy gap between valence and conduction band = 0.72 electron volt for germanium; k is Boltzmann's constant = 1.4×10^{-23} joule per degree Kelvin; T = temperature in degrees Kelvin. From Eqs. (8-26a) to (8-26d) it follows that G_{11}, G_{12}, G_{21}, or G_{22} may be written

$$G_{xy} \propto \frac{\sigma_i^2}{\sigma_b} \tag{8-76a}$$

Thus

$$G_{xy} \propto e^{-Eg/kT}T^{3/2} \tag{8-76b}$$

$$\frac{dG_{xy}}{dT}\frac{1}{G_{xy}} = \frac{1}{T}\left(\frac{Eg}{kT} + \frac{3}{2}\right) = 0.1 \text{ per degree Kelvin}$$

where use is made of values given above.

The currents I_{CO}, I_{CBO}, I_{ES}, I_{CS}, and I_{BS} can be shown to have a

[22] The curves are reproduced from P. J. Herkart and J. Kurshan, "Theoretical Resistivity and Hall Coefficient of Impure Germanium Near Room Temperature," *RCA Rev.*, Vol. 14, Sept. 1953.

[23] W. Shockley, M. Sparks, and G. K. Teal, "P-N Junction Transistor," *Phys. Rev.*, Vol. 83, p. 158, July 1951.

temperature sensitivity almost equal to that of G_{xy}, i.e., about 10 per cent per degree Kelvin. The slight difference here is due to the factor $\Lambda \equiv q/kT$ volt^{-1} which, as can be seen, is inversely proportional to the absolute temperature.

The elements of the small-signal equivalent circuit are generally less affected by temperature than is G_{xy} above. This may be seen by considering, for example, Eq. (8-30a).

$$g_{11} = G_{11}\,\epsilon^{\Lambda V_E}$$

It is apparent that although G_{11} rises with temperature, $\epsilon^{\Lambda V_E}$ will decrease with temperature, and thus g_{11} is less temperature-sensitive than G_{11} (see Problem 8.9).

APPENDIX 1

CONDUCTIVITY RELATIONSHIPS

The mobility of an electron or hole is defined by

$$v_d = \mu E$$

where v_d is drift velocity and E is electric field intensity.

In any region where free electrons and holes are present, the total current will be due to the movement of both these charge carriers. Thus the conductivity, defined as the ratio of total current crossing a unit area to the electric field intensity perpendicular to this area, is

$$\sigma = \frac{1}{\rho} = q\mu_n n + q\mu_p p \tag{8-77}$$

where σ is conductivity (ohm^{-1}cm^{-1}); ρ is resistivity (ohm-cm); q is electronic charge; n is density of free electrons in the region; p is density of free holes in the region; μ_n is mobility of electrons; μ_p is mobility of holes. In the case of intrinsic materials, the conductivity is

$$\sigma_i = q\mu_n n_i + q\mu_p n_i \tag{8-78}$$

since the number of holes and electrons are equal to a temperature-dependent constant n_i.

In the case of n-type or of p-type material, where most carriers are of one type, the conductivities are, respectively,

$$\sigma_n \doteq q\mu_n n_n \tag{8-79}$$

and
$$\sigma_p \doteq q\mu_p p_n \tag{8-80}$$

It can also be shown[24] that when both holes and electrons are present under thermal equilibrium conditions, such as in the n and p regions of a p-n junction, then

$$n_n p_n = p_p n_p = n_i^2 \tag{8-81}$$

where p_n is the thermal equilibrium value of hole density in the n region, and n_p is the thermal equilibrium value of electron density in the p region.

Thus for n-type or p-type material having conductivities σ_n and σ_p, respectively, it follows from Eqs. (8-78), (8-79), (8-80), and (8-81) that[25]

$$q\mu_p p_n = \frac{b\sigma_i^2}{(1 + b)^2\sigma_n} \tag{8-82}$$

and
$$q\mu_n n_p = \frac{b\sigma_i^2}{(1 + b)^2\sigma_p}, \quad \text{where} \quad b \equiv \frac{\mu_n}{\mu_p} \tag{8-83}$$

Thus from Eqs. (8-82) and (8-83),

$$\frac{\sigma_p}{\sigma_n} = \frac{\mu_p p_n}{\mu_n n_p} = \frac{D_p p_n}{D_n n_p} = \frac{1}{b}\frac{p_n}{n_p}$$

where use is made of the Einstein relationship of Eq. (8-24).

PROBLEMS

8-1. Derive an expression for I_{CBO}, the collector direct current, when the base current is zero, in terms of the d-c conductances G_{11}, G_{12}, G_{21}, and G_{22}. Express I_{CBO} now in terms of the conductivities of the p and n regions by means of Eqs. (8-26a) to (8-26d), and compare it with the expressions for I_{CO} given in Eq. (8-29).

8-2. Using Fig. 7-3a, give a physical interpretation of both terms of K given by Eq. (8-33d). (In the derivation of Eq. (8-33c) only the first term of K is interpreted by using Fig. 8-4.)

8-3. (a) Derive the open-circuit input, transfer and output impedance for a transistor, z_{11}, z_{12}, z_{21}, and z_{22}, from the admittances

[24] Shockley, *loc. cit.*, p. 460.
[25] Shockley, *loc. cit.*, p. 461.

given by Eqs. (8-43a) to (8-43d), using the conversion formula given in Eq. (2-21). Note that $\coth^2 \theta - \operatorname{cosech}^2 \theta = 1$.

(b) From these impedances derive a T circuit, using Fig. 7-25, assuming $(W/L_p)^2 \ll 1$.

8-4. (a) Show that the common-emitter, small-signal, short-circuit current amplification factor, α_{cbo} may be written

$$\alpha_{cbo} = \frac{I_C - I_{CS}}{I_B - I_{BS}} = -\frac{G_{21}}{(G_{11} + G_{21})}$$

where I_C and I_B are the collector and base direct currents, while I_{CS} and I_{BS} are defined in Eqs. (8-28b) and (8-28c). Neglect surface recombination.

(b) Derive an expression for α_{ceo} in terms of I_C, I_E, I_{CS}, and I_{ES}.

8-5. (a) The atomic weight of germanium is 72.6, while its density is 5.35 g per cc. Taking Avogadro's number as 6.02×10^{23} (i.e., number of atoms per gram molecule), calculate the number of atoms per cubic centimeter.

(b) The resistivity of intrinsic germanium is 70 ohm-cm. The mobility constant for holes at room temperature for germanium is $\mu_p = 1700$ cm^2 per volt-sec, while for electrons it is 2.1 times greater. The electronic charge $q = 1.6 \times 10^{-19}$ coulomb. From Appendix 1 calculate the number of free electrons per cubic centimeter for intrinsic germanium.

(c) Consider n-type germanium having a resistivity $\rho = 10$ ohm-cm. Calculate the number of free electrons per cubic centimeter. In what atomic ratio must a donor impurity be added to intrinsic germanium to achieve this resistivity? Assume all impurity atoms in the germanium are ionized.

8-6. (a) Prove that the lumped-parameter π circuit, which is used to approximate the transmission line as mentioned in Sec. 8.10, has elements whose values are approximately given by Eqs. (8-46a) to (8-46f), i.e., they are virtually independent of frequency if $(W/L_p)^2 \ll 1$. Estimate the degree of approximation if $W/L_p = 0.1$.

(b) Show that if $C_{Dp} \doteq C_e$, then

$$\frac{L_d}{r_d} = \frac{1}{n\alpha_{cbo}\,\omega_{cb}} = \frac{1}{n\alpha_{cbo}}\frac{C_e}{g_e}$$

where $n \doteq 3$. *Hint:* make use of Eqs. (7-9) and (7-11).

8-7. (a) Calculate the injection efficiency, the volume recombination transport factor, and the surface recombination transport factor for a *p-n-p* transistor having the following values: $\sigma_n = 0.45$ mho/cm; $\sigma_p = 10^3$ mhos/cm; $\tau_p = 500$ μsec (lifetime of holes in base); $L_n = 1.55 \times 10^{-3}$ cm (diffusion length of electrons into emitter); $D_n = 93$ cm^2/sec; $b = 2.1$; and $s = 350$ cm/sec. The transistor is of the wafer type shown in Fig. 8-5, having a base width $W = 1.9 \times 10^{-3}$ in., and an emitter dot diameter of 15×10^{-3} in. Assume that most of the surface recombination on the base occurs in a ring around the emitter dot; the width Δd of this ring being approximately the same as that of W, i.e., 1.9×10^{-3} in.

(b) Find the value of α_{cbo} for this transistor.

8-8. (a) The dielectric constant for germanium is $\kappa = 16$, while the permittivity for free space in mks units is $\epsilon_o \approx (1.11/9) \times 10^9$. The mobility constant for holes in germanium is $\mu_p = 1700$ cm^2/volt sec near room temperature. The field intensity corresponding to the breakdown voltage is $E_z = 2 \times 10^5$ volts/cm. Using these values, show that for a Schottky type *p-n* junction the width of the transition region d (Eq. 8-70), the capacitance C_T (Eq. 8-72), and the breakdown voltage V_z (Eq. 8-74) are as follows:

$\rho_n \gg \rho_p$	$\rho_n \ll \rho_p$
$d = 0.0399\sqrt{V\rho_n} \times 10^{-3}$ in.	$d = 0.0273\sqrt{V\rho_p} \times 10^{-3}$ in.
$C = \dfrac{0.0707D^2}{\sqrt{V\rho_n}}\ \mu\mu\text{f}$	$C = \dfrac{0.103D^2}{\sqrt{V\rho_p}}\ \mu\mu\text{f}$
$V_z = 102\rho_n$ volts	$V_z = 48.1\rho_p$ volts

where V is in volts, ρ is in ohms-cm, and D is the transverse diameter in mils.

(b) Show that the factor K of the K amplifier is given by

$$K = \frac{\Lambda V_c}{n}\frac{W}{d}$$

where $n = \frac{1}{2}$ for a Schottky type barrier; $1/\Lambda = 0.026$ volt at room temperature; V_C is the collector bias voltage in volts, and W and d are the base and collector transition widths, respectively, in the same units. *Hint:* use Eqs. (8-44e) and (8-71b), assuming $(W/L_p)^2 \ll 1$.

(c) Calculate K for $W = 1.9$ mils, $\rho_b = 2$ ohm-cm, and $V_C = 6$

volts. It is assumed that the resistivity of the base region ρ_b is much larger than that of the collector.

8-9. (a) Assuming $\sigma_i^2 \propto \exp(-E_g/kT)$ and $\sigma_b \propto T^{-3/2}$, where E_g and k are as given in Sec. 8.16, evaluate the percentage variation per degree Kelvin of the currents I_{CO}, I_{CBO}, I_{CS}, I_{ES}, and I_{BS} to three significant figures.

(b) As in (a), find the temperature sensitivity of the small-signal conductances, e.g. g_{11}, for $V_E = 0.1$ volt. What is the effect of V_B on the temperature sensitivity of g_{11}?

Chapter 9

HIGH-FREQUENCY AMPLIFIERS

9.1 Introduction

The chapters on generalized network representation (Chapters 2 and 3) and high-frequency properties of transistors (Chapters 7 and 8) provide the fundamentals for operating the transistor as a high-frequency amplifier. In this chapter, use will be made of this basic information to design high-frequency amplifiers for both narrow-band and wide-band applications employing either short-circuit stable or short-circuit unstable transistors. Comparisons between transistor amplifiers and their vacuum tube counterparts will be given first; differences in their properties and the consequent differences in design method will be discussed. In particular, problems of the selection and design of different kinds of coupling networks which satisfy the selectivity and power matching requirements are considered, and, gain control, neutralization, and unilateralization of transistor amplifiers are treated in detail.

Though the maximum operating frequency of present-day transistors has been continually increasing, there are still certain limitations which in their present form restrict their application. Special triode transistors designed for high-frequency operation, such as the *p-n-i-p* and the *n-p-i-n* junction triodes are being given serious attention, while applications of tetrode junction transistors have been explored and have been used effectively as high-frequency amplifiers.

9.2 Comparison between transistor amplifiers and vacuum tube amplifiers at high frequencies

Since both a transistor and a vacuum tube are capable of a comparable amount of amplification, especially at the lower frequencies, it is instructive to compare the basic features of the transistor amplifier with those of the vacuum tube amplifier. In particular, it will be helpful to bring out similarities between them so that some of the fundamental techniques in designing tube amplifiers can be used directly to design transistor amplifiers, while setting forth their differences so that certain modifications in design methods can be introduced.

Consider a conventional common-cathode class-A vacuum tube amplifier, Fig. 9-1, and assume that it is operated at a frequency such that both the interelectrode capacitances and the transit time effect can be neglected. On comparing this amplifier with a transistor amplifier operated in the same frequency range, we find that the main differences include the relative magnitude of the input impedances, the gain considerations, the internal feedback properties, and the frequency responses. The input impedance of a vacuum tube triode is normally so high that special difficulties are encountered (such as those caused by stray capacitances) when attempting to match the source impedance to the triode for maximum power transfer. This is one of the reasons that voltage gain, rather than power gain, is used to describe the performance of a vacuum tube amplifier.

On the other hand, the transistor amplifier has comparatively *low* input impedance, while the output impedance is of the same order of magnitude as that of a vacuum tube triode. Thus, it is more convenient to speak here of current amplification. Also, since impedance matching can be accomplished without undue difficulties, the *maximum power gain* is a practical and useful concept. In general, the power gain, current gain, and voltage gain, as well as the matched input and output impedance, are related at low frequencies as follows:

$$
\begin{aligned}
\text{power gain} &= K_p = 10 \log_{10} \frac{V_o^2/R_o}{V_{in}^2/R_{in}} \\
&= 20 \log_{10} \frac{V_o}{V_{in}} - 10 \log_{10} \frac{R_o}{R_{in}} = 10 \log_{10} \frac{i_o^2 R_o}{i_{in}^2 R_{in}} \\
&= 20 \log_{10} \frac{i_o}{i_{in}} + 10 \log_{10} \frac{R_o}{R_{in}} \\
\text{voltage gain} &= K_v = 20 \log_{10} \frac{V_o}{V_{in}} \\
&= K_p + 10 \log_{10} \frac{R_o}{R_{in}} \\
\text{current gain} &= K_i = 20 \log_{10} \frac{i_o}{i_{in}} \\
&= K_p - 10 \log_{10} \frac{R_o}{R_{in}}
\end{aligned}
\tag{9-1}
$$

As a consequence of the comparatively low input impedance of transistors, the input electrode of one stage may not be simply connected to the output electrode of the preceding stage in cascaded, parallel-tuned narrow-band amplifiers, as may be done when vacuum tubes are used, since the overall Q will generally be too low. Thus the coupling of such transistor stages requires a somewhat more elaborate coupling network than is necessary in cascaded vacuum tube amplifiers.

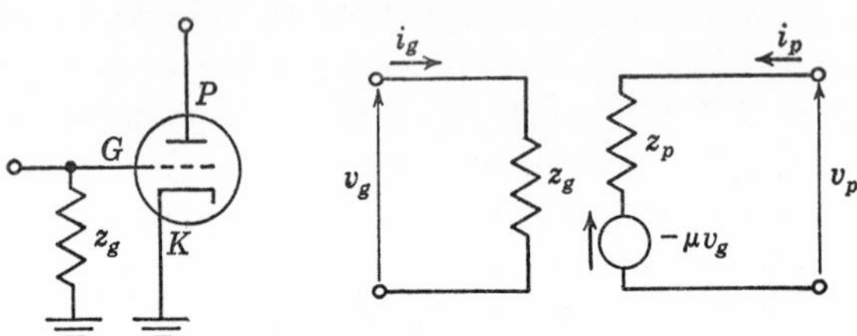

Fig. 9-1. Simplified equivalent circuit of common-cathode vacuum tube amplifier.

The second main difference between a vacuum tube amplifier and a transistor amplifier originates from the feedback properties of the latter. A vacuum tube amplifier at low frequencies, i.e., neglecting the interelectrode capacitances and the transit-time effect, has negligible internal feedback and acts as a unilateral network which may be characterized as having zero reverse transfer impedance ($Z_{12} = 0$). The mesh (loop) equations (from Fig. 9-1) of such an amplifier are, at low frequencies.

$$v_g = z_g i_g \,, \quad v_p = -\mu z_g i_g + z_p i_p \tag{9-2}$$

where z_g represents the externally connected grid impedance. The open-circuit impedance matrix of the amplifier is

$$\|z\| = \begin{Vmatrix} z_g & 0 \\ -\mu z_g & z_p \end{Vmatrix} \tag{9-3}$$

An advantage afforded by the zero reverse transfer impedance of the vacuum tube amplifier is its isolation property; changes occurring at the output terminals will not affect voltage-current relationships existing at the input terminals. But the transistor is, in general, a bilateral network having both nonzero reverse and forward transfer impedance, (i.e., $Z_{12} \neq 0$, $Z_{21} \neq 0$) in its open-circuit impedance matrix. These matrices are listed in Table 3-1. This implies that a transistor amplifier is a poor isolation stage, and interaction occurs between its input and output terminals. The effects of such interaction introduce special problems of aligning cascaded narrow-band amplifiers. By the same token, stage isolation and neutralization of transistor amplifiers are also important problems.

A further limitation of the transistor high-frequency amplifier is its signal power-handling capacity, which is limited by several factors: three factors mentioned in Sec. 6.2 limit the maximum voltage which can be applied, the heat generation and dissipation limit the power dissipation, and the small linear region in its static characteristics limits the range of operation.

9.3 Evaluation of maximum power gain

As stated in the previous section, the power gain (and to a lesser extent the current gain) is an important measure of the capabilities of a transistor. In this and the following section the conjugate matched (i.e., maximum) power gain will be calculated from a knowledge of four independent parameters in complex form.

Determination of Maximum Power Gain from the h Parameters

It has been shown in Chapter 3 that once the four parameters of a four-terminal network are measured, the matched input and output impedances and the matched power gain of the network can be calculated.

As an illustrative example let us examine the matched power gain of a common-emitter, 455 kc intermediate-frequency amplifier which uses a junction-type transistor with the following equivalent circuit element (Fig. 9-2): $1/g_e = 1300$ ohms; $1/g_{c'} = 1000$ ohms; $r_d = 30$ ohms; $C_e = 0.001$ μf; $C_{c'} = 0.006$ μf; $L_d = 0.3$ μh. Thus from Eq. (7-39) the common-emitter h parameters at 455 kc are:

$$h_{11} = r_{bb'} + z_e = 238 - j328 \text{ ohms}$$

$$h_{12} = z_e/Kz_{c'} = (11.35 + j2.35) \times 10^{-3}$$

$$h_{21} = z_e/z_d = 11.3\underline{/-75^\circ} = 2.93 - j10.9$$

$$h_{22} = (1/z_{c'} + 1/z_d + z_e/z_{c'}z_d)/K$$
$$= (0.444 + j0.111) \times 10^{-3} \text{ mhos}$$

The derived constants η_n, η_m, and A' are determined from Eqs. (3-51) and (3-52) as:

$$\eta_n = \frac{m_{12}n_{21} + m_{21}n_{12}}{2m_{11}m_{22}} = -0.565$$

$$A' = \frac{m_{12}m_{21} - n_{12}n_{21}}{m_{11}m_{22}} = 0.552$$

$$\eta_m = \sqrt{1 - A' - \eta_n^2} = 0.37$$

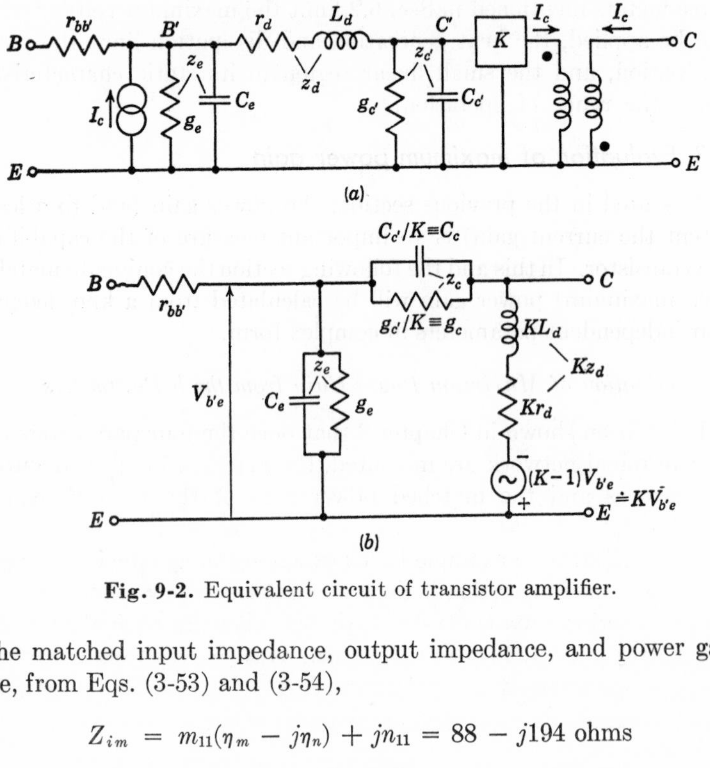

(a)

(b)

Fig. 9-2. Equivalent circuit of transistor amplifier.

The matched input impedance, output impedance, and power gain are, from Eqs. (3-53) and (3-54),

$$Z_{im} = m_{11}(\eta_m - j\eta_n) + jn_{11} = 88 - j194 \text{ ohms}$$

$$Y_{om} = m_{22}(\eta_m - j\eta_n) + jn_{22}$$

$$= (0.164 + j0.362) \times 10^{-3} \text{ mhos}$$

$$K_{pm} = \frac{|h_{21}|^2}{m_{11}m_{22}[(1 + \eta_m)^2 - \eta_n^2]} = 27.4 \text{ db}$$

Approximate Calculation

As an alternative to the exact calculation of the matched power gain from the h parameters, it may in some instances be estimated fairly closely as follows:

Let the input and the output impedances of a transistor amplifier be represented by two parallel combinations of resistances and reactances R_i, X_i, and R_o, X_o, respectively; and let the output terminals be connected to a load Z_L and the input terminals to a current

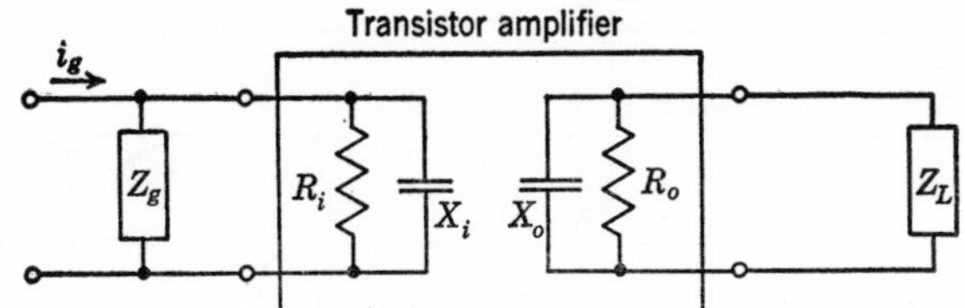

Fig. 9-3. Network representation of transistor amplifier.

generator with internal impedance Z_g as shown in Fig. 9-3. Since at the conjugate matched condition

$$R_L = R_o, \qquad X_L = X_o^*$$
$$R_g = R_i, \qquad X_g = X_i^*$$

and the power output is at its maximum, the power gain is then determined by

$$K_p = 10 \log_{10} \frac{V_L^2/R_L}{i_g^2 R_g/4} = 10 \log_{10} \frac{4V_L^2}{i_g^2 R_g R_L} \tag{9-4}$$

The problem is now to find R_g and R_L. In this connection we are reminded, however, that in a general network, if the matching impedance has a restriction placed on it, such as a fixed phase angle or a fixed reactive part, then the maximum power transfer occurs when the *magnitude* of the matching impedance equals the magnitude of the impedance to be matched. For practical reasons conjugate matching at the *input* side of a common-emitter transistor amplifier is often not considered worthwhile or may even prove impossible. Thus, on the input side, resistance matching is often considered adequate. The power gain of a typical junction transistor measured under the input resistance-matched and output conjugate-matched condition is shown in Fig. 9-4.[1]

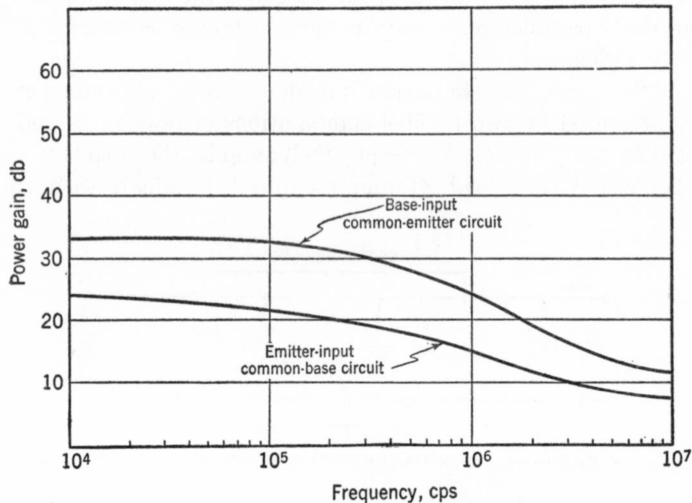

Fig. 9-4. Power gain vs. frequency of a typical *p-n-p* high-frequency junction-type transistor.

9.4 Some general considerations in the design of narrow-band and wide-band amplifiers

Since the properties of narrow-band and wide-band amplifiers are quite different, their respective circuit analysis, synthesis, and design also differ. In general, narrow-band amplifiers require high-Q coupling circuits, while low-Q coupling circuits are generally required for wide-band amplifiers. Amplifiers having an effective circuit Q greater than 10 will be designated as narrow-band amplifiers.

It is well known that spurious oscillations may result in vacuum tube amplifiers because of the presence of sufficiently large interelectrode capacitances and lead inductances which provide positive feedback. The same difficulties may exist in a high-gain transistor amplifier, whether of the junction or point-contact type. The actual stray elements which cause these spurious oscillations will, however, differ in detail in the junction and point-contact transistors, due to the

[1] **C. W. Muller and J. L. Pankove, "A *PNP* Triode Alloy Junction Transistor for Radio-Frequency Amplification," *RCA Rev.*, pp. 586–598, Dec. 1953.**

different phase relationships existing in these two devices. For the various modes of oscillations the reader is referred to Chap. 10. Neutralization methods for avoiding these difficulties are discussed in Sec. 9.10.

In the design of *point-contact* transistor amplifiers, special attention must be paid to the coupling networks in order to avoid two-terminal oscillations. Such oscillations are likely to occur if short-circuit unstable transistors are used, or if sufficient external base resistance is present.

Generally, the impedance of the coupling network between stages must here be larger than the negative resistance to be found at the transistor terminals over the whole frequency range where the negative resistance exists. Thus, a parallel resonant coupling network which may be suitable for junction transistors will be unsuitable for tuned amplifiers using short-circuit unstable transistors, for even if it offers high impedance at resonance it presents a low impedance at frequency removed from resonance, so that oscillations are likely to occur.

9.5 Coupling networks for narrow-band amplifiers with short-circuit stable transistors

In the design of a narrow-band amplifier, it is assumed that the matched power gain and the input and output impedances are known. The problem then becomes one of determining a suitable interstage coupling network to realize the desired selectivity, while maintaining the matched power gain in the pass band. Unavoidable losses in circuit resistances and in magnetic cores will, of course, subtract a small amount of gain from the matched figure.

Figure 9-5a shows two cascaded stages in block diagram form; R_o and C_o are the equivalent parallel-output resistance and output capacitance of the first stage; R_i and C_i represent the input resistance and capacitance of the second stage. It is often more convenient to consider the reactive parts as part of the coupling networks, as shown in Fig. 9-5b. Let K_p be the power gain per stage, f_o the resonant frequency, $Q = f_o/\Delta f$, the loaded Q of the coupling network, where Δf = the 3 db down bandwidth. The problem, then, is to design a coupling network to satisfy both the matching and the selectivity requirements. We shall discuss these coupling networks in detail.

Single-tuned Circuits

Design procedures for various kinds of coupling networks have been summarized in Table 9-1, where the quantities a, C_T, C_m, L_T, L_m and k have been introduced to simplify the computations. The origin of these quantities is explained in the following analysis of two basic interstage-coupling networks.

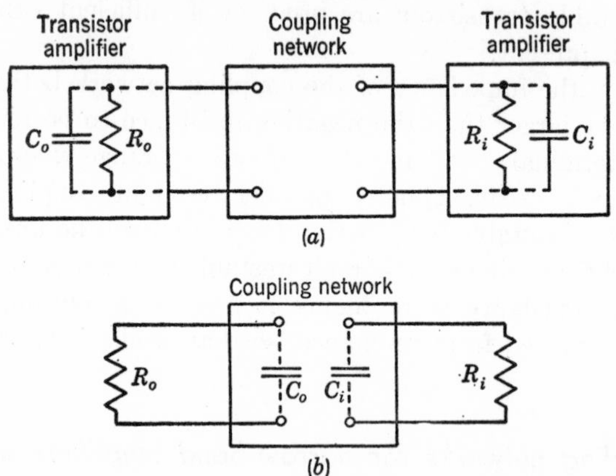

Fig. 9-5. Method to include input and output reactances of amplifier in the coupling network.

Consider a parallel-tuned circuit with an ideal transformer having a turns ratio of a connected to it, as shown in Fig. 9-6a. This is the first basic interstage-coupling network that will be considered. The matched condition neglecting coil loss is

$$R_o = a^2 R_i, \quad a = \sqrt{R_o/R_i} \tag{9-5}$$

and the selectivity or bandwidth relation is

$$Q = \frac{f_o}{\Delta f} = \pi R_o C_T f_o \quad \text{or} \quad C_T = \frac{1}{\pi R_o \Delta f} = \frac{Q}{\pi R_o f_o} \tag{9-6}$$

where C_T is defined as the capacitance needed to satisfy the required bandwidth when it is connected in parallel with $R_o/2$. Let L_T be the inductance required to resonate with C_T at the given frequency, f_o, i.e. $L_T = 1/\omega_o^2 C_T$.

Since this is an "ideal" situation, in which the coil is assumed to be without resistance, we relate all quantities for the practical situation (i.e., using coils that have some resistance) to these "ideal" quantities. Thus, if the coil has an equivalent parallel resistance R_C, and the same bandwidth and resonant frequency are specified as for the ideal case, then new values for the transformer turns ratio, capacitance, and inductance are required (see Fig. 9-6b). Thus inclusion

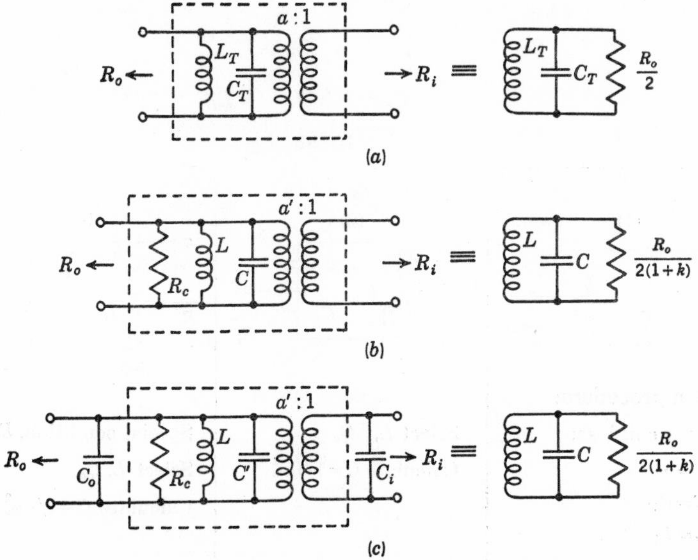

Fig. 9-6. (a) Parallel tuned LC circuit with an ideal transformer as coupling network. (b) Parallel LC circuit including coil loss. (c) Redesign of (b) including C_o and C_i.

of the coil resistance with the output resistance R_o results in a new equivalent-output resistance R_o' which is related to the old value R_o by

$$R_o' = \frac{1}{1/R_o + 1/R_c} = \frac{R_o}{1 + k}$$

where $k = R_o/R_c$, $R_c = Q_c\omega_o L$; L is the new coil inductance, and Q_c is the Q of the coil alone. The matched condition is now

$$R_o' = a'^2 R_i$$

From these considerations, the turns ratio a' is related to the old turns ratio a by

$$a' = \frac{a}{\sqrt{1 + k}}$$

Table 9–1

DESIGN PROCEDURE OF COUPLING NETWORKS FOR TUNED TRANSISTOR AMPLIFIERS

Given data: $R_o,\ R_i,\ f_o,\ Q,\ (Q = f_o/\Delta f)$

Derived constants:

$$a = \sqrt{R_o/R_i} \qquad (9\text{–}5)$$

$$C_T = Q/\pi f_o R_o \qquad (9\text{–}6)$$

$$C_m = 1/(2\pi f_o \sqrt{R_o R_i}) \qquad (9\text{–}8)$$

$$k = R_o/R_i$$

Circuit: (1)	(2)	(3)
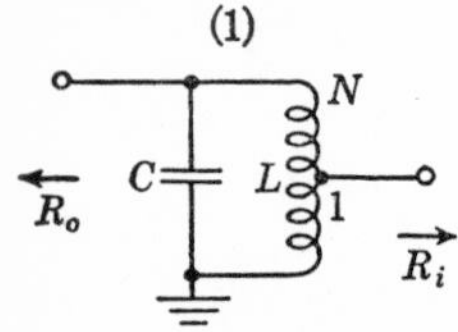	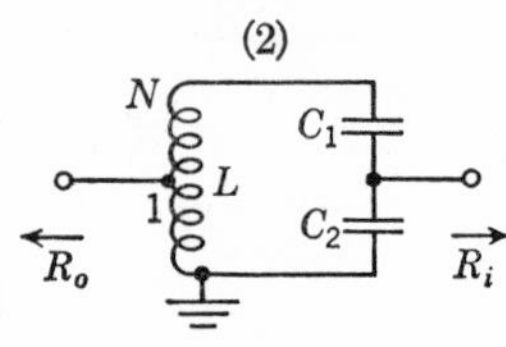	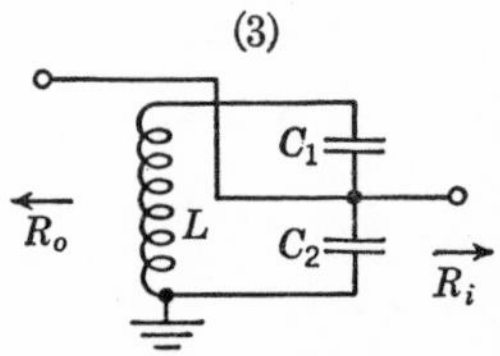
Design procedure: Neglect coil loss: $N=a$ $C=C_T$ $L=L_T$	Select L, Q_c Calculate $C=1/L\omega_o^2$	Special condition, $R_o=R_i$ Select L, Q_c, Calculate $C=1/L\omega_o^2$
Include coil loss: $N=\dfrac{a}{\sqrt{1+k}}$ $C=C_T(1+k)$ $L=\dfrac{L_T}{1+k}$ $P_c=10\log_{10}(1+k)$	Include coil loss: $N=\dfrac{1}{\sqrt{\dfrac{C}{C_T}-k}}$ $C_1=\dfrac{C}{1-\dfrac{1}{a}\sqrt{\dfrac{C}{C_T}}}$ $C_2=a\sqrt{CC_T}$ $P_c=10\log_{10}(1+kN^2)$	Include coil loss: $C_1=\dfrac{C}{1-\sqrt{\dfrac{C}{C_T}}}$ $C_2=\sqrt{CC_T}$ $P_c=10\log_{10}\left(1+k\dfrac{C_T}{C}\right)$
Modification for C_o, C_i: $C'=C_T(1+k)-C_o-\dfrac{C_i}{N^2}$	Modification for C_o, C_i: $C_1'=\dfrac{C-C_o/N^2}{1-\dfrac{1}{a}\sqrt{\dfrac{1}{C_T}\left(C-\dfrac{C_o}{N^2}\right)}}$ $C_2'=a\sqrt{\left(C-\dfrac{C_o}{N^2}\right)C_T}-C_i$	Modification for C_o, C_i: $C_2'=C_2-C_o-C_i$

Table 9–1 (Concluded)

Circuit: (4) 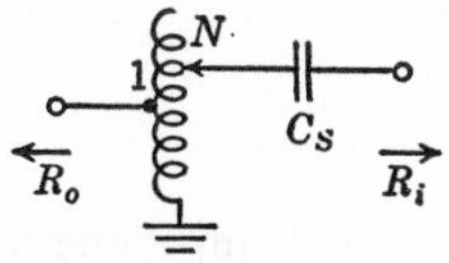	(5) 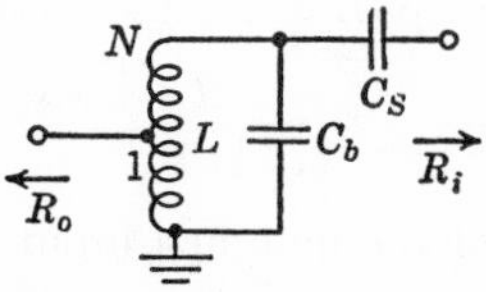	(6) 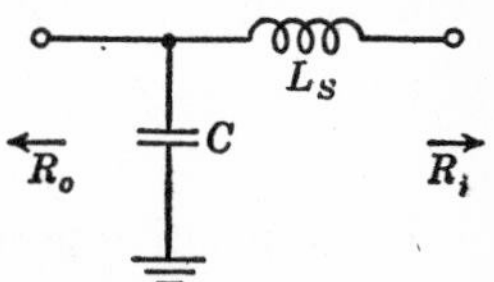
Design procedure:		
Neglect coil loss: $C_s = C_m^2/C_T$ $L = L_m^2/L_T$ $N = C_T/C_m$ $Q > \frac{a}{2}$, $N > 1$ $Q = \frac{a}{2}$, $N = 1$ $Q < \frac{a}{2}$, $N < 1$	Select L, Q_c Calculate $C = 1/L\omega_o^2$	Neglect coil loss: $L_s = L_m$ $C = C_m$
Include coil loss: $C_s = \frac{C_m^2}{C_T}$, $L = \frac{L_m^2}{L_T}$ $N = \frac{1}{\sqrt{\left(\frac{C_m}{C_T}\right)^2 - k}}$ $P_c = 10 \log_{10}(1 + kN^2)$	Include coil loss: $C_s = C_m\sqrt{\frac{C}{C_T}}$ $C_b = C - C_s$ $N = \sqrt{\frac{1}{\frac{C}{C_T} - k}}$ $P_c = 10 \log_{10}(1 + kN^2)$	Include coil loss (Q_s, k_s): $L_s = L_m\sqrt{1 + \frac{Q_s^2 k_s}{a^2}}$ $C = \frac{C_m}{\sqrt{1 + \frac{a^2}{Q_s^2 k_s}}}$ $P_c = 10 \log_{10}\left(1 + \frac{Q_s^2 k_s}{a^2}\right)$
Modification for C_o: $L' = \frac{L}{1 + C_o/N^2 C_s}$	Modification for C_o: $C_b' = C_b - \frac{C_o}{N^2}$	Modification for C_o: $C' = C + C_o$

Also, the selectivity requirement gives (for the same bandwidth)

$$\Delta f = \frac{1}{\pi R_o' C}$$

where C is the new capacitance required and is seen to be related to the old capacitance C_T by

$$C = (1 + k)C_T$$

Finally, the new inductance, L, is related to the old inductance L_T by

$$L = \frac{L_T}{1 + k}$$

If the reactive parts of the matched input and output impedances can be represented, respectively, by a capacitance C_i in parallel with R_i, and a capacitance C_o in parallel with R_o, as shown in Fig. 9-6c, then the actual capacitance to be connected externally is simply the difference between C and $(C_o + C_i/a'^2)$, i.e.,

$$C' = (1 + k)C_T - C_o - \frac{C_i}{a'^2}$$

The efficiency of a coupling network may be defined as the ratio of the actual maximum power delivered to the load, to the theoretical power which would be delivered to the load if the coupling network were lossless. In the preceding example the efficiency is shown as

$$\text{efficiency} = \frac{1/R_o}{1/R_o + 1/R_c} = \frac{1}{1 + k}$$

The reciprocal of the efficiency is termed the *coil loss,* which may be conveniently expressed as

$$P_C = 10 \log_{10} (1 + \text{k}) \quad \text{db} \tag{9-7}$$

The advantage of this form is that the coil loss can be simply subtracted from the amplifier gain (in decibels) to obtain the overall gain of the stage.

The second interstage-coupling network to be examined is based on the series-to-parallel impedance transformation shown in Figs. 9-7a and 9-7b. This transformation is approximate and holds only for high-Q circuits at a frequency range. Under matched conditions, the equivalent parallel resistance X_m^2/R_i should equal the output resistance R_o (if coil loss is neglected) and, thus,

$$X_m^2 = R_o R_i = \left(\frac{1}{\omega_o C_m}\right)^2 \tag{9-8a}$$

and

$$C_m = \frac{1}{\omega_o \sqrt{R_o R_i}} \tag{9-8b}$$

where C_m is defined as the capacitance required to satisfy the matching requirement by series-parallel impedance transformation which transforms R_i to R_o. Since C_m is not generally equal to C_T, this circuit will satisfy the matching requirement but not the selectivity

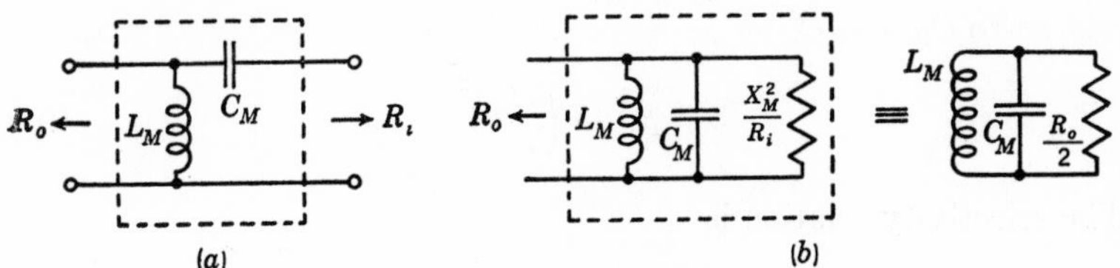

Fig. 9-7. (a) Simple LC coupling network; (b) transformed form of (a).

requirement. This lack of design freedom is imposed because of the limited number of circuit elements used. Finally, the inductance for the specified frequency of operation, ω_o, is

$$L_m = \frac{1}{\omega_o^2 C_m} \tag{9-8c}$$

A detailed circuit analysis is required to explain how the design procedures listed in Table 9-1 are derived. Circuit 4 is selected and redrawn in Fig. 9-8a, and may be transformed to the circuit of Fig. 9-8b.

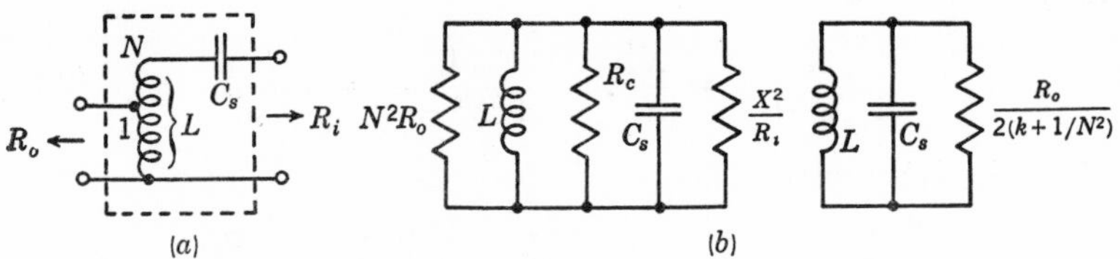

Fig. 9-8. (a) Circuit 4 of Table 9-1; (b) transformed form of circuit 4.

The coil loss must be neglected in the beginning of the analysis since neither the inductance nor the coil Q is known. Under matched conditions, neglecting coil loss,

$$N^2R_o = \frac{1}{(\omega_o C_s)^2 R_i}$$

where $1/N$ is the turns ratio of the autotransformer. By definition,

$$C_m^2 = \frac{1}{\omega_o^2 R_o R_i}$$

substituting this into the preceding expression, the turns ratio is related to C_m and C_s by

$$N^2 = \left(\frac{C_m}{C_s}\right)^2 \qquad (9\text{-}9)$$

The selectivity relation is

$$\frac{Q}{\pi f_o} = R_o C_T = R_o N^2 C_s \qquad (9\text{-}10)$$

Rearranging (9-10) and replacing $Q/\pi f_o R_o$ by C_T, we obtain

$$N^2 = \frac{C_T}{C_s} \qquad (9\text{-}11)$$

Combining (9-11) with (9-9) provides

$$C_s = \frac{C_m^2}{C_T}, \qquad L = \frac{L_m^2}{L_T} \qquad (9\text{-}12)$$

The value of inductance and its loss can now be determined. Let us select a coil of small size, having the highest possible Q_c, for mechanical convenience. The matched condition, considering the coil loss, is therefore

$$\frac{R_o}{1/N^2 + k} = \frac{X_s^2}{R_i}, \qquad \frac{1}{1/N^2 + k} = \left(\frac{C_m}{C_s}\right)^2 \qquad (9\text{-}9a)$$

The selectivity relation is

$$\frac{Q}{\pi f_o} = R_o C_T = \frac{R_o C_s}{1/N^2 + k}, \quad \frac{1}{N^2} + k = \frac{C_s}{C_T} \qquad (9\text{-}10a)$$

Combining Eqs. (9-9a) and (9-10a) yields the following expressions for circuit constants in the presences of coil loss:

$$C_s = \frac{C_m^2}{C_T}, \qquad L = \frac{L_m^2}{L_T} \qquad (9\text{-}12a)$$

$$N = \frac{1}{\sqrt{(C_m/C_T)^2 - k}} \qquad (9\text{-}11a)$$

Equations (9-11) and (9-12) offer satisfactory results if the coil selected has negligible loss; if the coil selected has appreciable loss, Eqs. (9-11a) and (9-12a) should be used. In the latter case coil loss is given by

$$P_C = 10 \log_{10} (1 + KN^2) \qquad (9\text{-}13)$$

A typical design of the coupling networks for a 455 kc amplifier with 60 db power gain and total bandwidth of 8 kc is included to illustrate the design method discussed previously.

Three stages of base-input, common-emitter junction transistor amplifiers are sufficient to realize 60 db of power gain. Four coupling networks, with individual bandwidth of 15.7 kc, synchronously tuned to 455 kc, will give a total bandwidth of 8 kc. The matched input and output resistances are $R_i = 60$ ohms, $R_o = 6000$ ohms. Since circuits 4 and 5 of Table 9-1 require a minimum number of elements, they are selected. Calculations for Q, a, C_T, and C_m yield

$$Q = 29, \quad a = 10, \quad C_T = 3360\ \mu\mu\text{f}, \quad C_m = 580\ \mu\mu\text{f}$$

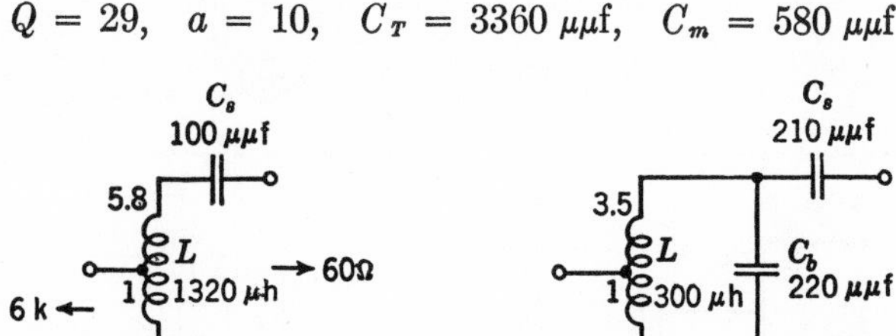

Fig. 9-9. Two coupling networks for a 455 kc i-f amplifier.

Circuit elements, calculated from equations in Table 9-1, are listed as follows:

Circuit selected from Table 9-1	No. 4	No. 5
C_s (μμf)	100	
L (μh)	1320	use 300 μh, $C_s = 210$ μμf
C_b (μμf)		220
Q_c	100	150
R_c (1000 ohms)	530	135
N	5.8	3.5
P_c (decibels)	1.4	1.9

Two types of coupling networks thus derived which satisfy the design criteria are shown in Fig. 9-9. These derived coupling networks include the amplifier capacitances, C_o and C_i, implicitly. The actual coupling circuits should be modified from these networks to exclude these capacitances.

Double-tuned Circuits

In certain applications, sharp skirt selectivity is required but cannot satisfactorily be obtained by use of synchronous-tuned, cascaded, single-tuned stages. In this event, other coupling-network types should be used; one possible solution is the use of the double-tuned

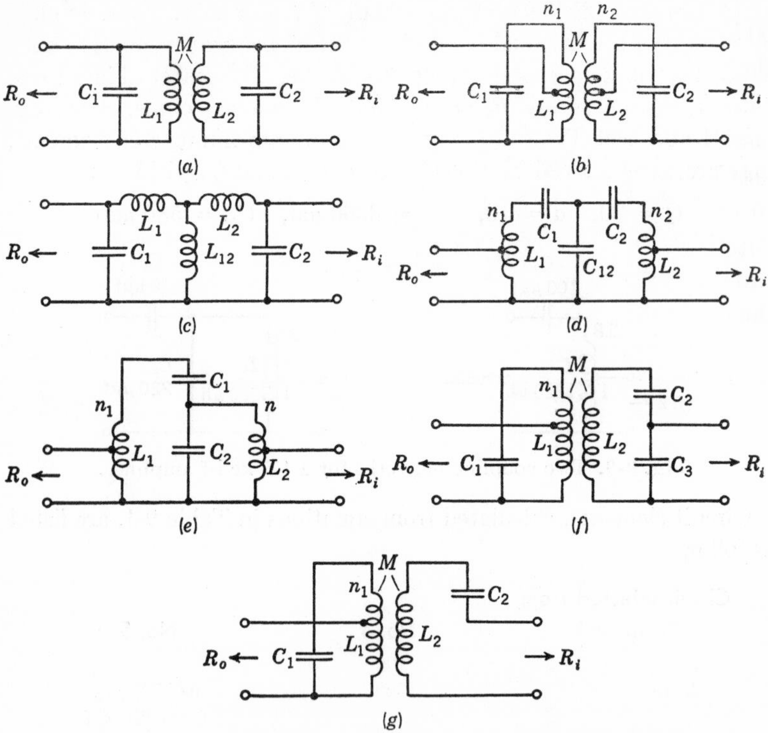

Fig. 9-10. Various types of double-tuned coupling networks.

circuit. Also, if the power gain per stage is so high that the number of stages and hence the number of coupling networks must be reduced, then the required individual circuit Q of each stage for the correct selectivity may be higher than can conveniently be obtained with single-tuned circuits, and thus double-tuned circuits are preferable.

Different types of double-tuned circuits can be used as the coupling networks for high-frequency amplifiers using short-circuit stable transistors. The double-tuned circuits may be magnetically coupled as shown in Fig. 9-10a, b, c, or they may be capacitively coupled as in Fig. 9-10d, or e, or they may be coupled with various impedance-transforming schemes as shown in Fig. 9-10f or g. For detailed treatment of double-tuned circuits the reader is referred to the literature.[2]

9.6 Narrow-band amplifiers using short-circuit unstable transistors

As illustrated earlier, the simple LC parallel resonant circuit and its modified forms are not suitable for application as coupling networks for high-frequency amplifiers using short-circuit unstable transistors, and, accordingly, other coupling network types will be examined.

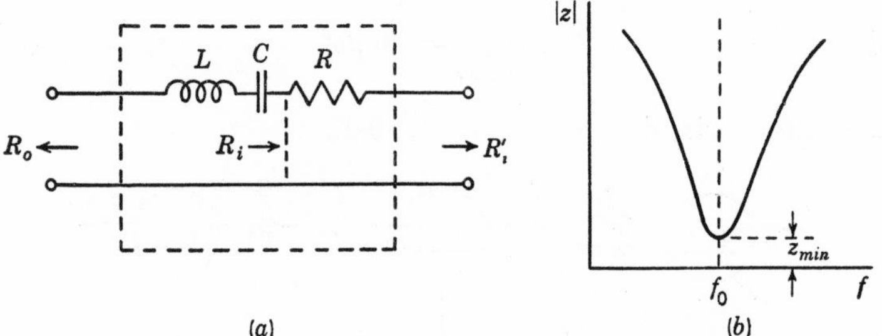

Fig. 9-11. (a) Simple LCR series circuit as a coupling network; (b) frequency response of the network.

Consider a simple series resonant circuit consisting of an inductance L, a capacitance C, and a resistance R used as the coupling network between stages, as shown in Fig. 9-11a, for which the impedance vs. frequency curve is shown in Fig. 9-11b. If R_{min} is the minimum resistance which will make the amplifier stable (considering both the preceding and the following stage) and if $|z_{min}| = R_{min}$, then the circuit

[2] A detailed analysis of coupled circuits is given by the staff of the Cruft Laboratory. Harvard University, *Electronic Circuits and Tubes*, McGraw-Hill Book Co., Inc., New York 1947, pp. 176–206; F. E. Terman, *Radio Engineer's Handbook*, McGraw-Hill Book Co., Inc., New York, 1943, pp. 148–173; G. E. Valley and H. Wallman, *Vacuum Tube Amplifiers*, McGraw-Hill Book Co., Inc., New York, 1948, pp. 201–226; C. B. Aiken, "Two Mesh Tuned Coupled Filters," *Proc. I.R.E.*, Vol. 35, Feb. 1937.

will be stable at all frequencies ($|z_{min}|$ is the minimum impedance of the coupling network).

In practice it is often desirable that $|z_{min}|$ exceed R_{min} by a considerable margin in order to insure stability. In the series resonant circuit of Fig. 9-11a, z_{min} is equal to the coil resistance. Thus, it is seen that the series coupling network should have a high enough resistance to insure stability, and the overall Q of the circuit should permit the required selectivity. Consider the following example:

Example 1: Design a simple series coupling network for a 455 kc intermediate-frequency amplifier using short-circuit unstable transistors. For stability it is found that the input resistance R_1 of the stabilized transistor is 300 ohms. The required circuit Q is 30.

From the properties of a series resonant circuit

$$L = \frac{QR_i}{\omega_o} = 3.2 \quad \text{mh} \tag{9-14}$$

and

$$C = \frac{1}{\omega_o^2 L} = 40 \ \mu\mu\text{f} \tag{9-15}$$

The resultant circuit is shown in Fig. 9-12.

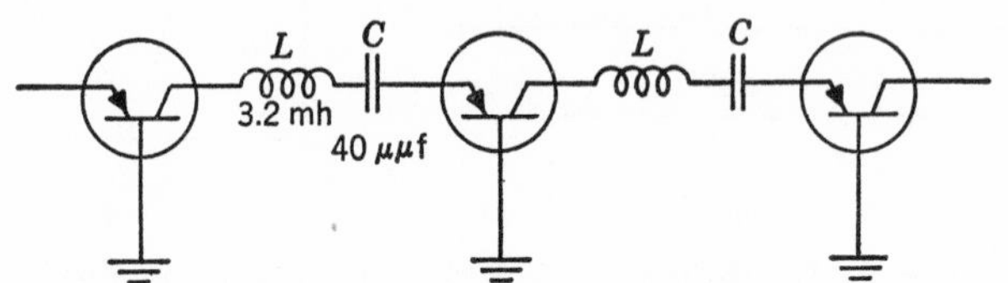

Fig. 9-12. A 455 kc i-f amplifier using simple series LC coupling circuits.

A number of double-tuned circuits can also be used as the coupling networks for high-frequency amplifiers, using short-circuit unstable transistors. The simplest network, using double series-tuned circuits with magnetic coupling is shown as Fig. 9-13; its impedance Z_1 at the resonant frequency can be transformed into the circuits of Fig. 9-14 and the effective Q of the circuit is

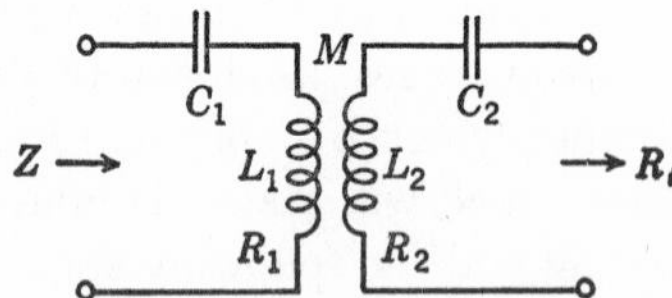

Fig. 9-13. Double-tuned series LC coupling network.

$$Q = \frac{\omega_o \left[L_1 + \dfrac{M^2/C_2}{R_i^2 + (\omega_o L_2 - (1/\omega_o C_2))^2} \right]}{R_1 + \dfrac{(\omega_o M)^2 R_i}{R_i^2 + (\omega_o L_2 - (1/\omega_o C_2))^2}} \tag{9-16}$$

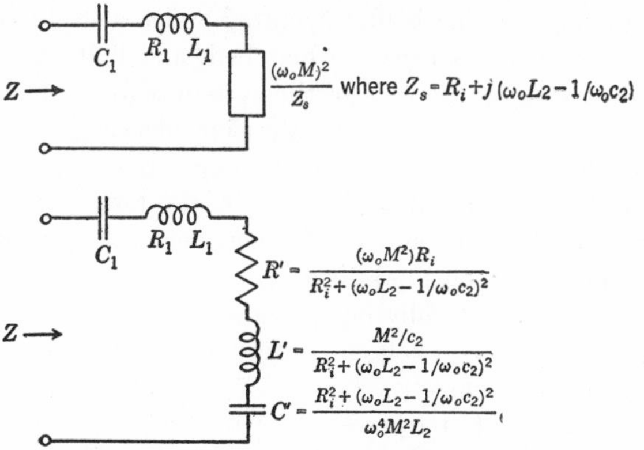

C_1 R_1 L_1

$Z \rightarrow$ $\dfrac{(\omega_o M)^2}{Z_s}$ where $Z_s = R_i + j(\omega_o L_2 - 1/\omega_o C_2)$

C_1 R_1 L_1

$Z \rightarrow$

$R' = \dfrac{(\omega_o M^2) R_i}{R_i^2 + (\omega_o L_2 - 1/\omega_o C_2)^2}$

$L' = \dfrac{M^2/C_2}{R_i^2 + (\omega_o L_2 - 1/\omega_o C_2)^2}$

$C' = \dfrac{R_i^2 + (\omega_o L_2 - 1/\omega_o C_2)^2}{\omega_o^4 M^2 L_2}$

Fig. 9-14. Equivalent series circuits of the double-tuned coupling network of Fig. 9-13.

9.7 Automatic gain control system

Automatic gain control systems[3,4] are generally used in radio receivers to maintain a relatively constant carrier input voltage to the detector over a wide range of input signal carrier levels to the receiver. This function is generally performed by using the rectified output of the detector to control the gain of the radio frequency amplifier, the converter, and/or the intermediate frequency amplifiers. In vacuum tube circuits, the rectified d-c output from the detector is used to control the grid bias of the vacuum tubes in a nonlinear region in order to control their voltage gain. Similar principles can also be applied to transistor circuits. The problem is the selection, from among the various d-c parameters of transistor circuits, of one controlling parameter which will act effectively in circuit gain control. An example of an automatic gain control system applied to a junction-type

[3] F. E. Terman, *Radio Engineer's Handbook*, McGraw-Hill Book Co., Inc., 1943, pp. 39–642.

[4] F. Langford-Smith, *Radiotron Designer's Handbook*, 4th ed., RCA Manufacturing Co., New York, 1954, Chap. 27.

transistor 455 kc intermediate-frequency amplifier will be discussed here; however, similar principles can be applied to the control of the radio-frequency amplifier or converter stages as well.

Selection of the Controlling d-c Parameter

If a transistor amplifier is first operated under such d-c bias conditions that the various stages are matched, and if its d-c operating point is then changed, the gain of the system will be affected simply because of the mismatch caused by the dependence of the input and output impedance of each stage on the bias values. Concomitantly, the gain of the system will be affected by the fact that the gain of each stage is itself dependent on the bias currents and voltages regardless of matching considerations.

Since a transistor is usually biased on the input side from a current source or (less often) by a voltage source, and on the output side by a voltage source, the quantities I_E, I_B, V_{EB}, and V_C are the ones to be considered for AGC purposes. We will now show, however, that in practice the most suitable controlling parameter is the d-c emitter bias I_E. For junction transistors three of the above quantities, I_E, I_B, and V_E are approximately related as follows (see Sec. 11–1):

$$I_E \doteq \frac{G_{11}}{\Lambda} \epsilon^{\Lambda(V_E + I_B r_{bb'})} + I_{ES} \tag{9-17a}$$

and

$$I_B \doteq -\frac{G_{11} + G_{21}}{\Lambda} \epsilon^{\Lambda(V_E + I_B r_{bb'})} + I_{BS} \tag{9-17b}$$

where G_{11} and G_{21} are conductances which are a function of the properties of the material constituting the transistor, and of its geometry, and as a first order approximation may be considered to be independent of the operating point; I_{ES} and I_{BS} are the currents that flow in the emitter and base, respectively, when strong reverse biases are placed across *both* junctions; $1/\Lambda = 0.026$ volts at room temperature; $r_{bb'}$ = base spreading resistance; and V_E = emitter to base voltage V_{EB} or $-V_{BE}$. Normally, I_E is considerably larger than I_B, while I_{BS} and I_{ES} are of the same order of magnitude. Thus, it is seen that variation in I_{ES} and I_{BS} in different transistors, such as may be caused by extraneous elements shunting the junctions, or by temperature, will cause large variations in the base currents for the same value of emitter current or emitter voltage; i.e., the base current is most sensitive to these extraneous factors. This is illustrated in Fig. 9-15, which shows a plot of voltage gain vs. base bias current for two common emitter amplifiers employing transistors which are nominally identical except that the collector current at zero base current I_{CBO} is different in the two units. It is readily seen that if AGC were applied to two such intermediate frequency amplifiers in cascade by

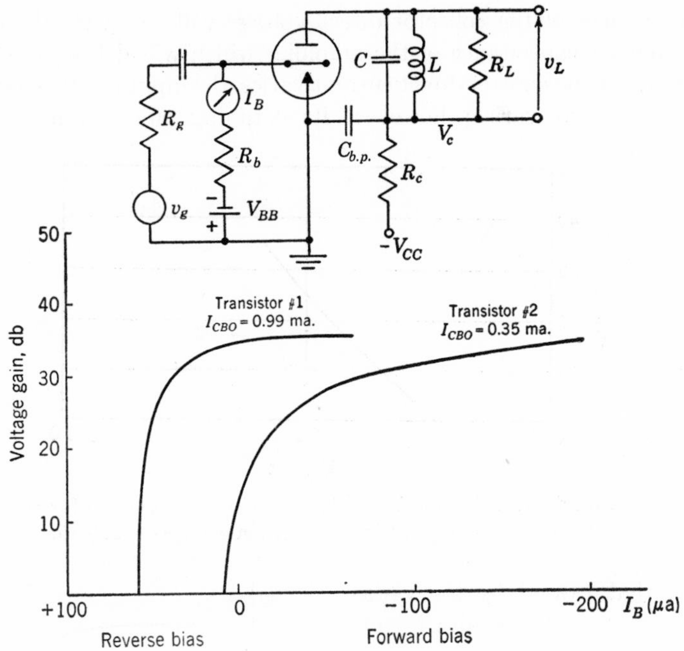

Fig. 9-15. Voltage gain vs. base bias current for a 455 kc i-f amplifier.

varying the *base currents*, very great care would have to be taken in a setting of the bias of each unit or, while the voltage gain of one unit had changed from 35 db to 0, the other unit would hardly be affected.

Figure 9-16 shows a plot of voltage gain vs. base to emitter voltage, V_{BE}. The use of V_{BE} as the controlling parameter is quite feasible but rarely used. The reason for this is that voltage biasing on the input side (which is the type of biasing best adapted to this method of control) is not commonly used since batteries having the required low voltage are not readily available. (Various artifices may of course be used to simulate voltage source biasing, but are usually uneconomical).

One of the limitations in the use of the collector voltage as the controlling parameter is the detuning effect. Since the collector capacitance is directly related to collector direct voltage by Eq. (7-2), as

$$C_c = AV_c^{-m}$$

any changes of the collector direct voltage will also vary the effective output capacitance of the amplifier which will detune the load circuit. As the emitter direct current varies, the input reactance of the amplifier also varies; however, its detuning effect is much less

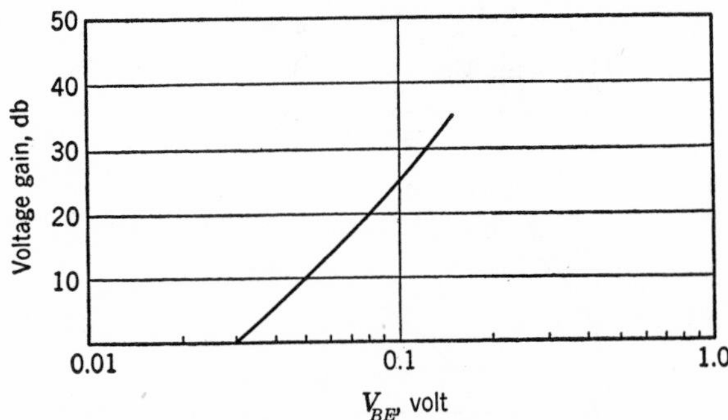

Fig. 9-16. Voltage gain vs. base-emitter bias voltage for a 455 kc i-f amplifier. Circuit diagram same as Fig. 9-15.

than that caused by the variation of its collector direct voltage. Therefore V_c is not generally used as the controlling parameter (Fig. 9-17).

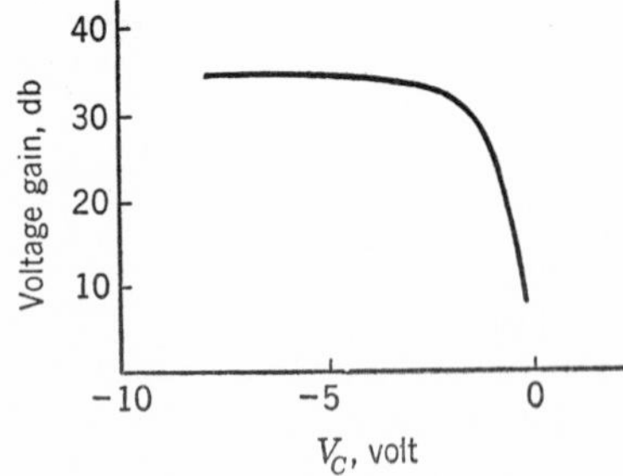

Fig. 9-17. Voltage gain vs. collector bias voltage for a 455 kc i-f amplifier. Circuit diagram same as Fig. 9-15.

Consider a common-emitter junction transistor intermediate-frequency amplifier as the controlled stage and its emitter direct current as the controlling parameter. The input impedance and the voltage gain of this amplifier are approximately given by

$$Z_{in} = r_{bb'} + z_e \tag{9-18}$$

and

$$K_v = \frac{K}{\left[1 + \left(\frac{K}{Z_L} + \frac{1}{z_{c'}}\right)z_d\right]\left[1 + \frac{r_{bb'} + Z_s}{z_e}\right] + \frac{r_{bb'} + Z_s}{z_{c'}}} \tag{9-19}$$

where Z_L and Z_S are the load and source impedances as shown in Eq. (7-32). Now it can be shown that z_d and z_e are strongly dependent on I_E, (see Sec. 11.1),

$$z_d \propto 1/(I_E - I_{ES}), \qquad z_e \propto 1/(I_E - I_{ES}) \tag{9-20}$$

Thus, Eq. (9-19) may be rewritten as:

$$K_v \doteq -\frac{K}{A_1 + A_2 I_E + A_3/I_E} \tag{9-21}$$

where A_1, A_2 and A_3 are independent of I_E.

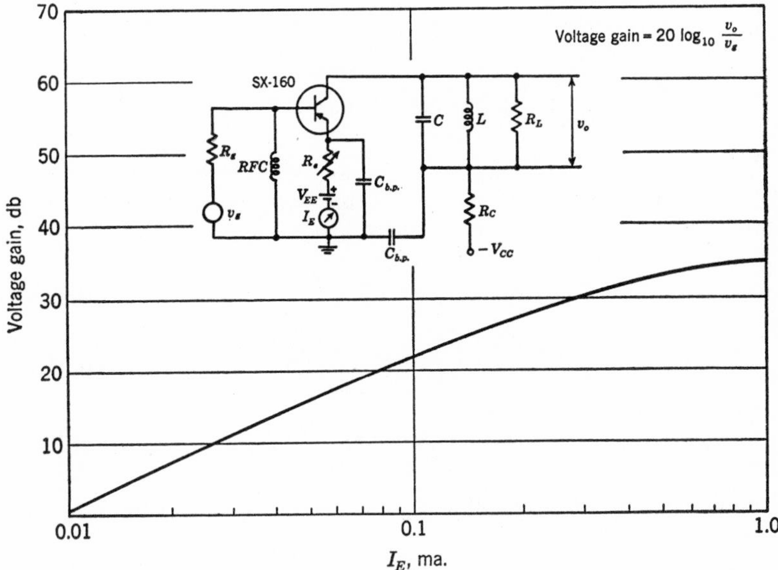

Fig. 9-18. Voltage gain vs. emitter bias current for a 455 kc i-f amplifier.

These analytic expressions show only the approximate results; no attempt is made to provide rigorous analysis. Experimental results shown in Fig. 9-18 verify the relationship between the gain of the amplifier and its emitter direct current.

Analysis of Typical Transistor Automatic Gain Control System

A block diagram and schematic diagram of a typical transistor automatic gain control system using the emitter current as the controlling parameter and the intermediate-frequency amplifiers as the controlled stages are shown in Figs. 9-19 and 9-20a, respectively. There are, in general, N controlled stages. Consider the d-c biasing

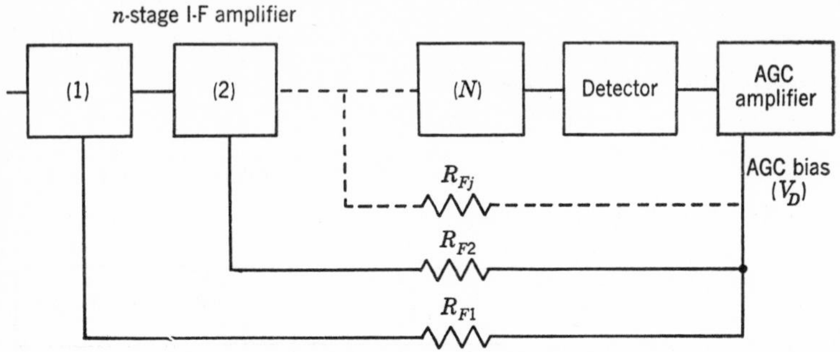

Fig. 9-19. Block diagram of an AGC system.

system of the Jth stage as shown in Fig. 9-20b, where r_j is the effective d-c resistance between the emitter and the base of the Jth amplifier; we have

$$I_{Ej} = \frac{V_{Ej}}{r_j} \tag{9-22a}$$

$$I_{Fj} = \frac{V_{Ej} + V_D}{R_{Fj}} \tag{9-22b}$$

$$I_{Ej} + I_{Fj} = \frac{V_{EE} - V_{Ej}}{R_{Ej}} \tag{9-22c}$$

Combining Eqs. (9-22a), (9-22b), and (9-22c) and solving I_{Ej}, we obtain

$$I_{Ej} = \frac{V_{EE} - R_{Ej}V_D/R_{Fj}}{R_{Ej} + r_j(1 + R_{Ej}/R_{Fj})} = \frac{V_{EE}}{R_{Ej}}\left[\frac{1 - R_{Ej}V_D/R_{Fj}V_{EE}}{1 + r_j(1/R_{Ej} + 1/R_{Fj})}\right] \tag{9-23}$$

$$I_{Ej} \doteq \frac{V_{EE}}{R_{Ej}}\left[1 - \frac{R_{Ej}}{R_{Fj}}\frac{V_D}{V_{EE}}\right] \quad \text{when} \quad \begin{matrix} r_j \ll R_{Ej} \\ r_j \ll R_{Fj} \end{matrix} \tag{9-23a}$$

Hence the entire automatic gain control system can be designed by the known relationship between voltage gain vs. I_E (Fig. 9-18) and the known relationship between the bias voltage vs. emitter current I_E, assuming the detector characteristic (V_{in} vs. V_D) is also given.

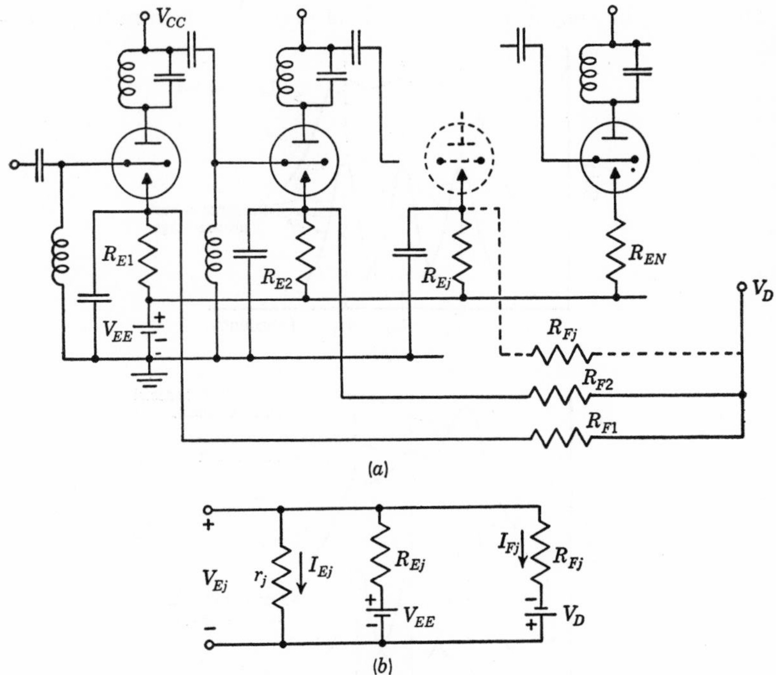

Fig. 9-20. (a) Simplified schematic diagram of an AGC system; (b) d-c biasing condition of the Jth stage of the amplifier.

9.8 Wide-band amplifiers

The bandwidth requirements of wide-band transistor amplifiers present different problems from those encountered in the design of narrow-band transistor amplifiers. However, the design techniques of narrow-band transistor amplifiers can still be indirectly applied to the wide-band case if we consider a wide-band amplifier as being composed of several stagger-tuned narrow-band amplifiers. Alternatively, a transistor wide-band amplifier can also be made by simply coupling transistors in cascade and relying only on current amplification at each stage. Another alternative approach involves the use of peaking circuits, equalization circuits, and padding circuits to form the desired frequency response.

Wide-band amplifiers using stagger-tuned amplifiers. If a wide-band amplifier is to be composed of several stagger-tuned narrow-band amplifiers, the conventional methods of design of vacuum tube stag-

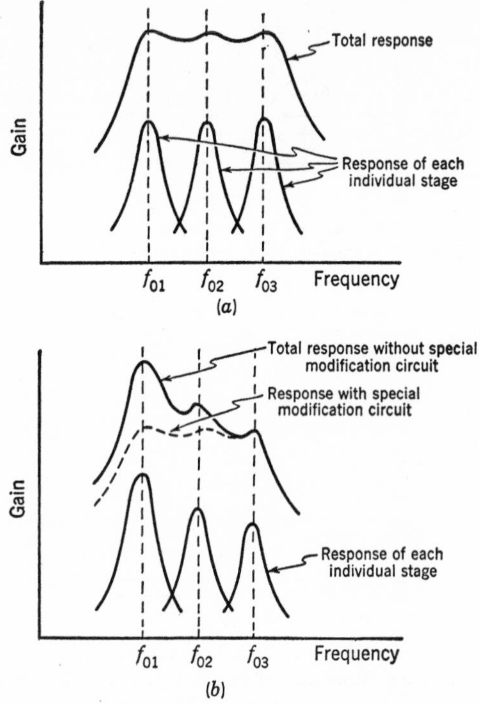

Fig. 9-21. Frequency responses of wide-band amplifiers composed of stagger-tuned narrow-band stages.

ger-tuned amplifiers[5] can be applied directly. The design of narrow-band amplifiers, as discussed in the first part of this chapter, is directly applicable to the wide-band case, provided that the center frequencies of each individual stage (f_{01}, f_{02}, f_{03} in Fig. 9-21a) are located in the frequency range so that a constant gain is obtained from the overall transistor amplifier.

[5] G. E. Valley and H. Wallman, *op. cit.*, Chap. 4; S. Seeley, *Electron Tube Circuits*, McGraw-Hill Book Co., Inc., New York, 1950, Chap. 10.

If the gain of each individual stage is different, as shown in Fig. 9-21b, special networks are required to reduce the gain of the high-gain stages so that the specified frequency response can be obtained; therefore the conventional methods of determining the center frequencies and the band-width of each individual stage for a specified total frequency response of the wide-band amplifier must be modified.

Wide-band amplifiers using cascaded current amplifiers of identical stages. Consider several stages of common-emitter junction transistor amplifiers or several stages of common base point-contact transistor amplifiers, simply connected in cascade. Now, each follower stage acts as a low impedance load to its previous stage, and the current gain of each stage is approximately equal to its short circuit current gain as discussed in Chapter 5. Let n = number of stages of cascaded current amplifiers as shown in Fig. 9-22; $\alpha_k = i_{ok}/i_{ik}$ = the short-circuit current amplification factor of stage k; f_{ck} = the α_k cutoff frequency of stage k; α_{ok} = the low-frequency short-circuit amplification factor of stage k; $K_i = i_{on}/i_{i1}$ = the total current gain of the n-stage cascade current amplifier; f = the frequency of operation; and i_{ik} and i_{ok} represent the input current and the output current of the kth stage respectively. Furthermore let

Fig. 9-22. Block diagram of a cascade current amplifier.

$$\alpha_k = \frac{\alpha_{ok}}{1 + jf/f_{ck}} \tag{9-24}$$

Then the current gain becomes

$$K_i = \frac{i_{on}}{i_{i1}} = \prod_{k=1}^{n} \left(\frac{\alpha_{ok}}{1 + jf/f_{ck}} \right) \tag{9-25a}$$

provided that the input circuits of the various stages may be considered to be short circuits. If the stages are identical then

$$\alpha_K = \alpha, \quad f_{ek} = f_e \qquad (k = 1, 2, \cdots n)$$

and

$$K_i = \left(\frac{\alpha_o}{1 + jf/f_c} \right)^n \tag{9-25b}$$

and the total current gain at low frequency (K_{io}) becomes

$$K_{io} = \alpha_o^n \tag{9-26}$$

The number of stages required can therefore be determined from the total low-frequency current gain K_{io} required, and the low-frequency short-circuit current amplification factor α_o of each individual stage by

$$n = \frac{\log_{10} K_{io}}{\log_{10} \alpha_o} \tag{9-26a}$$

If we define the normalized total current gain of this cascaded current amplifier as

$$A_i = \frac{K_i}{\alpha_o^n}$$

then

$$A_i = \frac{1}{(1 + j(f/f_c))^n} \tag{9-27}$$

$$|A_i| = 20 \log_{10} \left| \frac{1}{(1 + j(f/f_c))^n} \right| \quad \text{db} \tag{9-27a}$$

A plot of Eq. (9-27a) gives the universal frequency response curves of the n-stage cascaded amplifier as shown in Fig. 9-23 for different values of n. The asymptotic expression of Eq. (9-27a)

$$\begin{aligned} |A_i| &= 0, \qquad \frac{f}{f_c} \ll 1 \\ |A_i| &= 20 \log_{10} \left(\frac{f_c}{f}\right)^n, \qquad (f/f_c \gg 1) \end{aligned} \tag{9-27b}$$

is displayed as the solid lines of Fig. 9-23.

Figure of merit for transistor wide-band amplifiers. The wide-band amplifier can be characterized by a simple figure of merit.[6] For example, the figure of merit of a wide-band vacuum tube amplifier is given by the well-known factor, the "gain-band-width product," which is defined as the product of its voltage gain K_v at band center to its band-width B. The gain band-width product of a single-stage vacuum tube amplifier having a transconductance g_m, and only the tube output capacitance C as the tuning capacitance, is given as

[6] Valley and Wallman, *op. cit.*, Chap. 4.

$$K_v B = \frac{g_m}{2\pi C} \tag{9-28}$$

Similarly, a figure of merit can be assigned to the transistor wide-band current amplifier by defining its gain band-width product as the product of its low-frequency short-circuit current amplification factor α_{21o} and its appropriate α cutoff frequency f_c, i.e.,

$$K_i B = \alpha_{21o} f_c \tag{9-29}$$

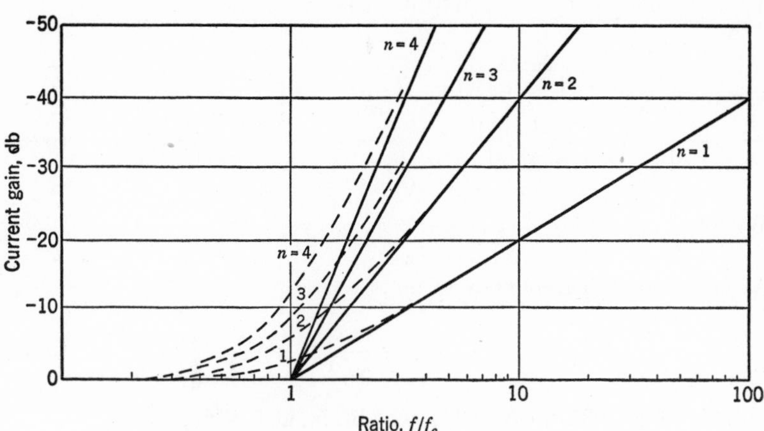

Fig. 9-23. Normalized current gain vs. frequency curve:

$$|A_i| = 20 \log_{10} \left| \frac{1}{[1 + j(f/f_c)]^n} \right| \text{ db.}$$

The figure of merit for three basic amplifier circuits—the common-base circuit, the common-emitter circuit, and the common-collector circuit—therefore, are defined respectively as

$$(K_i B)_b = -\alpha_{ceo} f_{ce} = \alpha_o f_{ce} \tag{9-29a}$$

$$(K_i B)_e = \alpha_{cbo} f_{cb} \tag{9-29b}$$

$$(K_i B)_c = \alpha_{ebo} f_{eb} \tag{9-29c}$$

A definite relationship exists between these expressions. If the relationship

$$\alpha_{cbo} = \frac{\alpha_o}{1 - \alpha_o} \tag{9-30}$$

is combined with
$$f_{cb} = (1 - \alpha_o)f_{ce} \tag{9-31}$$
we obtain
$$\alpha_{cbo}f_{cb} = \alpha_o f_{ce}$$
Therefore
$$(K_iB)_e = (K_iB)_b \tag{9-32}$$

Thus, the gain band-width product of a transistor current amplifier is the same for both the common-base circuit and common-emitter circuits. The relationship between the gain band-width product of the common-collector circuit to that of the other two basic circuits can be derived from the known equations listed in Table 3-1.

$$\alpha_{eb} = \frac{-1}{1-\alpha} = \frac{-1}{1 - \alpha_o/(1 + jf/f_{ce})}$$
$$= \frac{-1}{1-\alpha_o}\frac{1 + jf/f_{ce}}{1 + jf/(1-\alpha_o)f_{ce}} = \alpha_{ebo}\frac{1 + jf/f_{ce}}{1 + jf/(1-\alpha_o)f_{ce}} \tag{9-33}$$

Where
$$|\alpha_{ebo}| = \left|\frac{1}{1-\alpha_o}\right| \tag{9-34}$$

At f_{eb}, the cutoff frequency of α_{eb},

$$\alpha_{eb} = \frac{\alpha_{ebo}}{\sqrt{2}} \tag{9-35}$$

Substituting (9-35) into (9-33), we obtain, at $f = f_{eb}$,

$$\left|\frac{1 + jf_{eb}/f_{ce}}{1 + jf_{eb}/(1-\alpha_o)f_{ce}}\right| = \frac{1}{\sqrt{2}} \tag{9-36}$$

For junction transistors, it is true that

$$\frac{1}{1-\alpha_o} \gg 1 \tag{9-37}$$

From Eqs. (9-36) and (9-37), we obtain

$$f_{eb} \doteq f_{ce}(1 - \alpha_o) \doteq f_{cb} \tag{9-38}$$

In accordance with the approximation (Eq. 9-37), the relationship between the gain band-width product of the transistor in the three configurations is

$$(K_iB)_c = \alpha_{ebo}f_{eb} \doteq (K_iB)_e \doteq (K_iB)_b \tag{9-39}$$

Equation (9-39) indicates that the gain band-width product of the transistor is essentially the same in any of the three configurations.

Cascaded wide-band amplifiers using stages of different circuit configurations. A wide-band amplifier can be designed in which cascaded stages of different circuit configurations may be utilized to achieve a desired resultant frequency response. Experimental results on several circuit configurations for a video amplifier are shown here to illustrate the design of a wide-band amplifier of this type.

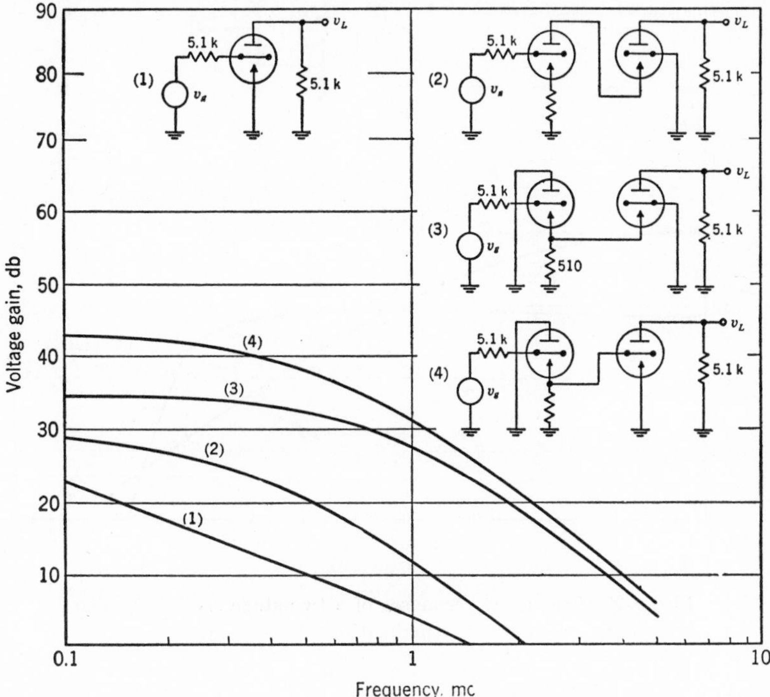

Fig. 9-24. Frequency response of cascaded video amplifier.

The frequency response of several video amplifiers operating between equal source and load impedances of 5100 ohms are shown in Fig. 9-24. Curve 1 shows the frequency response of a single-stage common-emitter circuit; curve 2, a two-stage cascaded-amplifier circuit consisting of a common-emitter stage followed by a common-base stage; curve 3, a common collector stage followed by a common base stage; and curve 4, a common collector stage followed by a common emitter stage.

Wide-band amplifiers using frequency response correction means. It is well known that peaking circuits, equalization circuits, or compensation circuits may be incorporated in a vacuum tube circuit[7] to improve frequency response; similar techniques may be applied to transistor amplifiers.

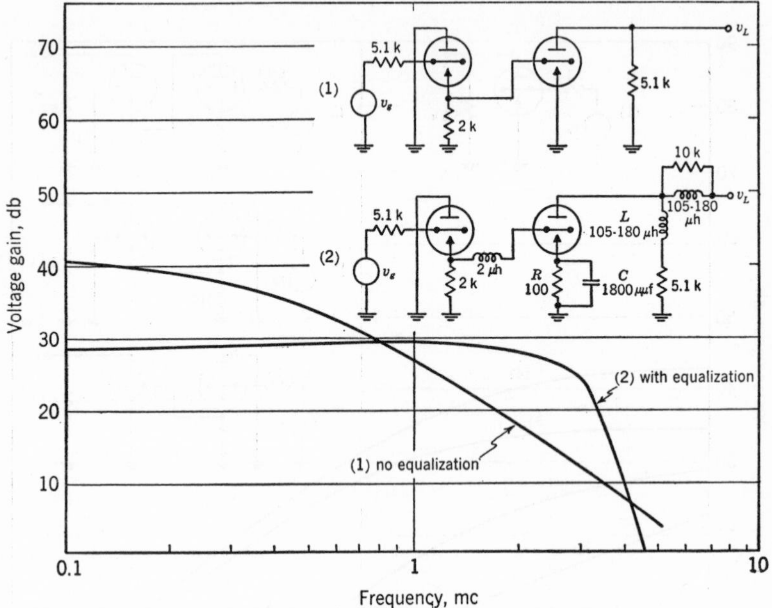

Fig. 9-25. Frequency responses of a two-stage cascaded video amplifier: (1) without equalization; (2) with equalization.

One of the most commonly used peaking circuits utilizes a peaking coil which is connected in series with the load, so that the effective load impedance and hence the effective gain of the amplifier is increased at high frequencies. Another type of frequency response correction may utilize either degenerative or regenerative feedback. Regenerative compensation circuits are designed so that positive feedback effects are predominant at high frequencies, thereby im-

[7] R. B. Dome, *Television Principles*, McGraw-Hill Book, Co., Inc., New York 1951; S. W. Seeley and C. N. Kimball, "Analysis and Design of Video Amplifiers," *RCA Rev.*, Jan. 1940.

proving the high-frequency gain.[8] The regenerative type of compensation circuit is usually not recommended because of distortion and instability which may be introduced by the positive feedback.

Degenerative compensation circuits are designed in such a way that their negative feedback effects are predominant at the lower frequencies. This provides an improvement in the frequency response of the amplifier by the low-frequency gain reduction, while the high-frequency gain remains relatively unaffected. A typical example of this type of compensation circuit is shown in Fig. 9-25, in which equalization of a video amplifier is obtained by connection of a degenerative parallel RC network in the emitter circuit.

The frequency response curves of Fig. 9-25 illustrate the effects of both the previously degenerative compensation and an inductive peaking circuit. Comparison of the frequency response of the amplifier without equalization (curve 1) with that of the circuit with equalization (curve 2) shows that the gain at low frequencies has been decreased, the gain at high frequencies has been increased, and the overall flatness of the frequency response has been greatly improved.

9.9 Amplifiers using special high-frequency transistors

As mentioned in the introduction to this chapter, a number of new approaches in the development of transistors of better high-frequency response have been brought forward by workers in this field. Some of the more significant contributions in this respect are set forth in this section.

The junction tetrode transistor,[9] first announced by Bell Telephone Laboratories, consists essentially of a conventional junction transistor to which a second base electrode has been added. The high-frequency gain of the junction tetrode can be extended appreciably by proper adjustment of the bias of the second base. The improvement in high-frequency response may be attributed to a lowered base resistance (controlled by the bias of the second base) and lowered collector capacitance (the active area of the collector junction is reduced). A video amplifier utilizing the junction tetrode is shown in Fig. 9-26. When

[8] G. C. Sziklai, R. D. Lohman, G. B. Herzog, "A Study of Transistor Circuits for Television," *Proc. I.R.E.* Vol. 41, pp. 708–717, June 1953.

[9] R. L. Wallace, Jr., L. G. Schimpf, and E. Dickton, "A Junction Transistor Tetrode for High-Frequency Use," *Proc. I.R.E.* Vol. 40, pp. 1396–1400, Nov. 1952.

the transistor is operated as a tetrode by proper biasing of the second base, a low frequency voltage gain of 22 db and a 3 db cutoff frequency of 5 megacycles is realized. If the transistor is operated as a triode, the 3 db cutoff frequency drops by a factor of 10 or more.

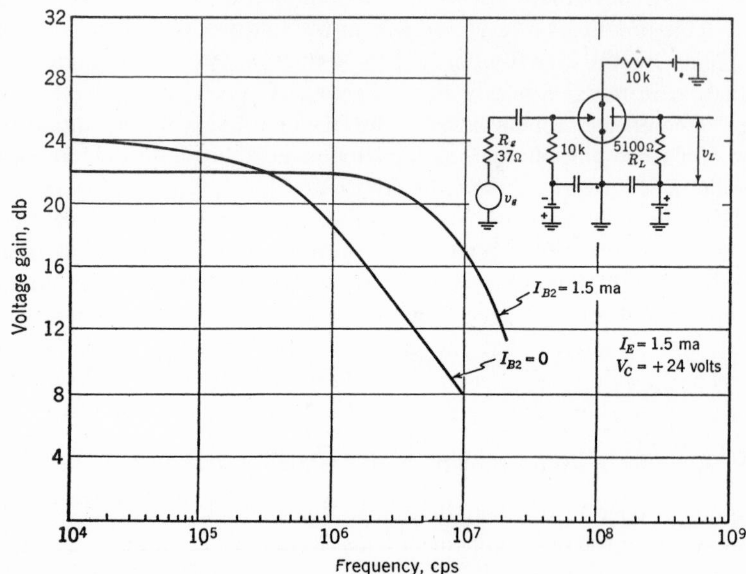

Fig. 9-26. Voltage gain vs. frequency for a tetrode junction transistor amplifier.

The surface barrier transistor[10, 11] utilizes highly specialized fabrication techniques in which precise electrochemical etching and plating means are used to control the base width to precise tolerances. The thickness may be reduced by this means, thereby giving increased power gain at high frequencies.

The p-n-i-p and n-p-i-n junction triode transistors[12] differ from conventional *p-n-p* and *n-p-n* junction transistors in that the base

[10] Members of the Technical Staff, Philco Research Division, "The Surface Barrier Transistor," *Proc. I.R.E.*, Vol. 41, pp. 1702–1720, Dec. 1953.

[11] J. B. Angell and F. P. Keiper, "The Surface-Barrier Transistor, Part 3, Circuit Applications of Surface-Barrier Transistors," *Proc. I.R.E.*, Vol. 41, pp. 1709–1714, Dec. 1953.

[12] J. M. Early, "P-N-I-P and N-P-I-N Junction Transistor Triodes," *B.S.T.J.*, Vol. 33, pp. 517–533, May 1954.

and collector regions are separated by a thick depletion layer of *i*-type semiconductor. The wide collector depletion layer results in relative small collector capacitance and gives a high reverse breakdown voltage, and permits the base region to be made extremely thin and of low resistivity, thus giving simultaneously a low base lead resistance and a very high α cutoff frequency f_{ce}.

Experimental results for an uncompensated common-emitter *p-n-i-p* transistor amplifier show a gain of 20.5 db at 10 megacycles, with 3 megacycles band-width. The frequency response is limited by the thickness (of the order of 0.3 thousandth of an inch) of the base layer of the available *p-n-i-p* transistors. The frequency range of operation is expected to be increased into the microwave frequency range as the fabrication technique is improved. According to theoretical calculation, a power gain of 10 db or more may be expected from a *p-n-i-p* or an *n-p-i-n* common-emitter amplifier at 1000 megacycles.

9.10 Neutralization and unilateralization of transistor high-frequency amplifiers

Neutralization

Neutralization is used to balance out undesirable reactive feedback effect and has been employed for years in vacuum tube circuits. For example, it is used in the vacuum tube triode common-cathode amplifier to eliminate the effect of grid-to-plate interelectrode capacitance, which may introduce positive feedback possibly leading to undesired oscillation.

Unilateralization

Unilateralization can be defined as the process of converting a bilateral four-terminal network into a unilateral four-terminal network. (Refer to Sec. 3.1 for definitions of bilateral and unilateral four-terminal networks.) Unilateralization therefore is a particular neutralization process which eliminates the undesirable inherent feedback property of a bilateral four-terminal network and converts it into a unilateral four-terminal network.

Since transistor amplifiers can in general be classified as bilateral four-terminal active networks, unilateralization may be utilized. One of the advantages of the unilateralized amplifier is that isolation between stages is afforded, and interaction between them is minimized.

In the case of a nonunilateralized junction transistor amplifier stage with a parallel-tuned load, for example, the input admittance will exhibit a peak at the resonant frequency of the output load. When this amplifier is unilateralized however, the input admittance in the vicinity of the operating frequency becomes independent of frequency.

The analysis by which a unilateralized amplifier is obtained may be simplified by using the matrix method. Consider two four terminal networks in parallel (as in Fig. 9-27), one of which is the unneutral-

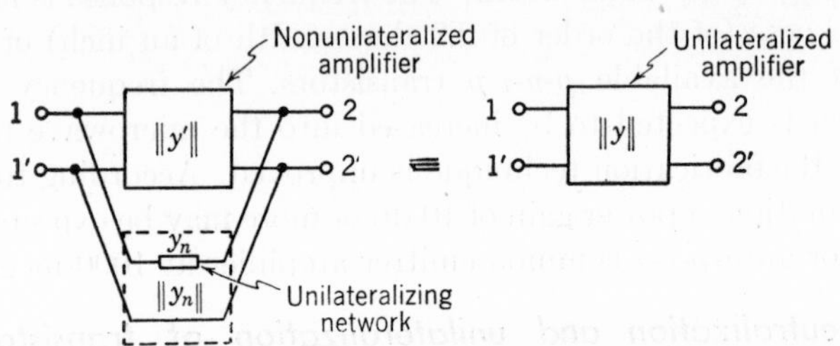

Fig. 9-27. Network representation of two four-terminal networks connected in parallel.

ized transistor amplifier having the short-circuit admittance matrix $\| y' \|$, and the other is the unilateralizing network having the short-circuit admittance matrix $\| y_n \|$, where

$$\| y' \| = \begin{Vmatrix} y'_{11} & y'_{12} \\ y'_{21} & y'_{22} \end{Vmatrix}$$

and

$$\| y_n \| = \begin{Vmatrix} y_n & -y_n \\ -y_n & y_n \end{Vmatrix}$$

The short-circuit admittance matrix $\| y \|$ of the unilateralized amplifier becomes

$$\| y \| = \begin{Vmatrix} y'_{11} + y_n & y'_{12} - y_n \\ y'_{21} - y_n & y'_{22} + y_n \end{Vmatrix} \tag{9-40}$$

The required condition for a unilateralized system with a parallel tuned output load is $y_{12} = 0$. Therefore

$$y_n = y'_{12} \tag{9-41}$$

which is the design criterion for the unilateralizing network y_n.

The reverse transfer admittance y'_{12} of a common-emitter junction transistor amplifier can be obtained, by using the equivalent circuit shown in Fig. 9-2. Thus from Eq. (7-39) and the relation $y_{12} = -h_{12}/h_{11}$,

$$\begin{aligned} y'_{12} &= -z_e/Kz_{c'}(r_{bb'} + z_e) \\ &= -(g_{c'} + j\omega C_{c'})/K(1 + r_{bb'}g_e + j\omega C_e r_{bb'}) \end{aligned} \tag{9-42}$$

which may be written in the form of a ratio of polynomials,

$$y'_{12} = -(as + b)/(cs + d) \tag{9-43}$$

where a, b, c, and d are constants and $s \equiv j\omega$. This expression is readily synthesized into a circuit consisting of a resistance in series with a parallel RC network, as shown in Fig. 9-28. The negative sign indicates a phase-reversing transformer.

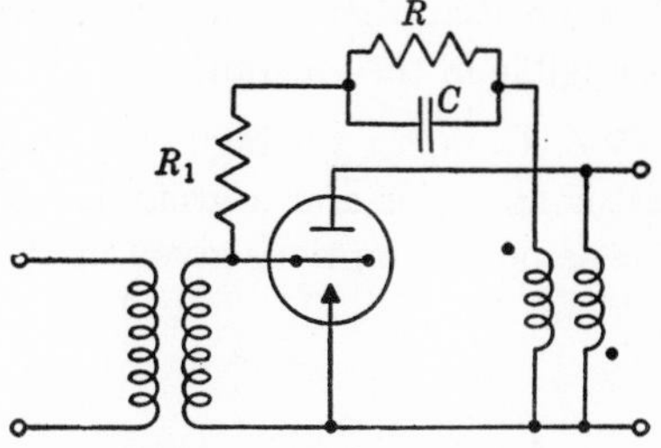

Fig. 9-28. Circuit connection of a neutralized amplifier.

Another method which may be used to compensate for the effect of the reverse transfer impedance in a transistor tuned amplifier is shown in the circuit of Fig. 9-29.[13] By applying out-of-phase signals to the emitter and base electrodes, effective unilatralization is accomplished.

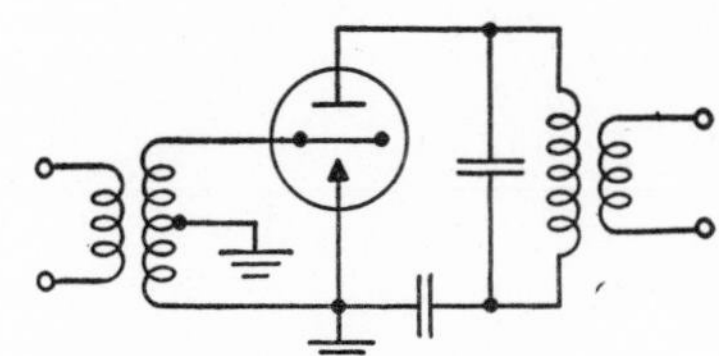
Fig. 9-29. A split input tuned amplifier.

PROBLEMS

9-1. Derive the design equations listed for the coupling network (2) in Table 9-1.

9-2. Derive Eq. 9-16.

9-3. Design a band-pass amplifier operated at 200 kc with a power gain of 60 db and a bandwidth of 6 kc. The amplifier is to consist of identical common-emitter amplifier stages coupled by a single-tuned coupling network. The individual stage has a matched input imped-

[13] L. E. Barton, U. S. patent 2,644,859.

ance of 150 ohms and a matched output impedance of 3000 ohms at 200 kc. The power gain of the individual stage is 31 db, and the effective output capacitance is 10 $\mu\mu$f. The amplifier is designed to be used for a signal source with a generator resistance of 300 ohms and a load impedance of 3000 ohms.

9-4. Repeat Problem 9-3, using double-tuned coupling networks.

9-5. Compare the high frequency operation of a common-emitter transistor amplifier and a grounded-cathode vacuum tube amplifier. Assume that there is no grid current and the transit time effect is negligible in the vacuum tube.

9-6. Compare the high frequency operation of a common-base transistor amplifier and a grounded-grid vacuum tube amplifier. Follow the same assumptions given in Problem 9-5.

Chapter 10

OSCILLATORS

10.1 Introduction

The transistor, by virtue of the fact that it is a device capable of amplification of power, is also capable of producing sustained oscillations. Generally speaking, a device which is characterized by a power output greater than its power input may be made to oscillate if a sufficient amount of the output signal is fed back to the input terminals of the device in proper phase relationship. Certain "current-multiplication" type transistor devices, such as the point-contact transistor, the double-base diode, and the hook transistor will oscillate if sufficient positive feedback is introduced by an impedance in a proper branch of the circuit. These devices may be considered members of a family of two-terminal oscillators with common circuit behavior. In the following sections two-terminal oscillators are discussed in detail, using the point-contact transistor as a working example because of the ease with which its circuit operation is analyzed. The basic principles of operation of the point-contact transistor circuit may then be extended to cover operation of circuits using other "current-multiplication" type devices with little change. Oscillators which depend on external feedback networks are discussed in the latter sections of this chapter.

It is conventional in vacuum tube work to classify oscillators into any one of a number of general class types. Such convention may also be carried over into transistor oscillator circuits. The reader should be reminded, however, that classification of oscillators is chiefly for the convenience of identification. In this chapter oscillators will be grouped under either of the two class types, *negative resistance* or *two-terminal* oscillators, and *feedback* or *four-terminal* oscillators, according to their general structure. For the sake of simplicity, the general discussion and analysis of transistor oscillators will be made with reference to sinusoidal-wave oscillators, while oscillators of nonsinusoidal waveform will be treated specifically in Sec. 10.9.

The two basic oscillator types are shown symbolically in Fig. 10-1. The negative-resistance oscillator consists of two parts; an active *maintaining* circuit and a *frequency discrimination* circuit. The maintaining circuit is characterized by a two-terminal active network which exhibits in its voltage-current characteristic a region of negative resistance; that is, in this region a positive increment in

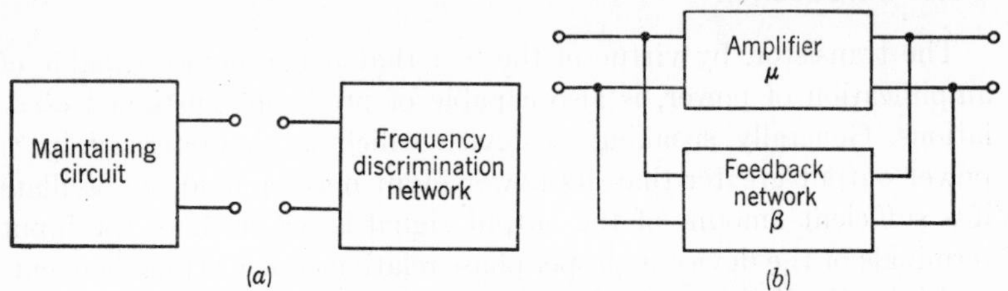

Fig. 10-1. Basic oscillator types: (a) negative-resistance oscillator; (b) feedback oscillator.

voltage results in a negative increment of current. Sustained oscillation is obtained by connecting a frequency discrimination circuit, usually an *LC* resonant circuit, to the maintaining circuit. Familiar examples of vacuum tube negative resistance oscillators are the dynatron oscillator, and the transitron, or "negative transconductance" oscillator. The feedback oscillator, as shown in Fig. 10-1b, is characterized by a four-terminal amplifier with a feedback path returning a part of the output voltage or current, in the ratio β, to the input terminals in the proper phase relationship. At some point in the circuit a frequency-discrimination circuit must also be included to select the desired frequency of oscillation. Examples of vacuum tube feedback oscillators are the common Hartley and Colpitts oscillators, or the tuned-plate tuned-grid oscillator.

As mentioned in Chapter 2, point-contact type transistors usually have a collector-to-emitter current gain greater than unity while the emitter and collector voltages are in phase. This type of transistor is most conveniently incorporated in negative-resistance oscillator circuits. It is not necessarily restricted to this type of operation, however, and may be operated as a four-terminal oscillator. In fact, those point-contact transistors which either do not have α greater than unity, or are operated at higher frequencies, above the frequency where α drops below unity, must be operated in four-terminal oscillator circuits. The junction triode, on the other hand, must operate in four-terminal type oscillator circuits. This is because the junction transistor does not offer a current gain greater than unity while the input and output voltages are in phase. In the discussion which follows it is understood that point-contact transistors are used in the two-terminal circuits, and junction triodes are used in the four-terminal circuits unless otherwise specified.

10.2 Condition of sustained oscillation

It was pointed out above that all oscillators can basically be considered feedback oscillators, since feedback, whether intentionally introduced or an inherent characteristic of the circuit, is requisite to sustained oscillation. In a like manner it may be shown that all

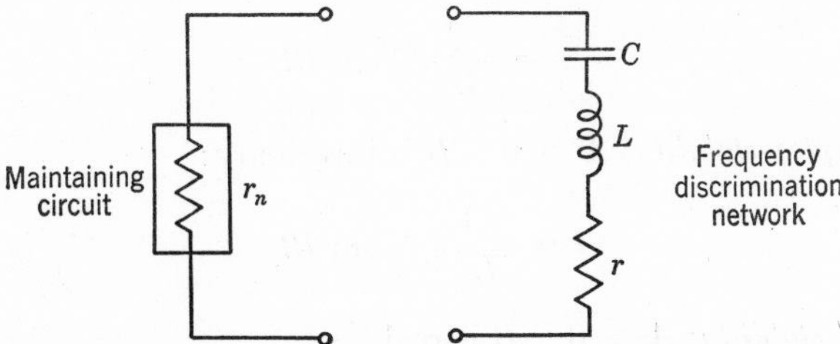

Fig. 10-2. Basic oscillator equivalent circuit.

oscillators may, with equal accuracy, be considered negative-resistance oscillators. The voltage or current in such a circuit may be represented by a differential equation as a variable of time. An approximate condition for sustained oscillation is that the damping factor in the differential equation for the circuit be zero or negative. This may be shown with the aid of the equivalent circuit of the basic oscillator shown in Fig. 10-2. In the frequency-discrimination network, L and C are the reactive components of the resonant circuit, and r represents the ohmic losses of the network. In the maintaining circuit, the dynamic resistance is represented by r_n. A summation of voltages around the loop yields the circuit equation which, in differential form is

$$\frac{d^2i}{dt^2} + \frac{R}{L}\frac{di}{dt} + \frac{1}{LC}\,i = 0 \qquad (10\text{-}1)$$

where $R = (r + r_n)$

The solution of the circuit equation is

$$i = \frac{-1}{L} \epsilon^{-At}(\epsilon^{Bt} - \epsilon^{-Bt}) \tag{10-2}$$

where $A = \frac{R}{2L}$, and $B = \sqrt{(A^2 - 1/LC)}$

An examination of the solution reveals that the circuit will be unstable if the damping factor A is negative. This implies that r_n must be negative and have an absolute value equal to or greater than r.

The behavior of the circuit is described by three distinct solutions of Eq. (10-2), dictated by the values of A and B, which are functions of the circuit parameters. These solutions are

1. *Complex instability:* $A < 0$, B is imaginary:

$$i = \frac{-1}{L} \epsilon^{At} \sin Bt \tag{10-3}$$

2. *Complex stability:* $A > 0$, B is imaginary:

$$i = \frac{-1}{L} \epsilon^{-At} \sin Bt \tag{10-4}$$

3. *Real stability:* $A > 0$, B is real

$$i = \frac{-1}{BL} \epsilon^{-At} \sinh Bt \tag{10-5}$$

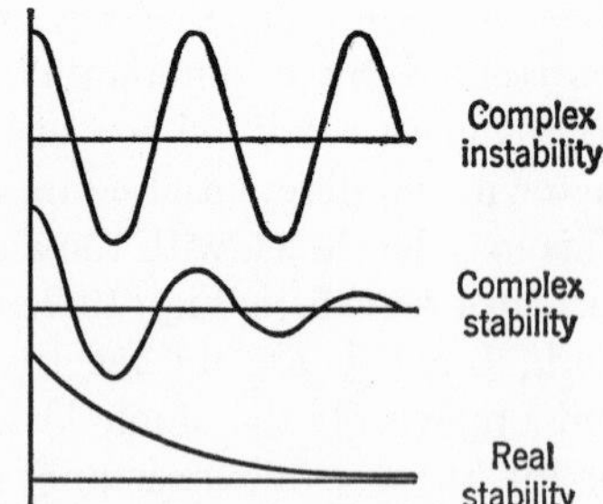

Fig. 10-3. Transient behavior of basic oscillator circuit.

As seen above, the condition of complex instability obtains when the net circuit resistance is negative and B is imaginary, e.g., $(R/2L)^2 < (1/LC)$. Under these conditions oscillations will start from an initial disturbance and will increase in amplitude until limited by circuit nonlinearities. Sustained oscillation is maintained thereafter. Complex stability obtains when the net circuit resistance is positive and B is imaginary. Under these conditions the oscillation produced by an initial disturbance will decay exponentially to zero. The third case of real stability, or sometimes called an *aperiodic discharge*, results when A is positive and B is real, that is, $R > 2\sqrt{L/C}$. Waveforms of these three special solutions are shown in Fig. 10–3.

10.3 Negative-resistance two-terminal networks

The negative resistance requirement having been generally established in the operation of oscillator circuits, the operation of two-

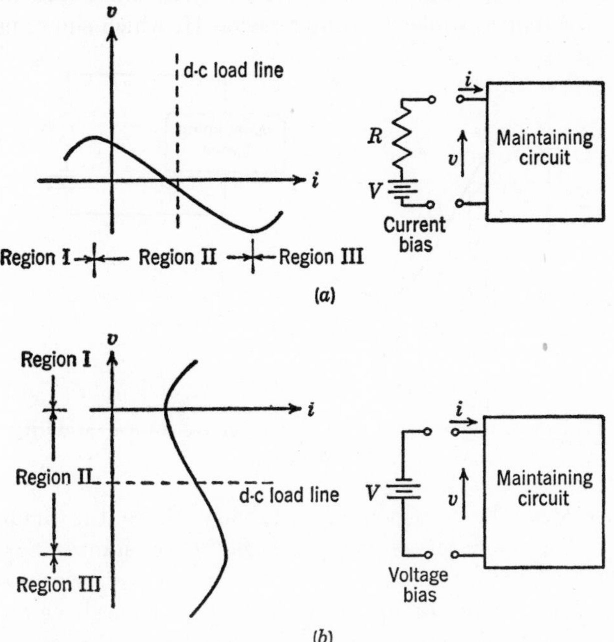

Fig. 10-4. Generalized negative-resistance characteristics: (a) current controlled; (b) voltage controlled.

terminal oscillators in particular will be further developed from that basis. Negative-resistance two-terminal circuits may be classified under either of two categories depending on the characteristics of the direct voltage-current relation at the terminals.[1] This voltage-

[1] E. W. Herold, "Negative Resistance and Devices for Obtaining It," *Proc. I.R.E.*, Vol. 23, Oct. 1935.

current curve is referred to as the *driving-point resistance* characteristic, or the *negative-resistance* characteristic. The two categories are the *current-controlled* and the *voltage-controlled* driving point resistance. Generalized characteristics illustrating these two types of negative resistance are shown in Fig. 10-4. In Fig. 10-4a the region of negative resistance is specified by the magnitude of current, while in Fig. 10-4b the region of negative resistance is specified by the magnitude of voltage. The regions I and III in the characteristic curves of these two figures show positive resistance, and they are regions of stability, while the center region II, which shows negative

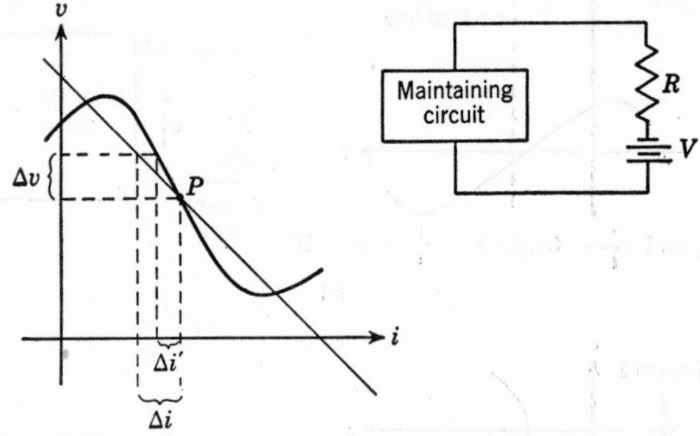

Fig. 10-5. Current-controlled negative resistance—stability considerations.

resistance, may be a region of instability. Since the maintaining circuit of an oscillator requires a negative resistance, the center region is of particular interest in consideration of oscillator operation. To establish a quiescent operating point in the negative-resistance region for sustained oscillation it is essential that the d-c load line does not intersect the characteristic in the stable regions I and III.[2] Thus for the current-controlled circuit a constant current bias, usually consisting of a battery in series with a high resistance R, is required, and such an arrangement is shown in Fig. 10-4a. In the voltage-controlled circuit a constant voltage bias is required as shown in Fig. 10-4b.

Obviously, a negative-resistance network composed of resistive elements only is incapable of oscillation with a resistive load. Con-

[2] Detailed discussion of this requirement is given in Chapter 12.

sider, for example, the current-controlled characteristic of Fig. 10-5. A voltage change Δv from the operating point P corresponds to a current change Δi through the load resistor, and a current change $\Delta i'$ occurs in the maintaining circuit. Thus

Δi = current variation through the load resistor R

$\Delta i'$ = current variation through the negative resistance R_n in the maintaining circuit

$\Delta i \neq \Delta i'$

This, of course, is an absurdity, since the resistance R and the network are in series; hence the circuit is not complete. Accordingly, let us examine the circuit of Fig. 10-6, wherein a capacitor C is included in shunt with the negative resistance. Here for a voltage change Δv across R, part of the current flows into C to charge it up to $V + \Delta V$. This fulfills the basic condition that the summation of currents at any point in the circuit is zero. The circuit is then capable of being un-

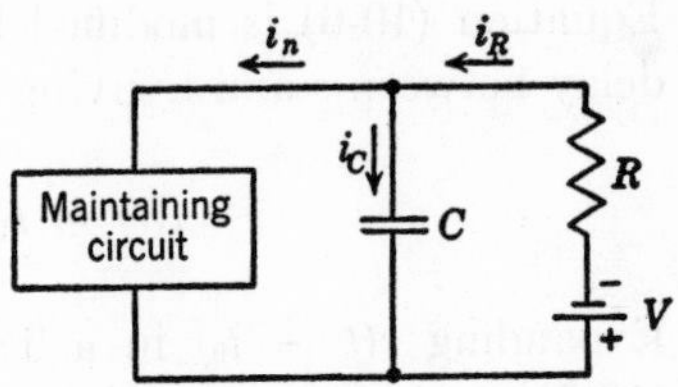

Fig. 10-6. Unstable configuration of current-controlled negative resistance.

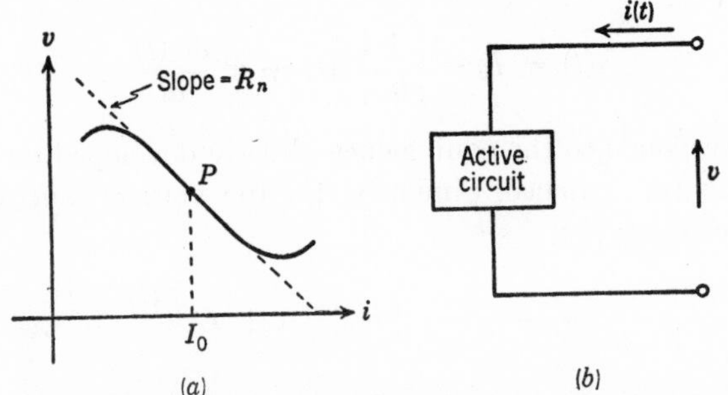

Fig. 10-7. (a) Driving point impedance characteristic; (b) two-terminal negative-resistance circuit.

stable. In a like manner it may be shown that the voltage-controlled type of negative-resistance two-terminal network may be made unstable when it is coupled to an inductive element.

Mathematically, an interpretation of the reactive elements for instability can be obtained by a consideration of the characteristic and circuit of Fig. 10-7.[3] Taking a point P on the static characteristic of the two-terminal current-controlled negative resistance, we can write for the characteristic itself in the neighborhood of the point P,

$$i = I_0 - \left|\frac{1}{R_n}\right| v \tag{10-6}$$

and

$$i = i(t)$$

Equation (10-6) is modified by postulating the existence of a time delay between v and i, giving

$$i(t) = I_0 - \left|\frac{1}{R_n}\right| v(t - t_0) \tag{10-7}$$

Expanding $v(t - t_0)$ in a Taylor series and substituting into Eq. (10-7),

$$i(t) = I_0 - \left|\frac{1}{R_n}\right| [v(t) - t_0 v'(t) + t_0^2 v''(t) - \dots] \tag{10-8}$$

We may drop the terms beyond $v'(t)$ as being of second order, and so negligible, and letting $\left|\frac{1}{R_n}\right| t_0 = C$, one has

$$i(t) = I_0 - \left|\frac{1}{R_n}\right| v(t) + C\,\frac{dv\,(t)}{dt} \tag{10-9}$$

which corresponds to the equivalence already developed on the basis of experimental evidence. Similarly, for the voltage-controlled type of negative resistance,

$$v(t) = V_0 - |R_n|\, i(t) + L\,\frac{di(t)}{dt} \tag{10-10}$$

Accordingly, the current-controlled type of negative resistance becomes unstable when the d-c instability conditions have been satisfied and the maintaining circuit is shunted by a capacitance as shown in Fig. 10-8a. The voltage-controlled type of negative resistance becomes unstable when the d-c instability conditions have been

[3] Private communication with P. L. Bargellini, Moore School of Electrical Engineering, University of Pennsylvania.

N. Carrara, *Teoria dei Bipoli non Lineari*, Tipografia Accademia Navale, Leghorn (Italy), 1948.

satisfied and when the maintaining circuit is connected in series with an inductive element (Fig. 10-8b).

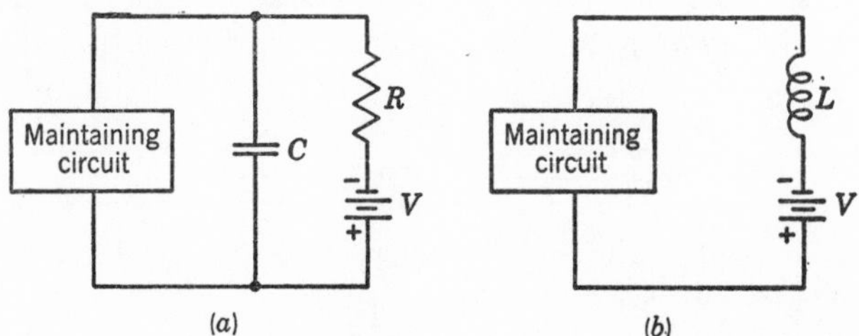

Fig. 10-8. Instability configurations for negative-resistance circuits: (a) current-controlled circuit; (b) voltage-controlled circuit.

10.4 Transistor negative-resistance circuits

Two-terminal, negative-resistance oscillators using point-contact transistors are classified according to the circuit position of the frequency-controlling reactive networks. Looking into certain branches of a properly biased point-contact transistor circuit, driving point resistances with regions of negative slope similar to those of Fig. 10-4 can be seen. For example, current-controlled negative resistance is seen looking into the emitter or the collector circuits, and a voltage-controlled negative resistance is seen looking in at the base. Recalling the a-c load requirements for each of these negative resistance types, *LC* resonant circuits may be coupled to the emitter, collector, or base circuits as follows:

1. *Base-controlled oscillator.* Voltage-controlled negative resistance is seen looking in at the base terminal of a properly connected transistor. The quiescent operating point is provided by the base voltage V_{BB}. The frequency-controlling network consists of a parallel resonant circuit for sinusoidal oscillation at a desired frequency. Positive feedback is provided across the resonant circuit, which provides a high impedance at resonance.

2. *Emitter-controlled oscillator.* Current-controlled negative resistance is seen looking in at the emitter of a properly connected transistor. The quiescent operating point is determined by the voltage V_{EE} and the series resistor R_e. The frequency-controlling network consists of a series resonant *LC* circuit. The base resistance R_b provides the required positive feedback which, in this case, is not

frequency-sensitive, and the series resonant circuit passes only the desired frequency in the emitter circuit.

3. *Collector-controlled oscillator.* The characteristics of this circuit are generally similar to those of the emitter-controlled circuit.

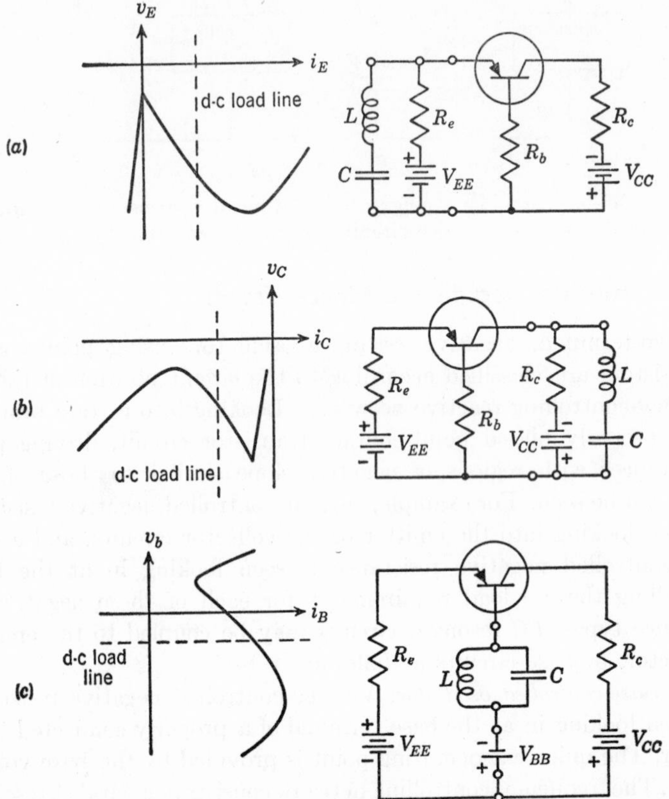

Fig. 10-9. Three basic two-terminal negative-resistance oscillator circuits. (a) emitter controlled; (b) collector controlled; (c) base controlled.

The series circuit offers minimum degeneration at resonance enabling oscillation at the prescribed frequency.

Typical negative-resistance characteristics and oscillator configurations for each of the above three cases are shown in Fig. 10-9.

A general circuit analysis will illustrate the role of the individual impedances in the three basic circuits. Consider the simple transistor circuit with internal resistances r_e, r_b, and r_c, and external impedances Z_e, Z_b, and Z_c shown in Fig. 10-10. The condition for oscillation is that the determinant of the characteristic equations of the circuit be equal to zero. Thus in this case the condition is

$$\Delta \equiv (Z_e + r_e)(Z_c + r_c) + (Z_b + r_b)(Z_e + r_e) + (Z_c + r_c) - (Z_b + r_b)r_m \leq 0 \tag{10-11}$$

The energy condition for oscillation is obtained by equating the real part of the determinant to zero, and the frequency of oscillation is obtained by equating the imaginary part to zero. The conditions which must be imposed on individual impedances for oscillation can then be derived from the determinant. Thus we see that high impedance in the base circuit tends to facilitate oscillation, while high impedances in the emitter and collector circuits tend to prevent oscillation.

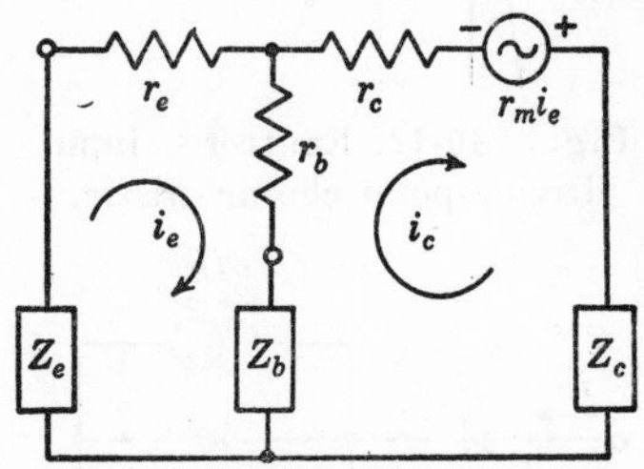

Fig. 10-10. Generalized transistor oscillator.

A fourth oscillator configuration should be included in discussion of basic point-contact transistor oscillators. This circuit, Fig. 10-11, obtains direct in-phase feedback from collector to emitter through the series *LC* resonant circuit. It is similar to the base-controlled oscillator in that feedback takes place only at the resonant frequency.

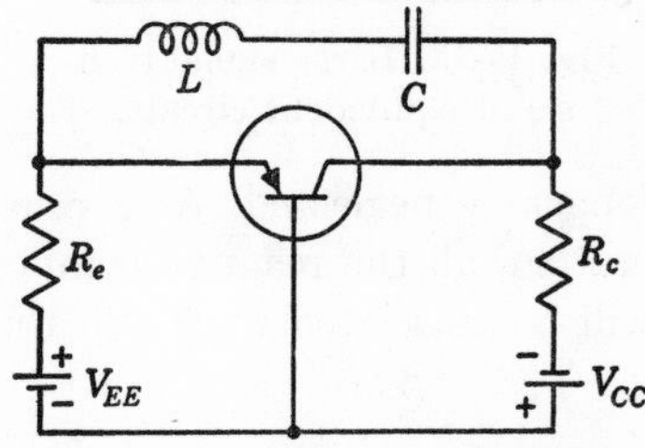

Fig. 10-11. Collector to emitter feedback oscillator.

In the driving-point characteristics shown in Fig. 10-9, each curve has three distinct regions. In each region the curve may be approximated by a straight line as shown in Fig. 10-12. The transistor may now be represented by the large-signal equivalent circuit shown in Fig. 10-13. The equivalent circuit is characterized by the emitter junction diode D_1, the collector junction diode D_2, and the fictitious current source $\alpha' i_E$. In the first region of operation both diodes are biased in the reverse direction, and the transistor is in the *cutoff state* with high internal resistances. In the second region the emitter doide is biased in the forward direction, while the collector diode remains biased in the reverse direction, and the transistor is in the *active state* capable of power amplification. In the third region both diodes conduct in the forward direction, and the transistor is in the *saturation state* with low internal resistances. Analytical expressions for the derivation of driving-point characteristics are given in Sec. 12.3.

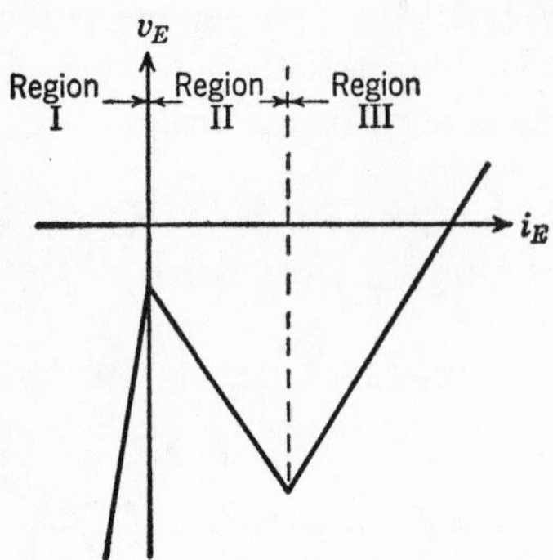

Fig. 10-12. Emitter input driving-point characteristic.

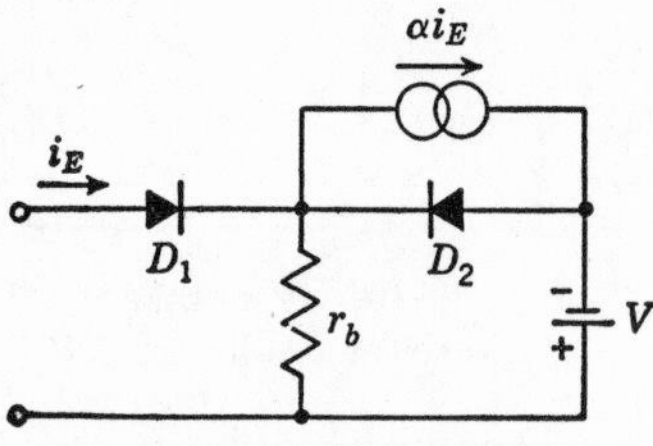

Fig. 10-13. Large-signal transistor equivalent circuit.

10.5 High-frequency considerations

So far in this chapter the transistor has been treated as a purely resistive device with certain prescribed dynamic characteristics. For oscillation at the higher frequencies, however, it soon becomes evident that the reactive components in the transistor itself can no longer be neglected. As a rough approximation for practical consideration, all the reactive components in the point-contact transistor will be associated with α in the relation

$$\alpha = \frac{\alpha_0}{1 + j\omega/\omega_{ce}} \tag{10-12}$$

where α_0 is the low-frequency value for α, and ω_{ce} is the angular cutoff frequency.

To illustrate the behavior of the transistor at high-frequency oscillation let us examine the simple circuit in Fig. 10-14, for a grounded base point-contact transistor with short circuited collector. The impedance looking into the emitter may be expressed as

$$R_{in} = r_e + r_b(1 - \alpha) \tag{10-13}$$

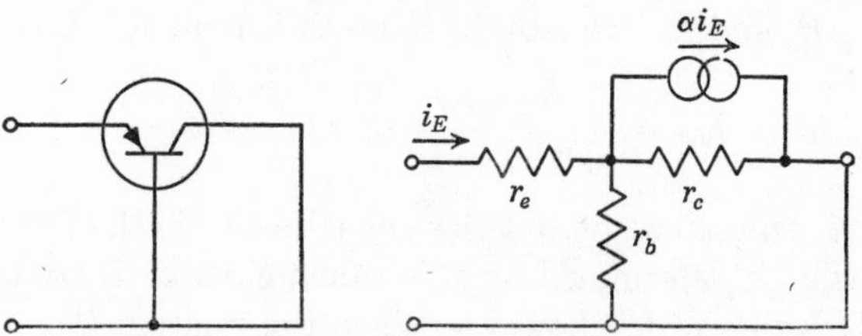

Fig. 10-14. A point-contact transistor circuit and its equivalent circuit.

Substituting the high-frequency expression for α as given in Eq. (10-12) into Eq. (10-13), the input impedance becomes

$$Z_{in} = r_e + r_b \left(1 - \frac{\alpha_0}{1 + j\omega/\omega_{ce}}\right) \tag{10-14}$$

which is no longer resistive.

From this expression we can now develop the equivalent circuit for the transistor short-circuit input impedance, Fig. 10-15. The

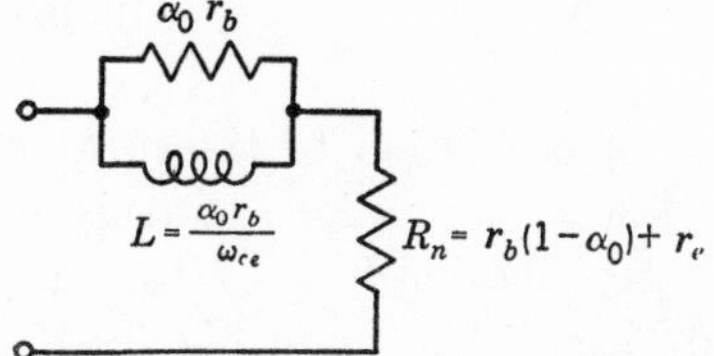

Fig. 10-15. Equivalent circuit for short-circuit input impedance.

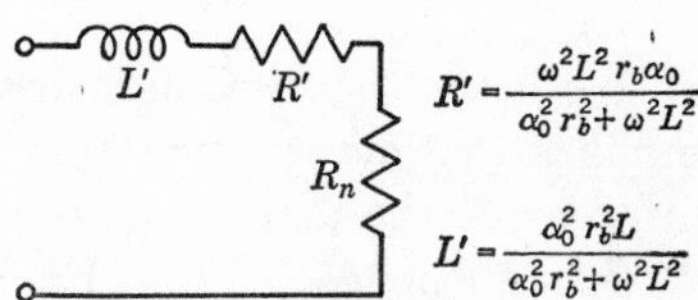

Fig. 10-16 Series LR circuit equivalent.

value for L is $\alpha_0 r_b/\omega_{ce}$. Hence, if α_0 is greater than unity, and r_e is sufficiently small, it is seen from Fig. 10-15 that the equivalent circuit consists of a negative resistance of magnitude $r_b(1 - \alpha_0) + r_e$ in series with a linear passive network. Since we are interested in the total effective circuit resistance, let us convert the parallel RL circuit to a series $R'L'$ circuit as seen in Fig. 10-16, where

$$R' = \frac{\omega^2 L^2 r_b \alpha_0}{\alpha_0^2 r_b^2 + \omega^2 L^2} \tag{10-15}$$

$$L' = \frac{\alpha_0^2 r_b^2 L}{\alpha_0^2 r_b^2 + \omega^2 L^2} \tag{10-16}$$

Now adding R' and R_n, we obtain the total circuit resistance,

$$R' + R_n = \frac{\omega^2 L^2 r_b \alpha_0}{\alpha_0^2 r_b^2 + \omega^2 L^2} + r_b(1 - \alpha_0) + r_e \qquad (10\text{-}17)$$

Hence if L' is tuned out by a series capacitance C', the frequency of oscillation will be determined by this tuned circuit. There is a lower limit for the value of C', however, since the relation $R' + R_n \leqslant 0$ must be fulfilled for sustained oscillation. The maximum frequency of oscillation is obtained with the smallest value of C' that fulfills the condition $R' + R_n = 0$.

$$\frac{\omega^2 L^2 r_b \alpha_0}{\alpha_0^2 r_b^2 + \omega^2 L^2} + r_b(1 - \alpha_0) + r_e = 0 \qquad (10\text{-}18)$$

Substituting $L = \alpha_0 r_b/\omega_{ce}$, and rearranging, we obtain

$$\frac{\omega_m}{\omega_{ce}} = \sqrt{\frac{r_b(\alpha_0 - 1) - r_e}{r_b + r_e}} \qquad (10\text{-}19)$$

In practical applications $r_e \ll r_b$, and Eq. (10-19) becomes

$$\frac{\omega_m}{\omega_{ce}} = \sqrt{(\alpha_0 - 1)} \qquad (10\text{-}20)$$

which relates the maximum frequency of oscillation to the current amplification factor cutoff frequency. For example, for a transistor with $\alpha = 3$, the maximum frequency of oscillation is 1.4 times the cutoff frequency ω_{ce}. From Eq. (10-16), Eq. (10-20), and Fig. 10-15, we obtain the magnitude of the equivalent series inductance L'.

$$L' = \frac{L}{\alpha_0} = \frac{r_b}{\omega_{ce}} \qquad (10\text{-}21)$$

From Eq. (10-21) we observe that the equivalent series inductance is dependent on the value of r_b; and then the maximum oscillation frequency is a function of r_b. The necessary series capacitance to resonate with L' now follows.

$$C = \frac{\omega_{ce}}{\omega_m^2 r_b} = \frac{\omega_{ce}}{\omega_{ce}^2(\alpha_0 - 1)r_b} = \frac{1}{\omega_{ce}(\alpha_0 - 1)r_b} \qquad (10\text{-}22)$$

The above analysis neglects the collector capacitance and assumes that the only reactive effect which is of consequence is the phase shift associated with α. In practice it is found[4] that by virtue of the collector capacitance, internal oscillations and their higher modes may occur at frequencies above that predicted by Eq. 10-20. The mechanism of oscillation is analogous to electron oscillations around a positive grid, the so-called Barkhausen oscillations.[4]

10.6 Frequency stability

We shall find the basic problems of frequency stability in transistor oscillator circuits not too unlike those encountered in vacuum tube oscillators and subject to like means of analysis.[5] The oscillation frequency of an oscillator is determined by the following three factors:

1. The natural frequency of the resonant circuit—the LC tank circuit.
2. The reactive elements of the maintaining circuit.
3. The curvature of the maintaining circuit voltage-current characteristic, i.e., the nonlinearity of the negative-resistance curve.

We shall discuss each of these factors with the help of a typical transistor oscillator, the base-controlled oscillator of Fig. 10-9c.

1. *Tank circuit.* Mechanical stability of the component parts should, of course, be assured in the presence of vibration and changes of atmospheric conditions. The Q of the circuit should be *high* to make the tank highly frequency-selective, while the resonant impedance of the tank *looking from the maintaining circuit* should be kept *low* so that circuit Q will not suffer when the tank is loaded by the maintaining circuit. A high-Q, low-Z_0 parallel resonant circuit can be obtained by tapping the inductance of the tank, Fig. 10-17. The L/C ratio of the tank should be low to filter out harmonics, which tend toward frequency instability.

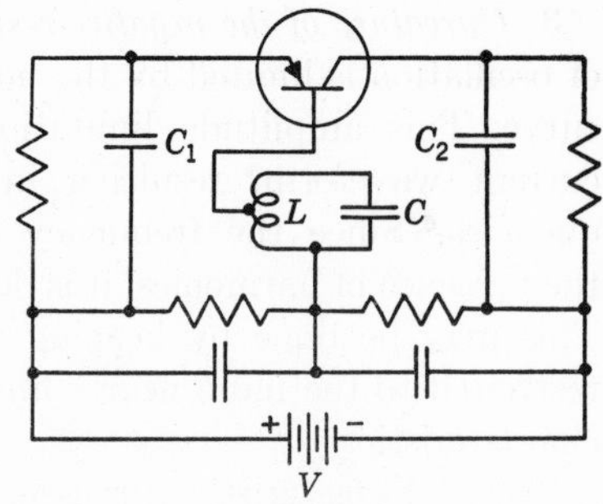

Fig. 10-17. Stabilized base resonant circuit oscillator.

2. *Transistor reactance.* The subject of internal transistor reactance is accorded more thorough discussion in Chapter 7; accordingly, only

[4] H. E. Hollman, "Internal Transistor Oscillations," *Proc. I.R.E.*, Vol. 42, p. 1323, August 1954.

[5] H. A. Thomas, *Theory and Design of Valve Oscillators*, Chapman and Hall, London, 1951.

a brief qualitative treatment is considered here. The presence of reactive elements in the maintaining circuit which remain constant do affect frequency of oscillation, but do not cause frequency instability. The reactive elements in a transistor, however, do not remain constant, but can vary to a great extent with changes of circuit biases and with changes of temperature. This results mostly from the change of *effective thickness* of the junctions within the transistor with applied voltage. Accordingly, frequency variation caused by changes of bias voltages can be minimized to some extent by using a common bias source for both emitter and collector as shown in Fig. 10-17. Of course, the advantages of a common bias source are also obtained in circuits which provide self-bias to the emitter electrode. At best, however, complete compensation of the effect of bias voltage changes is difficult to obtain. The relatively large "swamping capacitors" C_1 and C_2 will tend to minimize changes of internal capacitance while simultaneously improving the high-frequency response of the circuit. The effect of changes of transistor reactances can also be *minimized* by having the maintaining circuit loosely coupled to the resonant tank circuit. One form of loose coupling is produced by tapping the inductance, as shown in Fig. 10-17.

3. *Curvature of the negative-resistance characteristic.* The amplitude of oscillation is limited by the nonlinearity of the negative-resistance curve. This amplitude limitation produces distortion of the base current waveform, resulting in the production of harmonic frequencies.[6] Since the frequency of the fundamental is affected by the presence of harmonics, it is desirable to minimize their generation. This may be done by keeping the oscillation amplitude small and restricted to the more nearly linear region of the negative resistance characteristic.

Three characteristic curves of the base resonant circuit oscillator will aid in understanding some details of the operation of the oscillator. The i_B-v_B curve, which is the driving-point impedance characteristic at the base, defines the shape of the negative-resistance curve. The i_C-v_B curve is the collector transfer characteristic, and dictates the waveshape of the collector current. The i_C-v_B curve is the emitter transfer characteristic, and dictates the waveshape of the emitter current. These three curves are displayed jointly in Fig. 10-18, and the three distinct regions of operation are identified.

[6] H. A. Thomas, *op. cit.*

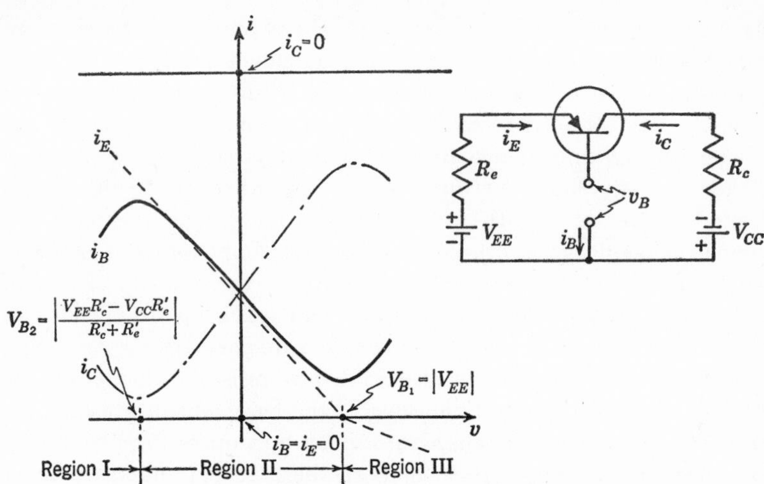

Fig. 10-18. Base voltage characteristics.

Analytically it can be shown (see Chapter 12) that the extent of the negative resistance region of the base characteristic is defined by the two voltages approximately as

$$V_{B_1} = V_{EE} \tag{10-23}$$

and

$$V_{B_2} = \frac{V_{EE}R_c' - V_{CC}R_e'}{R_c' + R_e'} \tag{10-24}$$

where

$$R_e' = R_e + r_e$$

$$R_c' = R_c + r_c$$

The negative resistance characteristic approaches a straight line except in the neighborhood of the limits.

To obtain good symmetrical waveform, it is obvious that the quiescent operation point should lie at the center of the negative-resistance region. By making the relative magnitude of the emitter bias and the collector bias in the ratio

$$\frac{V_{EE}}{V_{CC}} = \frac{R_e'}{2\alpha R_c' + R_e'} \tag{10-25}$$

no base bias is required.

It should be mentioned at this point that while the analysis based on the low-frequency equivalent circuit and the d-c characteristics may tell us much about the fundamental operation of a circuit, it is only an approximation at best in practice. The reactive effects within the transistor cannot be shown in d-c characteristics; a much more complicated high-frequency equivalent circuit is needed.

Returning to the characteristics of Fig. 10-18, we observe that in normal operation of the two-terminal base resonant circuit oscillator, wherein a high-impedance resonant circuit is coupled to the base circuit, a high degree of distortion occurs when the base voltage swing extends outside the approximately linear negative-resistance region. Accordingly, the need for loose coupling is emphasized, and voltage swings at the base should be limited to the more linear region.

The importance of maintaining a constant d-c operating point is also evident by an inspection of this figure. Ideally, the d-c operating point should lie at the center of the negative-resistance region so that the positive and the negative swing of the base current are of equal amplitude. One way to help assure a constant operating point is by use of a common bias source for both the collector and the emitter circuits so that the ratio of the two biases remains constant.

10.7 Crystal-controlled oscillators

The transistor oscillator is readily adapted to crystal frequency control, providing the same flexibility of circuit configuration as may be obtained in the simple two-terminal oscillators just discussed. The crystal itself may be operated either as a resonant circuit or as an antiresonant circuit, of very high Q. Figure 10-19 describes the basic crystal oscillator, in which the equivalent circuit of the crystal is shown as the resonant circuit coupled to a two-terminal negative-resistance network of either the voltage-controlled type or the current-controlled type.

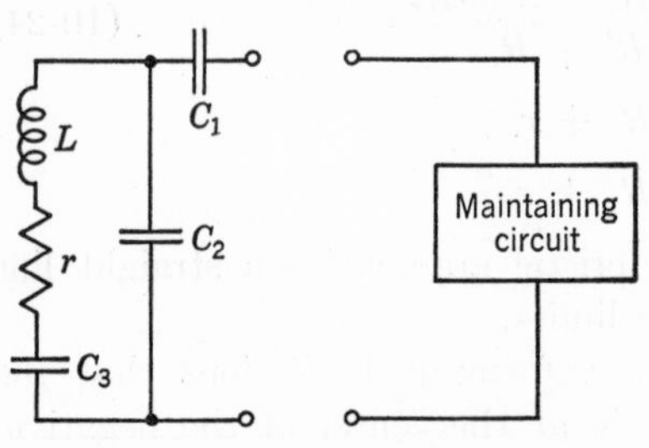

Fig. 10-19. Equivalent circuit of basic crystal oscillator.

Here C_1 is the equivalent capacitance of the air gap between the crystal faces, C_2 is the mounting capacitance, and C_3 and L are the effective reactive components of the crystal itself; r represents the crystal losses. Since the crystal may operate either at resonance, in which event it presents a low resonant impedance, or at antiresonance, in which event it presents a high resonant impedance, it may be placed at any one of the various branches of the two-terminal oscillator to achieve precision control of oscillation frequency. As an illustrative example, Fig. 10-20a shows the crystal operating at antiresonance in the base circuit. A d-c path must be provided in shunt to the crystal for bias currents, and this may be

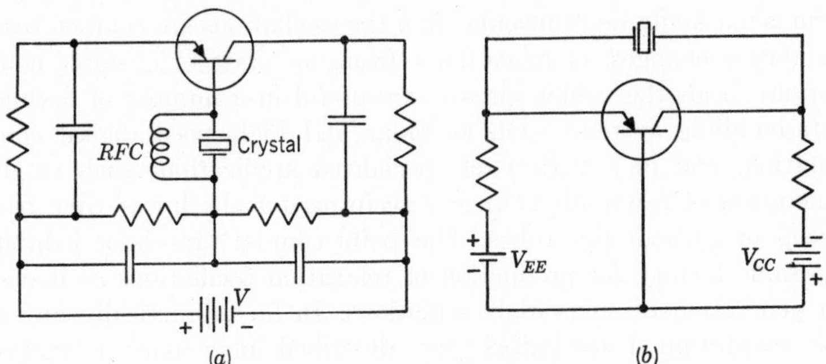

Fig. 10-20. Crystal controlled oscillators.

either the RF choke shown, or a high resistance. Figure 10-20b shows the crystal operating at resonance to form a feedback path between the collector and the emitter. In practical oscillator circuits an *LC* resonant circuit may also be employed; the crystal is loosely coupled to the maintaining circuit to achieve good frequency stability.

10.8 Oscillator-frequency multipliers

The basis for harmonic frequency generation has been touched upon in Sec. 10.6, in which it was pointed out that operation of the transistor beyond its linear regions leads to harmonic frequency generation. Figure 10-21 illustrates an oscillator-frequency multiplier in which a parallel resonant circuit L_2-C_2, tuned to an integral multiple of the fundamental frequency determined by the tank circuit L_1-C_1, has been placed in the collector circuit. At the resonant frequency of the base tank the collector tank circuit, which is tuned to a harmonic frequency, still presents a low impedance to the collector and thus enhances oscillation at the

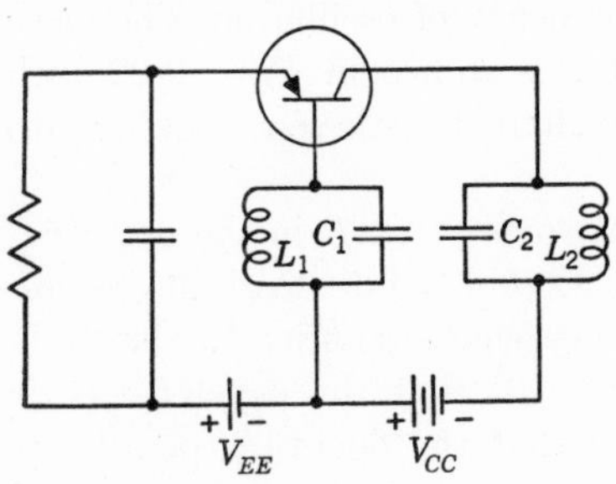

Fig. 10-21. Oscillator-frequency multiplier.

fundamental frequency. The harmonic output is taken from the L_2-C_2 tank circuit.

10.9 Relaxation oscillators

Relaxation oscillators are those oscillators in which output waveform is markedly nonsinusoidal, and the oscillations are characterized by abrupt changes, or relaxations, from one state of unstable equilibrium to another. Such circuits are useful in a number of discrete data-handling systems such as radar and high-speed digital computation, and in a variety of specialized applications such as the generation of sawtooth voltage waveforms for the linear time base sweep of cathode-ray tubes. The point-contact transistor exhibits the same facility for production of relaxation oscillations as it does for generation of sinusoidal oscillations. In fact, practically any of the two-terminal oscillators just described may offer relaxation oscillations with proper selection of parameters in the circuit design.

Emitter Control

The emitter-controlled relaxation oscillator is one of the simplest, and at the same time one of the most effective relaxation oscillation circuits. A reactive element is employed at the emitter to control the mode of oscillation of the circuit and the operation of this circuit is easily analyzed in a qualitative manner from a consideration of the driving-point resistance characteristic displayed at the emitter.

The characteristic is of the current-controlled type and a capacitive element C_e is employed to satisfy the conditions for instability. The size of C_e influences the repetition frequency of oscillation. The basic emitter-controlled relaxation oscillator is shown in Fig. 10-22 with an idealized driving-point impedance characteristic seen looking into the emitter.

The circuit is biased quiescently at some point P in the negative-resistance region, which is the intersection of the d-c load line (representing R_e) and the negative resistance characteristic. In the cycle of operation, consider initially (at $t = 0$) that the capacitor C_e is charged to a negative voltage V_1, so that the operation point is at M_1 on the characteristic. At this point the transistor is in its *cutoff* state, and the emitter reverse resistance is very high. Thus the capacitor C_e essentially discharges through R_e with a time constant C_eR_e. Eventually the voltage across C_e reaches the value V_2 at point M_3 on the characteristic, and the transistor enters into its dynamic

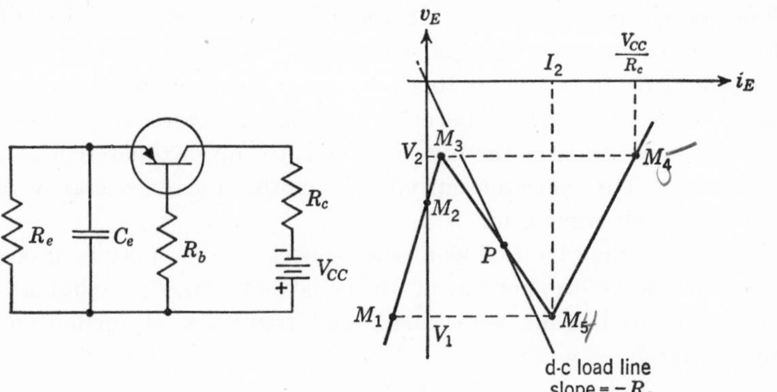

Fig. 10-22. Emitter-controlled relaxation oscillator.

transition region. In the waveform plots of Fig. 10-23 this occurs at time t_0. When the transistor enters into its transition region, the positive feedback action in the circuit causes the emitter current to increase very rapidly until the transistor reaches saturation. This

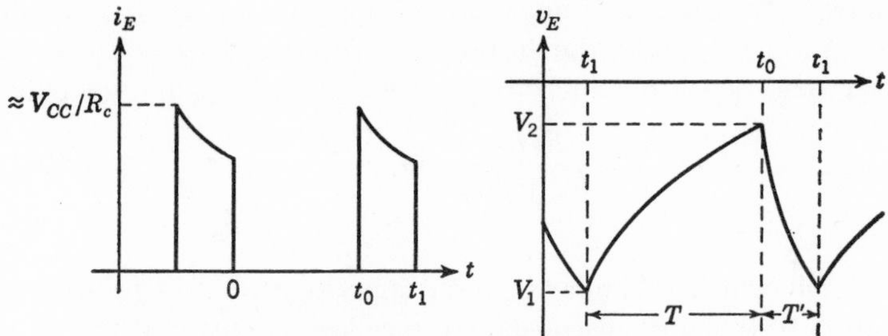

Fig. 10-23. Emitter waveforms of emitter-controlled relaxation oscillator.

corresponds to the sudden jump of the operation point from M_3 to M_4. While the transistor is in the saturation region, it acts like a low-impedance passive device, and the capacitor C_e is charged by the power supply voltage with a time constant

$$C_e \frac{R_b R_c}{R_b + R_c}$$

The operation point moves from M_4 to M_5. When M_5 is reached, the transistor enters the transition region again, and the emitter current drops very rapidly, corresponding to the sudden jump of the operation point from M_5 to M_1 (at $t = t_1$ in the waveform plot).

Thus the cycle is completed. In the emitter voltage waveform plot (Fig. 10.23), we see that the capacitor C_e discharges with a time constant C_eR_e from $t = 0$ to $t = t_0$; C_e then charges during the time $t = t_0$ to $t = t_1$. The emitter current is essentially zero for $0 < t < t_0$ (because of the high R_e); and it is approximately V_{CC}/R_c at time t_0. The collector current waveform resembles closely the emitter current waveform.

The circuit may be used as a pulse generator, or it may be used as a sawtooth waveform generator. In the latter event, R_c is eliminated, causing T' to become very small, and frequency of oscillation is approximately

$$f \approx \frac{1}{R_e C_e \ln (V_1/V_2)} \tag{10-26}$$

Note that under these conditions the frequency of oscillation is essentially independent of the value of the collector bias voltage V_{CC}. If the circuit is used as a pulse generator, pulse width is controlled by adjustment of the sizes of C_e and R_c. Resistance R_b is also involved in the determination of pulse width, but is generally fixed in size to satisfy the instability criterion. The width of the emitter (and hence the collector) current pulse T' is approximately

$$T' \approx \frac{R_c R_b}{R_c + R_b} C_e \ln \frac{V_{CC} - V_2}{V_{CC} - V_1} \tag{10-27}$$

Collector Control

A circuit which is similar in both appearance and in principle of operation to that just discussed is the collector-controlled relaxation oscillator, Fig. 10-24. The voltage-current characteristic appearing at the collector of the regenerative point-contact circuit is shown in Fig. 10-9b. The negative-resistance characteristic is of the current-controlled type, and accordingly the capacitance C_c is required for instability. The circuit is not so generally useful as the emitter-controlled circuit, since considerably poorer control is obtained at the collector terminal.

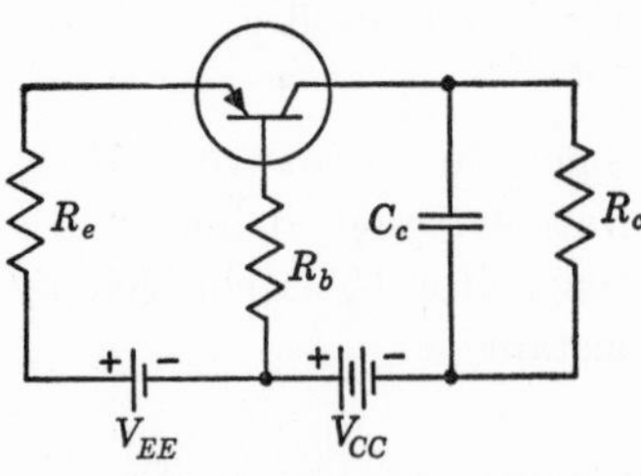

Fig. 10-24. Collector-controlled relaxation oscillator.

Base Control

Although the basic principle is the same, the operation of the base-controlled relaxation oscillator is somewhat different from that of the emitter-controlled and the collector-controlled circuits. Since, as we

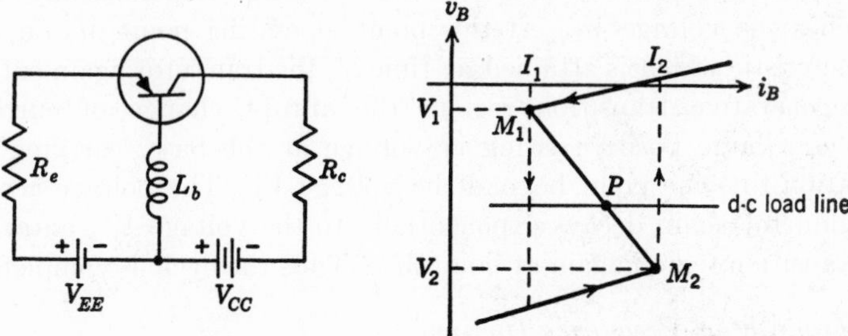

Fig. 10-25. Base-controlled relaxation oscillator.

have pointed out in Sec. 10.4, the base terminal of a point-contact transistor may exhibit a voltage-controlled negative-resistance characteristic, it follows that a series inductance is required for oscillation. The basic circuit of the base-controlled relaxation oscillator is shown in Fig. 10-25 with a linearized driving-point resistance characteristic. Operation of the circuit is as follows. With a proper base voltage bias the d-c load line can be made to intersect the characteristic in the negative-resistance region as shown. The voltage and the current waveforms appearing at the base terminal are as shown in Fig. 10-26. Assume at time t_0 the instantaneous operating point of the circuit is M_1 on the characteristic. The abrupt change of current in the transistor as the operating point moves into the transit-

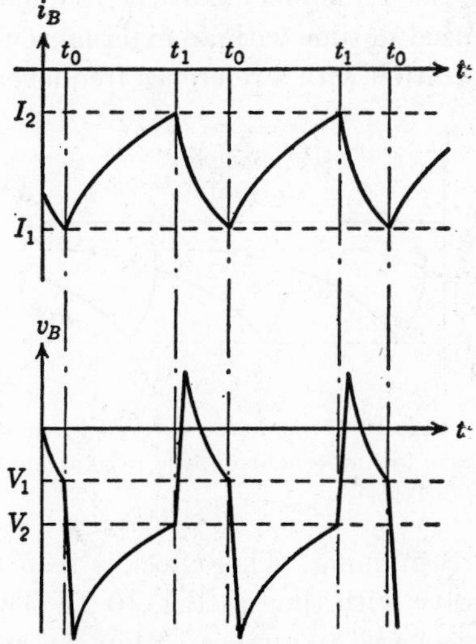

Fig. 10-26. Base waveforms of base-controlled relaxation oscillator.

ion region induces a large (depending on the Q of the inductor) negative voltage pulse at the base. Accordingly, operation of the circuit is carried well beyond the voltage V_2 by the inductive "kick" of the inductor. The field in the inductance now begins to collapse at a rate determined by the size of the inductor and the circuit resistances, and the base voltage exponentially approaches the voltage V_2. At this point, operating point M_2 on the characteristic which is attained at time t_1, the transistor again enters its regenerative transition region; the abrupt change of current induces a large positive swing of voltage at the base, carrying its operation to some point beyond the voltage V_1. The voltage across the inductor again decays exponentially to the voltage V_1, entering the transition region again at point M_1. Thus the cycle is completed.

Synchronization, Frequency Division

Any of the relaxation oscillators so far discussed may be operated in such a manner that the frequency of their oscillations are synchronized in time with an external source of periodic excitation. Synchronization with a reference frequency may be accomplished by choosing the time constants of the relaxation circuit to provide a free-running frequency with a period slightly greater than that of the reference frequency. The reference signal, in the form of a positive pulse at the emitter, or a negative pulse at the base, will cause the circuit to fire at a time τ before the circuit would normally have fired had it been free-running. This effect is seen in the plot of the emitter voltage wave with time in Fig. 10-27. The emitter voltage wave must have recovered to a point within the amplitude of the synchronizing pulse to the critical firing level V_2 when the synchronizing pulse is applied.

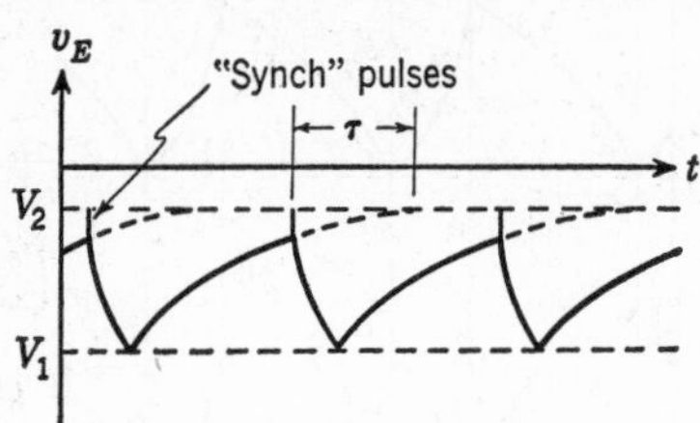

Fig. 10-27. Emitter voltage waveform of a synchronized relaxation oscillator.

The principles outlined above may be extended to cover those cases where the control signal has a frequency which is an approximate multiple of the free-running frequency of the oscillator. An example of the frequency division arrangement is described in Fig. 10-28. In the example shown, the control frequency has a period of T seconds, and the output frequency has a period of nT seconds. In this case, positive input pulses of frequency $1/T$ are applied at the emitter of the transistor, and are shown diagramatically superimposed on the emitter voltage wave in the upper figure. Every third input pulse

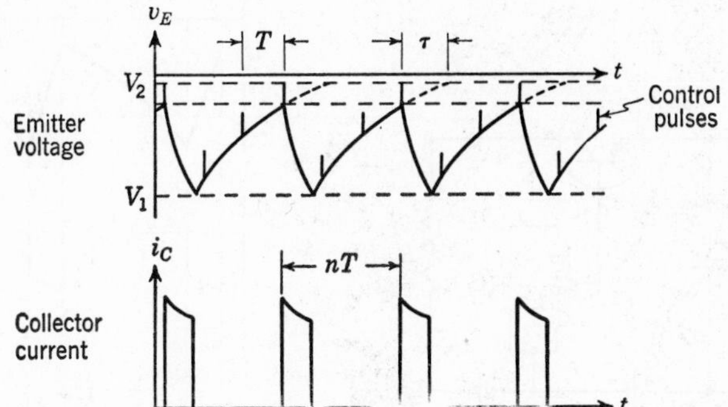

Fig. 10-28. Waveforms of a relaxation oscillator operating as a frequency divider.

causes the circuit to enter its regenerative state before the time it normally would have if free-running. Thus the repetition frequency of the current pulse is a subharmonic frequency of the control frequency. Frequency divisions by factors of three or greater may be developed, but for reliability the slope of the emitter voltage wave must be steep near the firing point if consistent discrimination between adjacent control pulses is to be obtained.

10.10 Self-quenching oscillators

Self-quenching, or sometimes called "squegging," oscillators may be designed by effectively combining the operation of a sinusoidal oscillator and a relaxation oscillator. Such a circuit is shown in Fig. 10-29, in which the operation of an emitter-controlled relaxation oscillator is combined with the operation of a base-controlled sinusoidal oscillator. Figure 10-30 describes the pertinent current and voltage waveforms for this circuit.

10.11 Four-terminal oscillators

The junction triode transistor is most commonly used as the active element in four-terminal, or feedback type, oscillator circuits. Generally speaking, the point-contact transistor may be used in both negative-resistance oscillator circuits or in feedback oscillator circuits;

however, under certain circumstances the feedback configuration is required. For example, point-contact transistors with a current amplification factor which is less than unity must employ an external

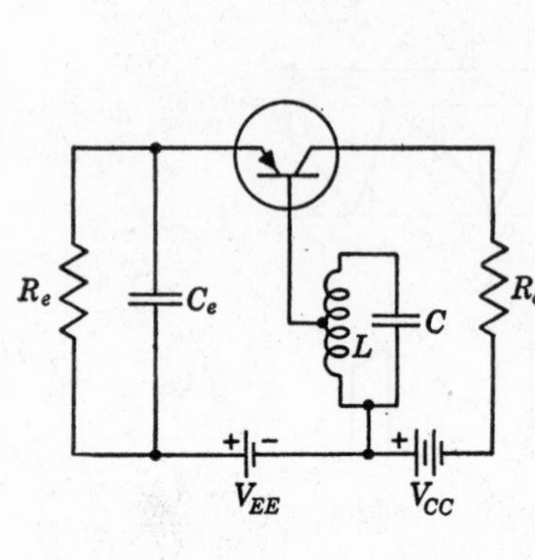

Fig. 10-29. Self-quenching oscillator.

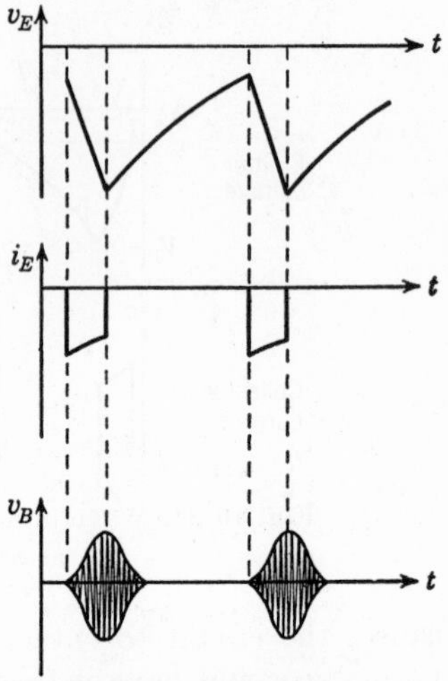

Fig. 10-30. Self-quenching oscillator waveforms.

feedback path to return some of the output power to the input. Again, at those frequencies where the phase shift associated with alpha cutoff becomes great enough, it may be found that emitter and collector currents are no longer in phase, and an external phase-shifting network is needed.

The junction transistor oscillator is similar in many respects to some of the more common vacuum tube oscillators, and precise duals of such circuits as the vacuum tube Hartley, Colpitts, and the tuned-plate oscillators may be derived.[7] However, the principles of duality are frequently cumbersome to carry along in practical circuit design and analysis. In the following discussion we shall compare transistor and vacuum tube circuits of similar structure rather than following the dual analogy of each circuit. The reader will soon see the similarities in structure and operation between some transistor feedback oscillators and their vacuum tube counterparts. Circuit analysis and design technique well known in vacuum tube work can be readily adopted for a study of transistor circuits.

[7] G. Raisbeck, "Transistor Circuit Design," *Electronics*, Vol. 24, pp. 128–134, Dec. 1951.

Two transistor oscillator circuits which closely resemble their vacuum tube counterparts in physical appearance are the Hartley and the Colpitts type oscillators. The physical similarity is indeed quite close if, as has been shown in other sections of this book, the base and the emitter of the transistor are treated circuitwise as the

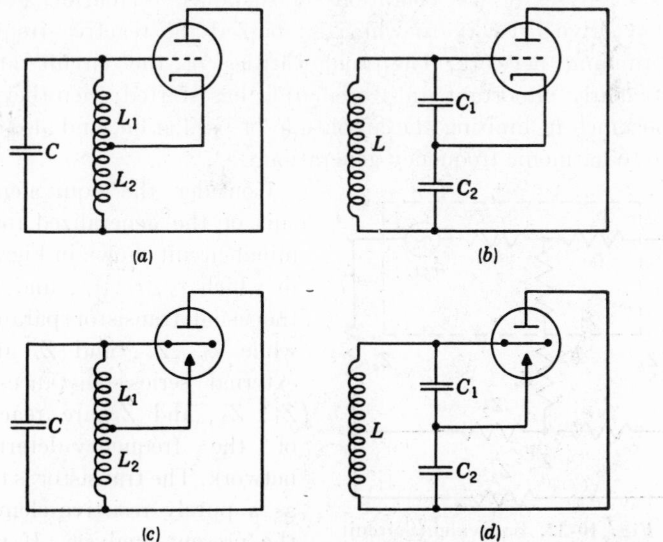

Fig. 10-31. Four-terminal oscillators: (a) vacuum tube Hartley; (b) vacuum tube Colpitts; (c) transistor Hartley; (d) transistor Colpitts.

vacuum tube control grid and cathode, respectively. Alternating-current circuit diagrams of the vacuum tube Hartley and Colpitts oscillators are compared with the transistor versions in Fig. 10-31. Similar as their physical appearances may be, however, there is a marked departure in operating characteristics between the vacuum tube oscillators and the transistor oscillators occasioned by the loading presented to the tuned circuit by the low input impedance of the transistor. The loading effect is appreciable, and demands a departure in the analysis of the transistor circuit from the typical linear analysis of the vacuum tube circuit.[8] This will be shown in the analyses of these two circuits in the succeeding sections.

[8] F. B. Llewellyn, "Constant-Frequency Oscillators," *Proc. I.R.E.*, pp. 2063–2094, 1931.

10.12 The generalized four-terminal oscillator

There are a large number of ways in which the condition of sustained oscillation may be determined, but a very precise analysis is usually unwarranted, since the computed value of any parameter in the active circuit is modified immediately once oscillation is started. Most analyses of the conditions of sustained oscillation assume a linear active network to which is coupled the reactive frequency-determining network. The nonlinearities of the circuit are not particularly important until oscillation has started; then they are of importance in limiting the amplitude of oscillation, and also contribute to harmonic frequency generation.

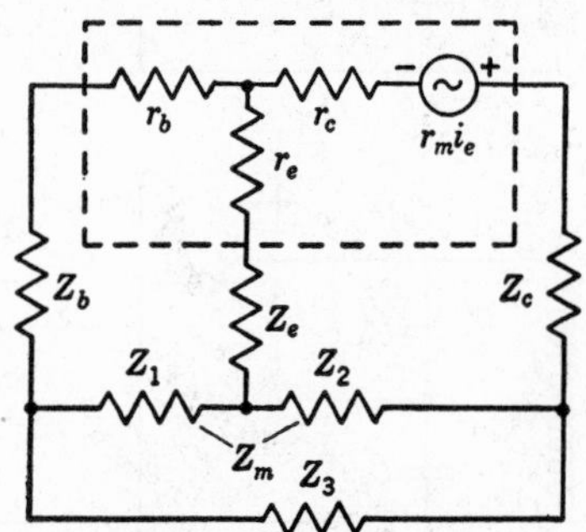

Fig. 10-32. Equivalent circuit of generalized four-terminal transistor oscillator.

Consider the equivalent circuit of the generalized four-terminal circuit shown in Fig. 10-32, in which r_b, r_e, r_c, and r_m are the usual transistor parameters, while Z_b, Z_e, and Z_c are the external series reactances, and Z_1, Z_2, and Z_3 are reactances of the frequency-determining network. The transistor is treated as a purely resistive element in the present analysis. If mutual inductance exists between the reactances Z_1 and Z_2, the additional circuit impedance Z_m is also included, as indicated in the equivalent circuit.

Application of Kirchhoff's laws to the three loops of the equivalent circuit yields the circuit equations:

$$i_1(Z_b' + Z_e' + Z_1) + i_2(Z_e' - Z_m) - i_3(Z_1 + Z_m) = 0$$

$$i_1(Z_e' - Z_m - r_m) + i_2(Z_c' + Z_e' + Z_2 - r_m) + i_3(Z_2 + Z_m) = 0$$

$$i_1(Z_1 + Z_m) + i_2(Z_2 + Z_m) + i_3(Z_0) = 0 \quad (10\text{-}28)$$

where
$$Z'_b = r_b + Z_b = r_b + jX_b$$
$$Z'_e = r_e + Z_e = r_e + jX_e$$
$$Z'_c = r_c + Z_c = r_c + jX_c$$

and
$$Z_0 \equiv Z_1 + Z_2 + Z_3 + 2Z_m$$
$$= \text{series impedance of the frequency-determining network}$$

Following Llewellyn's vacuum tube analysis, we can separate out the real terms from the imaginary terms from the determinant of the above circuit equations; equating each to zero we shall have expressions giving the stability condition and the operating frequency, respectively. Thus, equating the real terms to zero we have

$$\begin{aligned} Z_0(X_1 + X_b)(r_c + r_e - r_m) &+ (X_c + X_e + X_2)(r_b + r_c) \\ &+ X_m(2r_e - r_m) \\ &+ (2r_e - r_m)(X_2 + X_m)(X_1 + X_m) \\ &+ (X_2 + X_m)^2(r_b + r_e) \\ &+ (X_1 + X_m)^2(r_c + r_e - r_m) = 0 \end{aligned} \tag{10-29}$$

Equating the imaginary terms of the circuit determinant to zero, we have

$$\begin{aligned} Z_0(r_br_c + r_br_e + r_er_c - r_br_m) &- (X_1 + X_b)(X_c + X_e + X_2) \\ &- X_e(X_2 + X_c) - X_m(2X_e - X_m) \\ &+ 2(X_e - X_m)(X_2 + X_m)(X_1 + X_m) \\ &+ (X_1 + X_m)^2(X_c + X_e + X_2) \\ &+ (X_2 + X_m)^2(X_b + X_e + X_1) = 0 \end{aligned} \tag{10-30}$$

These two equations are not very different from those derived for the case of vacuum tube circuit analysis. However, there is the important difference that in the vacuum tube circuit

$$R_g \gg R_a\,,\ X_1\,,\ X_2\,,\ \text{and}\ X_m$$

where R_g = grid resistance; R_a = anode resistance. In the transistor circuit, r_e is quite small compared with r_c, and is appreciable compared with the effective series resistance of the resonant circuit. This loading of the resonant circuit by the low input impedance of the transistor is a source of frequency instability which is not therefore encountered in vacuum tube oscillators. Equations (10-29) and (10-30) will be used in the succeeding sections to analyze the Colpitts and the Hartley oscillator configurations for the starting conditions and for oscillation frequency.

10.13 The Colpitts oscillator; starting condition

The starting condition for the Colpitts oscillator is found from Eq. (10-29), in which the real terms of the circuit determinant have been equated to zero. Assuming that the series reactances, Z_b, Z_c, and Z_e are zero (they will be introduced later in the discussion on frequency stability), and that X_m is zero for the Colpitts configuration, we can solve for the starting conditions by making the substitutions:

$$X_1 = -1/\omega C_1, \quad X_2 = -1/\omega C_2, \quad \text{and} \quad X_3 = \omega L$$

At resonance the series reactance of the tank circuit is nearly zero; letting $Z_0 = 0$, Eq. (10-29) reduces to

$$X_2^2(r_b + r_e) + X_1X_2(2r_e - r_m) + X_1^2(r_c + r_e - r_m) \approx 0 \quad (10\text{-}31)$$

Solving for the ratio of the capacitances, we have

$$\frac{X_2}{X_1} = \frac{C_2}{C_1} \approx \frac{(r_m - 2r_e) \pm \sqrt{(2r_e - r_m)^2 - 4(r_b + r_e)(r_c + r_e - r_m)}}{2(r_b + r_e)} \quad (10\text{-}32)$$

We can simplify this expression for the average transistor, since $r_e \ll r_m$, and $4(r_b + r_e)(r_c + r_e - r_m) \ll (2r_e - r_m)^2$. The starting condition becomes

$$\frac{C_1}{C_2} \approx \frac{r_m}{r_b + r_e} \approx \frac{r_{21}}{r_{11}} \quad (10\text{-}33)$$

In general then, the condition of sustained oscillation for the Colpitts oscillator is

$$C_1/C_2 \geq r_{21}/r_{11} \quad (10\text{-}34)$$

10.14 The Colpitts oscillator; frequency stability

Loading of the resonant circuit of an oscillator will not of itself cause frequency instability; *load changes* will, however, cause frequency instability, and must be guarded against in practical oscillator design. The electron-coupled oscillator in vacuum tube circuits, for example, was designed primarily to avoid frequency instability from load variations. Other means for the enhancement of frequency stability include:

1. *Loose coupling of the tank circuit to the maintaining circuit* (minimizing the effect of maintaining circuit load changes on the tank circuit).

2. *High ratio of C to L.*[9] It has been shown that a large capacitance in the parallel resonant tank reduces the magnitude of the harmonic components in the oscillation current, which tends to stabilize frequency.

3. *Use of stabilizing reactance:*[10,11] Frequency stabilization by the insertion of reactive elements in the element leads.

The first of these measures can be taken into account only in the initial design of the oscillator circuit. A high ratio of C to L is easily designed into most oscillator circuits. The use of external stabilizing reactances is an especially effective means of stabilizing frequency in the transistor oscillator.

This is true, for the stabilizing series reactances in the transistor circuit not only eliminate the reactive effects of the transistor, but also minimize frequency shift from changes in d-c loading on the tank circuit by the maintaining (transistor) circuit.

When the transistor is coupled to the resonant circuit, it is found in the steady-state oscillation condition that every transistor parameter is involved in the determination of frequency. Since it is known that these parameters *do not* stay constant, but vary with operating conditions, environmental conditions, and life, it is well to isolate them from the resonant circuit. This step was considered in Sec. 10.6 in the discussion of point-contact transistor oscillator stability. The measures which are developed here for junction transistor oscillators can be applied equally well to the point-contact transistor oscillators in most of their circuit configurations.

At resonance the series reactance of the tank circuit is zero ($Z_0 = 0$); substituting this into Eq. (10-30) and using the tank circuit substitutions for the Colpitts oscillator, we have an expression relating

[9] H. A. Thomas, *op. cit.*

[10] F. B. Llewellyn, *op. cit.*

[11] J. B. Oakes, "Analysis of Junction Transistor Audio Oscillator Circuits," *Proc. I.R.E.*, Vol. 42, Aug. 1954.

oscillation frequency to tank circuit parameters and transistor parameters.[12]

$$f = \frac{1}{2\pi}\sqrt{\frac{1}{LC_T} + \frac{1}{AC_1C_2}} \qquad (10\text{-}35)$$

where
$$C_T = \frac{C_1C_2}{C_1 + C_2}$$

and
$$A = (r_b r_c + r_b r_e + r_c r_e - r_b r_m)$$

The transistor itself is effective in the circuit only through the term A, which we note includes all the transistor parameters. If the term $1/AC_1C_2$ is eliminated from the expression, oscillation frequency becomes

$$f = \frac{1}{2\pi\sqrt{LC_T}}$$

which is now independent of the transistor parameters.

Base Stabilization

Let us examine means whereby oscillation frequency may be stabilized against changes of the transistor parameters by insertion of a stabilizing reactance in the base lead. Let

$$X_m = Z_e = Z_c = 0, \qquad Z_b \neq 0$$

and assume the circuit to oscillate at the natural frequency of the tank circuit such that $Z_0 = 0$. Making these substitutions in Eq. (10-30), we have

$$X_1^2X_2 + X_2^2(X_b + X_1) = 0$$

or
$$X_b = -X_1(1 + X_1/X_2) \qquad (10\text{-}36)$$

Since X_1 and X_2 are capacitive, X_b must be inductive. Hence X_b is the value of the inductive reactance that must be inserted in the base lead to cause oscillations at the natural frequency of the tank circuit independent of transistor parameters. Care should be exercised in the stabilization of this type oscillator, since the calculated value for X_b is valid for but one ratio of the capacitances C_1 and C_2.

[12] J. B. Oakes, *loc. cit.*

Collector Stabilization

Collector stabilization is achieved by finding that value of collector series reactance which will cause the circuit to oscillate at the natural frequency of the LC tank. Let

$$X_m = Z_e = Z_b = 0, \qquad Z_c \neq 0, \qquad Z_0 = 0$$

Substituting into Eq. (10-30) and reducing, we have

$$X_c = -X_2(1 + X_2/X_1) \tag{10-37}$$

which indicates an inductive reactance in the collector lead for stabilization.

10.15 The Hartley oscillator; starting condition

The starting condition for the Hartley oscillator is found in an analogous manner to that used for finding the starting condition for the Colpitts oscillator.

Let us assume

$$Z_b = Z_c = Z_e = 0$$

The tank circuit constants are

$$X_1 = \omega L_1\,, \qquad X_2 = \omega L_2\,, \qquad X_3 = \frac{-1}{\omega C}\,, \qquad X_m = \omega M$$

Also, $$Z_0 \approx 0$$

These values are substituted into the real part of the circuit determinant, Eq. (10-29), yielding the expression for the starting condition,

$$\frac{L_2 + M}{L_1 + M} \approx \frac{r_{21}}{r_{11}} \tag{10-38}$$

That is, the condition of sustained oscillation is

$$\frac{L_2 + M}{L_1 + M} \geq \frac{r_{21}}{r_{11}} \tag{10-39}$$

10.16 The Hartley oscillator, frequency stability

The oscillation frequency of the unstabilized Hartley oscillator is

$$f = \frac{1}{2\pi}\,\frac{1}{\sqrt{C(L_1 + L_2 + 2M) - [(L_1L_2 - M^2)/A]}} \tag{10-40}$$

The determination of the stabilizing reactances for the Hartley oscillator can be carried out in the same manner as the determination of these reactances for the Colpitts oscillator, with the exception that the mutual reactance X_m is included in this case.

10.17 Tuned-collector oscillator

Another common type of feedback oscillator is shown in Fig. 10-33. In this circuit, the tuned-collector oscillator, the base of the transistor is coupled to the collector inductively, and the sense of the secondary winding is such as to allow for the 180° phase reversal inherent between base and collector currents. The capacitor C_e offers an easy path for oscillating frequency currents; R_e is selected to provide proper emitter-base bias.

Self-modulation (quenching) of this type of oscillator may be obtained by using a large RC time constant in the emitter circuit. The operation may be described qualitatively as follows: Assume the emitter capacitor C_e is initially charged to a sufficiently negative voltage so that the transistor is in the cutoff state. The charge on the emitter capacitor gradually leaks off through R_e until a point is reached where the transistor enters the active region, and oscillation starts. As the amplitude of oscillation increases, emitter current (which is rectified at the emitter junction) flows and charges the capacitor. The bias builds up gradually in this manner and ultimately damps out the oscillation, completing the cycle.

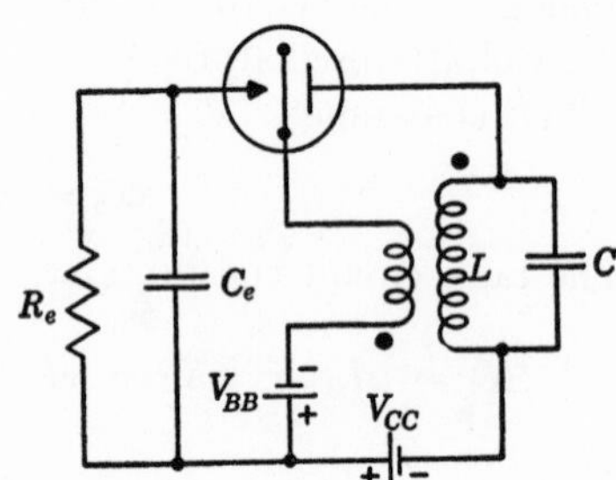

Fig. 10-33. Tuned-collector oscillator.

10.18 Crystal control

An effective crystal-controlled oscillator, somewhat similar in appearance to a Colpitts oscillator, is shown in Fig. 10-34. The circuit will exhibit very stable operating characteristics by use of the crystal as the principal control element in conjunction with the tuned circuit in the collector, which helps to reduce the harmonic content. If collector bias is adjusted to permit "bottoming" of the characteristic in operation, excellent amplitude stability is achieved.

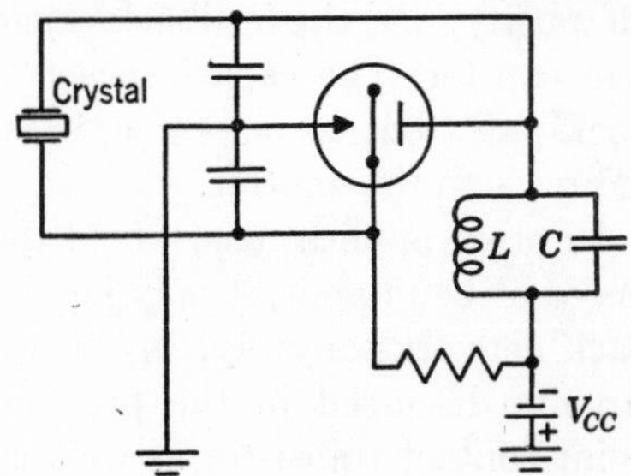

Fig. 10-34. Crystal-controlled junction transistor oscillator.

10.19 Feedback oscillators using point-contact transistors

Earlier in this chapter it was pointed out that while the point contact transistor lends itself easily to operation in negative-resistance type oscillators, its use as an oscillator is not limited to this type of circuit. Operation in feedback type circuits is not only possible so long as the power gain of the transistor is great enough, but may be necessary in those instances where the current amplification factor may be less than unity, or where a combination of alpha phase shift and decreased gain at higher frequencies takes place.

We have seen in Sec. 10.3 that the theoretical upper frequency limit of oscillation of the *negative-resistance* type of oscillator is roughly $\sqrt{2} \times f_c$. Oscillations at frequencies well above this limit may be achieved provided sufficient gain is still available, and provided that the phase shift associated with alpha cutoff is compensated for by an equal and opposite phase shift elsewhere in the circuit.[13] At these higher frequencies the oscillator circuit of Fig. 10-35 may be used. In this circuit stray capacitances are neglected for

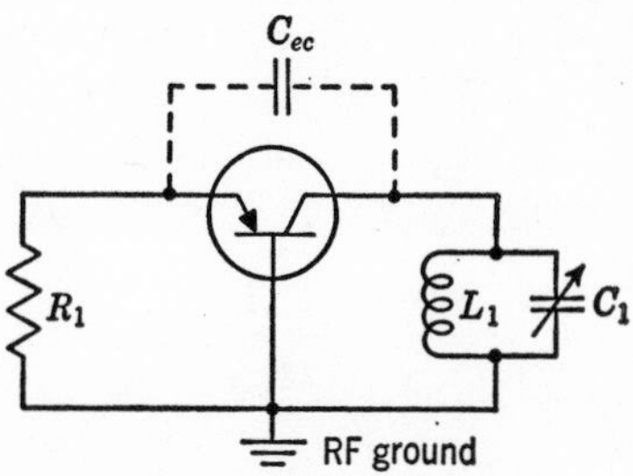

Fig. 10-35. Feedback type point-contact transistor oscillator.

[13] D. E. Thomas, "A Point-Contact Transistor VHF FM Transmitter," Bell Telephone Laboratories, Inc., Aug. 1953.

simplicity, and the feedback capacitor C is inserted between collector and emitter. The capacitance C not only provides an external feedback path, but corrects the phase of the collector currents which are fed back to the emitter.

In other applications, where the complication of alpha phase shift may not be present, it may be desirable to incorporate external feedback networks anyway. In this event, any of the feedback oscillator circuits discussed in the previous sections may be used with the point-contact transistor as well as with the junction transistor.

PROBLEMS

10-1. Prove the equivalence of setting $Z_{in} = 0$ to setting the circuit determinant $\Delta = 0$ in deriving the stability criterion.

10-2. Develop Eqs. 10-26 and 10-27, and develop a new equation for the free running frequency of a relaxation oscillator with finite R_c.

10-3. Develop an expression relating the free running frequency of oscillation of the base-controlled relaxation oscillator of Fig. 10-25 to the circuit and device parameters. Draw the pertinent equivalent circuits for each region of operation of the circuit.

Chapter 11

MODULATION AND DEMODULATION

In order to perform the functions of modulation or demodulation a device with a nonlinear characteristic is required. Such nonlinear operation is usually obtained either by the use of a crystal or a vacuum tube diode, or by driving an amplifier into its nonlinear region. In fact, because the voltage-current relationships are seldom linear in nature, the term "linear operation" is only relative.

The choice between a crystal and a vacuum tube diode is to some extent determined by the frequency response and noise considerations. Thus at microwave frequencies the crystal diode mixer has established its superiority over its vacuum tube counterpart. In addition, the crystal (or semiconductor) diode also has the advantages of small size and absence of filament power. It can therefore be expected that the transistor, which in some respects may be viewed as consisting of semiconductor diodes, should possess some of the advantages of the crystal diode in addition to being capable of power amplification.

In this chapter we shall examine the nonlinearities of transistor characteristics and discuss operation of a transistor as a modulator and demodulator.

11.1 Nonlinearities in transistor characteristics

In order to obtain an exact solution to a circuit problem containing nonlinear elements, a knowledge of nonlinear mechanics is required. Such problems are usually much more involved than those dealing only with linear elements. However, in practice it is often sufficient if only an approximate solution is obtained, and hence various simplifying assumptions are made; e.g., the nonlinearities may be represented by "ideal" diodes (i.e., they have zero resistance in the forward direction, and an infinite resistance in the reverse direction) in series with linear resistances. Another approximation is to neglect all but a limited number of frequency components of a complex waveform.

In this section the exact theoretical expressions for the nonlinearities in junction transistors are given so that the type and degree of approximation, when needed, can be made judiciously.

The Resistive Large-Signal Characteristics

The d-c characteristics of a junction transistor (neglecting any extraneous elements which may be shunting the junctions) are given by Eqs. (8.27a) to (8.27c).

$$I_E = [\epsilon^{\Lambda(V_E + I_B r_{bb'})} - 1] \frac{G_{11}}{\Lambda} + [\epsilon^{\Lambda(V_C + I_B r_{bb'})} - 1] \frac{G_{12}}{\Lambda} \tag{11-1a}$$

$$I_C = [\epsilon^{\Lambda(V_E + I_B r_{bb'})} - 1] \frac{G_{21}}{\Lambda} + [\epsilon^{\Lambda(V_C + I_B r_{bb'})} - 1] \frac{G_{22}}{\Lambda} \tag{11-1b}$$

$$I_B = -\left\{ [\epsilon^{\Lambda(V_E + I_B r_{bb'})} - 1] \frac{(G_{11} + G_{21})}{\Lambda} + [\epsilon^{\Lambda(V_C + I_B r_{bb'})} - 1] \frac{(G_{12} + G_{22})}{\Lambda} \right\} \tag{11.1c}$$

where G_{11}, G_{12}, G_{21}, and G_{22} are conductances, each of which is a function of the properties of the material constituting the transistor, and of its geometry; $1/\Lambda = 0.026$ volt at room temperature; $r_{bb'}$ = base spreading resistance; I_E, I_C, and I_B = d-c emitter, collector, and base currents, respectively; V_E and V_C = emitter to base, and collector to base, direct voltages, respectively. (The sign convention is as indicated in Fig. 8-3.)

In normal transistor operation the collector junction is biased in the "reverse" direction, and V_C in the above expressions is a negative number (as is I_B and I_C). Thus for collector voltages greater than about 0.5 volt, the exponential terms containing V_C are entirely negligible, and we may write Eqs. (11-1a) to (11.1c) as follows:

$$I_E = \frac{G_{11}}{\Lambda} \epsilon^{\Lambda(V_E + I_B r_{bb'})} + I_{ES} \tag{11-2a}$$

$$I_C = \frac{G_{21}}{\Lambda} \epsilon^{\Lambda(V_E + I_B r_{bb'})} + I_{CS} \tag{11-2b}$$

$$I_B = -\frac{G_{11} + G_{21}}{\Lambda} \epsilon^{\Lambda(V_E + I_B r_{bb'})} + I_{BS} \tag{11-2c}$$

where

$$I_{ES} = -\frac{1}{\Lambda}(G_{11} + G_{12}) \tag{11-3a}$$

$$I_{CS} = -\frac{1}{\Lambda}(G_{21} + G_{22}) \tag{11-3b}$$

$$I_{BS} = -(I_{ES} + I_{CS}) = \frac{1}{\Lambda}(G_{11} + G_{12} + G_{21} + G_{22}) \tag{11-3c}$$

Figure 11-1 shows exaggerated details near the origin of the curves V_E vs. I_E, of V_E vs. $(-)I_C$, and of V_E vs. $(-)I_B$, which follow from

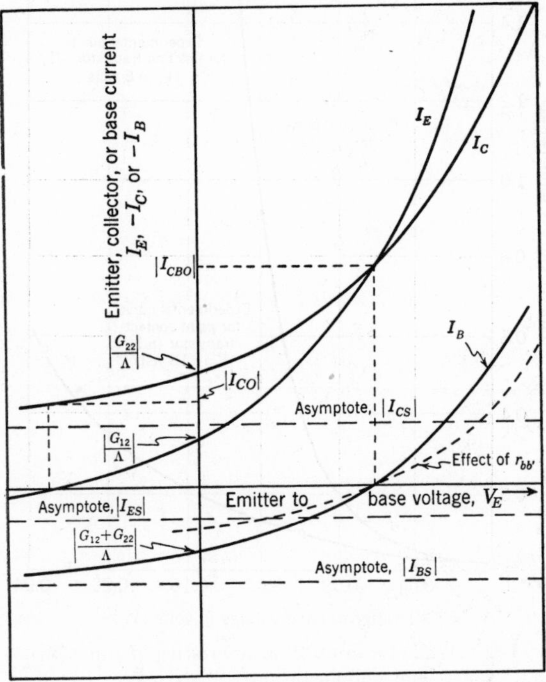

Fig. 11-1. D-c input and transfer characteristics for junction transistors (not to scale).

Eqs. (11-2a) to (11-2c) for $r_{bb'} = 0$. The dctted curve shows the effect of $r_{bb'}$ on the base current curve. The effect on the other curves is similar, i.e., their slopes decrease. It is obvious that for a given value of V_E, $I_E = |I_C| + |I_B|$. Thus at the point where the I_E

and I_C curves intersect, the value of I_B is 0, while the current flowing in the collector is the maximum "saturation" current I_{CB0}. (It is the *maximum*, because Eqs. (11-2a) to (11-2c), which are the basis of these curves, assume that V_C is very large). The saturation current I_{CO} is also indicated, corresponding to where $I_E = 0$.

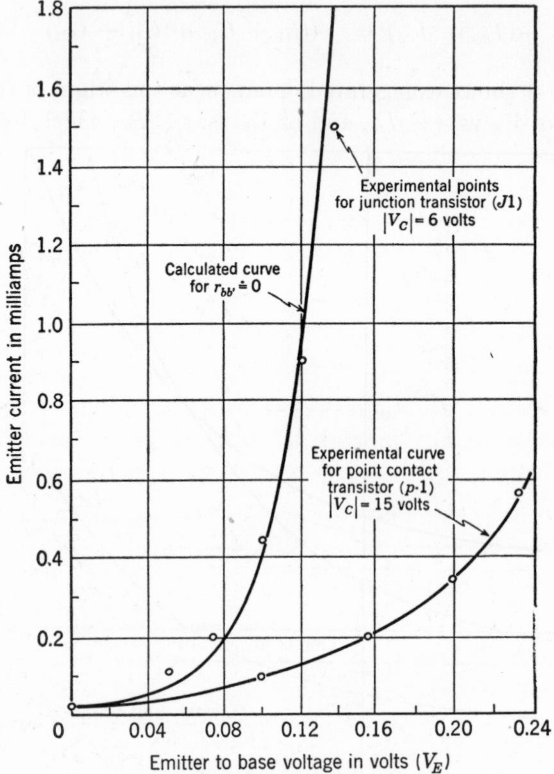

Fig. 11-2. D-c input characteristics of junction and point-contact transistors.

The theoretical expressions for G_{11}, G_{12}, G_{21}, and G_{22} are independent of current or *emitter* voltage according to the "first-order" theory of Shockley, *et al.*[1] Thus the large-signal resistive input and forward-transfer characteristics are over a limited range in the form of ex-

[1] W. Shockley, M. Sparks, and G. K. Teal, "P-N Junction Transistors," *Phys. Rev.*, Vol. 83, pp. 151, July 1951.

ponentials as indicated by the above equations. Figure 11-2 shows experimental points and a calculated curve (using Eqs. 11-2a with $r_{bb'} = 0$) for a junction transistor, and an experimental curve for a point-contact transistor, for a constant voltage on the collector.

The conductances G_{11}, G_{12}, G_{21}, and G_{22}, however, are dependent on *collector* voltage by virtue of their dependence on the effective base width, $W \doteq (W' - d)$, where W' is the width measured between the metallurgical junctions and d is the width of collector transition region. It can be shown (Eq. 8-70) that $d \propto V_C^n$, where n is a fraction which in practice varies from about ½ to ⅓.

It should also be noted that Eqs. (11-1) and (11-2) hold only for collector voltages below the breakdown voltage. At the breakdown point the above equations are drastically affected, since small increases in collector voltage result here in large changes of collector current.

The Resistive and Reactive Small-Signal Parameters

The small-signal equivalent circuit of a device helps in some respects to gain an insight into the response of the device for large signals. Thus we examine the individual elements of the high-frequency equivalent circuit of a junction transistor, shown in Fig. 11-3 (see

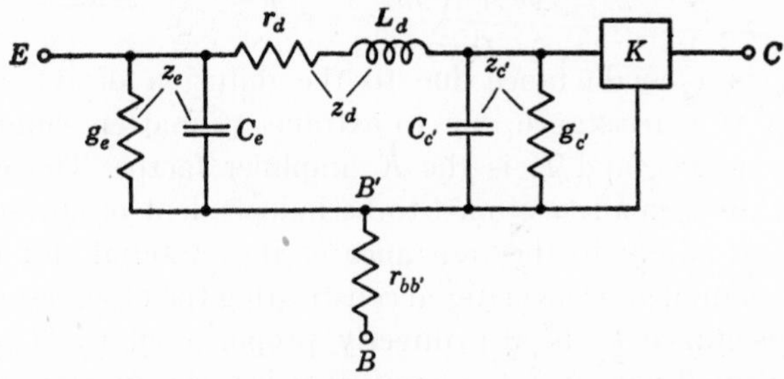

Fig. 11-3. Small-signal equivalent circuit of junction transistors.

Sec. 7-7 *et seq.*). The only significant approximation contained in this circuit as compared with the "exact" equivalent circuit is the replacement of distributed elements by lumped constant elements.

As a result of the exponential relationships in the d-c characteristic described above, the values of some of the small-signal resistive parameters are approximately inversely proportional to current.

This is to be expected, since by differentiating, for example, Eq. (11-2a) (ignoring the element $r_{bb'}$), we obtain

$$g_{11} = \left.\frac{dI_E}{dV_E}\right|_{V_C=0} = G_{11}\epsilon^{\Lambda V_E} \tag{11-4a}$$

$$= \Lambda(I_E - I_{ES}) \tag{11-4b}$$

that is, for emitter bias direct currents $|I_E| \gg |I_{ES}|$, g_{11} is proportional to the emitter direct current. Similarly, r_d and g_e may be written (from Sec. 7-7),

$$r_d = \left|\frac{1}{\Lambda(I_C - I_{CS})}\right| \doteq \left|\frac{1}{\Lambda(I_E - I_{ES})}\right| \tag{11-5a}$$

$$g_e = \frac{1}{\alpha_{cbo} r_d} \tag{11-5b}$$

where α_{cbo} is the low-frequency value of the short-circuit current amplification factor, which according to the first-order theory is independent of current. Similarly, $g_{c'}$ is approximately proportional to $(I_E - I_{ES})$ provided its dominating component is that which is due to the diffusion of the minority carriers,[2] i.e. (from Eq. 7-15),

$$g_{c'} \equiv \left(g'_{Dp} + \frac{K}{r_\lambda}\right) \tag{11-6}$$

where g'_{Dp} is a conductance due to the diffusion of the minority carriers; r_λ is a resistance due to extraneous matter shunting the collector junction; and K is the K amplifier factor. The elements r_λ and $r_{bb'}$ are normally assumed to be independent of current, since they are due purely to the resistance of the material shunting the collector junction, and the material constituting the base, respectively.

The capacitance C_e is also directly proportional to $(I_E - I_{ES})$ for not too small values of I_E; however, when the emitter current is zero, or when there is a reverse bias on the emitter junction, C_e depends mostly on the emitter bias *voltage*. The reason for this behavior may be seen by examining the components of C_e (from Eq. 7-12).

$$C_e \equiv C_{Dp} + C_n + C_{SR} + C_{TE} \tag{11-7}$$

[2] This fact follows from Eq. (8-46b), where $g'_{Dp} \propto G$, and from Eq. (8-44b), where $G \propto (I_E - I_{ES})$, approximately. For a symmetrical transistor $g_{Dp} = g'_{Dp}$.

For approximately $I_E > 0$ the diffusion capacitance C_{Dp} is the dominating term, and it is proportional to g_{Dp} (from Eq. 8-46c), which in turn is proportional to $(I_E - I_{ES})$ as explained above. For approximately $I_E < 0$ the emitter transition capacitance C_{TE} dominates, its dependence on the emitter voltage being of the form given in Eq. (11-9).

It should be noted that although g_e and C_e are each proportional to $(I_E - I_{ES})$ their quotient is obviously independent of current; i.e., ω_{cb} is independent of current, since $g_e/C_e \doteq \omega_{cb}$, where ω_{cb} is the "cutoff" angular frequency at which the magnitude of the short-circuit current amplification factor has decreased by 3 db from its low-frequency value (see Eq. 7-11). Similarly, although the inductance L_d is dependent on the emitter direct current, *viz.*, $L_d \propto 1/(I_E - I_{ES})$, the time constant L_d/r_d is independent of current.

The capacitance $C_{c'}$ is nearly independent of voltage or current. This is evident from below. The components of $C_{c'}$ are,

$$C_c' = C_{Dp} + KC_{TC} \tag{11-8a}$$

However, the collector capacitance[3] C_c *is* dependent on collector voltage, as

$$C_c(\equiv C_{c'}/K) = C_{Dp}/K + C_{TC} \tag{11-8b}$$

In contrast to C_e, the transition capacitance (C_{TC}) is here of major importance under normal operating conditions, while the diffusion component is often negligible. From Eq. (8-72) the expression for C_{TC} may be written

$$C_{TC} = A\,|\,V_C\,|^{-n} \tag{11-9}$$

where V_C = the reverse voltage across the collector junction; n = a fraction such as ½ or ⅓, depending on the distribution of the "impurities" (donor and acceptor atoms) in the vicinity of the junctions; and A is a function of the geometry and the resistivities of the material constituting the transistor. Thus an increase in collector voltage results in a decrease in capacitance.

The K amplifier factor increases with collector voltage,

$$K \propto |\,V_C\,|^{n}$$

[3] Capacitance C_c is the resultant capacitance when $C_{c'}$ is transferred to the right of the K amplifier in Fig. 11-3.

where n is a fraction as defined above. This follows from Eqs. (8-44e) and (8-71b). It is now clear that the product KC_{TC} and hence $C_{c'}$ is virtually independent of voltage.

The expressions for the nonlinearities described in this section, as stated earlier, are a result of a "first-order" theory. On this basis the expressions for G_{11}, G_{12}, G_{21}, and G_{22} are independent of current. Accordingly, the short-circuit current amplification factor at low frequency α_{cbo} (which also relates r_d with g_e as in Eq. 11-5b) also appears to be independent of current, since we may write

$$\alpha_{cbo} = \frac{I_C - I_{CS}}{I_B - I_{BS}} = \frac{-G_{21}}{G_{11} + G_{21}} \tag{11.10}$$

Experimentally, however, it is found that this is not quite correct, as seen, for example, from Fig. 8-6, showing an experimental curve of α_{cbo} vs. I_E. Thus the above-listed conductances *are* somewhat dependent on current, especially G_{11} (cf. Sec. 8.12). The exact analytical expression for this dependence is, however, too complicated to be of direct use in practical circuit calculations.

Finally, it should be emphasized that since an explicit solution to most nonlinear differential equations seldom exists, there is no single approach in the analysis of nonlinear networks which could be followed as a matter of routine, analogous to the solution of linear circuit problems. Thus various artifices are used, depending on the problem in hand.

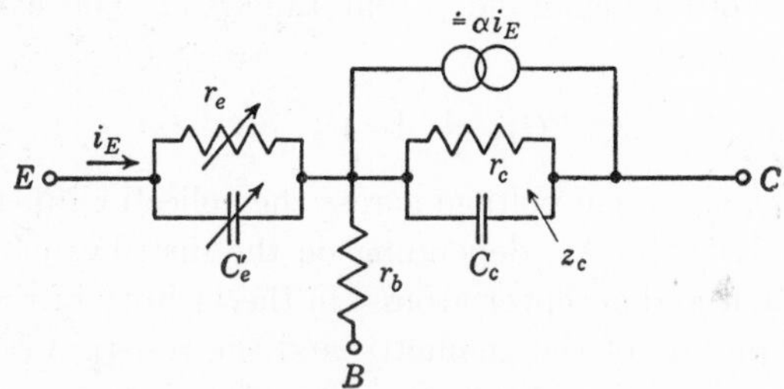

Fig. 11-4. Approximate equivalent T circuit for some nonlinear applications.

For example, consider the T equivalent circuit shown in Fig. 11-4. If we identify $r_{bb'}$, r_d, and C_e of Fig. 11-3 with r_b, r_e, and C_e' of Fig. 11-4, the input impedances of these circuits are approximately equal (see Sec. 7.14). Similarly, by making the collector impedance z_c

equal to $K(z_e + z_{c'})$, the output impedances of the two circuits will be approximately equal at all but the highest frequency range. However, the reverse transfer impedance (or reverse voltage amplification factor) of Fig. 11-4 is now quite inaccurate at all but very low frequencies when compared with that of Fig. 11-3. Hence the T circuit could in some cases be used for finding the modulation products resulting from the nonlinearities in the *input* circuit, and for the resultant *output* we can resort to Fig. 11-3. (This procedure is particularly suitable for the analysis of mixer operation as in Sec. 11.8.) The merit of the T circuit here is that as a first-order approximation only a limited number of nonlinear elements are assumed, viz, r_e and C'_e as indicated in Fig. 11-4.

11.2 Harmonics generated on an exponential curve

In Sec. 11.1 it is shown that some of the large-signal transistor characteristics are in the form of exponentials. The presence of a comparatively linear element like $r_{bb'}$ tends to reduce this nonlinearity. In Class A amplifiers, where linear operation is desired, the presence of a large source impedance will further "pad" the nonlinearity. With modulation or demodulation, however, a nonlinear voltage-current relationship is essential, and thus we consider the "ideal" case where $r_{bb'} = 0$. Accordingly, from Eq. (11-2a),

$$I_E = I_{ES} + \frac{G_{11}}{\Lambda}\epsilon^{\Lambda V_E} \tag{11-11}$$

Let

$$V_E = V_{EE} + V_e' \cos \omega t \tag{11-12}$$

where V_{EE} is the applied direct voltage, and V'_e is the peak value of alternating voltage. Substituting Eq. (11-12) into Eq. (11-11), it follows by Fourier analysis that

$$I_E = I_{ES} + I'_0 + I'_1 \cos \omega t + I_2 \cos 2\omega t + \dots + I_n \cos n\omega t \tag{11-13a}$$

where

$$I'_0 = \left[\frac{1}{2\pi}\int_0^{2\pi} \epsilon^{\Lambda V'_e \cos\omega t}\, d(\omega t)\right]\frac{G_{11}}{\Lambda}\epsilon^{\Lambda V_{EE}} = I_0^*(\Lambda V'_e)\frac{G_{11}}{\Lambda}\epsilon^{\Lambda V_{EE}}$$

and

$$I'_n = \left[\frac{1}{\pi}\int_0^{2\pi} \epsilon^{\Lambda V'_e \cos\omega t} \cos n\omega t\, d(\omega t)\right]\frac{G_{11}}{\Lambda}\epsilon^{\Lambda V_{EE}} = I_n^*(\Lambda V'_e)\frac{G_{11}}{\Lambda}\epsilon^{\Lambda V_{EE}}$$

where $I_n^*(\Lambda V_e')$ is the modified Bessel function of order n. Thus we may write

$$I_E = I_{ES} + \frac{G_{11}}{\Lambda} \epsilon^{\Lambda V_{EE}} \sum_{n=0}^{n=\infty} I_n^*(\Lambda V_e') \cos n\omega t \qquad (11\text{-}13\text{b})$$

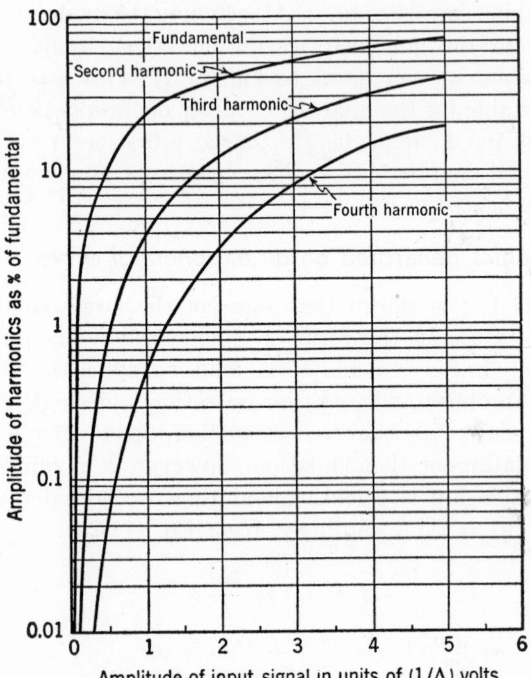

Fig. 11-5. Dependence of lowest-order harmonics, generated with exponential nonlinearity, on signal level.

Figure 11-5 shows the amplitudes of the second, third, and fourth harmonics (expressed as a percentage of the amplitude of the fundamental) plotted against the amplitude of the input signal. Thus, for example, for an input signal amplitude $V_e' = 1/\Lambda(= 0.026$ volt at room temperature) the relative amplitudes of the first, second, third, and fourth harmonics are 1:0.24:0.039:0.0048, respectively.

11.3 Modulated amplifiers

A transistor amplifier may be modulated in a somewhat analogous manner to the method used for a vacuum tube amplifier. Thus modulation will be achieved by varying the collector voltage (similar to plate modulation) or the voltages on the other electrodes of Class A, B, or C amplifiers. As an example, Fig. 11-6 shows an emitter-modulated common-base amplifier with the modulating and carrier generators virtually connected in parallel at the input. The inductance L to which the modulating voltage is connected presents a low impedance to this frequency and a high impedance to the carrier frequency source. The capacitance C on the other hand is of such a magnitude that it passes carrier frequency currents easily but presents a high impedance at the lower frequencies.

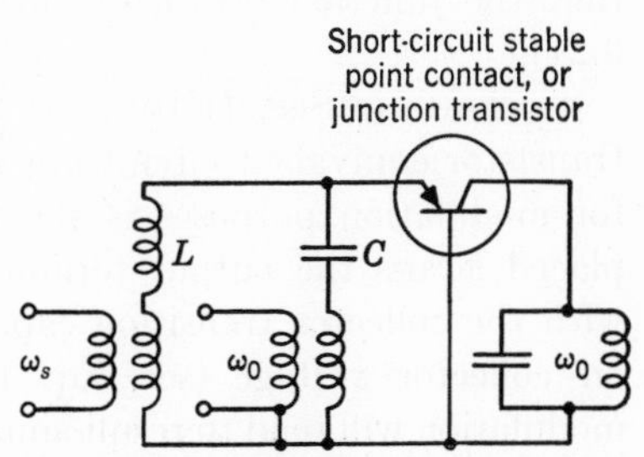

Fig. 11-6. Modulated common-base tuned amplifier.

Note that there is a considerable difference between the nonlinearities of a point-contact and that of a junction transistor, as may be seen for example from the d-c input characteristics plotted in Fig. 11-2. Another difference is in the magnitude of the transition capacitances; in point contacts, because of the small dimensions of the active region, it is much smaller than in junction transistors. In general, larger modulating voltages (or currents) are required in circuits using point-contact transistors, mostly because the equivalent emitter resistance r_e (Fig. 11-4) is here several times larger than that of junction transistors for the same emitter current. An indication of the nonlinearity of the transfer characteristics of a common-base tuned amplifier, for both a point-contact and a junction transistor, may be obtained from Fig. 11-7, which shows the small signal voltage gain

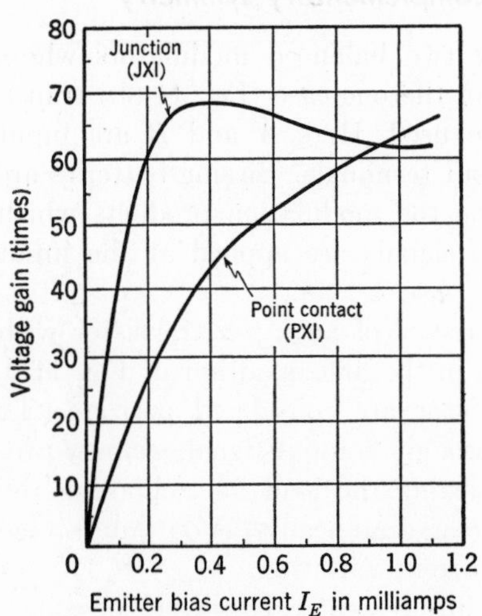

Fig. 11-7. Experimental curves showing dependence of two tuned amplifiers on emitter current.

vs. emitter base current. The low gain at low emitter bias current is mostly due to the high emitter resistance; at higher currents the emitter resistance decreases, but the current amplification factor for the particular junction transistor has decreased to such an extent that the junction transistor curve has a finite maximum. (see Eq. 9-21).

As shown in Sec. 11.1b, most resistive and reactive elements of a transistor equivalent circuit are nonlinear. Of particular importance for modulation purposes is the capacitance C_c, which is virtually placed across the output terminals.[4] This capacitance is associated with the collector transition capacitance and is therefore dependent on collector voltage (see Eq. 11-8b). This means that frequency modulation will tend to result simultaneously with amplitude modulation. This problem is dealt with in connection with modulated oscillators in Sec. 11-6.

Balanced modulation, as known in the vacuum tube art, is also possible with transistors. Indeed, here additional design freedoms are present as a result of the availability of transistors of opposite conductivity, *n-p-n* and *p-n-p*. This is treated in the following section.

11.4 Balanced modulation and complementary symmetry

Figures 11-8a and 11-8b show two balanced modulators whose circuits are identical except that in the one case (Fig. 11-8b) transistors of opposite conductivity are used. Here A and B are input terminals, while C and D are output terminals. Biasing batteries are not shown. We shall now examine the modulation products which result in these circuits when two signals are applied at the input terminals.

Consider the collector characteristics of an *n-p-n* transistor with I_B as a running parameter as seen in the first quadrant of Fig. 11-9. (Currents flowing into the transistor are considered positive.) To determine the output waveform for a given input signal, we may proceed in the usual manner by inserting the load line, choosing the quiescent operating point, and tracing graphically the output voltage at the collector for a given base current variation.

For a *p-n-p* transistor this procedure is similar. However, the collec-

[4] See footnote, p. 391.

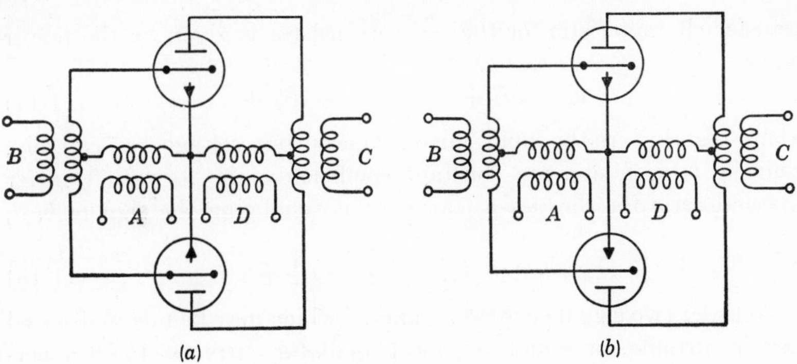

Fig. 11-8. Conventional and complementary symmetrical operation.

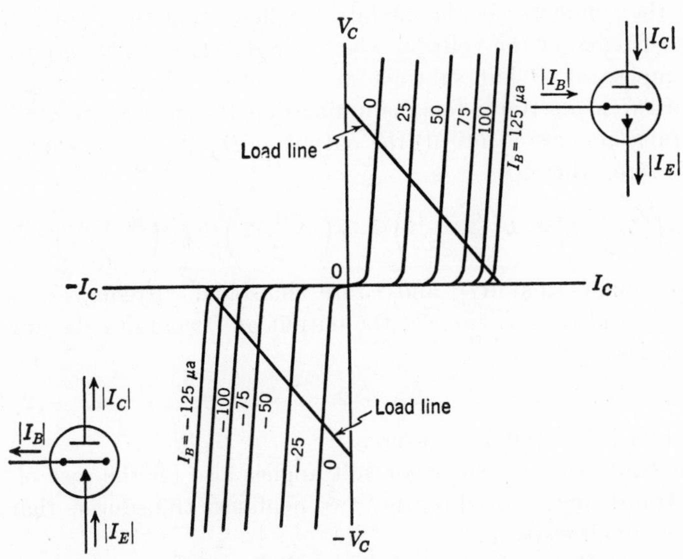

Fig. 11-9. *n-p-n* and *p-n-p* collector characteristics.

tor characteristic curves are now situated in the third quadrant, as seen in Fig. 11-9. The mathematical difference between two similar curves that lie in the first and third quadrants is that the coefficients of the even powers of the one curve, when expressed as a power series, have an opposite sign to the other. In other words, if the forward transfer characteristic for the *n-p-n* transistor is given by the power series

$$v_o = ai_i + bi_i^2 + ci_i^3 + di_i^4 + \dots \tag{11-14}$$

where i_i and v_o are the input current and output voltage, respectively, while a, b, c, d, etc. are constant coefficients, the forward transfer characteristic for the *p-n-p* transistor is (changing the sign of b, d, etc.)

$$v_o = ai_i - bi_i^2 + ci_i^3 - di_i^4 + \dots \tag{11-15}$$

Consider two signal currents, i_s and i_c (which may be modulator and carrier currents, or signal and local oscillator currents) to be superimposed at the input terminals A, both in Fig. 11-8a and in Fig. 11-8b, i.e.,

$$i_i = (i_s + i_c)/2 \tag{11-16}$$

From the symmetry of the circuits it follows that the resulting collector currents, or the voltages which will develop at the output, will superimpose at D but subtract at C. Thus in Fig. 11-8a for the case of two *n-p-n* transistors (assuming that the characteristics of the two transistors are identical) the output at D will be $2v_0$, while that at C is zero, where

$$v_0 = a\left(\frac{i_s + i_c}{2}\right) + b\left(\frac{i_s + i_c}{2}\right)^2 + c\left(\frac{i_s + i_c}{2}\right)^3 + d\left(\frac{i_s + i_c}{2}\right)^4 \tag{11-17}$$

It now follows that if i_s and i_c are sinusoidal currents, i.e., $i_s = I'_s \sin \omega_s t$ and $i_c = I'_c \sin \omega_c t$, the output at D contains the angular frequencies

$$\omega_s, \quad \omega_c, \quad (\omega_c \pm \omega_s), \quad 2\omega_s, \quad 2\omega_c, \quad (2\omega_c \pm \omega_s), \quad (\omega_s \pm 2\omega_c)$$

etc., while the output at C is zero.

It is easily shown that this result applies also for the case of two *p-n-p* transistors—indeed for any two nonlinear transducers that are identical in all respects.

To obtain the modulation products for *complementary symmetrical operation*, Fig. 11-8b, we proceed as above. Thus the output from the *n-p-n* transistor is as given by Eq. (11-17), but for the *p-n-p* transistor the output is from Eqs. (11-15) and (11-16),

$$v'_0 = a\left(\frac{i_s + i_c}{2}\right) - b\left(\frac{i_s + i_c}{2}\right)^2 + c\left(\frac{i_s + i_c}{2}\right)^3 - d\left(\frac{i_s + i_c}{2}\right)^4 + \dots \tag{11-18}$$

As before, we add the output of the two transistors to get the output at D

$$v_o + v_o' = 2a\left(\frac{i_s + i_c}{2}\right) + 2c\left(\frac{i_s + i_c}{2}\right)^3 + \dots \qquad (11\text{-}19)$$

while the output at C is

$$v_o - v_o' = 2b\left(\frac{i_s + i_c}{2}\right)^2 + 2d\left(\frac{i_s + i_c}{2}\right)^4 + \dots \qquad (11\text{-}20)$$

Again by substituting the sinusoidal expressions for i_s and i_c in Eqs. (11-19) and (11-20), it is seen that the output at D contains the fundamentals ω_s and ω_c as well as $3\omega_s$, $3\omega_c$, $(\omega_c \pm 2\omega_s)$, $(2\omega_c \pm \omega_s)$, etc., while that at C contains the second harmonics $2\omega_s$ and $2\omega_c$, the sidebands $(\omega_c \pm \omega_s)$, etc.

By similar reasoning, the outputs at C and D can be obtained when

Table 1

SIMILAR TRANSISTOR OPERATION

Input at A	Input at B	Output at C	Output at D
$s + c$	0	0	$s, c, c \pm s, 2c, 2s$
0	$s + c$	$s, c, c \pm 2s, 2c \pm s$	$s \pm c, 2c, 2s$
s	c	$c, s \pm c, c \pm 2s$	$s, 2c, 2s, 2c \pm s$
c	s	$s, s \pm c, 2c \pm s$	$c, 2s, 2c, c \pm 2s$

Table 2

COMPLEMENTARY SYMMETRICAL OPERATION

Input at A	Input at B	Output at C	Output at D
$s + c$	0	$s \pm c, 2c, 2s$	$s, c, c \pm 2s, 2c \pm s$
0	$s + c$	$s, c, c \pm s, 2c, 2s$	0
s	c	$c, 2s, 2c, c \pm 2s$	$s, c \pm s, 2c \pm s$
c	s	$s, 2c, 2s, 2c \pm s$	$c, c \pm s, c \pm 2s$

both i_s and i_c are applied at B or when one signal is applied at A and the other at B. In the latter case the input at B may be treated as two separate inputs applied to each half of the winding.

The modulation products for various input combinations for the circuits of Fig. 11-8a and Fig. 11-8b are summarized in Tables 1 and 2, respectively. (Here $s \equiv \omega_s$ and $c \equiv \omega_c$.) By inspection it is seen that, for example, in *suppressed carrier modulation*, the carrier and the modulating signal should be applied to terminals A and B, respectively, when like conductivity transistors are used, but in the reverse order when utilizing complementary symmetry. Furthermore, the output is taken at C in the former case and D in the latter.

11.5 Amplitude modulated junction transistor oscillator[5]

Amplitude modulation or frequency modulation may to some extent be obtained with most oscillating systems merely by varying an element of a circuit or the operating point. However, in order to obtain relatively linear modulation, the elements of the circuit must be correctly proportioned, and the operating point must be established with care. In this and the following sections an approximate analysis is presented which aims to give some insight into the operation of junction and point-contact modulated transistor oscillators. In particular, the conditions for linear modulation, the modulation input impedance, and the modulating power will be derived for the three cases of collector, base, and emitter modulation.

Analysis of Waveforms and Method of Operation

Figure 11-10 shows an *n-p-n* junction transistor oscillator of the feedback type discussed in Chapter 10. The transistor is biased from two bias batteries, V_{CC} and V_{BB}. A sinusoidal voltage of peak amplitude V_0' is developed across the tank circuit, and part of this voltage (peak amplitude V_f') is fed back to the base in the correct phase by means of the transformer. Resistor R_E is a biasing resistor; C_E is a by-pass capacitor for oscillator frequencies; v_C and v_B are instantaneous interelectrode voltages; i_C is the instantaneous collector current, while I_E is the direct or average emitter bias current.

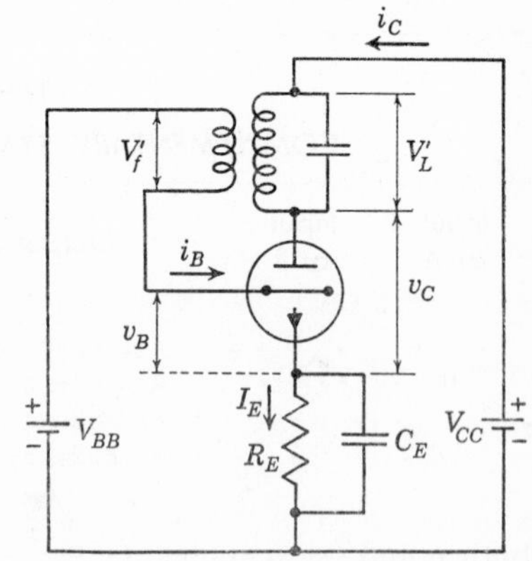

Fig. 11-10. Junction transistor oscillator.

[5] The basic analysis of modulated oscillators is due to H. C. Lin.

The voltage and current waveforms for a particular load are shown in Fig. 11-11. Thus suppose that V_0' is smaller than V_{CC}; i.e., there is always some positive voltage on the collector as seen in Fig. 11-11a. Let the minimum instantaneous voltage from collector to emitter be v_{CM}. Therefore

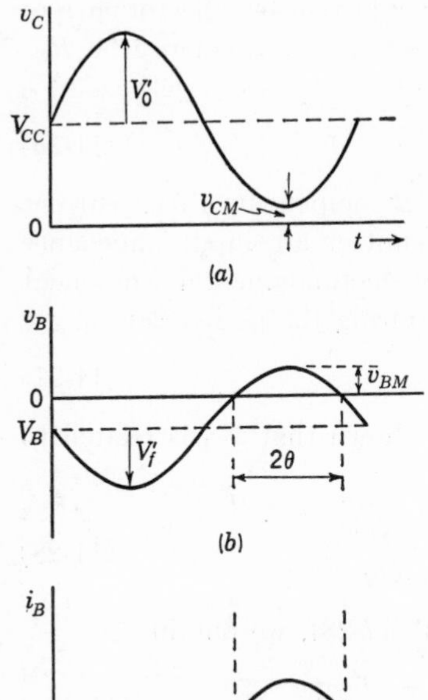

Fig. 11-11. Waveforms.

$$v_{CM} = V_{CC} - V_0'$$

since the alternating voltage drop across R_E at the oscillator frequency is negligible. Now the base to emitter voltage v_B is also sinusoidal as shown in Fig. 11-11b, and the peak value of the alternating voltage is

$$V_f' = \beta V_0' \qquad (11\text{-}21)$$

where β is the fraction of voltage fed back by transformer. Also the effective (applied) base to emitter direct voltage is

$$V_B = V_{BB} - I_E R_E \qquad (11\text{-}22)$$

Since base current can flow only when the base is biased positively with respect to the emitter, it is seen that the maximum base current will flow when v_B reaches the value v_{BM}, where

$$v_{BM} = V_f' - V_B \qquad (11\text{-}23)$$

as shown in Fig. 11-11b. The base current waveform is shown in Fig. 11-11c and we define it as flowing through an angle 2θ. The resulting collector current is seen in Fig. 11-11d.

Examine now the relationship between the different waveforms in Fig. 11-11. From Fig. 11-11b

$$V_B = V_f' \cos \theta \qquad (11\text{-}24)$$

Thus from Eqs. (11-21) to (11-24) we obtain

$$\frac{v_{BM}}{\beta V_0'} = 1 - \cos \theta \tag{11-25}$$

Let the amplitude of the fundamental component of collector current in Fig. 11-11d be I_c' and the load impedance at resonance be R_L. Hence

$$V_0' = I_c' R_L \tag{11-26}$$

Also let the amplitude of the *fundamental* component of base current in Fig. 11-11c be I_b' and the base-to-emitter a-c input impedance (Class A) be R_{in}. Thus the amplitude of the fundamental component of "clipped" base voltage (which acts during the period 2θ), is

$$V_{b1}' = I_b' R_{in} \tag{11-27}$$

Now, by Fourier analysis, it is readily shown that V_{b1}' is related to v_{BM} in Fig. 11-11b by the expression

$$\frac{V_{b1}'}{v_{BM}} = \frac{\theta - \sin\theta \cos\theta}{\pi(1 - \cos\theta)} \tag{11-28}$$

Hence, from Eqs. (11-25), (11-26), and (11-28), we obtain

$$\theta - \sin\theta\cos\theta = \frac{\pi}{\beta R_L} \frac{I_b'}{I_c'} R_{in} \tag{11-29a}$$

$$= \frac{\pi}{\beta R_L} \frac{R_{in}}{\alpha_{cb}'} \tag{11-29b}$$

where

$$\alpha_{cb}' \equiv \frac{I_c'}{I_b'} \tag{11-29c}$$

i.e., α_{cb}' is the a-c current gain for the transistor when a load R_L is present. Equation (11-29b) states that the flow angle for a given transistor depends on the load R_L and the turns ratio of the transformer.

Another relationship to which reference will be made later is the dependence of the radio frequency load current I_c' on the voltage V_{BB}. This is found as follows: from Eqs. (11-21), (11-22), (11-24), and (11-26),

$$V_{BB} = \left(\frac{I_E R_E}{I_c'} - \beta R_L \cos\theta\right) I_c' \tag{11-30}$$

The d-c amplification factors[6] are defined as

$$\alpha_{CB} \equiv \frac{I_C}{I_B} \tag{11-31a}$$

and

$$\alpha_{CE} \equiv \frac{I_C}{I_E} \tag{11-31b}$$

Also, the d-c input impedance is defined as

$$R_{IN} \equiv \frac{V'_B}{I_B} \tag{11-32}$$

where V'_B is the average, forward-bias, base voltage, and I_B is the resultant current. Voltage V'_B is related to V'_{b1}, the amplitude of the fundamental frequency component, by Fourier analysis,

$$\frac{V'_B}{V'_{b1}} = \frac{\sin\theta - \theta\cos\theta}{\theta - \sin\theta\cos\theta} \tag{11-33}$$

Thus from Eqs. (11-27), (11-29), (11-31), (11-32), and (11-33), Eq. (11-30) may be rewritten

$$V_{BB} = \left[\left(\frac{\sin\theta - \theta\cos\theta}{\theta - \sin\theta\cos\theta}\right)\frac{\alpha_{CB}}{\alpha'_{cb}}\cdot\frac{R_{in}}{R_{IN}}\frac{R_E}{\alpha_{CE}} - \beta R_L\cos\theta\right]I'_c \tag{11-34}$$

Collector Modulation

In collector modulation the collector voltage is varied, causing a change in I'_c. Consider therefore that V_{CC} is the modulating voltage.

The condition for linear modulation may be obtained as follows: From Fig. 11-11a,

$$v_{CM} = V_{CC} - V'_0 \tag{11-35}$$

Substitute for V'_0 from Eq. (11-26).

$$v_{CM} = V_{CC} - I'_c R_L \tag{11-36}$$

Hence if $v_{CM} = 0$,

$$I'_c R_L = V_{CC} \tag{11-37}$$

Equation (11-37) states that linear modulation is possible by varying

[6] It can be seen from Eq. (11-10) that for increasing values of direct current, α_{CB}, tends to α_{cbo}, the short-circuit alternating current amplification factor. Similarly, α_{CE}, tends to α_{ceo}, which for a good transistor is near unity.

the collector voltage, provided that the negative peak of the collector voltage, as seen in Fig. 11-11a, is close to zero. Thus for this to occur, R_L should be high or V_{CC} should be sufficiently low.

The modulation input impedance, $R_{cm} \equiv dV_{CC}/dI_C$ (where I_C = d-c component of collector current) may be obtained by utilizing Eqs. (11-27), (11-29c), (11-31), (11-32), (11-33), and (11-36). Thus for the case where collector cutoff occurs ($v_{CM} = 0$),

$$\frac{V_{CC}}{I_B} = \frac{\theta - \sin\theta\cos\theta}{\sin\theta - \theta\cos\theta} \frac{\alpha'_{cb}}{\alpha_{CB}} \frac{R_{IN}}{R_{in}} R_L \qquad (11\text{-}38)$$

which when combined with Eq. (11-29b) yields

$$\frac{V_{CC}}{I_C} = \frac{\pi}{\beta} \frac{R_{IN}}{\alpha_{CB}(\sin\theta - \theta\cos\theta)} \qquad (11\text{-}39)$$

Hence R_{cm} ($\equiv dV_{CC}/dI_C$) may now be found from this equation by differentiation. Note that as a rough approximation at high emitter currents R_{cm} is actually given by Eq. (11-39), although for a more exact value, the dependence of R_{IN}, α_{CB}, and θ on current should be considered.

The modulating power for 100 per cent modulation is

$$P_{cm} = \frac{V_{CC}^2}{2R_{cm}} \qquad (11\text{-}40)$$

where V_{CC} = peak collector modulating voltage and where R_{cm} may be obtained from above. A practical value is in the order of 10 mw.

Base Modulation

In base modulation, the base voltage V_{BB} is changed, causing a change in I'_c, and thus in V'_c.

The condition for linear modulation may be obtained from Eqs. (11-34) and (11-29b). Combining these equations,

$$V_{BB} = \beta R_L I'_c \left(\frac{\sin\theta - \theta\cos\theta}{\pi} \frac{\alpha_{CB}}{\alpha_{CE}} \frac{R_E}{R_{IN}} - \cos\theta \right) \qquad (11\text{-}41)$$

from which it is seen that in order for V_{BB} to be proportional to I'_c the quantities θ, and $\alpha_{CB}/\alpha_{CE}R_{IN}$ should be constant. Furtheremore, θ depends on α'_{cb} and R_{in} as seen from Eq. (11-29b). Thus in order to keep the flow angle from varying, the collector voltage should not swing into the cutoff region[7] where α'_{cb} and R_{in} vary strongly. Furthermore, adding a padding resistance in series with the emitter or base will tend to keep both R_{IN} and R_{in} constant.

Summarizing: In order to achieve linear modulation not only can padding resistance be used, but more important, the collector voltage should be prevented from going to zero. This means that v_{CM} in Fig. 11-11b must be kept large, which from Eq. (11-36) implies that the load resistance R_L must be kept small, or the supply voltage V_{CC} must be adjusted to a sufficiently high value.

The modulation input impedance $R_{bm} \equiv dV_{BB}/dI_B$ may be obtained by substituting Eq. (11-32) into (Eq. 11-41). Also eliminating $(R_L I'_c)$ from Eq. (11-41) by the use of Eq. (11-29), and rearranging, we obtain

$$\frac{V_{BB}}{I_B} = \frac{V'_f}{V'_B} \frac{\sin\theta - \cos\theta}{\pi} \left(\frac{\alpha_{CB}}{\alpha_{CE}} R_E - \frac{\pi \cos\theta \, R_{IN}}{(\sin\theta - \theta\cos\theta)} \right) \tag{11-42}$$

By Fourier analysis it follows that the ratio of V'_f to V'_B, the d-c component of base voltage, is

$$\frac{V'_f}{V'_B} = \frac{\pi}{\sin\theta - \theta\cos\theta}$$

Hence Eq. (11-42) can be written

$$\frac{V_{BB}}{I_B} = \left(\frac{\alpha_{CB}}{\alpha_{CE}} R_E - \frac{\pi \cos\theta \, R_{IN}}{\sin\theta - \theta\cos\theta} \right) \tag{11-43}$$

from which R_{bm} follows.

Note that for values of θ which are not too small the second term in Eq. (11-43) is small, and hence $R_{bm} \doteq \alpha_{cb} R_E$; i.e., R_{bm} may be very large—a practical value of 150,000 ohms for $R_E = 5000$ ohms being quite feasible as compared with 30,000 ohms for R_{cm}. In order to obtain a large flow angle it is seen from Eq. (11-29b) that β, the feedback ratio, must be made as small as possible while still sustaining oscillation.

The modulating power for 100 per cent modulation of the collector r-f current is

$$P_{bm} = \tfrac{1}{8} I_B^2 R_{bm} \tag{11-44}$$

[7] Below about 0.1 volt, where the collector characteristics bend over sharply.

where I_B is the d-c component of base current. (Since 100 per cent modulation occurs by varying I_B from zero to some value, it also represents the modulation peak to peak current.) From Eqs. (11-27), (11-29c), (11-31), (11-32), and (11-33),

$$I_B = \frac{I_c'}{\alpha_{cb}'}\left(\frac{\sin\theta - \theta\cos\theta}{\theta - \sin\theta\cos\theta}\right)\frac{R_{in}}{R_{IN}} \tag{11-45}$$

To form a basis for comparison with the modulation power required for collector modulation, let the maximum zero to peak alternating voltage on the collector be $2V_{CC}$, i.e., $I_c'R_L = 2V_{CC}$. Thus the modulation power is

$$P_{bm} = \frac{1}{2}\frac{R_{bm}}{(\alpha_{cb}')^2}\frac{V_{CC}^2}{R_L^2}\left(\frac{\sin\theta - \theta\cos\theta}{\theta - \sin\theta\cos\theta}\right)^2\frac{R_{in}^2}{R_{IN}^2} \tag{11-46}$$

A practical value is in the order of 20 μw.

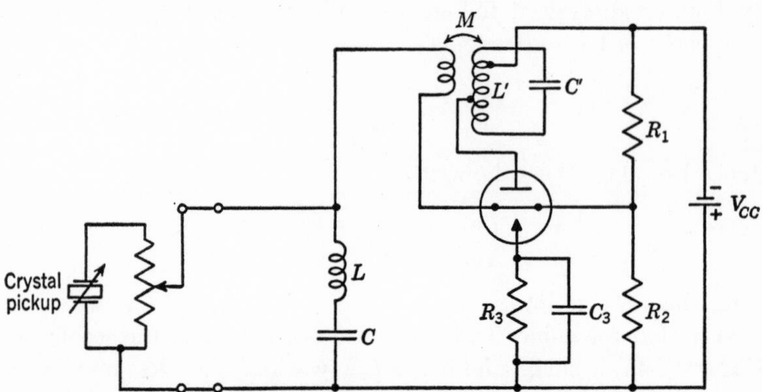

Fig. 11-12. High input impedance modulated oscillator.

The high input impedance for modulating frequencies in base modulation makes it possible for the oscillator to be modulated from a high-impedance source. Figure 11-12 shows a base-modulated junction transistor oscillator which is modulated directly from a crystal pickup. The series resonant circuit at the input, whose resonant frequency corresponds to the frequency of oscillation, presents an open circuit to the modulating voltage. The bias voltage for the base is obtained from a voltage divider, R_1, R_2.

Emitter Modulation

In emitter modulation the modulating voltage is inserted in series with the emitter.

The condition for linear modulation when the emitter voltage is varied, is virtually the same as that for base modulation, since the emitter to base impedance at the oscillator frequency is low compared with the collector impedance.

The emitter modulation impedance $R_{em} \equiv dV_{BB}/dI_E$ can be shown to be

$$R_{em} = R_E - \frac{\pi \cos\theta}{\sin\theta - \theta\cos\theta}\,\frac{R_{IN}}{\alpha_{CB}}\,\alpha_{CE} \tag{11-47}$$

in the region where α_{cb} and R_{IN} are substantially constant. A practical value for R_{em} is 2500 ohms if $R_E = 5000$ ohms.

The modulation power for 100 per cent emitter modulation can be shown to be (in a similar manner as for base modulation)

$$P_{em} = \frac{1}{2}\,\frac{V_{CC}^2}{R_L^2}\,\frac{R_{em}}{\alpha_{CE}^2}\,\frac{\alpha_{CB}^2}{(\alpha_{cb}')^2}\,\frac{R_{in}}{R_{IN}}\,\frac{\sin\theta - \theta\cos\theta}{\theta - \sin\theta\cos\theta} \tag{11-48}$$

A practical value is in the order of 1 mw.

11.6 Frequency modulation and stabilization

The result of nonlinear reactances in a device is that some frequency modulation usually occurs simultaneously with amplitude modulation.

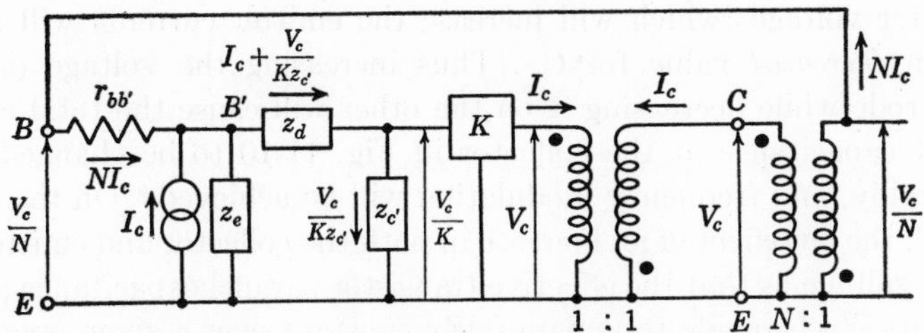

Fig. 11-13. Common-emitter equivalent circuit of a junction transistor with feedback transformer.

Consider, for example, the equivalent transistor capacitance which appears in parallel with the tank circuit of the oscillator shown in Fig. 11-10. This can be estimated from the equivalent circuit shown in Fig. 11-13 as follows. (See Sec. 7.9.)

Let the feedback transformer have a turns ratio of N:1. If the collector to emitter voltage is V_c while the collector current is I_c, the base voltage is V_c/N and the current is NI_c. Also, since the current through $z_{c'}$ is $V_c/Kz_{c'}$, the current flowing in z_d is $I_c + V_c/Kz_{c'}$. Thus by Kirchhoff's law, summing the current at B',

$$NI_c + I_c - \left(I_c + \frac{V_c}{Kz_c'}\right) = \left(\frac{V_c}{N} - r_{bb'}NI_c\right)\frac{1}{z_e}$$
$$\frac{V_c}{I_c} = \left(1 + \frac{r_{bb'}}{z_e}\right)\left(\frac{1}{1/N^2z_e + 1/NKz_c}\right) \tag{11-49}$$

The second factor in Eq. (11-49), which is the most important as far as frequency considersations are concerned, consists of two impedances in parallel, viz., N^2z_e and $NKz_{c'}$. Also, z_e and $z_{c'}$ each consists of a resistance in parallel with a capacitance, as seen from Fig. 11-3. Hence the total equivalent capacitance at the collector terminals is

$$C_{total} = \frac{1}{N}\left(\frac{C_e}{N} + \frac{C_{c'}}{K}\right) = \frac{1}{N}\left(\frac{C_e}{N} + C_c\right) \tag{11-50}$$

where[8] $$C_c = \frac{C_{c'}}{K}$$

It now follows from Sec. 11.1b that an increase in the collector voltage will result in a decrease in C_c (see Eq. 11-9). However, an increase in emitter voltage (which will increase the emitter current) will result in an *increased* value for C_e. Thus increasing the voltage on one electrode while decreasing it on the other will cause the total equivalent capacitance at the collector in Fig. 11-10 to be changed considerably, and frequency modulation will be achieved.[9] On the other hand, the net effect of an increase in both the collector and emitter-to-base voltage, is that the effective transistor parallel capacitance at the ouptut can be made to remain fairly constant over a given operating range, thereby keeping the frequency stabilized. The above principle

[8] See footnote, p. 391.

[9] From the analysis of the amplitude modulated oscillator in Sec. 11.5, it follows that in order to obtain an FM signal having a constant amplitude, virtually the opposite rules must be followed to those for achieving linear amplitude modulation. For example, in collector frequency modulation a low load impedance must be used, so that collector cutoff does not occur.

is utilized in the Lin modulated oscillator shown in Fig. 11-14, which shows a modulation frequency amplifier in cascade with an oscillator of the feedback type. Here V_{CC} is the collector supply voltage for both transistors. Resistors R_1 and R_2 constitute a potential divider for proper base bias stabilization of the modulator amplifier, while C_1 is a by-pass capacitor for modulation frequencies. Inductor L_1

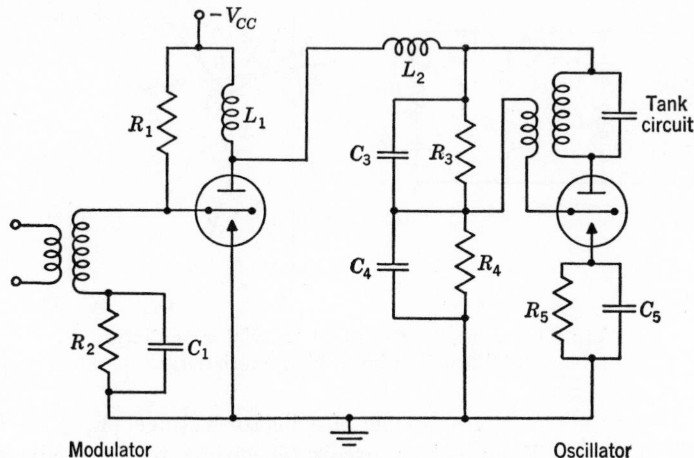

Fig. 11-14. Frequency stabilized amplitude modulated oscillator.

has a high reactance, while L_2 has a low reactance at modulator frequencies, so that the output current (or voltage) of the first stage appears in series with the oscillator transistor. Furthermore, the potential divider R_3 and R_4 is by-passed for oscillator frequencies only, by C_3 and C_4. This divider supplies a portion of the modulator voltage to the base as shown, so that an increase in the modulator voltage simultaneously increases the collector and base voltages of the oscillator transistor to a degree required for maintaining a constant frequency.

11.7 Modulated point-contact oscillators

Consider the point-contact transistor oscillator shown in Fig. 11-15a. This oscillator is of the two-terminal type with the resonant circuit in the emitter as described in Chapter 10. The analyses of the other types of two terminal oscillators follow by analogy.

Figure 11-15b shows the idealized negative-resistance emitter characteristics described in Sec. 12.4. Here P_0 is the virtual d-c quiescent operating point at the intersection of the loadline and the negative-resistance characteristic. For satisfactory operation, P_0 should appear approximately halfway between P_1 and P_2.

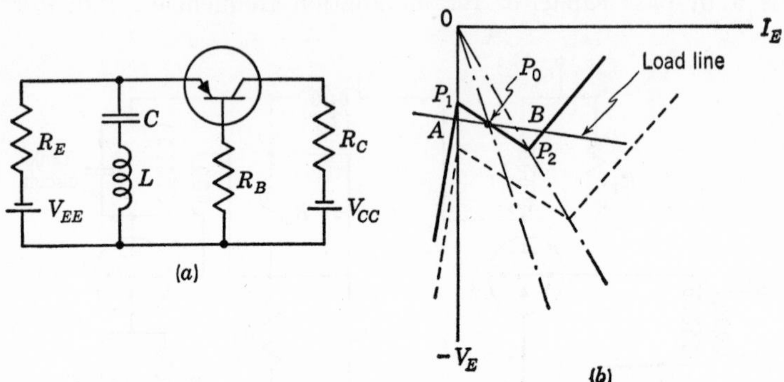

Fig. 11-15. (a) Point-contact transistor oscillator; (b) linearized input characteristics.

Consider the effect of a change of collector voltage (V_{CC}) on Fig. 11-15b. Using a T equivalent circuit (according to the analysis in Section 12.4) at P_1,

$$I_{E1} = 0, \qquad \text{and} \qquad V_{E1} = -\frac{R_b V_{CC}}{R_b + R_c + r_c}$$

where r_c is the "collector resistance" and R_b is the total resistance in the base lead. At P_2,

$$I_{E2} = \frac{V_{CC}}{\alpha(R_b + R_c) - R_b}, \qquad \text{and} \qquad V_{E2} = \frac{R_b(1 - \alpha)V_{CC}}{\alpha(R_b + R_c) - R_b}$$

At P_0,

$$I_{E0} = \frac{V_{CC}}{2[\alpha(R_b + R_c) - R_b]}, \qquad \text{and} \qquad V_{E0} = \frac{V_{E1} + V_{E2}}{2}$$

From these expressions it is seen that the length of the negative portion of the characteristic is proportional to V_{CC}. Also, the length of the loadline AB that the emitter characteristic intercepts, and which is directly proportional to the amplitude of oscillation, can also be shown to be proportional to V_{CC}, provided that the load line intersects the negative resistance portion at its center (which can be accomplished by adjusting the emitter battery V_{EE} and/or R_E).

The condition for linear modulation is that the "quiescent" operating-point voltage P_0 be simultaneously adjusted with the collector voltage, so that the two remain proportional to each other, and hence to the amplitude of oscillation. If only the emitter-to-base voltage is changed, as is the case with emitter (or base modulation), then P_0 is shifted from its central position and the wave becomes distorted. This means that the ratio of amplitudes of the fundamental frequency component to the harmonics changes, thereby affecting the frequency stability of the circuit (cf. Chapter 10).

The modulation input resistance for collector modulation can be found as follows. While the emitter current is as indicated at P_1 and P_2 (Fig. 11-15b), the currents at the collector are

$$I_{C1} = \frac{V_{CC}}{R_b + R_c + r_c} \tag{11-51a}$$

$$I_{C2} = \frac{-\alpha V_{CC}}{\alpha(R_b + R_c) - R_b} \tag{11-51b}$$

The operating point is midway between P_1 and P_2 ; i.e.,

$$I_C = -\frac{1}{2}\left[\frac{1}{R_b + R_c + r_c} + \frac{\alpha}{\alpha(R_b + R_c) - R_b}\right] V_{CC} \tag{11-51c}$$

Hence the collector modulation input impedance is

$$R_{cm} = \frac{dV_{CC}}{dI_C} = \frac{2}{\{1/(R_b + R_c + r_c) + \alpha/[\alpha(R_b + R_c) - R_b]\}} \tag{11-52}$$

The modulating power for an excursion in collector voltage of ΔV_{CC} volts is

$$P_{cm} = \frac{1}{2R_{cm}}\left(\frac{\Delta V_{CC}}{2}\right)^2 = \frac{\Delta V_{CC}^2}{16} \left[\frac{1}{R_b + R_c + r_c} + \frac{\alpha}{\alpha(R_b + R_c) - R_b}\right] \tag{11-53}$$

A practical value is 20 mw.

11.8 Transistor mixer

A transistor will perform the functions of a mixer in a circuit similar to that of a vacuum tube triode. The local oscillator and signal voltages may be applied either to the same input electrode or to separate electrodes.

A typical junction or point-contact transistor mixer circuit is shown in Fig. 11-16. Here V_o and V_s are the local oscillator and signal open-circuit voltages, respectively, while R_o and R_s are the corresponding source resistances. The intermediate frequency voltage is obtained across the parallel tuned circuit C', L'. The collector is usually biased from a constant voltage source, while the input side may be biased either from a constant current source (hence the blocking capacitor C) or a constant-voltage source, or by using one of the circuit arrangements described in Chapter 4.

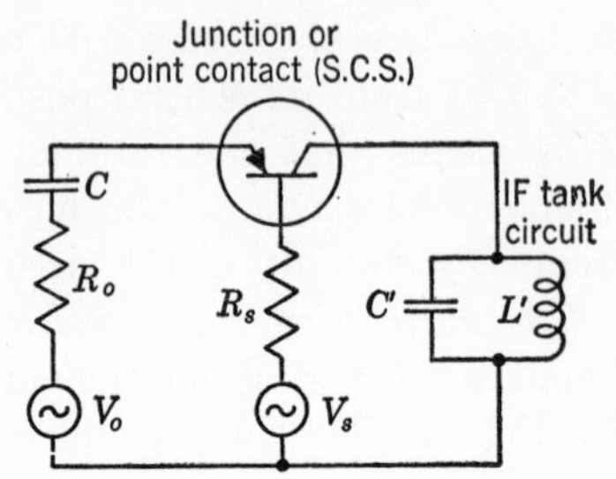

Fig. 11-16. Mixer circuit.

Equivalent Circuit of a Transistor Mixer[10]

Consider a T equivalent circuit as shown in Fig. 11-17a to which all the external elements are connected as in Fig. 11-16, except for the signal voltage source V_s, which for simplicity is relocated from the

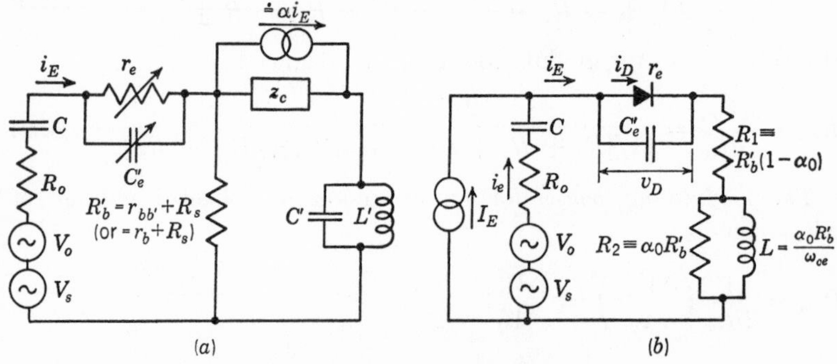

Fig. 11-17. Equivalent mixer circuit.

base lead to the emitter lead. This relocation does not alter the emitter to base voltage (from E to B) and has only a negligible effect

[10] J. Zawels, "The Transistor as a Mixer," *Proc. I.R.E.*, Vol. 42, March 1954.

on collector current, since the collector impedance is high. Resistance R_b' is the sum of the "base resistance" r_b and R_s, and α_{ce} is the common-base short-circuit current amplification factor. From Eq. (7-38) it may be written

$$\alpha_{ce} = \frac{\alpha_{ceo}}{1 + j\omega/\omega_{ce}}; \qquad \alpha_0 \equiv -\alpha_{ceo}; \qquad \alpha \equiv -\alpha_{ce} \tag{11-54}$$

where α_{ceo} is the low-frequency value of α_{ce}, and ω_{ce} is the angular "cutoff" frequency. Furthermore, in Fig. 11-17a the elements r_e and C_e' (equivalent to r_d and C_e as described in Sec. 11.1) are nonlinear, causing the conversion from signal to intermediate frequency to occur in the input circuit. The intermediate frequency current is then amplified and the resultant voltage appears across the tank circuit.

Assume the emitter to be biased from a constant d-c source; a practical value is, say, $I_E = 250\ \mu a$. The local oscillator (large signal) will vary the current flowing into the emitter. A practical value for local oscillator voltage may be 200 mv for junction transistors, and 500 mv for point-contact transistors. (The higher voltage for the latter is due to the higher ratio of forward to reverse resistance in point-contact transistors as may be seen from Fig. 11-2.) Experimentally it is found that for optimum operation it places a reverse voltage on the emitter junction for only a small fraction of its cycle. Also at local oscillator and signal frequencies the tank circuit has nearly zero impedance.

Thus the short-circuit input impedance is[11]

$$Z_{in} = \frac{1}{1/r_e + j\omega C_e'} + R_b'(1 - \alpha) \tag{11-55}$$

Substituting Eq. (11-54),

$$Z_{in} = \frac{1}{1/r_e + j\omega C_e'} + R_b'(1 - \alpha_o) + \frac{1}{1/\alpha_0 R_b' + 1/j(\omega/\omega_{ce})\alpha_0 R_b'} \tag{11-56}$$

This impedance Z_{in} may now be synthesized into the equivalent

[11] As stated in Sec. 11.1 (with reference to Fig. 11-4) the T circuit yields a sufficiently accurate expression for the input impedance of a junction transistor in the useful frequency range.

circuit shown in Fig. 11-17b, which bears a resemblance to a conventional diode mixer circuit.

This circuit is used in the analysis for both point-contact and junction transistor mixers. For point-contact transistor, C_e' is smaller and r_e is generally larger for the same emitter current.

Frequency Dependence

It is clear that both C_e' and the phase shift in α_{ce} (as manifested by the inductance L in Fig. 11-17b), will affect the conversion gain of the transistor. As shown in Sec. 11.1b, C_e' may be considered to consist mainly of the diffusion capacitance C_{Dp} when biased in the forward direction, and the emitter junction transition capacitance C_{TE} when biased in the reverse direction.

We may now define three frequency ranges for the operation of a transistor mixer.

Range A or "alpha range." This is the lowest frequency range, and here α_{ce} determines the input impedance level. For very low frequency the input impedance is essentially resistive; at the higher end of this frequency range α_{ce} has a phase shift (i.e., the inductance L in Fig. 11-17b becomes significant), and the input becomes partially reactive.

Range B or "base resistance range." This is the frequency range where α_{ce} has fallen to a very low value and the input impedance is determined primarily by the total base resistance. The inductance in Fig. 11-17b may now be neglected because of its high reactance in this frequency range, and the input impedance becomes

$$Z_{in} = z_e' + R_b'(1 - \alpha_0) + \alpha_0 R_b' = z_e' + R_b' \qquad (11\text{-}57)$$

where z_e' consists of r_e in parallel with C_e'.

Range C or "capacitance range." This is the highest frequency range; here the conversion ability is limited by the transition capacitance, which shunts the diode when it is biased in the reverse direction, (i.e., $C_e' \doteq C_{TE}$) as the case is in the conventional diode mixer.

Figure 11-18 shows experimental curves of conversion voltage gain (defined as the ratio of intermediate voltage at the collector to signal voltage) vs. signal frequency, for a junction transistor and a point-contact transistor. The three frequency ranges are indicated for the point-contact transistor (having an α_{ce} cutoff frequency of 4.5 megacycles). It is seen that the conversion voltage gain remains substantially constant in the B range and falls less than 3 decibels in the C frequency range. However, the curve for the junction transistor (with an α_{ce} cutoff of 8 megacycles), shows a continuous fall of gain with frequency, primarily as a result of the larger reverse bias emitter shunting capacitance C_{TE}.

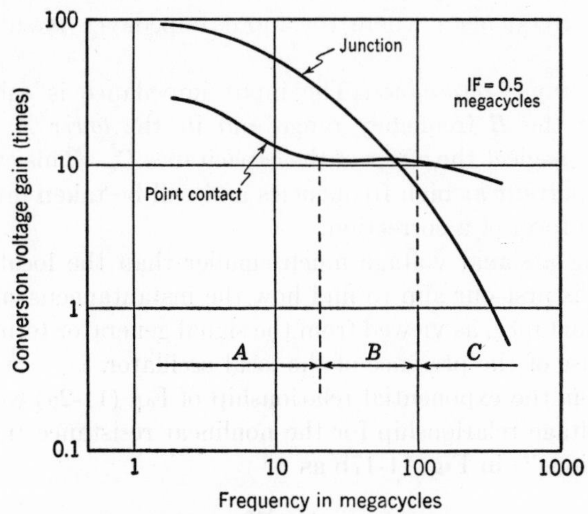

Fig. 11-18. Experimental curves showing dependence of conversion voltage gain on signal frequency for transistor mixers.

Thus the ultimate signal frequency limitation on the conversion ability of transistors is set by the reverse-bias emitter shunting capacitance. The maximum intermediate frequency, however, is limited by the same factors which limit the frequency in intermediate frequency amplifiers.

Evaluation of Conversion Gain

A measure of the conversion ability of transistors is the *conversion gain*, which is defined as

$$\text{conversion gain} = \frac{\text{available intermediate frequency power from mixer}}{\text{available power from signal source}}$$

Thus the conversion gain is a function of source resistance and will be a maximum when both the signal source and the intermediate frequency amplifier are matched to the mixer. Experimentally, it is found that conversion gain has a broad maximum when it is plotted as a function of signal source resistance.[12] In the low-frequency A range a conversion of 6 decibels below the gain of the transistor as an intermediate frequency amplifier is common.

Two methods are given here for calculation of the conversion gain. The first method is simpler to apply, but unlike the second, it is restricted to frequencies where the input impedance is substantially resistive.

Resistive input impedance. The input impedance is substantially resistive in the B frequency range and in the *lower* A frequency range, if we neglect the effect of the capacitance C_e'. This capacitance is most important at high frequencies and will be taken into account later in the form of a correction.

Assuming a signal voltage much smaller than the local oscillator voltage, it is first our aim to find how the instantaneous small-signal input conductance, as viewed from the signal generator terminals, will vary because of the presence of the local oscillator.

Thus from the exponential relationship of Eq. (11-2a) we write the current voltage relationship for the nonlinear resistance (i.e., for the "emitter diode") in Fig. 11-17b as

$$i_D = A'(\epsilon^{\Lambda v_D} - 1) \tag{11-58}$$

where A' = function of the geometry and the properties of the material constituting the transistor; v_D = total instantaneous voltage across diode; i_D = total instantaneous current in diode; and $1/\Lambda = (kT/q)$ 0.026 volt at room temperature.[13] Alternatively, from Eq. (11–58),

$$v_D = \frac{1}{\Lambda} \ln (i_D + A') - \frac{1}{\Lambda} \ln A' \tag{11-59}$$

Now, let i_e = alternating component of current in emitter, and I_E = direct current in emitter. Then

$$i_D \doteq i_e + I_E$$

[12] J. Zawels, *loc. cit.*

[13] Although Eq. (11-58) applies here to junction transistors, this equation may also be used, and a similar analysis may be followed, for the case of point-contact transistors provided a suitably modified value is used for Λ.

From Fig. 11-17b, writing the voltage drops around the loop,

$$V_{in} \equiv (V_0 \cos \omega_o t + V_s \sin \omega_s t)$$
$$= R_0 i_e + v_D + R_1(i_e + I_E) + V_C + i_e R_X \qquad (11\text{-}60)$$

where V_C = average direct voltage across blocking capacitor and $R_X = R_2 \equiv \alpha_{ceo}(r_b + R_s)$ in the B frequency range where the reactance due to the inductor is assumed to be infinite, whereas $R_X = 0$ in the lower A frequency range where the inductor reactance is assumed to be zero. Substituting Eq. (11-59) into (11-60),

$$V_{in} = \frac{1}{\Lambda} \ln (i_e + I_E + A') + (i_e + I_E + A') (R_0 + R_1 + R_X) + V_1 \qquad (11\text{-}61)$$

where

$$V_1 = V_C - I_E(R_0 + R_X) - \frac{1}{\Lambda} \ln A' - A'(R_0 + R_1 + R_X)$$

Differentiating Eq. (11-61) and taking the reciprocal

$$g_{in} \equiv \frac{di_e}{dV_{in}} = \frac{\Lambda(i_e + I_E + A')}{1 + \Lambda(i_e + I_E + A')R} \qquad (11\text{-}62)$$

where

$$R \equiv R_0 + R_1 + R_X \equiv R_0 + (r_b + R_s)(1 - \alpha_o) + R_X$$

From the definition of R_X it directly follows that in the B frequency range, $R = R_o + R_s + r_b$, while in the lower A frequency range the value of R is smaller, viz., $R = R_o + (R_s + r_b)(1 - \alpha_o)$. In Fig. 11-19, g_{in} is plotted[14] against V_{in} for various values of R by making use of Eqs. (11-61) and (11-62). The effect of V_1 in Eq. (11-61) is to merely shift the curves parallel to the abscissa. In Fig. 11-19, V_1 is arbitrarily taken equal to 0.12 volts. Also shown are loci for $(i_e + I_E + A')$ = constant.

The intermediate frequency current in the emitter circuit can now be found from Fig. 11-19 in a manner analogous to that used in the

[14] For an alternative method for obtaining the curve corresponding to $R_x = 0$ in Fig. 11-19 see Problem 11.5.

case of diode mixers.[15] The local oscillator voltage, $V_0 \cos \omega_o t$, will cause g_{in} to vary with time, viz., $g_{in}(t)$. Expanding $g_{in}(t)$ into a cosine series of period $2\pi/\omega_o$,

$$g_{in}(t) = G_0 + G_1 \cos \omega_o t + G_2 \cos 2\omega_o t + G_3 \cos 3\omega_o t + \ldots + Gn \cos n\omega_o t \qquad (11\text{-}63)$$

where $$\frac{\omega_0}{2\pi} = \text{local oscillator frequency}$$

$$G_0 = \frac{1}{2\pi} \int_0^{2\pi} g_{in}(t)\, d(\omega_o t) \qquad (11\text{-}64a)$$

$$G_n = \frac{1}{\pi} \int_0^{2\pi} g_{in}(t) \cos n\omega_o t\, d(\omega_o t) \qquad (11\text{-}64b)$$

Thus if the signal voltage is $V_s \sin \omega_s t$, where $V_s \ll V_o$, then the small-signal current in the emitter lead is

$$\begin{aligned} i_e' &= g_{in}(t) V_s \sin \omega_s t \\ &= G_0 V_s \sin \omega_s t + \tfrac{1}{2} V_s \sum_{n=1}^{\infty} G_n \sin (\omega_s - n\omega_0)t \\ &\qquad + \tfrac{1}{2} V_s \sum_{n=1}^{\infty} G_n \sin (\omega_s + n\omega_o)t \end{aligned} \qquad (11\text{-}65)$$

The intermediate frequency current in the emitter lead for nth harmonic operation of the local oscillator is now given by[16]

$$i_e = \frac{G_n}{2} V_s \qquad (11\text{-}66)$$

and the resulting intermediate frequency voltage developed at the output, as well as the conversion gain, follows by treating it as an amplifier problem.

As an alternative to Eqs. (11-64a) and (11-64b), the coefficients G_0, G_1, G_2, etc. can be evaluated by a 7-point analysis as shown in Fig. 11-19, where the circle diameter equals the local oscillator peak-

[15] E. W. Herold, "The Operation of Frequency Converters and Mixers for Superheterodyne Reception," *Proc. I.R.E.*, Vol. 30, p. 84, Feb. 1942; E. G. James and J. E. Houldin, "Diode Frequency Changers," *Wireless Engineer*, Vol. 20, p. 15; Jan. 1943.

[16] By analogy with diode mixers $G_n/2$ may be referred to as the *conversion conductance*.

to-peak voltage. Thus projecting 30° intervals onto the $R = 300$ ohm curve, we obtain

$$G_1 = \frac{1}{6}[(g_7 - g_1) + (g_5 - g_3) + 1.73(g_6 - g_2)] \tag{11-67}$$

where $g_1, g_2, g_3, \ldots, g_7$ are the 7-point conductances.

From Fig. 11-19 the emitter bias direct current which corresponds to the given position of the circle can be obtained by noting the value

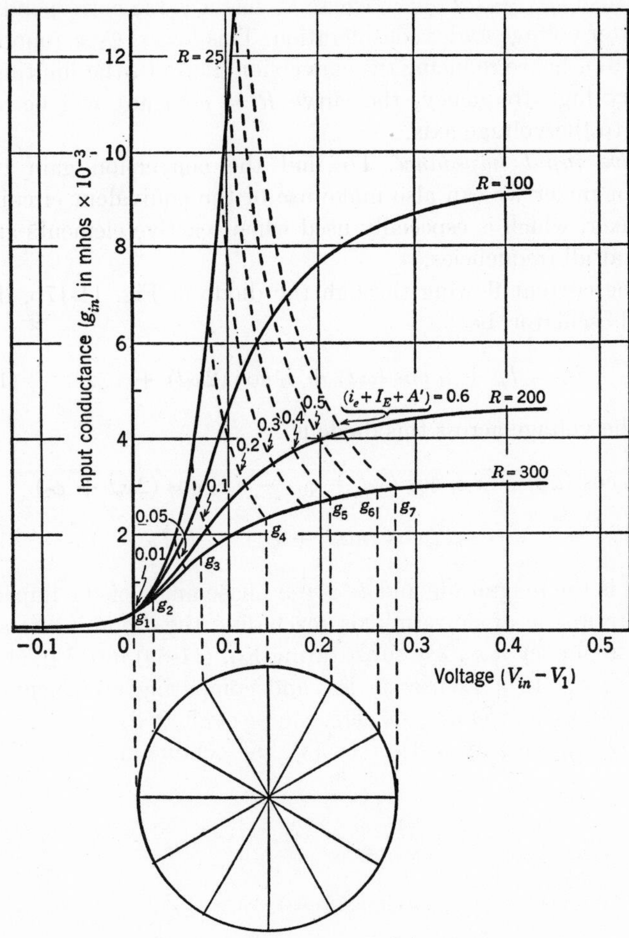

Fig. 11-19. Calculations of Fourier coefficients of time-varying input conductance.

of $(i_e + I_E + A')$ at g_1, g_2, g_3, etc., and taking the average over one cycle. This average is $(I_E + A') = I_E$, since A' is normally quite small (in the order of about 0.01 ma) and can be neglected.

As stated earlier, the capacitance C_e' is most important in the C frequency range, since the value of its reactance is now significant when compared with the emitter resistance when a reverse bias is present. The effect of C_e' can be approximately taken into account in Fig. 11-19 by raising the curve especially near the origin—a rough value is also $[g_{in}^2 + (\omega C_e')^2]^{1/2}$, where C_e' has a value corresponding to the emitter voltage under consideration. This lowers G_1 as found from Eq. (11-67), hence reducing the conversion gain. In the limiting case of a very high frequency, the curve R = constant will be almost parallel to the voltage axis.

Reactive input impedance. To find the conversion gain of the transistor mixer we can also make use of the equivalent circuit of a *diode* mixer, which is especially used when reactive elements are important at all frequencies.

Let the current flowing through the diode in Fig. 11-17b, due to the local oscillator, be

$$i_D = I_E + i_1 \cos(\omega_0 t) + i_2 \cos(2\omega_0 t) + \dots \tag{11-68}$$

Hence the voltage across this diode is

$$\begin{aligned} v_D = V_0 \cos(\omega_0 t) - i_1 z_1 \cos(\omega_0 t + \phi_1) - i_2 z_2 \cos(2\omega_o t + \phi_2) \\ - \dots - \dots - i_n z_n \cos(n\omega_0 t + \phi_n) - R_1 I_E - V_C \end{aligned} \tag{11-69}$$

where z_n is the magnitude and ϕ_n is the phase angle of the impedance as seen from the diode terminals (excluding the diode itself) at the angular frequency $n\omega_0$. By substituting Eq. (11-69) into Eq. (11-58), expanding it into a Fourier series, and comparing coefficients with Eq. (11-68), the currents i_1, i_2, etc. can be evaluated.

Next by differentiating Eq. (11-58), the conductance of the diode alone is

$$g_{in}' \equiv \frac{di_D}{dv_D} = \Lambda(i_D - A') \tag{11-70}$$

Substitute Eq. (11-68) into Eq. (11-70).

$$g_{in}'(t) = G_0' + G_1' \cos(\omega_0 t + \phi_1) + G_2' \cos(2\omega_0 t + \phi_2) + \dots \tag{11-71}$$

where $G_0' = (I_E - A')$; $G_1' (\equiv 2g_1') = \Lambda i_1$; $G_2' (\equiv 2g_2') = \Lambda i_2$, etc.[17] Using these conductances, the small-signal diode equivalent circuit of Fig. 11-20 now follows,[18] from which the necessary matching conditions for any required power transfer (and the mismatching conditions for parasitic currents) can be calculated. In Fig. 11-20, E_s, indicates terminals where the open-circuit signal-generator

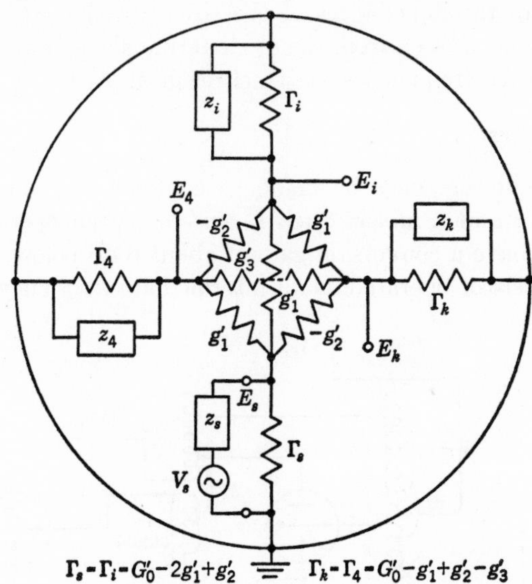

Fig. 11-20. Five-pole equivalent circuit for diode mixer showing i-f, signal, image and sum frequency impedances.

voltage V_s acts in series with Z_s. (A current generator representation may obviously also be used.) Also E_i indicates terminals where the intermediate frequency voltage appears which is responsi-

[17] The use of the conductances g_1', g_2', etc. instead of $G_1'/2$, $G_2'/2$, etc. in Fig. 11-20 is a matter of convenience.

[18] J. Zawels, "A Generalized Treatment and the Sum Frequency of the Diode Mixer," to be published. Fig. 11-20 is derived from general considerations and should be regarded as an approximation. Depending on the degree of accuracy required, this circuit may be simplified still further by the omission of the third harmonic conductance g_3' or by the grounding of the terminal E_4 which reduces it to the circuit of E. W. Herold, R. R. Bush, and W. R. Ferris, "Conversion Loss of Diode Mixers having Image Frequency Impedance," *Proc. I.R.E.*, Vol. 33, p. 605, Sept. 1945.

ble for the intermediate frequency current in Z_i. *This intermediate frequency current flows in the emitter and causes the intermediate frequency voltage in the collector tank circuit, in a manner identical to that in an intermediate frequency amplifier.* E_k indicates terminal where image frequency voltage appears. E_4 indicates terminal where sum frequency voltage appears. It should be noted that Z_s, Z_i, Z_k, and Z_4 are the impedances of the circuit, excluding the emitter diode impedance, as seen from the diode terminals, and are calculated at the respective frequencies at which each applies.

11.9 Converters

Various oscillators may be made to combine the functions of a local oscillator and a mixer. Such a *converter* when operating satisfactorily will have a conversion gain of about 6 db below the gain of the same transistor operated as an intermediate frequency amplifier.

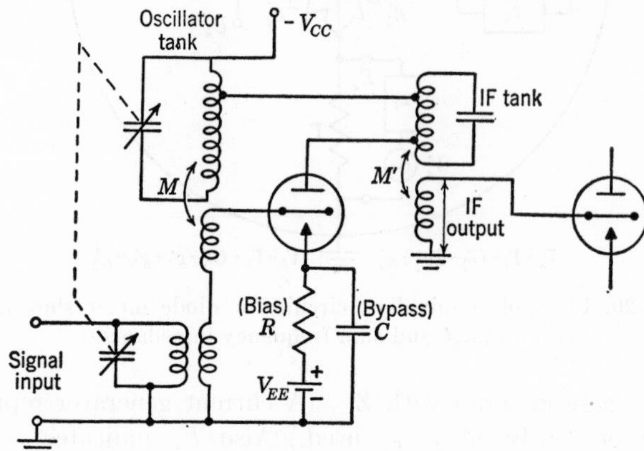

Fig. 11-21. Junction transistor converter.

Figure 11-21 shows a junction transistor converter[19] consisting of an oscillator of the feedback type, described in Chapter 10, to which two additional tank circuits are connected. The input signal tank circuit is transformer coupled and feeds into the base, while the intermediate frequency is developed across the tank circuit connected to the collector. A practical conversion gain is about 25 db with an intermediate frequency of 455 kc.

[19] The circuit was proposed by D. D. Holmes.

A simple point-contact converter (excluding bias batteries) is shown in Fig. 11-22. It has three tank circuits situated in the base, emitter, and collector leads for the oscillator, signal, and intermediate frequencies, respectively. The oscillation occurs approximately at the resonant frequency of the tank circuit in the base, as described in

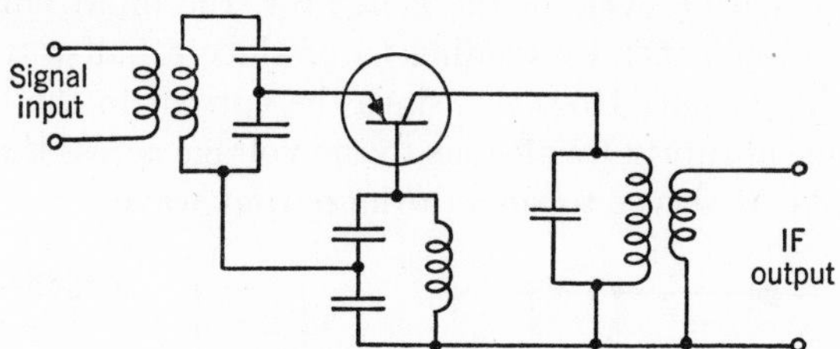

Fig. 11-22. Point-contact transistor converter.

Chapter 10. The capacitor dividers shown are for the purpose of matching the high-impedance tank circuits to the low input impedance of the transistor. Tapped inductor coils may obviously also be used.

11.10 Diode detector

A conventional diode detector which is followed by a vacuum tube amplifier is usually of the voltage output type. An example of such a detector is that shown in Fig. 11-23a; it is commonly called an *envelope detector*. The rectified signal input voltage, from which the high-frequency component is largely removed by the capacitor, appears across the output resistance. Thus the envelope of the input signal voltage is reproduced, and this is used to drive the vacuum tube amplifier.

When a diode detector is followed by a transistor it would appear desirable that the detector be of a "current output" type. This is because in contrast to a vacuum tube triode, which has a high input impedance and is "voltage controlled", a transistor has a relatively low input impedance and may be considered[20] to be "current con-

[20] Note that the terms "current output," "voltage controlled" and "current controlled" are used for reasons of a simplified explanation only and are not to be taken too literally since with each change of current there must obviously be some change of voltage and vice versa. Thus, under some circumstances a voltage output detector may also be used in conjunction with transistors.

trolled." Thus the dual of the detector of Fig. 11-23a may be taken; this is shown in Fig. 11-23b.

The method of operation is as follows: When the direction of current flow in the current generator is as shown, the diode is biased in the reverse direction and the total current flows through the load. During the negative cycle of the generator, the input current flows through the diode, thereby tending to produce a half-wave rectified current at the output. However, since the current in the inductance cannot change abruptly (analogous to the voltage across the capacitor in Fig. 11-23a) it serves to smooth the output wave.

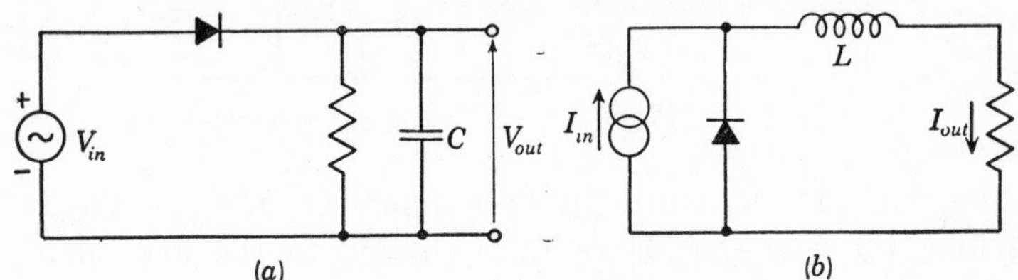

Fig. 11-23. (a) "Voltage output" diode detector. (b) "Current output" diode detector.

The quantitative analysis for the current detector follows by the principle of duality from the analysis of the voltage detector, and therefore in this connection the reader is referred to texts dealing with this subject.

11.11 Collector detection[21]

There are two distinct modes of operation of a vacuum tube triode detector. One mode makes use of the nonlinearity of the transfer characteristic, and with this method the grid is normally biased near cutoff. The plate detector is an example of such operation. The other mode makes use of the nonlinearity of the *input* circuit, and with this method the grid is biased near the point where grid current starts to flow; the *grid-leak detector* being an example.

In transistors there is no such sharp distinction, since the input characteristics very closely resemble the transfer characteristic, both being in the form of exponentials. Thus the *collector detector* (shown

[21] The basic analysis of collector detection is due to H. C. Lin.

in Fig. 11-24) may be viewed as operating either by virtue of the nonlinear transfer characteristic, or as a result of rectification in the input circuit and subsequent amplification. Indeed it is shown in Sec. 11.12 that irrespective of which nonlinearity is considered basic, the calculated optimum[22] emitter-voltage bias point for the two nonlinearities is the same.

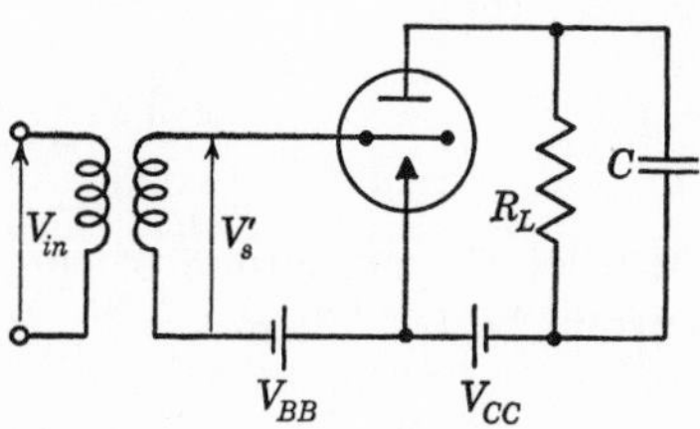

Fig. 11-24. Collector detector.

Furthermore, the plate detector may be considered to have an infinite input impedance (although this is of course only relatively true). Thus impedance matching is here not so important a consideration as it is in the collector detector. In order to measure the power transfer ability of a detector we define the detection power gain as,

$$K_{pd} = \frac{\text{modulation frequency power output}}{\text{available modulation power in carrier wave}}$$

Consider the collector detector of Fig. 11-24, which has a load R_L, by-passed for carrier frequencies by the capacitor C. To find an approximate expression for the detection power gain, let a 100 per cent modulated carrier, whose amplitude at the peak of the modulation wave is V_s', be applied at the input. Let us also use a straight-line approximation for the input characteristic I_B vs. V_B as seen in Fig. 11-25, instead of the exact exponential curve (a portion of which is shown dotted in Fig. 11-1). The floating potential of the base, i.e., where $I_B = 0$, is assumed to be equal to V_F volts.

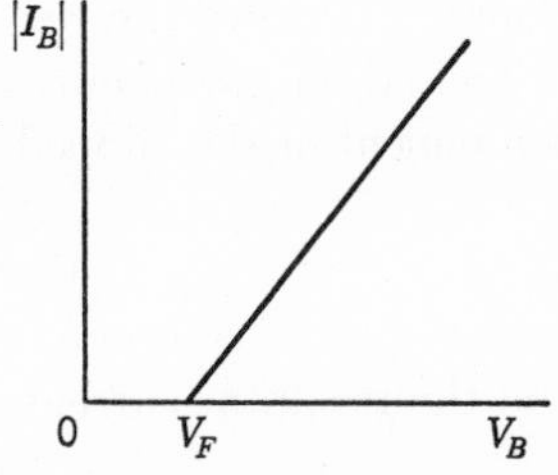

Fig. 11-25. Linearized base input characteristics.

The bias direct voltage V_{BB} in combination with the signal V_s', as shown in Fig. 11-24, will cause current to flow during a flow angle 2θ, which is less than 180° if $V_{BB} < V_F$, and greater than 180° if $V_{BB} >$

[22] "Optimum" refers here to detection linearity, i.e., linearity between the input signal and the desired output signal.

V_F. Thus by Fourier analysis it is easily shown that if the amplitude of the fundamental component of the clipped voltage wave is V'_{b1}, then

$$\frac{V'_s}{V'_{b1}} = \frac{\pi}{\theta - \sin\theta\cos\theta} \tag{11-72}$$

Also let the amplitude of the fundamental component of the base current be I'_b. Then

$$\frac{V'_{b1}}{I'_b} = Z_{in} \tag{11-73}$$

where Z_{in} is the Class A input impedance at the carrier frequency. Now under matched conditions the *modulation* power input will equal the available modulation power from the 100 per cent modulated carrier wave, and as an approximation from Eqs. (11–72) and (11-73) it is

$$P_{ma} = \mathcal{R}\left(\frac{1}{2}\frac{V'_s}{2} \times \frac{I'_b}{2}\right) = \frac{1}{8}\mathcal{R}(V'_s I'_b) \tag{11-74}$$

From Eqs. (11-72), (11-73), and (11-74),

$$P_{ma} = \mathcal{R}\left(\frac{\theta \sin\theta\cos\theta}{8\pi Z_{in}} V'^2_s\right) \tag{11-75}$$

where $\mathcal{R}$ denotes the real part of an expression.

To find the *modulation power output* we note that the average direct component of the clipped input voltage is

$$V'_B = \frac{\sin\theta - \theta\cos\theta}{\pi} V'_s \tag{11-76}$$

and the resultant current is

$$I_B = \frac{V'_B}{R_{IN}} \tag{11-77}$$

where R_{IN} is defined as the d-c input resistance. Now this *average* current I_B represents also the peak-to-peak amplitude of the modulation frequency current in the base for a 100 per cent modulated wave. Thus if the peak amplitude of the modulation frequency current in the collector is I'_c, then

$$\alpha'_{cb} = \frac{2I'_c}{I_B} \tag{11-78}$$

where α'_{cb} is the current gain at modulation frequencies for a load R_L. Thus the modulation frequency power output at the collector is

$$P_{ml} = \frac{1}{2}(I'_c)^2 R_L \tag{11-79}$$

which from Eqs. (11-76) to (11-78) may be written

$$P_{ml} = \frac{1}{8}\frac{(\alpha'_{cb})^2}{R_{IN}^2}\left(\frac{\sin\theta - \theta\cos\theta}{\pi}\right)^2 R_L(V'_s)^2 \tag{11-80}$$

Thus the detection power again is, from Eqs. (11-75) and (11-80),

$$K_{pd} = \frac{P_{ml}}{P_{ma}} \doteq \frac{(\alpha'_{cb})^2}{\pi}\frac{R'_{in}}{R_{IN}}\frac{(\sin\theta - \theta\cos\theta)^2}{\theta - \sin\theta\cos\theta} R_L \tag{11-81}$$

where R'_{in} is the real part of Z_{in}.

11.12 Biasing for minimum distortion in collector detector and Class B amplifiers

Although the detection power gain of a detector is important, it is by no means the overriding consideration. Thus the optimum flow angle for a large detection gain in collector detectors does not necessarily coincide with the optimum flow angle for good linearity.

For the special case discussed in the previous section, where a straight-line approximation was assumed for the I_B versus V_B characteristic, it is seen that for good linearity the base bias voltage V_{BB} should equal V_F. In other words, the flow angle should be 180°. However, the more exact expressions for transistor characteristics are in the form of exponentials, and for linear detection (and also for satisfactory Class B amplifier operation) it is desirable to operate with a base bias voltage near the point where the slope of the forward transfer characteristic changes most abruptly. This optimum operation point may be found as follows.

From Eq. (11-2b),

$$I_C = \frac{G_{21}}{\Lambda}\epsilon^{\Lambda(V_E + I_B r_{bb'})} + I_{CS} = \frac{G_{21}}{\Lambda}[\epsilon^{-\Lambda(V_B - I_B r_{bb'})}] + I_{CS} \tag{11-81a}$$

where V_B ($\equiv -V_E$) is the base to emitter voltage in the intrinsic transistor, I_B = base current, and $r_{bb'}$ = base spreading resistance. The point where the slope changes most abruptly is where

$$\frac{d^3I_C}{dV_B^3} = 0 \tag{11-82}$$

and from Eq. (11-81a) it is where the collector current is

$$I_{C/opt} = -\frac{\alpha_{cbo}}{2r_{bb'}\Lambda} + I_{CS} \tag{11-83}$$

where
$$\alpha_{cbo} = \frac{dI_C}{dI_B}$$

Furthermore, the optimum base current $I_{B/opt}$ corresponding to $I_{C/opt}$ is, from Eqs. (11-10) and (11-83),

$$I_{B/opt} = \frac{1}{2r_{bb'}\Lambda} + I_{BS} \tag{11-84}$$

Hence the voltage V_B, which corresponds to $I_{B/opt}$ and to $I_{C/opt}$ is, using Eq. (11-2c),

$$V_{B/opt} = \frac{1}{\Lambda}\left[\ln\left(\frac{-2r_{bb'}G_{21}}{\alpha_{cbo}}\right) + I_{BS}r_{bb'}\Lambda - \frac{1}{2}\right] \tag{11-85}$$

A practical value is 0.1 volt.

By a similar method it can be shown from Eq. (11-2c) that the base-to-emitter voltage at the point where the input characteristic V_B vs. I_B changes most abruptly is also given by Eq. (11-85). Hence detection by virtue of the nonlinear *transfer* characteristic is identical to detection by virtue of the nonlinear *input* circuit for this type of detector.

11.13 Temperature dependence of optimum bias point in collector detectors and Class B amplifiers

The temperature dependence of the optimum base bias current for linear detection $I_{B/opt}$ is a result of its being a function of $r_{bb'}$, I_{BS}, and Λ, as shown by Eq. (11-84).

In Sec. 8.16 it is shown that $r_{bb'}$ rises with temperature (near room temperature), while Λ, being inversely proportional to the absolute temperature, falls with temperature. Hence the product $r_{bb'}\Lambda$ occuring in Eq. (11-84) changes very little with temperature, and the temperature dependence of $I_{B/opt}$ may be wholly ascribed to the temperature dependence of I_{BS}. In Sec. 8.16 it is also shown that the temperature sensitivity of I_{BS} is approximately 10 per cent per degree Kelvin.

The temperature dependence of the optimum base bias voltage is, from Eq. (11-85),

$$\frac{dV_{B/opt}}{dT} = \frac{1}{\Lambda}\left(\frac{1}{G_{21}}\frac{dG_{21}}{dT} + r_{bb'}\Lambda\frac{dI_{BS}}{dT}\right) \qquad (11\text{-}86)$$

where the temperature dependence of $r_{bb'}$ and Λ is neglected. The quantity $(1/G_{21})(dG_{21}/dT)$ describes the temperature sensitivity of G_{21}, and from Sec. 8.16 it is seen to be about 10 per cent per degree Kelvin. Also since $1/\Lambda \doteq 0.026$ volt at room temperature, it follows from Eq. (11-86) that for a transistor where the second term is negligible (i.e., comparatively small $r_{bb'}$, and no external resistance in base lead), $dV_{B/opt}/dT = 2.6$ millivolt per degree centigrade. It can be seen that this is the rate at which the applied forward bias between the base and emitter leads should *decrease* when the temperature increases, so that optimum operation is maintained.

11.14 Stabilization of operating point using nonlinear elements

In the previous section it was shown that for the sake of linearity between the input and output signals, the bias currents in collector detectors (and Class B amplifiers) should be suitably changed if the temperature changes. Such operating point stabilization in collector detectors is also essential, since it is often a source of automatic gain control.

By using nonlinear elements such as diodes and thermistors in circuits similar to those described in Chapter 4, a chosen operating point may still further be stabilized. For example, Fig. 11-26[23] may be considered, to be a modification of Fig. 4-15. The diode is placed in series with a high resistance R_1, thereby causing a constant current to flow in it. If a *p-n* junction diode is used, its temperature dependence resembles that of a junction transistor. Thus an increase in temperature will now cause the d-c resistance of the diode to fall,

[23] The circuit was proposed by L. Barton.

thereby reducing the voltage across it and also the current flowing in the base.

This effect can still further be enhanced by using another diode which is biased in the reverse direction, as seen in Fig. 11-27.[24] Again,

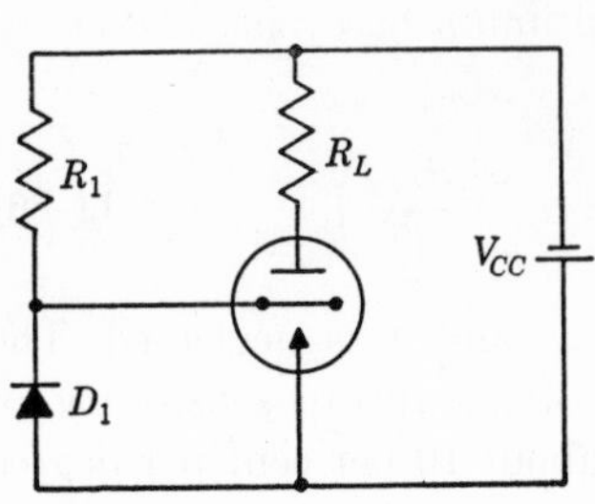

Fig. 11-26. Single-diode temperature stabilization of given operating point.

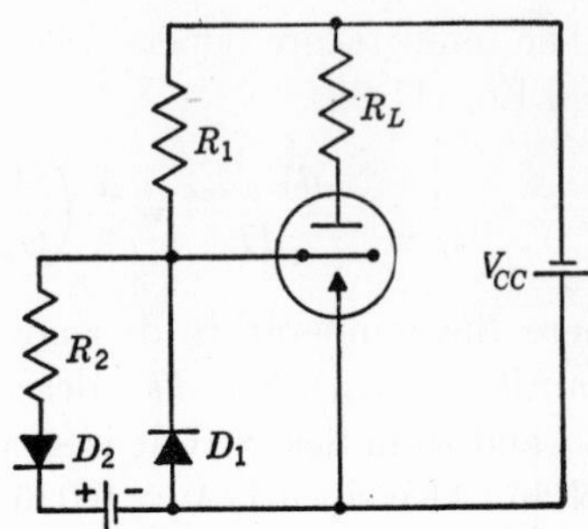

Fig. 11-27. Double-diode temperature stabilization of given operating point.

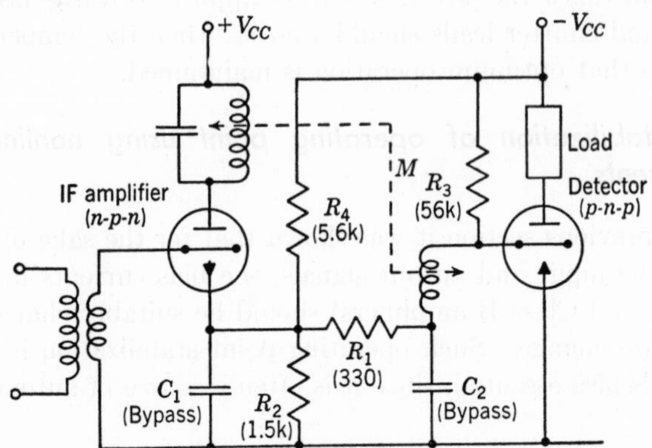

Fig. 11-28. Stabilization of operating point of i-f amplifier detector stages.

with a rise in temperature the resistance of the second diode drops, thereby tending to increase the reverse current of diode D_2 and to reduce the net current flowing in the base still further.

Instead of using diodes for stabilizing the bias, another transistor may be used as shown in Fig. 11-28.[24] This shows an intermediate frequency amplifier followed by a collector detector stage. The

[24] This circuit was proposed by H. C. Lin.

collector detector derives its bias from the base to emitter voltage of the intermediate frequency amplifier as well as from the R_2, R_4 potential divider.

PROBLEMS

11-1. (a) Using Eqs. (11-2a) to (11-2c) and assuming $G_{21} = G_{12}$, evaluate the emitter-to-base voltage V_E at which $I_B = 0$ if $|I_{BS}/I_{CS}| = 3$.

(b) Evaluate the emitter-to-base voltage corresponding to I_{C0} and I_{CB0} (i.e., the floating potentials of the emitter and base).

(c) Derive an expression for the base current and emitter-to-base voltage at which the slope of the I_B vs. V_E curve changes most abruptly, i.e., where $\partial^3 I_B/\partial V_E^3 = 0$. Compare this result with the emitter to base voltage for

$$\frac{\partial^3 I_C}{\partial V_E^3} = 0, \quad \text{and for} \quad \frac{\partial^3 I_E}{\partial V_E^3} = 0$$

(d) Show the effect of $r_{bb'}$ on the curves of Fig. 11-1 and indicate the values where the curves intersect the coordinates.

11-2. (a) Find an expression which relates I_E to V_E (but excludes I_B or I_C), using Eqs. (11-2a) to (11-2c).

(b) Now find expressions for amplitudes of the first, second, and third harmonics of emitter voltage if the emitter current is $I_E = I_{EE} + I_e' \cos \omega t$.

(c) Examine the case where a sinusoidal emitter to base voltage is given, i.e., $v_E = V_{EE} + V_e' \cos \omega t$, and the emitter current is required.

11-3. (a) Extend row 4 of Table 1, Sec. 11.4 to include all modulation products up to fourth harmonics and their sidebands, and also indicate their relative amplitudes in terms of the coefficients a, b, c, and d.

(b) By inspection extend Tables 1 and 2, utilizing the result in (a).

11-4. In a point-contact transistor oscillator shown in Fig. 11-15a, $R_c = 560$ ohm, R_b (external) $= 910$ ohms, r_b (internal) $= 300$ ohms, $r_c = 20{,}000$ ohms, $\alpha_{ce} = 3$, and collector supply voltage $= 22\frac{1}{2}$ volts. Calculate the collector modulation input impedance and modulation power.

11-5. (a) Show that common base short-circuit a-c amplification factor α_{ceo} may be written

$$\alpha_{ceo} = \frac{\partial I_C}{\partial I_E} = \left(\frac{I_C - I_{CS}}{I_E - I_{ES}}\right) = \frac{G_{21}}{G_{11}}$$

using Eqs. (11-2a) to (11-2c).

(b) Assuming a resistance R_s in series with the base lead and a resistance R_o in series with the emitter lead, evaluate $g_{in} \equiv 1/(dV_E/dI_E)$ as a function of I_E, α_{ceo}, I_{ES}, Λ, $r_{bb'}$ R_s, and R_o. Show that this equation is identical to Eq. (11-62) for the case of $R_X = 0$ if $I_{ES} \equiv A'$, and that the resultant shape of the g_{in} vs. V_E curve is the same as in Fig. 11-19.

11-6. (a) Using Fig. 11-19, plot the conversion conductance $G_1/2$ (as defined in Eq. 11-67), as a function of the input voltage V_{in} and also as a function of the emitter direct current I_E for a local oscillator voltage of 0.1 volt, assuming $A' = 10^{-5}$ amp.

(b) At the input voltage V_{in} which corresponds to the emitter current for which the curve in part (a) is a maximum, plot the conversion conductance $G_1/2$ as a function of local oscillator voltage.

(c) Show qualitatively how the magnitude and phase shift of α_{ce} affects (1) the local oscillator input impedance, (2) the conversion ability of the equivalent input circuit shown in Fig. (11-17b), and (3) the current flowing in the tank circuit of the transistor mixer described in Sec. 11.8.

11-7. (a) For the circuit shown in Fig. 11-23b, and assuming a sinusoidal input current, sketch the output voltage, the voltage across the inductance, and the voltage across the diode.

(b) Find analytical expressions for these voltages, assuming the diode to be ideal.

11-8. (a) Estimate the modulation power input for a collector detector, assuming a linearized input characteristic; flow angle = 180°, peak amplitude of carrier = 0.1 volt; $r_{bb'} = 500$ ohms, $\alpha_{cbo} = 30$, $\omega_{cb} = 300$ kc, carrier frequency = 0.5 megacycles. Assume a forward emitter series resistance of 15 ohms.

(b) Find the flow angle for which the detection gain is a maximum.

11-9. Assuming zero load, evaluate the voltage at room temperature where the V_B versus I_C characteristic changes most abruptly, i.e., $V_{B/opt}$ from Eq. (11-85) if $r_{bb'} = 300$ ohms, $\alpha_{cbo} = 20$, $W/L_p = 0.1$, $W = 10^{-3}$ in., the cross-sectional area $= 25 \times 10^{-4}$ in.^{2}, intrinsic resistivity = 60 ohm-cm, resistivity of base = 1 ohm-cm, and ratio of electron to hole mobilities $b = 2.1$.

Chapter 12

PULSE CIRCUITS

12.1 Introduction

In the previous chapters the transistor has been dealt with largely in continuous-wave circuits where the voltage and current waveforms are, or closely resemble, sinusoidal waves. The behavior of these circuits is usually expressed in terms of their response to steady-state sinusoidal-wave excitation of a specified frequency. Each circuit element, either passive or active, is conveniently represented by its a-c impedance; and steady-state analysis completely describes the characteristics of the circuit. In most cases where substantial nonlinearity is involved, the circuit may still be analyzed in the steady-state manner by taking into account not only the fundamental frequency but also the more important harmonic components derived from the driving signal.

In some more recently developed fields, e.g., radar, television, telemetering, and high-speed digital computation, there is a need for circuits that handle electric impulses rather than continuous waves. These circuits are generally referred to as *pulse circuits* or *switching circuits*. The primary functions performed by such circuits are summarized as follows:

1. Generation, amplification, and shaping of pulse waveforms
2. Storage of digital information
3. Switching and gating, for routing and transforming signals from one part of the circuit to another

Pulse circuits have certain distinct characteristics which set them apart from conventional continuous-wave circuits, i.e.,

1. The circuit undergoes abrupt and often discontinuous changes in the normal levels of voltage and current. This frequently implies that the active circuit elements experience radical changes of state (e.g., the transistor, as the active element, may change from its high-conduction state to its cutoff state in a very short time interval).
2. Large excursions of voltage and current usually cause the opera-

tion of the active element (possibly also some passive elements such as saturable magnetic devices) to extend to highly nonlinear regions.

3. Output of the circuit is usually controlled by the presence or absence of an input signal whose magnitude is greater than a prescribed threshold value. In such a circuit the faithful reproduction of the input signal is normally not required.

Because of these characteristics, the pulse circuit is not conveniently described by steady-state analysis; rather, its response to specific pulse waveforms is generally used to describe the circuit.

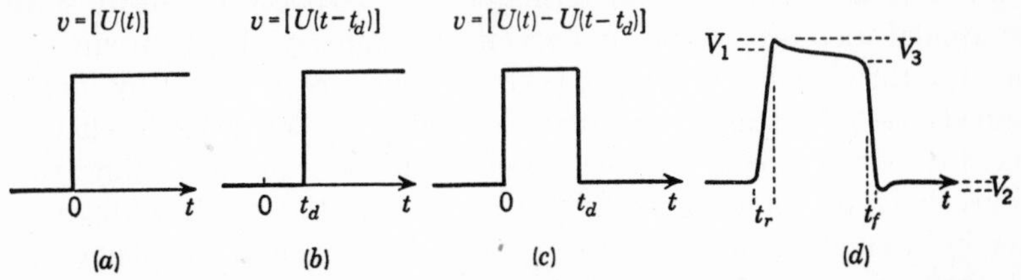

Fig. 12-1. Fundamental pulse waveforms: (a) unit step function; (b) delayed unit step function; (c) ideal rectangular pulse; (d) practical rectangular pulse.

The simplest pulse waveform, and one which is of prime importance in pulse circuit analysis, is the ideal *unit step function* shown in Fig. 12-1a. Analytically the unit step function is defined as

$$U(t) = 0, \qquad t < 0$$
$$U(t) = 1, \qquad 0 < t$$

This function may be employed to represent a physical quantity, e.g., current or voltage, which changes abruptly from one constant level to another. A circuit in which current or voltage undergoes such change is said to have two distinct states; the "off" state and the "on" state, or the "cutoff" state and the "saturation" state. In digital computation reference is made to the "0" state and the "1" state.

If a change of state occurs at a time other than $t = 0$, the event is represented by the *delayed unit step function* shown in Fig. 12-1b, and is defined as

$$U(t - t_d) = 0, \qquad t < t_d$$
$$U(t - t_d) = 1, \qquad t_d < t$$

An ideal rectangular pulse with a finite time duration may be considered the superimposition of two successive step functions, as,

$$v = V[U(t) - U(t - t_d)]$$

which implies

$$v = 0 \qquad \text{for } t < 0 \text{ and } t_d < t$$

$$v = V \qquad \text{for } 0 < t < t_d$$

The ideal pulse, as shown in Fig. 12-1c, may only be approached, of course, in practical circuitry. The most prominent departure from the ideal case is the finite time required for an electrical quantity to establish itself at either of its two stable states. Thus a rectangular pulse produced by a practical circuit may take the general form shown in Fig. 12-1d. The departures from the ideal rectangular pulse are measured by the following quantities indicated in the figure:

t_r	build-up (rise) time
t_f	decay (fall) time
V_1 and V_2	overshoots
V_3	droop

For a good approximation to the ideal pulse all these quantities should be kept small. The magnitudes of these quantities depend on the reactive components of the passive and active elements in the circuit. These elements, therefore, are of general concern in pulse circuit design.

The point-contact type transistor, by virtue of some of its unique properties, enjoyed an early success in the field of pulse circuits. Since, in such circuits, the junction transistor behaves quite differently from the point-contact transistor, we shall treat the two types of transistor separately. The frequency response of the transistor is a problem of major concern in the operation of pulse circuits. However, in the first part of this chapter, where emphasis lies in illustrating the modes of operation of the transistor as a resistive nonlinear active element, the transistor will be treated as a frequency-independent element. Later sections will treat the transistor as a frequency-dependent element. The operation, as well as the design and analysis techniques, of pulse circuits are usually more conveniently illustrated by point-contact transistor circuits, because of their susceptibility to treatments as two-terminal networks. In this chapter the discussion of point-contact transistor circuits will precede that of the junction transistor circuits.

12.2 Large-signal operation of point-contact transistors

For large-signal operation the point-contact transistor is a highly nonlinear device. This is quite evident in examining the static characteristics of the transistor over an extensive operating range. Consider

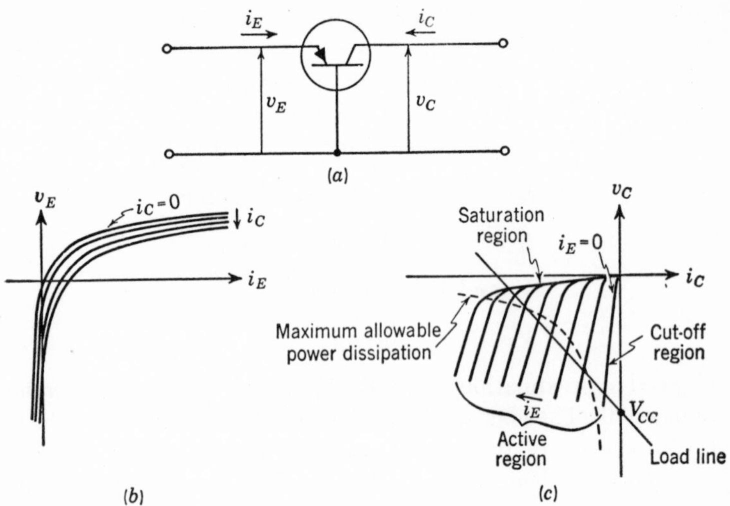

Fig. 12-2. Static characteristics of a point-contact transistor: (a) the transistor as a four-terminal network; (b) the emitter characteristics; (c) the collector characteristics.

the circuit arrangement shown in Fig. 12-2a, where a low-frequency input signal applied at the emitter controls the collector output voltage developed across the load resistor R_c. Referring to the collector static characteristics of the transistor (Fig. 12-2c), the excursion of the operation point of the transistor is confined along the load line. A negative input voltage tends to cause a negative current to flow into the emitter. However, for negative emitter currents the emitter junction offers a high resistance (as shown in Fig. 12-2b, for $i_E < 0$); and thus for any practical emitter voltage the excusion of the operating point is limited (on the low-conduction side) to a region slightly to the left of the $i_E = 0$ characteristic. For all practical purposes the $i_E = 0$ characteristic describes operation of the transistor in the region $i_E \leq 0$. This region is generally referred to as the *cutoff* region; and the transistor is said to be in the *off* state. For $i_E > 0$ the collector current increases rapidly with the emitter current; this region is referred to as the *active* region. When i_E becomes large enough, however, the operation point soon reaches the knee of the characteristic, and further increase of i_E produces no appreciable increase of i_C. The transistor is then said to be in the *saturation* region, or in the *on* state. The change in characteristics from the cutoff region to the active region is abrupt, and this transition is controlled solely by the emitter current. The change from the active region to the saturation region is less abrupt (and in some transistor units rather gradual); and the change of state is determined by the load line as well as by the emitter current.

The nonlinear static characteristics of a transistor resemble to a certain extent the voltage-current relation of a crystal diode. Adler[1] suggested a large-signal equivalent circuit for point-contact transistors (Fig. 12-3a). In the equivalent circuit, the nonlinear behavior of

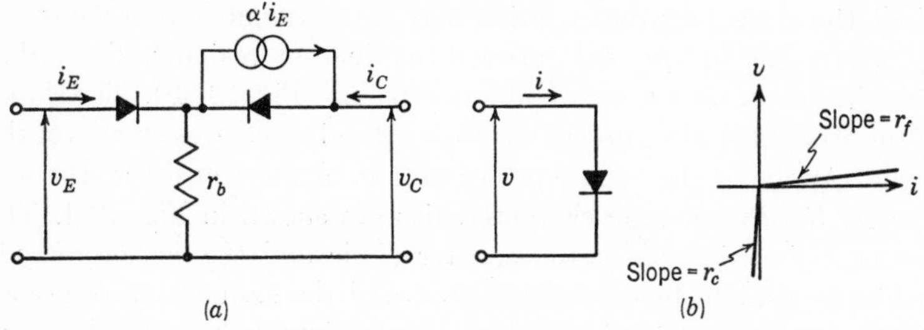

Fig. 12-3. (a) Large-signal equivalent circuit of the point-contact transistor; (b) sectionally linearized diode characteristic.

the emitter junction and the collector junction are represented by the emitter diode D_E and the collector diode D_C. The transistor action is represented by the fictitious current generator $\alpha' i_E$ across the collector diode. In normal operation the collector power supply biases the col-

[1] R. B. Adler, "A Large Signal Equivalent Circuit for Transistor Static Characteristics," *Transistor Group Report T-8*, Research Laboratory of Electronics, Massachusetts Institute of Technology, 1952.

lector diode in the reverse direction. The three regions of operation of the transistor may be defined by the direction of current flow in the two diodes. For $i_E < 0$ both diodes are operated in the reverse direction and the current generator is inactive. Thus in the cutoff region the transistor behaves as a passive element with a high emitter resistance and a high collector resistance. In the active region, where $i_E > 0$, the emitter diode conducts in the forward direction, while the collector diode is still biased in the reverse direction. The current generator is now active, and the transistor behaves as an active element with power amplification. For further increase of i_E the generator current $\alpha' i_E$ soon becomes greater than the collector current i_C, the collector diode begins to conduct in the forward direction, and the transistor enters the saturation region. In this region both the emitter resistance and the collector resistance are low. The current generator is now shunted by the low collector resistance. When there is an appreciable load resistance in the collector circuit (as in the case of many practical circuits) the transistor behaves like a passive element with a low internal resistance.

The highly nonlinear characteristics of the transistor make it difficult to perform precise circuit analysis; and in practical applications a certain degree of approximation is in order. In the case of a crystal diode the voltage-current relation may be represented approximately by a straight line in the forward conduction region and another straight line in the reverse conduction region (Fig. 12-3b). The slopes of the straight lines represent the forward and reverse resistances of the diode. Applying the same approximation to the transistor, the *sectionally linearized* static characteristics are shown in Fig. 12-4. The sectional linearization of the emitter diode and the collector diode results in straight-line characteristics, and the assumption of a constant current amplification factor α results in equal spacing between the characteristics. As is indicated in the figure, the slope of the linearized characteristics represents approximately the emitter resistance and the collector resistance in the three regions; and the spacing between the collector characteristics represents the short-circuit current amplification factor α. The value of α is defined as $\alpha \equiv \partial i_C / \partial i_E$ with v_C constant. The fictitious current generator amplification factor α' is defined as $\alpha' \equiv \alpha + (r_b/r_c)(\alpha - 1)$. In the active region, where $r_c \gg r_b$, α' is approximately equal to α. In the saturation region where the values of r_c and r_b may be of the same order, the relation $\alpha' \approx \alpha$ no longer holds. It is to be noted that α and α' are small-signal parameters, their values being different in different linear regions. The large-signal current gain of a circuit, however, can easily be obtained from the collector characteristics and the load line in the customary manner.

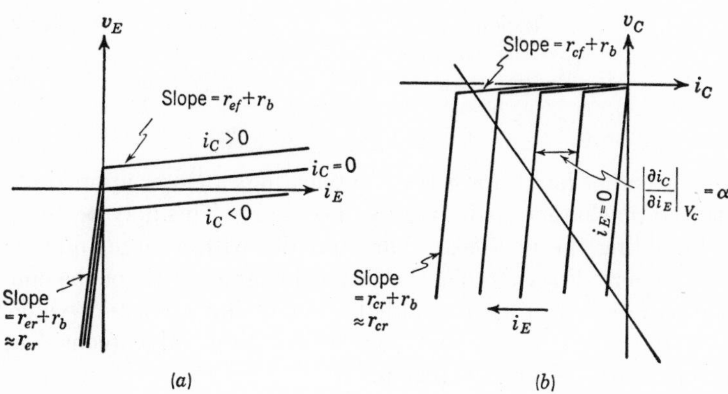

Fig. 12-4. Sectionally linearized static characteristics of a point-contact transistor: (a) the emitter characteristics; (b) the collector characteristics.

The small-signal T equivalent circuit may be adopted for large-signal operation by assigning one set of transistor parameters for each of the three regions, as shown in Table 12-1. In the table r_{ef} and r_{er} represent, respectively, the forward and reverse resistance of the emitter junction diode; and r_{cf} and r_{cr} represents the forward and reverse resistance of the collector diode.

Table 12-1

	Region I	Region II	Region III
State:	cutoff	active	saturation
i_E:	negative	positive, small	positive, large
v_C:	high	intermediate	low
Emitter diode:	reverse	forward	forward
Collector diode:	reverse	reverse	forward
r_e:	$r_{er} \approx$ 100,000 ohms	$r_{ef} \approx$ 50 ohms	$r_{ef} \approx$ 50 ohms
r_c:	$r_{cr} \approx$ 20,000 ohms	$r_{cr} \approx$ 20,000 ohms	$r_{cf} \approx$ 50 ohms
r_b:	$r_b \approx$ 50 ohms	$r_b \approx$ 50 ohms	$r_b \approx$ 50 ohms
α':	$\alpha_1' \approx 0$	$\alpha_2' \approx 2.5$	$\alpha_3' \approx 2.5$

In many pulse circuit applications the external resistance of the circuit is large enough so that $R_e \gg r_{ef}$, $R_c \gg r_{cf}$, and $R_b \gg r_b$. In such cases the equivalent circuit may be further simplified as shown in Table 12-2.

Table 12-2

	Region I	Region II	Region III
r_e	$r_{er} \approx$ 100,000 ohms	0	0
r_c	$r_{cr} \approx$ 20,000 ohms	$r_{cr} \approx$ 20,000 ohms	0
r_b	0	0	0
α'	0	$\alpha' \approx 2.5$	0

On the other hand, for certain applications a closer approximation of the static characteristics may be necessary. This may be achieved by simulating the nonlinear characteristics with a larger number of linear regions. For example, the forward characteristic of the emitter diode may be better approximated by assigning a constant value for r_{ef} for the active region and another constant value (considerably smaller) for the saturation region.

12.3 Trigger action and trigger-action circuits

Circuits employing one or more active elements with provision for regeneration may be designed to offer rapid change of state. In such circuits the input signal serves only to initiate a prescribed operation of change of state. Once initiated by the input signal the circuit will supply its own driving power to complete the operation even after the input signal is removed. This type of circuit usually has three or more distinct operation regions, so arranged that stable regions are separated by unstable regions. Let us consider the simple, yet most practical, case where a circuit has two stable regions separated by an unstable region as represented symbolically in Fig. 12-5. In Region I and in Region III the circuit behaves like a normal stable circuit where the operating point is dictated by the input signal. (The operating point is defined by the voltage and the current at a given junction of the circuit.) In Region II the circuit is unstable and the operating point may be shifted by the circuit itself. Assume the operating point is initially located in Region I. An input signal may displace the operating point in this region as it would in a normal stable circuit. However, once the operating point is carried into the unstable Region II, the circuit supplies its own driving power to carry the operating point through Region II into Region III without help from the externally applied input signal. When the operating point reaches the stable Region III, the circuit acts once more as a normal stable circuit. Similarly, if the circuit is originally operated in Region III, once the operating point is carried into Region II by an

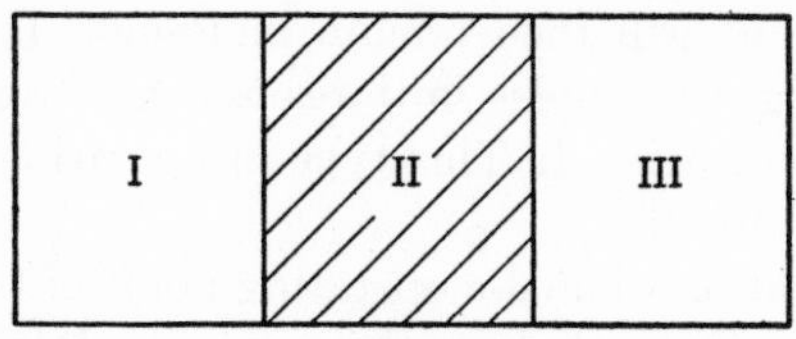

Region I	Region II	Region III
Stable	Unstable	Stable
Low-conduction	Transition	High-conduction
Cutoff	Active	Saturation
Off	Transition	On
Positive-resistance	Negative-resistance	Positive-resistance

Fig. 12-5. The three distinct regions of a trigger-action circuit.

external input signal the circuit itself will carry the operating point to the stable Region I. This process of transition through Region II, which may be quite fast and is independent of the input signal, is generally referred to as *trigger action.* We shall name such circuits *trigger-action circuits*, or simply, *trigger circuits.* The input signal which initiates the trigger action is generally called the *triggering pulse.*

The trigger action circuits may be arranged to operate in one of three principal modes:

1. *Monostable* operation. The operating point of the circuit is quiescently in the stable Region I. The presence of the triggering pulse carries the operating point into Region II and the circuit quickly moves the operating point to Region III. The operating point stays in Region III for a given length of time, depending on the reactive elements of the circuit, and then re-enters the unstable Region II and quickly returns to the original stable Region I. Similarly, the operating point may be quiescently in the stable Region III; and a triggering pulse may cause the operating point to move to Region I

for a length of time. A typical example of this type of operation is the *one-shot multivibrator*.

2. *Bistable* operation. The circuit is quiescently in a stable region, say Region I. The trigger pulse initiates the trigger action of the circuit, and the operating point moves through Region II to Region III. The operating point will then remain in Region III indefinitely, or until a second triggering pulse initiates another trigger action to return the circuit to Region I. This type of operation is typical of the common *flip-flop* circuits.

3. *Astable* operation. The d-c operating point of the circuit for this type of operation is located in the unstable Region II. Any disturbance of the circuit, such as circuit noise or the transients caused by switching on d-c power, will start the trigger action and carry the operating point to one of the stable regions, say Region I. The operating point stays in Region I for a length of time determined by the reactive elements in the circuit, re-enters the unstable region, and passes into Region III. The operating point stays in the Region III for a given time and re-enters the unstable region, thus completing one cycle of operation. In this way the circuit is seen to oscillate from one stable region to the other, which is typical of *free-running multivibrators*.

A quantitative study of the operation of trigger circuits may best be achieved by examining the driving-point impedance looking into a given branch of the circuit. As we are limiting our discussion to low-frequency operation at present we shall deal with the case in which the circuit is purely resistive. As illustrated in Chapter 10, the *driving-point characteristic* of a trigger action circuit may assume either of the two general forms shown in Fig. 12-6. In either curve the voltage-current relation indicates that the circuit exhibits positive resistance in the stable Regions I and III, and a negative resistance in the unstable Region II.

The mode of operation of trigger circuits is readily understood with the help of the *driving-point characteristic* and the *load line*. The load line represents the load resistance and the bias voltage to be connected to the driving point. Figure 12-7b illustrates monostable operation of a trigger circuit. The quiescent operating point P, which is the intersection of the driving-point characteristic and the load line, is in the stable Region I. The application of the triggering pulse is equivalent to shifting the load line without changing its slope. Let us consider a

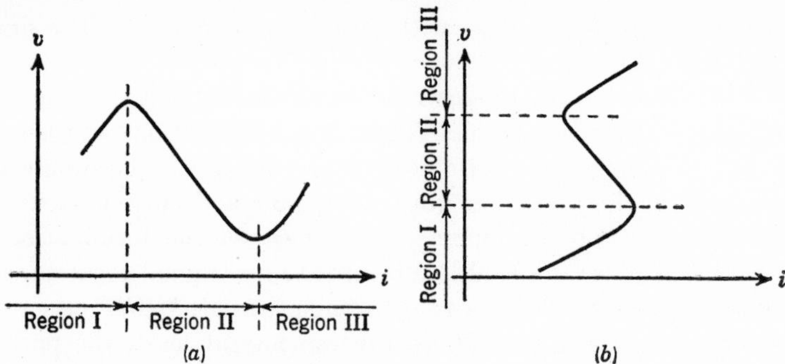

Fig. 12-6. Driving-point characteristics of trigger-action circuits: (a) current-controlled negative-resistance curve; (b) voltage-controlled negative-resistance curve.

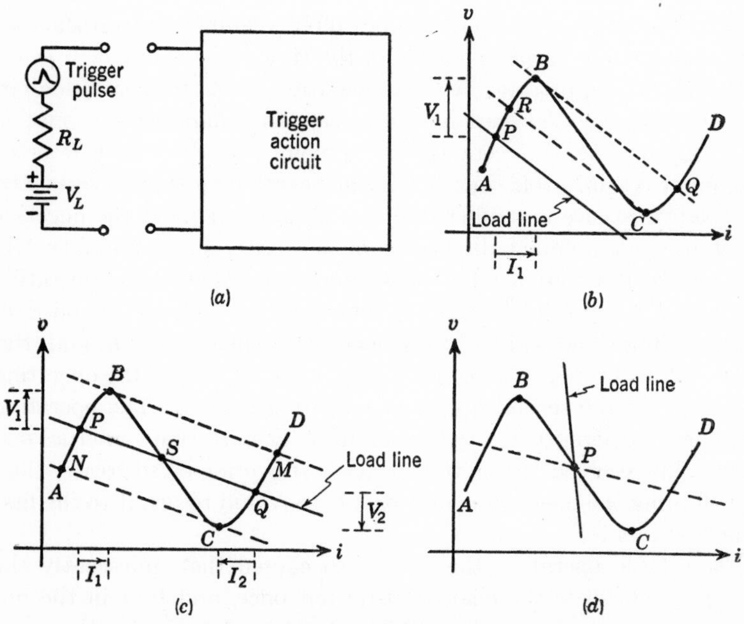

Fig. 12-7. The three principal modes of operation of a trigger-action circuit: (a) trigger-action circuit and driving-point load; (b) monostable operation; (c) bistable operation; (d) astable operation.

positive pulse applied in series with the driving-point load. The signal voltage shifts the load line upward and parallel to the quiescent load line moving the operating point P up along the curve AB. When the operating point moves beyond B the only intersection between the load line and the characteristic becomes the point Q. Accordingly, the circuit must make a sudden jump in voltage and current from the operating point B to the operating point Q. At the termination of the triggering pulse the load line returns to its original location, and the operating point falls back to P through the path $QCRP$ as shown. This complete path $PBQCRP$ is, theoretically at least, the path of the operating point in a complete cycle of monostable operation when there is no reactive element in the circuit. With reactive elements the path is substantially modified, because the d-c load-line and the d-c characteristic no longer fully describe the circuit. In practice, the effects of reactive elements usually cannot be neglected; and detailed discussion of these effects will be found in later sections. However, the pure resistive version does offer a simple and satisfactory description of the basic operation of the circuit.

Figure 12-7c illustrates bistable operation of the trigger-action circuit. Quiescently the load line intersects the characteristic once in each region. The quiescent operating point may be either P or Q. The point S is unstable since it is in the negative resistance region and the load resistance is smaller than the absolute value of the negative resistance. (A detailed discussion of the criterion of stability will appear in a later section.) Let us assume the initial quiescent operating point is P. A positive triggering pulse greater than V_1 applied in series with the load will move the operating point beyond B, and trigger action will bring the operating point to M. From M the operating point falls to the second quiescent operating point Q. The operating point may remain at point Q indefinitely, or until some external disturbance is received. From Q, a negative triggering pulse greater than V_2 will bring the operating point past C to N and return it to the first quiescent point P.

For astable operation the load is so chosen that quiescently the load line intersects the characteristic but once, and that in the unstable region as shown in Fig. 12-7d. Reactive elements in the circuit enable the operating point to oscillate from one stable region to the other. The path of operation depends almost entirely on the reactive elements in the circuit, as was discussed in Chapter 10.

12.4 Trigger action provided by the point-contact type transistor[2]

As explained in Chapter 10 a circuit employing a point-contact transistor is capable of trigger action if the emitter-to-collector current

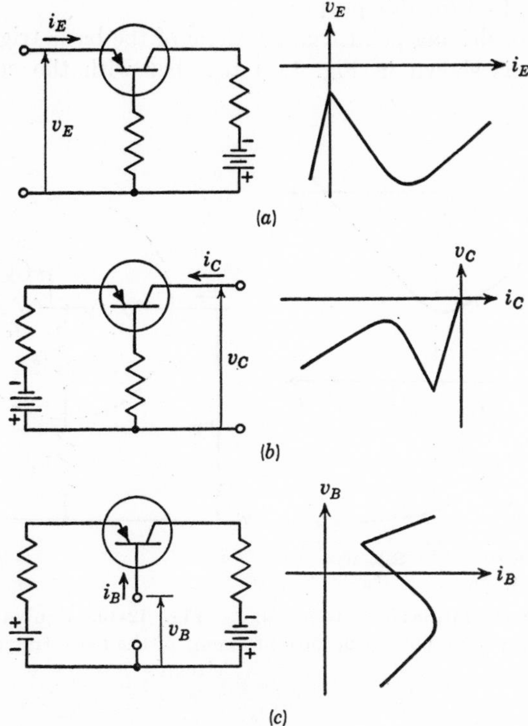

Fig. 12-8. Driving-point characteristics of a transistor trigger-action circuit: (a) emitter circuit; (b) collector circuit; (c) base circuit.

gain is greater than unity. Looking into any one of the three branches of a transistor trigger-action circuit we may see a driving-point characteristic similar to those of Fig. 12-6. The driving-point characteristic for the emitter branch and the collector branch exhibit the current-controlled negative resistance curve (Fig. 12-8a and Fig. 12-8b); while the driving-point characteristic for the base branch exhibits voltage-controlled negative resistance (Fig. 12-8c). For most

[2] A. W. Lo, "Transistor Trigger Circuits," *Proc. I.R.E.*, Vol. 40, Nov. 1952.

practical applications the collector current represents the output signal, and the emitter current is usually the controlling factor for the operation of the circuit. In such cases the emitter driving-point characteristic may be used most advantageously to determine the behavior of the circuit, although either of the other two characteristics may also be used for this purpose.

The emitter driving-point characteristic of the basic trigger circuit (Fig. 12-8a) is shown in Fig. 12-9 together with the collector-to-

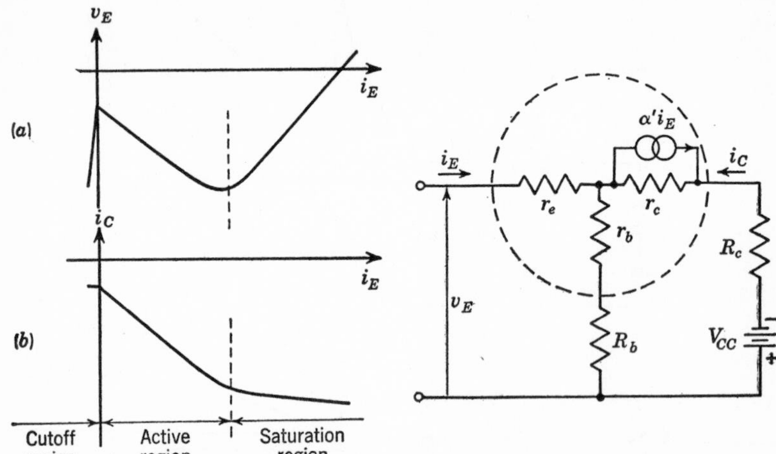

Fig. 12-9. Operation characteristics: (a) emitter driving point; (b) current transfer.

Fig. 12-10. Equivalent circuit of the basic trigger-action circuit.

emitter current transfer characteristic. The v_E-i_E curve and the emitter load line together determine the mode of operation of the circuit; and the i_C-i_E curve determines the amplitude and waveform of the output signal.

Analytically, with reference to the equivalent circuit of Fig. 12-10 the emitter driving-point characteristic may be represented by

$$v_E = \left\{ r_e + \frac{(R_b + r_b)[R_c + r_c(1 - \alpha)]}{R_b + r_b + R_c + r_c} \right\} i_E - \frac{(R_b + r_b)V_{CC}}{R_b + r_b + R_c + r_c} \qquad (12\text{-}1)$$

The current transfer characteristic may be represented by

$$i_C = -\frac{R_b + r_b + \alpha r_c}{R_b + r_b + R_c + r_c} i_E - \frac{V_{CC}}{R_b + r_b + R_c + r_c} \tag{12-2}$$

In normal operation of trigger circuits, the values of the currents and voltages are subject to changes over wide ranges. Over such wide ranges the equivalent circuit parameters of the transistor do not remain as constants, but change with respect to the currents and the voltages. Any attempt to express the equivalent circuit parameters as continuous functions of voltage or current, however, makes the analytical forms unduly complicated. For circuit design purposes, the sectional linearization technique outlined in Sec. 12.2 may be adopted.

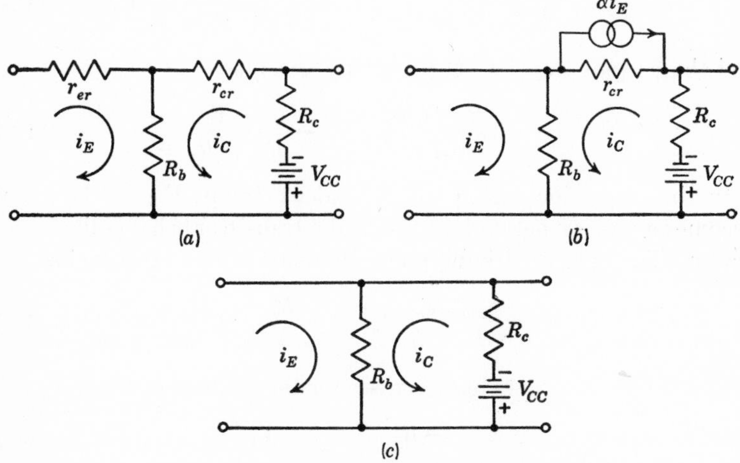

Fig. 12-11. Equivalent circuits for the three operation regions: (a) cutoff; (b) active; (c) saturation.

Based on the approximation outlined in Table 12-2 the equivalent circuits for the three regions become quite simple. They are shown in Fig. 12-11. Since the forward resistances r_{ef} and r_{cf} are neglected in this approximation, we shall, for simplicity in the following discussion, write r_e for r_{er} and r_c for r_{cr}.

In the cutoff region, the equivalent circuit becomes that of Fig. 12-11a, which is a passive network characterized by the high reverse emitter resistance r_e. Solving the network equations for v_E, the emitter driving-point characteristic for this region is

$$v_E = r_e i_E - \frac{R_b}{R_b + R_c + r_c} V_{CC} \tag{12-3}$$

The current transfer characteristic takes the form,

$$i_C = -\frac{R_b}{R_b + R_c + r_c} i_E - \frac{V_{CC}}{R_b + R_c + r_c} \tag{12-4}$$

In the active region the equivalent circuit, Fig. 12-11b, becomes an active network characterized by a current source $\alpha' i_E$, across the collector resistance r_c. The emitter driving-point characteristic in this region is derived as

$$v_E = \frac{R_b[R_c + r_c(1 - \alpha)]}{R_b + R_c + r_c} i_E - \frac{R_b}{R_b + R_c + r_c} V_{CC} \tag{12-5}$$

and the current transfer characteristic becomes

$$i_C = -\frac{R_b + \alpha r_c}{R_b + R_c + r_c} i_E - \frac{V_{CC}}{R_b + R_c + r_c} \tag{12-6}$$

In the saturation region the equivalent circuit, Fig. 12-11c, again becomes a passive network in which the transistor behaves like a conductor. The emitter driving-point characteristic is expressed as

$$v_E = \frac{R_b R_c}{R_b + R_c} i_E - \frac{R_b}{R_b + R_c} V_{CC} \tag{12-7}$$

The current transfer characteristic for the saturation region is

$$i_C = \frac{-R_b}{R_b + R_c} i_E - \frac{V_{CC}}{R_b + R_c} \tag{12-8}$$

The calculated characteristics based upon the simplified analysis and the characteristics obtained experimentally are plotted in Fig. 12-12 for a typical circuit. Close agreement between the experimental and analytical curves show that these approximations are justified. Agreement is not expected, of course, where the observed curve departs from linearity. In the active region the curves depart considerably from a straight line. This is because the values of α and r_c do not remain constant with change of i_E, as was assumed in the analysis. However, in most pulse-handling circuits the exact shape of the curve in the transition region is not important so long as the turnover points P_1 and P_2 of the emitter driving-point characteristic, and Q_1 and Q_2 of the current transfer characteristic are well defined. From

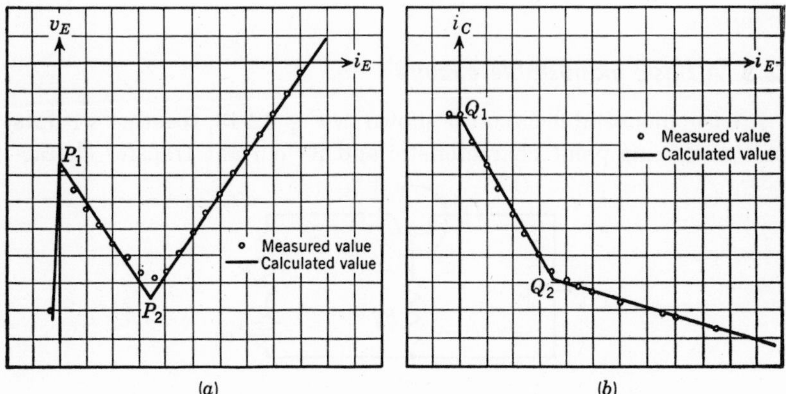

Fig. 12-12. Operation characteristics of a typical trigger-action circuit: (a) emitter driving point; (b) current transfer.

Eqs. (12-3) to (12-8), the calculated coordinates of the turnover points are

$$P_1: \quad i_E = 0, \quad v_E = \frac{-R_b}{R_b + R_e + r_c} V_{CC} \tag{12-9}$$

$$Q_1: \quad i_E = 0, \quad i_C = \frac{-V_{CC}}{R_b + R_e + r_c} \tag{12-10}$$

$$P_2: \quad i_E = \frac{V_{CC}}{\alpha(R_b + R_e) - R_b}, \quad v_E = \frac{R_b(1 - \alpha)}{\alpha(R_b + R_e) - R_b} V_{CC} \tag{12-11}$$

$$Q_2: \quad i_E = \frac{V_{CC}}{\alpha(R_b + R_e) - R_b}, \quad i_C = \frac{-\alpha V_{CC}}{\alpha(R_b + R_e) - R_b} \tag{12-12}$$

The points P_1 and Q_1, where the circuit is triggered from low conduction to high conduction, depend primarily on the value of r_c, which, unfortunately, is affected considerably by temperature and may vary from unit to unit. The points P_2 and Q_2, where the circuit is triggered from high conduction to low conduction, depend primarily on α, which often differs appreciably between individual transistor units. The stabilization of the turnover points P and Q is a problem of major importance in the design of practical pulse circuits. Stabilization techniques will be illustrated in a later section.

We shall now examine a few basic trigger-action circuits which are used as the building blocks for the design of practical pulse handling circuits.

12.5 A basic monostable circuit

A basic monostable circuit is shown in Fig. 12-13, together with its emitter driving-point characteristic and its current transfer charac-

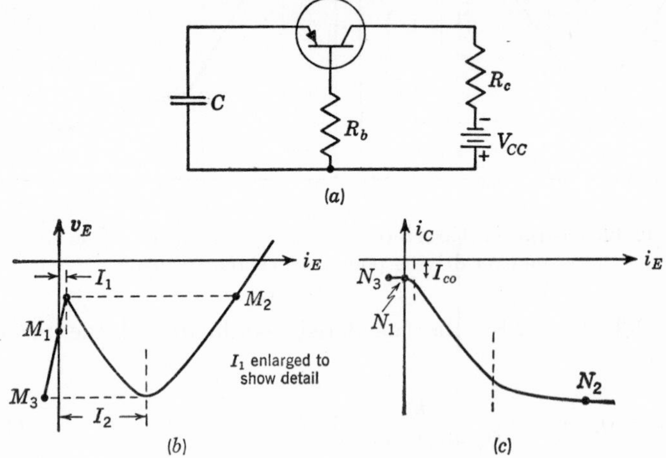

Fig. 12-13. A basic monostable circuit: (a) circuit configuration; (b) and (c) operation characteristics.

teristic. These two curves may be referred to jointly in the following discussion. The negative-resistance region of the v_E-i_E curve begins slightly to the right of the v_E axis. In the quiescent state the capacitor C constitutes an open circuit in the emitter loop. The quiescent operation point is M_1, which is the intersection between the open-circuit load line (the v_E axis) and the v_E-i_E curve. When a trigger source sends into the emitter a positive current greater than I_1, the circuit passes into its unstable negative-registance region. Because of the current amplification within the transistor and the positive feedback action afforded by the base resistance, the emitter and collector currents increase rapidly, resulting in the sudden jump of i_E to the point M_2 in the saturation region. The transition path P_1M_2 is suggested by the fact that at the instant when a voltage is applied across the capacitor, it behaves like a short circuit; and thus the a-c load line of the emitter circuit at that instant is P_1M_2. The transition path is modified if other reactive components including those associated with the transistor are also considered. A detailed discussion of the effects of these additional reactive elements will appear later in this chapter. Now that the capacitor C is being charged in the emitter loop, i_E diminishes until its value is less than I_2. At this point

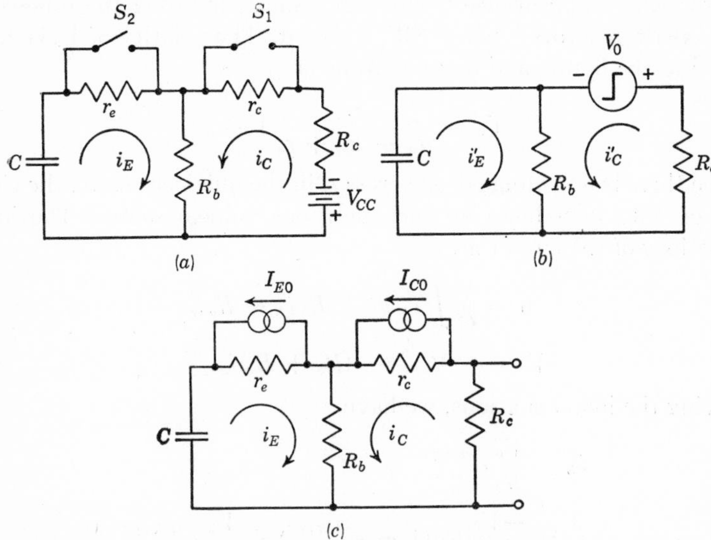

Fig. 12-14. (a) Equivalent circuit illustrating the trigger action of the basic monostable circuit; (b) effect of closing switch; (c) effect of opening switch.

the circuit re-enters the unstable region and quickly jumps back to point M_3 in the low-conduction stable state. The capacitor now discharges through the reverse resistance of the emitter junction, and eventually the initial quiescent operating point M_1 is attained.

The effect of the trigger action of the circuit is equivalent to switching the circuit from its cutoff state to its saturation state. Referring to the equivalent circuits shown in Fig. 12-11a and 12-11c, the event is seen to be equivalent to the switching operation shown in Fig. 12-14a, where r_e and r_c are values in the cutoff state. A detailed analysis of the operation is included here to illustrate the technique used in analyzing this type of circuit.

Quiescently, with both SW_1 and SW_2 open, the currents in the emitter loop and the collector loop are, respectively,

$$i_{E0} = 0, \qquad i_{C0} = \frac{V_{CC}}{R_b + R_c + r_c}$$

At $t = 0$ both switches are closed. The effect of closing these switches is illustrated in Fig. 12-14b. Here V_0 is a fictitious voltage source whose appearance results from short-circuiting the quiescent voltage drop across r_c when SW_1 is closed. The polarity of V_0 is indicated in the figure, and its magnitude is

$$V_0 = \frac{r_c}{R_b + R_c + r_c} V_{CC}$$

Since there is no voltage drop across r_e in the quiescent state, the closing of SW_2 introduces no such fictitious voltage source. The loop equations of the circuit are

$$0 = \frac{1}{C}\int i'_E\,dt + R_b i'_E + R_b i'_c$$

$$V_0 = -R_b i'_E - (R_b + R_c)i'_c$$

Solving the loop equations, we have

$$i'_E = \frac{V_0}{R_c}\epsilon^{-t/R_{11}C}$$

$$i'_c = \frac{-V_0}{R_bR_c}R_{11}(1 - \epsilon^{-t/R_{11}C}) + \frac{V_0}{R_c}\epsilon^{-t/R_{11}C}$$

where $$V_0 \equiv \frac{r_c}{R_b + R_c + r_c}V_{CC}, \qquad R_{11} \equiv \frac{R_bR_c}{R_b + R_c}$$

Now taking into consideration the initial currents i_{E0} and I_{C0}, the total currents are

$$i_E = i'_E + I_{E0} = \frac{V_0}{R_c}\epsilon^{-t/R_{11}C} + 0 = \frac{V_0}{R_c}\epsilon^{-t/R_{11}C}$$

$$\begin{aligned} i_C &= i'_C + I_{C0} \\ &= \frac{-V_0}{R_b + R_c}(1 - \epsilon^{-t/R_{11}C}) - \frac{V_0}{R_C}\epsilon^{-t/R_{11}C} - \frac{V_{CC}}{R_b + R_c + r_c} \\ &= \frac{-R_bV_0}{R_c(R_b + R_c)}\epsilon^{-t/R_{11}C} - \frac{V_{CC}}{R_b + R_c} \end{aligned}$$

The analysis reveals that i_E, the emitter current, jumps from zero to V_0/R_c when the trigger action is initiated by the triggering pulse, and then decreases exponentially with time at a rate determined by the time constant CR_{11}. This continues until i_E falls below the value of I_2, then the circuit re-enters the negative-resistance region and triggers back to the low-conduction state. The value of I_2, as calculated from Eq. (12-9), is

$$I_2 = \frac{V_{CC}}{\alpha(R_b + R_c) - R_b} \tag{12-13}$$

The second trigger action is equivalent to opening switches SW_1 and SW_2 at $t = T$, that is, when i_E reaches I_2. The time required for i_E to drop to I_2 is

$$T = R_{11}C \ln \frac{r_c[\alpha(R_b + R_c) - R_b]}{(R_b + R_c + r_c)R_c} \tag{12-14}$$

The currents i_E and I_C for $t > T$ may be calculated as an opening switch problem. The opening of switches SW_1 and SW_2 at $t = T$ is equivalent to inserting the fictitious current source I'_{E0} and I'_{C0} (Fig. 12-14c) at $t = T$. These values are

$$I'_{E0} = \frac{V_0}{R_c} \epsilon^{-(T+\tau)/R_{11}C}$$

$$I'_{C0} = \frac{R_b V_0}{R_c(R_b + R_c)} \epsilon^{-(T+\tau)/R_{11}C} - \frac{V_{CC}}{R_b + R_c}$$

where $\tau = t - T$. The expressions of i_E and i_C for $t > T$ may thus be calculated in a similar manner as the closing switch case mentioned earlier. A solution of close approximation, however, may be readily reached when one takes into consideration the fact that r_c and r_e are much larger than R_b and R_c. The opening of switches SW_1 and SW_2 results in the insertion of a large resistance r_e in the collector loop, which returns the circuit almost instantly to its quiescent state. The only factor which prevents the circuit from returning to its quiescent state instantaneously is the capacitor C, which is being charged up during the time interval $0 < t < T$. Capacitor C begins to discharge at $t = T$ and produces a discharge current which is in the opposite direction to i_E during $0 < t < T$. This discharge current causes i_E to be slightly below zero at $t > T$. However, since the discharge current is limited by the high emitter reverse resistance r_e, its magnitude is very small compared with i_E during the interval $0 < t < T$. As far as current waveforms are concerned, it is a good approximation to say that both i_E and i_C return to their quiescent value instantaneously at $t = T$. Summarizing, we have

$$\begin{aligned} i_E &= 0, \qquad \text{for } t < 0,\ T < t \\ &= \frac{V_0}{R_c}\epsilon^{-t/R_{11}C}, \qquad \text{for } 0 < t < T \end{aligned} \tag{12-15}$$

$$\begin{aligned} i_C &= \frac{-V_{CC}}{R_b + R_c + r_c}, \qquad \text{for } t < 0,\ T < t \\ &= \frac{V_0 R_b}{R_c(R_b + R_c)}\epsilon^{-t/R_{11}C} - \frac{V_{CC}}{R_b + R_c}, \qquad \text{for } 0 < t < T \end{aligned} \tag{12-16}$$

where $$V_0 = \frac{r_c}{R_b + R_c + r_c} V_{CC}, \quad R_{11} = \frac{R_b R_c}{R_b + R_c}$$

$$T = R_{11} C \ln \frac{r_c[\alpha(R_b + R_c) - R_b]}{(R_b + R_c + r_c)R_c}$$

The current waveforms are shown in Fig. 12-15a and 12-15b.

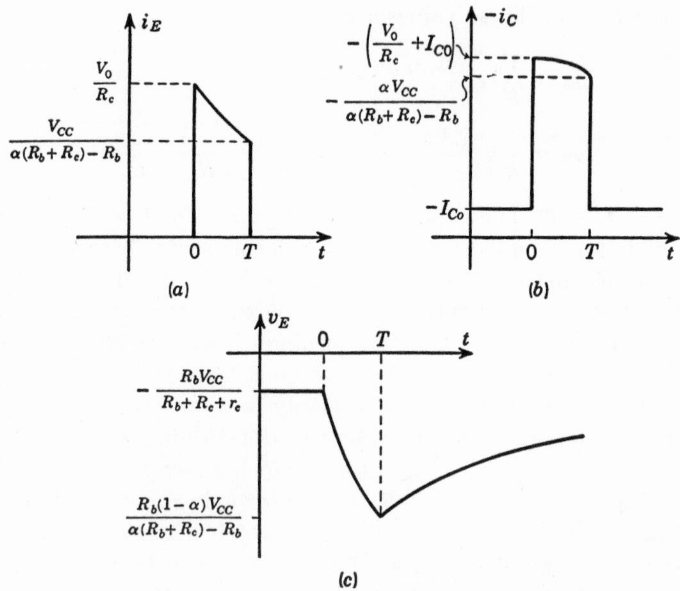

Fig. 12-15. Waveforms in the basic monostable circuit: (a) emitter current waveform; (b) collector current waveform; (c) emitter voltage waveform.

The voltage across C does not return to its quiescent value instantly at $t = T$, for the charge accumulating during the interval $0 < t < T$ must discharge through the high emitter back resistance r_e. Analytically, the voltage across the capacitor may be expressed as

$$\begin{aligned} v_E &= \frac{-V_{CC}}{(R_b + R_c + r_c)} \quad \text{for} \quad t < 0 \\ &= \frac{-R_b}{R_b + R_c} V_{CC} + \frac{R_b V_0}{R_b + R_c} \epsilon^{-t/R_{11}C}, \quad \text{for} \quad 0 < t < T \\ &= \frac{-R_b V_{CC}}{R_b + R_c + r_c} + \left[\frac{R_b(1 - \alpha) V_{CC}}{\alpha(R_b + R_c) - R_b} + \frac{R_b V_{CC}}{R_b + R_c + r_c} \right] \epsilon^{-(t-T)/r_e C}, \\ & \qquad \text{for} \quad T < t \qquad (12\text{-}17) \end{aligned}$$

The voltage waveform across C is shown in Fig. 12-15c. Because of the long time constant r_eC for the cutoff state, it is seen that the capacitor requires an appreciable time to discharge. This effect defines the upper limit of the circuit repetition frequency.

It is of interest to note that in the normal operation of a trigger-action circuit a major part of the load line may lie in the region where the dissipation in the transistor is higher than the allowable value (Fig. 12-2c). This is permissible because the operation point can stay for some length of time only in Region I and Region III; and the transition through Region II (where the dissipation is high) is very fast. Thus the average dissipation in the transistor is low.

Quantitative information furnished by the v_E-i_E and the i_C-i_E characteristics may be used as an alternative means for the analysis of the basic trigger-action circuit. The trigger-action circuit may be treated simply as a two-terminal network defined by the v_E-i_E characteristic (Fig. 12-16). This is shown graphically in Fig. 12-17, and illustrated as follows:

With the sectional linearization technique mentioned earlier, the two-terminal network may be adequately represented by a resistance R in series with a direct voltage source V. The resistances R_{I} and R_{II} and R_{III} are the slope of the linearized v_E-i_E curve in each of the three regions. The three segments of the curve intersect the v_E axis at V_1, V_2, and V_3, respectively. Analytically the v_E-i_E characteristic is represented by the expression

$$v_E = Ri_E + V \qquad (12\text{-}18)$$

which is a linear expression in each of the three regions. The general expressions for the current and the voltage in such a circuit are

$$i_E = \frac{V_{E0} - V}{R} \epsilon^{-t/RC} \tag{12-19A}$$

$$v_E = (V_{E0} - V)\epsilon^{-t/RC} + V \tag{12-19B}$$

where V_{E0} represents the initial voltage across the capacitor. Referring to the characteristic of Fig. 12-17 it is seen that in the quiescent state

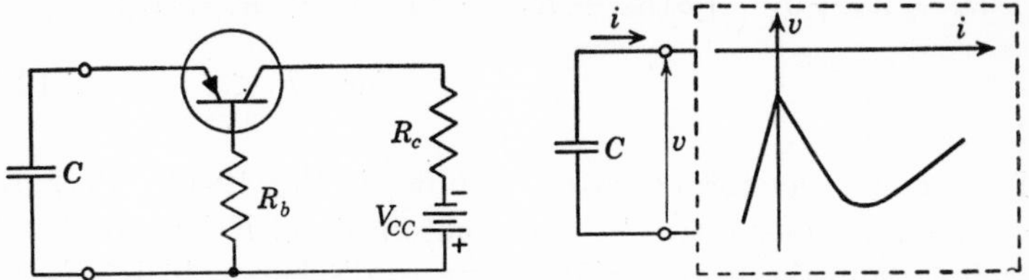

Fig. 12-16. Trigger-action circuit represented by the driving-point characteristic.

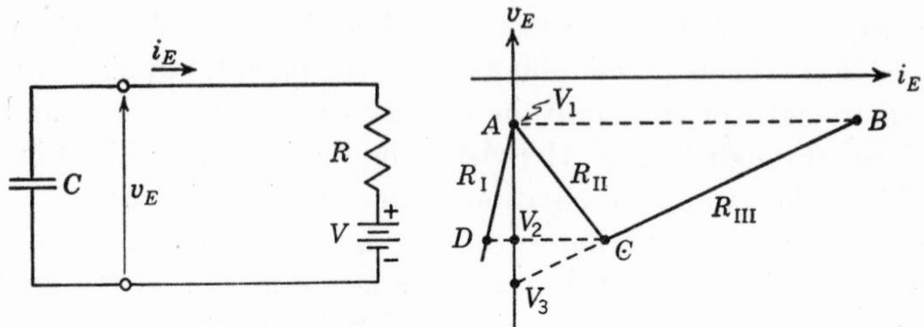

Fig. 12-17. Graphical analysis utilizing the linearized driving-point characteristic.

($t < 0$) the operating point remains at A. At $t = 0$ the operating point jumps to B, and it proceeds to move along BC while the capacitor is being charged during the interval $0 < t < T$. At $t = T$, the operating point jumps from C to D, and then proceeds to move along DA while the capacitor is being discharged for $t > T$. The excursion of the operating point produces the emitter current and voltage waveforms shown in Fig. 12-15.

Summarizing, operation through the three regions may be tabulated as in Table 12-3.

Table 12-3

Time	Region	R	V
$t < 0$	I	R_I	V_1
$t = 0$	II	R_{II}	V_1
$0 < t < T$	III	R_{III}	V_3
$t = T$	II	R_{II}	V_1
$T < t$	I	R_I	V_1

Substituting the values of R and V in Eqs. (12-19a) and (12-19b) we have

$$
\begin{aligned}
i_E &= 0 && \text{for } t < 0 \\
&= \frac{V_1 - V_3}{R_{III}} \epsilon^{-t/R_{III}C} && \text{for } 0 < t < T \qquad (12\text{-}20) \\
&= \frac{V_2 - V_1}{R_I} \epsilon^{-(t-T)/R_I C} && \text{for } T < t
\end{aligned}
$$

$$
\begin{aligned}
v_E &= V_1 && \text{for } t < 0 \\
&= (V_1 - V_3)\epsilon^{-t/R_{III}C} + V_3 && \text{for } 0 < t < T \qquad (12\text{-}21) \\
&= (V_2 - V_1)\epsilon^{-(t-T)/R_I C} + V_1 && \text{for } T < t
\end{aligned}
$$

The value of T may be readily solved by setting $v_E = V_2$ in Eq. (12-19). Thus,

$$T = \frac{1}{R_{III}C} \ln \frac{V_1 - V_3}{V_2 - V_3} \qquad (12\text{-}22)$$

The expressions for i_C may be calculated from the i_C-i_E characteristic (Fig. 12-18) as

$$
\begin{aligned}
i_C &= I_{C0} && \text{for } t < 0 \\
&= I_1 + K_{III} i_E && \text{for } 0 < t < T \qquad (12\text{-}23) \\
&= I_{C0} && \text{for } t < T
\end{aligned}
$$

where K_{III} is the slope of the i_C-i_E characteristic in Region III; the slope of the characteristic in Region I is practically zero. Thus we see that the operation of the basic monostable circuit can be completely analyzed graphically by the v_E-i_E and the i_C-i_E characteristics. Since the two characteristics can be easily obtained by point-to-point measurement or by simple cathode-ray tube display, they offer a simple means for the analysis of the operation of more complicated trigger-action circuits, where the analytical method may be lengthy and cumbersome.

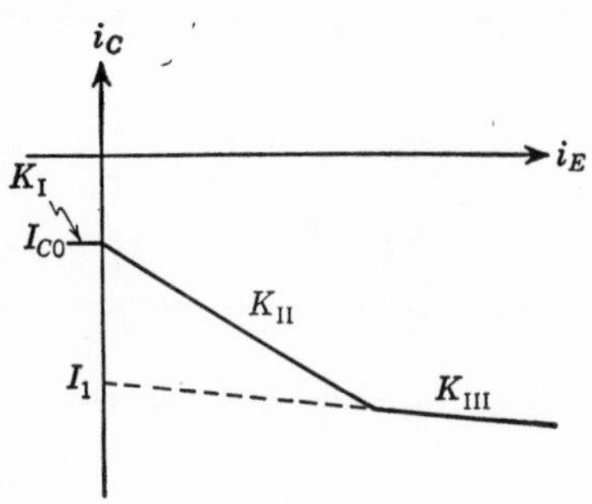

Fig. 12-18. Graphical analysis utilizing the linearized current transfer characteristic.

A convenient circuit arrangement for the display of the characteristics is shown in Fig. 12-19. A high resistance R is connected in series with the 60-cycle driving voltage V to insure that the circuit is stable in all regions. Since the emitter junction presents a high resistance in the reverse direction, a diode is included to prevent the appearance of a high voltage across the emitter junction during the

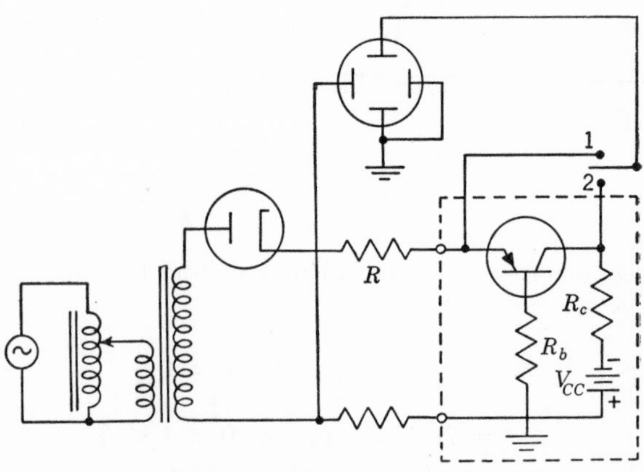

Fig. 12-19. A circuit for the display of operation characteristics.

negative half cycle of the driving voltage. The scope displays the v_E-i_E characteristics when the switch is at position 1; and it displays the i_C-i_E characteristic when the switch is in position 2.

12.6 Transmission-line control of the monostable circuit

The output pulse of the basic monostable circuit departs from an ideal rectangular pulse chiefly in the droop according to the exponential term $\epsilon^{-t/R_{11}C}$. This departure is more pronounced when R_c is small, which is the case when a high-current pulse is desired. Furthermore, the output pulse width is a function of α and r_c, which may vary from unit to unit and which are also temperature-dependent. For precise applications it is desirable to have a circuit whose output waveform is controlled by circuit parameters excluding those of the transistor. One such circuit employing a transmission line is shown in Fig. 12-20. For the following analysis let the emitter load be chosen as an open-circuited lossless line with a surge impedance of $Z_0 = R_b R_c/(R_b + R_c) \equiv R_{11}$, and of such length that the delay time t_1 is equal to $T/2$. The Laplace-transformed expression of the transmission line is[3]

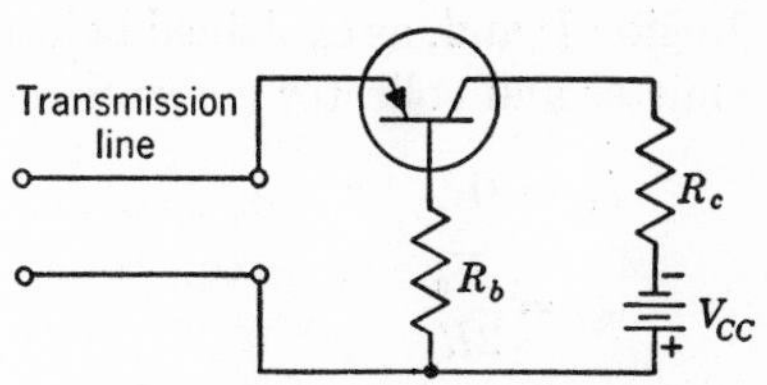

Fig. 12-20. Transmission-line controlled monostable circuit.

$$Z = Z_0 \frac{1 + \epsilon^{-2t_1 s}}{1 - \epsilon^{-2t_1 s}} = R_{11} \frac{1 + \epsilon^{sT}}{1 - \epsilon^{sT}}$$

The Laplace-transformed loop equations for the circuit are

$$0 = I_E(R_b + Z) + I_C R_b$$

$$\frac{V}{S} = -I_E R_b + I_C(R_b + R_c)$$

Solving, we have

$$i_E' = \frac{V_0}{2R_c}[U(t) - U(t - T)]$$

$$i_C' = -\frac{V_0(R_b + 2R_c)}{2(R_b + R_c)R_c} U(t) + \frac{V_0 R_b}{2(R_b + R_c)R_c} U(t - T)$$

Taking into account the initial conditions $i_{E0} = 0$ and $i_{C0} = I_{C0}$, we have

[3] S. Goldman, *Transformation Calculus and Electrical Transients*, Prentice-Hall, Inc., New York, 1949.

$$i_E = \frac{V_0}{2R_c}[U(t) - U(t - T)] \tag{12-24}$$

$$\begin{aligned} i_C = &-\frac{V_0(R_b + 2R_c)}{2(R_b + R_c)R_c}U(t) \\ &+ \frac{V_0 R_b}{2(R_b + R_c)R_c}U(t - T) - I_{C0} \end{aligned} \tag{12-25}$$

This analysis is valid only for $i_E > I_2$. Equation (12-22) shows that i_E drops to zero at $t = T$. Thus at $t = T$ the circuit triggers back into Region I; and, as explained before, i_C drops to I_{C0} for $t > T$. Thus the emitter and collector currents may be summarized as

$$\begin{aligned} i_E &= 0 && \text{for } t < 0, T < t \\ &= \frac{V_0}{2R_c} && \text{for } 0 < t < T \end{aligned} \tag{12-26}$$

$$\begin{aligned} i_C &= -I_{C0} && \text{for } t < 0, T < t \\ &= \frac{-R_b V_0}{2R_c(R_b + R_c)} - \frac{V_{CC}}{R_b + R_c} && \text{for } 0 < t < T \end{aligned} \tag{12-27}$$

From these equations it is evident that the values of i_E and i_C are constant (depending on circuit parameters only) during the time interval $0 < t < T$. The width of the current pulse is controlled solely

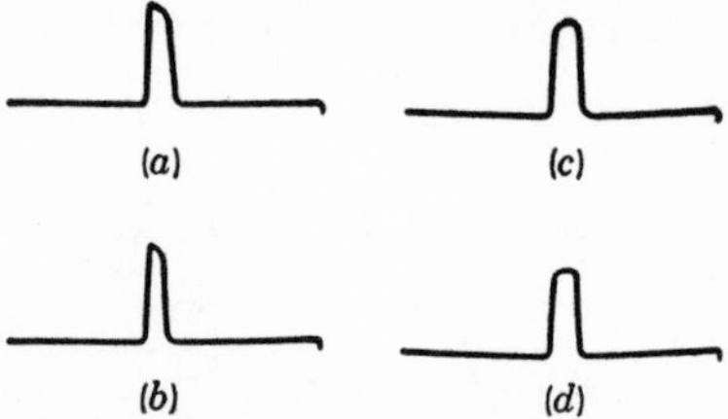

Fig. 12-21. Output waveforms of two monostable circuits: (a) condenser controlled, with transistor 1; (b) condenser controlled, with transistor 2; (c) transmission-line controlled, with transistor 1; (d) transmission-line controlled, with transistor 2.

by the transmission line, which may be precisely designed and built. The advantages of employing a transmission line instead of a capacitor as the emitter load of the basic monostable circuit is illustrated in a typical case as shown in Fig. 12-21.

12.7 Some practical monostable circuits

The basic monostable circuit may be used as a regenerative pulse amplifier with many applications. A practical pulse standardization circuit and some of the waveforms are shown in Fig. 12-22. A nega-

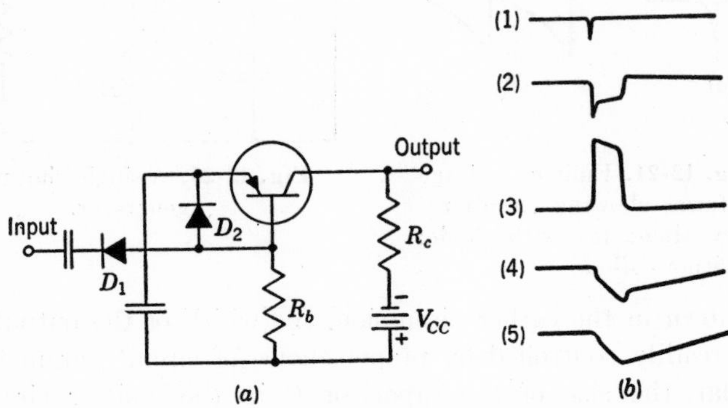

Fig. 12-22. A pulse standardization circuit: (a) circuit arrangement; (b) waveforms; (1) input pulse, (2) emitter current, (3) collect current, (4) base voltage, (5) emitter voltage.

tive triggering pulse, applied at the base of the transistor, initiates trigger action. Because of the presence of the crystal diode, D_1, the input source is isolated from the transistor circuit except for the instant when the initiation of trigger action takes place. The output pulse amplitude and width are practically independent of input pulse amplitude and width (Fig. 12-23).

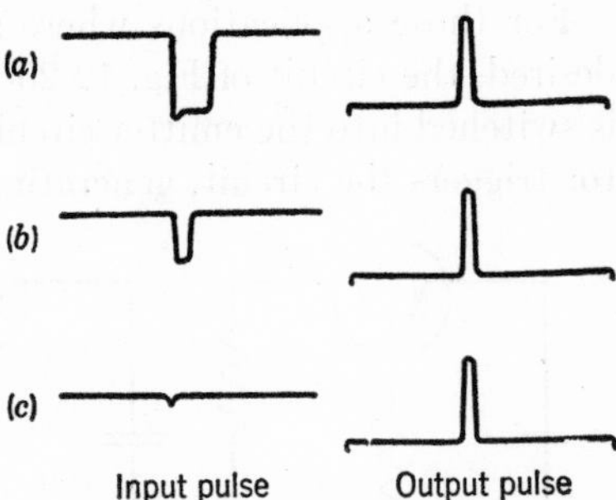

Fig. 12-23. Input and output waveforms of the pulse standardization circuit.

It is observed that after the circuit triggers from its saturation state to its cutoff state, the capacitor C starts to discharge through the internal emitter resistance r_e which is high in the cutoff state. This discharge time limits the repetition frequency at which the circuit can be operated. To reduce the discharge time, a second diode D_2 (Fig. 12-22a) is placed between emitter and collector to provide a low-impedance path for the discharge of the capacitor. The effectiveness of this measure is illustrated by the emitter voltage waveform photography of Fig. 12-24.

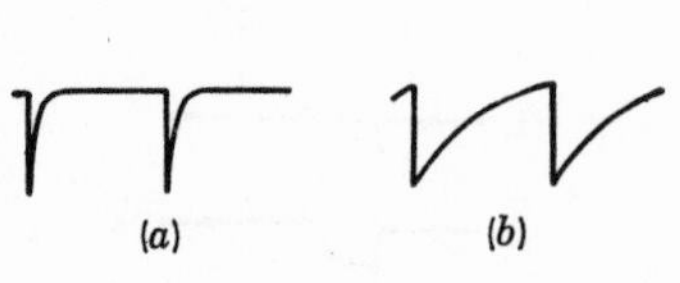

Fig. 12-24. Emitter voltage waveforms showing circuit recovery time: (a) with diode; (b) without diode.

Fig. 12-25. A single-shot pulse generator.

As shown in the earlier discussion, the width of the output pulse can be readily controlled by proper choice of circuit parameters, in particular, the size of the capacitor C in the emitter circuit. It is also possible to utilize the trailing edge of the output pulse to generate a pulse delayed from the triggering pulse by a prescribed time interval.

For those applications where a single, manually initiated pulse is desired, the circuit of Fig. 12-25 is useful. Each time the capacitor C is switched into the emitter circuit the charging current of the capacitor triggers the circuit, generating a single output pulse.

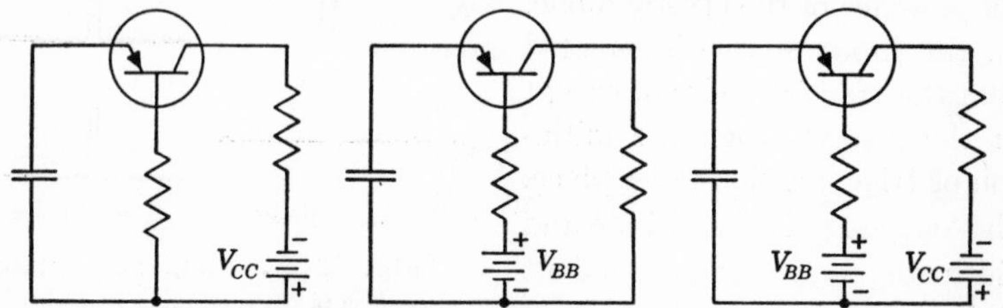

Fig. 12-26. Locations of the power-supply battery.

The power-supply voltage V_{CC} in the basic monostable circuit may be located either in the collector circuit or in the base circuit in order that the d-c level of the output may accommodate d-c coupling to associated circuits (Fig. 12-26). This will be found valuable when the monostable circuit is used to drive various d-c coupled circuits.

Frequently discrimination against spurious signals is more important than trigger sensitivity. In that event, the emitter of the transistor may be current-biased to insure that the transistor remains in its low-conduction quiescent state until a trigger pulse exceeding a prescribed level is applied. Two current-bias arrangements, and their effects on the emitter input characteristic, are shown in Fig. 12-27.

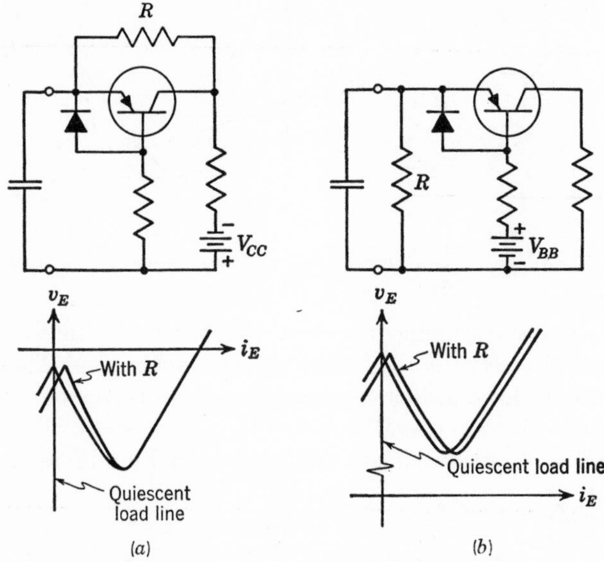

Fig. 12-27. The effect of an emitter current bias on the driving-point characteristics.

The high resistance R, in each case, allows a negative current to flow into the emitter when the transistor is in its quiescent state. The presence of the resistance has little effect on operation of the circuit when the transistor is in its active state. As mentioned earlier, a transmission line may be employed in place of the emitter capacitor for more precise control of the circuit.

In the monostable circuits mentioned above, the only reactive load is in the emitter circuit. Other arrangements, in particular an inductance or a short-circuited transmission line in the base circuit, or a capacitor or an open-circuited line in the collector circuit, may be used in various applications. The analysis of these circuits may be performed with the help of the respective driving-point characteristics and current-transfer characteristics as demonstrated before.

12.8 A basic bistable circuit

A basic bistable circuit and its operating characteristics are shown in Fig. 12-28a and 12-28b. The emitter load consists of a resistance R_e and a bias voltage V_{EE}.

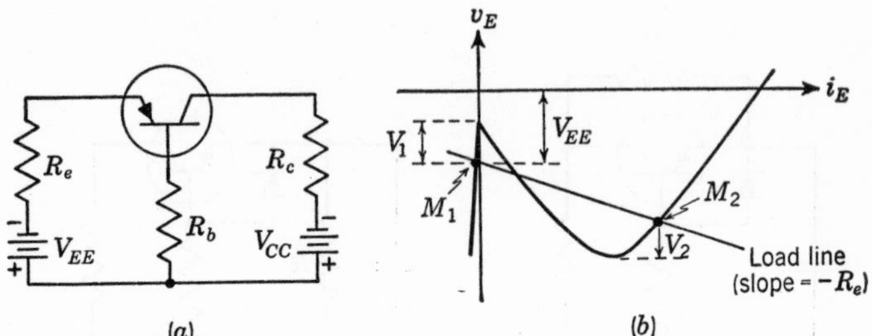

Fig. 12-28. A basic bistable circuit: (a) circuit arrangement; (b) emitter driving-point characteristic.

A fundamental requirement for bistable operation is that the emitter load line intersect the v_E-i_E curve once in each region. The circuit may stay at the low-conduction operation point M_1 (the off state), or at the high-conduction operation point M_2 (the on state). The equivalent circuits of the two states are shown in Fig. 12-29, and the

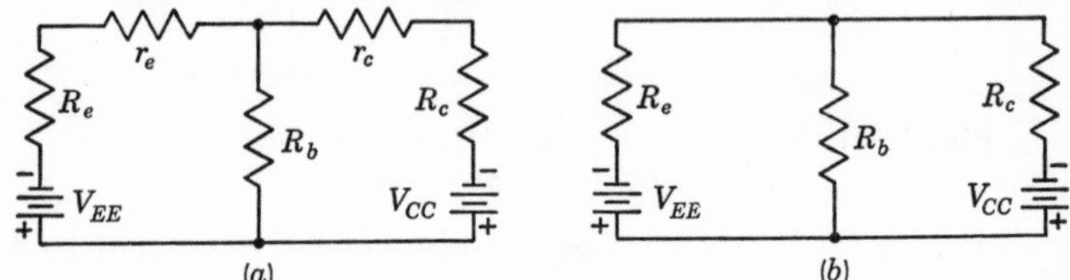

Fig. 12-29. Equivalent circuits of the basic bistable circuit: (a) cutoff state; (b) saturation state.

emitter and collector currents in either state may be computed accordingly. Referring to Fig. 12-28, a positive voltage greater than V_1 triggers the circuit from its off state to its on state, and a negative voltage greater than V_2 triggers the circuit from the on state to the off state. The values of V_1 and V_2 may be made small to favor trigger sensitivity, or they may be made fairly large to insure reliable operation in the presence of noise, temperature change, and individual differences from transistor to transistor. In practice, the chosen values of R_e and V_{EE} are a compromise between sensitivity and stability. However, the ultimate limits of the two parameters are

$$R_e < \left| \frac{R_b[R_c + r_c(1 - \alpha)]}{R_b + R_c + r_c} \right| \tag{12-28}$$

$$\frac{R_b V_{CC}}{R_b + R_c + r_c} < V_{EE} < \frac{R_b(1 - \alpha)V_{CC}}{\alpha(R_b + R_c) - R_b} \tag{12-29}$$

In other words, R_e must be smaller than the absolute value of the negative resistance, and V_{EE} must lie between the voltages of the two

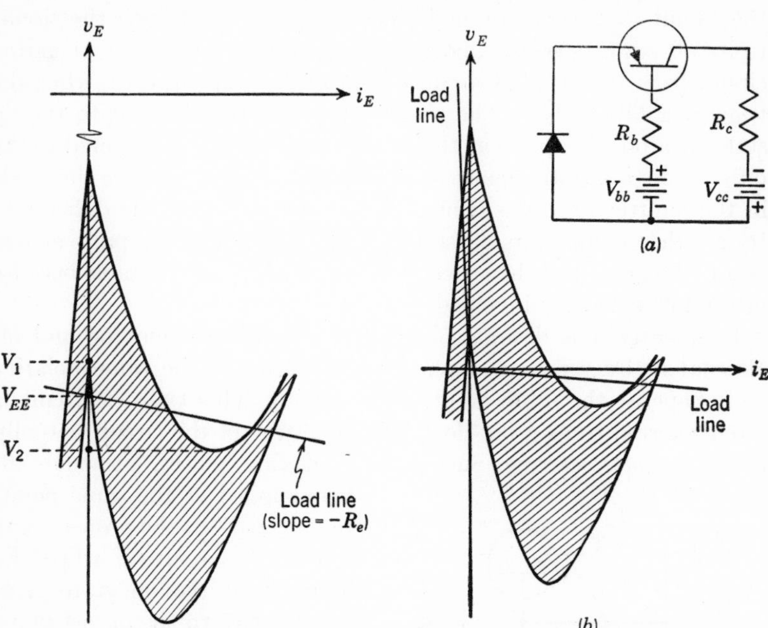

Fig. 12-30. Spreading of the emitter driving-point characteristics.

Fig. 12-31. A practical bistable circuit: (a) circuit arrangement; (b) emitter driving-point characteristic and the nonlinear load line.

turnover points. Individual transistors of the same type may exhibit considerable variation in the positioning of the $v_E - i_E$ curve, such as is shown by the spread of characteristics indicated by the shaded area of Fig. 12-30. To assure satisfaction of the three-point intersection condition, and to eliminate the relatively critical bias source V_{EE}, the circuit of Fig. 12-31a is introduced. Here the load resistor R_e is replaced by a crystal diode, and the bias source is moved to the base. The circuit parameters are so chosen that, for the majority of transistors, the center portion of the negative-resistance region of each $v_E - i_E$ curve lies on the i_E axis. The crystal diode, used as the emitter load, causes the emitter load line to have two straight portions as shown in Fig. 12-31, insuring the three-point intersection requirement for each $v_E - i_E$ curve.

The bistable circuit may be triggered at the base of the transistor as well as at the emitter. A negative pulse applied at the base will trigger the circuit to its on state; and a positive pulse will trigger the circuit to its off state. Crystal diodes may be used to isolate the triggering circuit from the bistable circuit except for the time interval when the triggering takes place. The circuit may also be triggered to the on state by a positive pulse at the emitter and it may be triggered to the off state by a negative pulse at the emitter. However, since the diode in the emitter circuit is conducting in the on state it is difficult to trigger the circuit to its off state by applying a negative pulse at this point. Triggering at the collector is possible but not desirable because of the low efficiency involved.

Frequently it is desirable to trigger a bistable circuit on and off alternately by repeated application of pulses of the same polarity and shape at the same point in the circuit. This type of circuit is often referred to as a flip-flop. The operation of the circuit actually involves *pulse steering*. Successive triggering pulses, although always applied at the same point, are "steered" to the proper point to turn the circuit off when the circuit is in the on state, and are "steered" to the proper point to turn the circuit on when the circuit is in the off state. Pulse-steering arrangements usually take advantage of the fact that the voltage at a certain point in the circuit is different in the two states. A pulse-steering circuit developed by Bangert[4] is typical of such operation. In this circuit (Fig. 12-32) a crystal diode D and a resistor R are added in the emitter circuit. In the on state the large emitter current I_{ON} develops a voltage

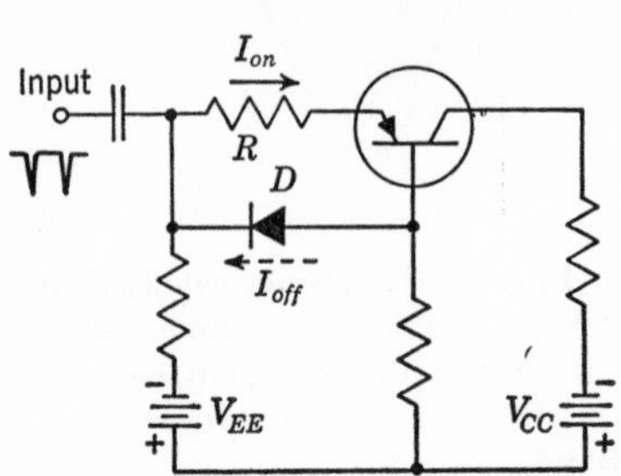

Fig. 12-32. A single-transistor flip-flop.

[4] I.R.E.-A.I.E.E. Transistor Circuit Conference, New York, 1953.

across R. This voltage biases the diode in the reverse direction. The negative input triggering pulse, blocked from going to the base by the diode, goes to the emitter through R and triggers the circuit to its off state. In the off state the emitter circuit current I_{OFF} flows through the diode in the forward direction. The input triggering pulse now goes through the diode to the base and triggers the circuit to its on state. The pulse-steering process, which depends on the small voltage difference in the two states, may be quite critical in practical operation.

12.9 Twin-transistor bistable circuits

An earlier bistable circuit developed by Trent[5] employs two transistors instead of one. The circuit arrangement follows closely the pattern of the vacuum tube Eccles-Jordan circuit. However, unlike the vacuum tube circuit, either half of the circuit possesses trigger-action property as in the single transistor trigger circuits. A simplified

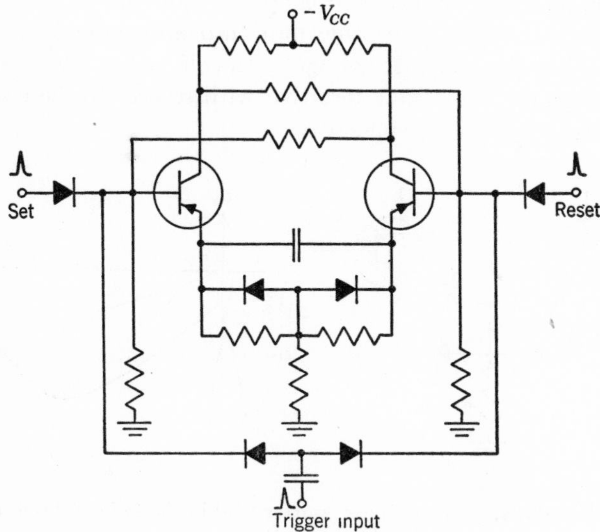

Fig. 12-33. A twin-transistor bistable circuit.

version of the circuit is shown in Fig. 12-33. Certain features of this circuit will be discussed here in detail to illustrate design technique.

[5] R. T. Trent, "A Transistor Reversible Binary Counter," *Proc. I.R.E.*, Vol. 40, Nov. 1952.

1. *Lock-in arrangement.* Similar to vacuum tube Eccles-Jordan circuits, the transistor in the on state helps to hold the other transistor in its off state, and vice versa. This lock-in feature is provided by the common emitter resistance R_e and the collector-to-base cross-coupling resistances R_1 and R_2 as shown in Fig. 12-34. The emitter current of the on unit develops a voltage drop across R_e (with polarity as shown) which biases the emitter of the other unit negative with respect to the base to hold the unit in the off state. Furthermore, the collector voltage of the off unit is more negative than that of the on unit. The collector potential of one unit is coupled to the base of the other unit through coupling resistors R_1 and R_2. Thus the collector voltage of the off unit tends to keep the base voltage of the on unit negative with respect to the emitter to assure its operation in the on state.

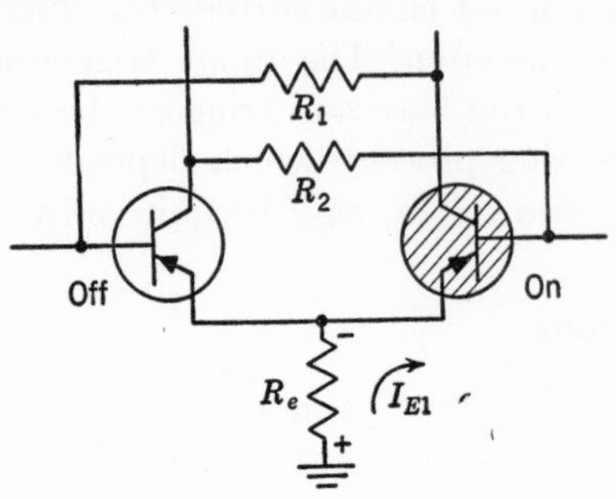

Fig. 12-34. The lock-in feature of the twin-transistor bistable circuit.

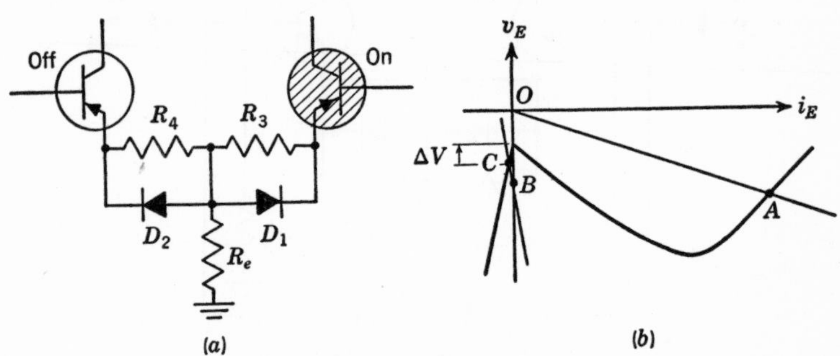

Fig. 12-35. The nonlinear emitter load in the twin-transistor bistable circuit.

2. *Nonlinear emitter load.* Two crystal diodes are included in the emitter circuit to give different load lines for the on unit and the off unit. Referring to Fig. 12-35, the emitter load line of the on unit is represented by the line OA, which represents the load resistance con-

sisting of R_e and the small forward resistance of the crystal diode. The load line of the off unit is represented by the line BC. Here OB represents the voltage developed across R_e by the emitter current of the on unit. The slope of the line BC is the reverse resistance of D_2 and R_4 in parallel. A triggering voltage greater than ΔV is required to trigger the off unit to the on state and thus reverse the states of the two units. Trigger sensitivity may be controlled by varying the value of R_4. The circuit design always involves a compromise between sensitivity and reliability, of course.

3. *Input pulse steering*. The base voltage of the on unit is more negative than that of the off unit. A pair of crystal diodes is used in the input circuit to steer the input pulse to the proper point. As shown in Fig. 12-36, the two diodes are biased automatically by the base voltage in such a way that the positive input pulse is steered to the

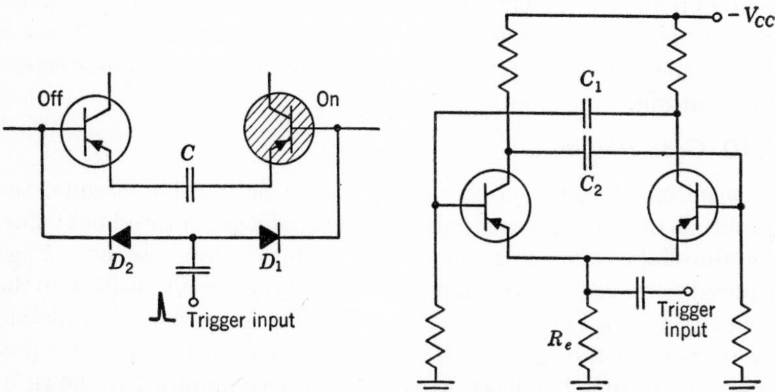

Fig. 12-36. The input pulse steering arrangement in the twin-transistor bistable circuit.

Fig. 12-37. A simplified twin-transistor bistable circuit.

base of the on unit. This tends to trigger the on unit to its off state. Furthermore, the low base-to-emitter impedance of the on unit passes the positive input pulse through C to the emitter of the off unit. This tends to turn the off unit to its on state.

Another version of the twin-transistor bistable circuit is shown in Fig. 12-37. *Lock-in* is accomplished solely by the common emitter resistance R_e. The arrival of a negative pulse at the common emitter junction turns both units off momentarily. The collector voltage of the on unit now undergoes a sudden change to a more negative value. This change of voltage sends a negative pulse through the cross-coupling capacitor to the base of the off unit and turns that unit on. Thus the on and off units remain reversed in the circuit until the arrival of the next input pulse. Simplicity is achieved in this circuit at the expense of the maximum repetition frequency and reliability.

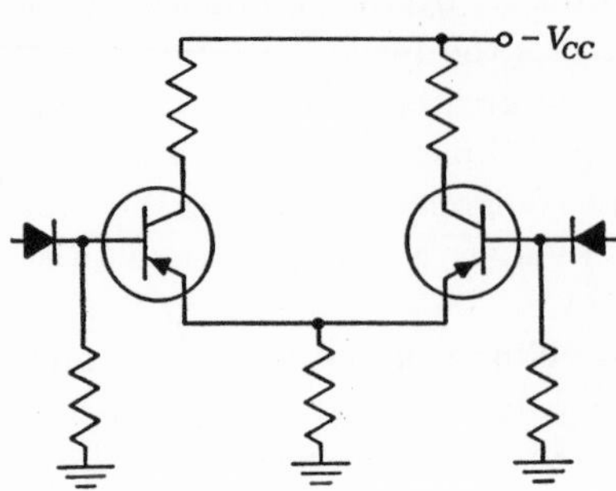

Fig. 12-38. A twin-transistor one-bit register.

With the cross-coupling capacitors removed, the circuit operates as a one-bit register (Fig. 12-38). Although two transistors are required, the circuit can achieve a high degree of reliability that is difficult for the single-transistor circuit to attain.

12.10 Gate circuits

To initiate trigger action in monostable or bistable circuits, the amplitude of the triggering pulse must exceed a given threshold value. The threshold value, as a function of the bias voltage, is the voltage required to move the operation point from its quiescent position to the turnover point. Thus the bias may act as a gate control to dictate whether or not the circuit will respond to a triggering pulse of a prescribed amplitude.[6] A basic gated regenerative amplifier is shown in Fig. 12-39. In this circuit the emitter is biased by the gate control voltage, which may be derived from a bistable circuit supplying either a voltage V_1 or a voltage V_2, depending on the state of the bistable circuit, so that the stable operation point is either at P_1 or at P_2 of the characteristic. The input pulse is of such amplitude that the circuit can be triggered into high conduction if the emitter is biased at P_1, but not while it is biased at P_2. The diode in the base circuit stabilizes the position of the first turnover point against changes of transistor parameters due to temperature, etc. Such stabilization

[6] R. T. Trent, *op. cit.*

techniques in trigger action circuits are important in practice, and they will be discussed in detail in the next section. With diode stabilization, the circuit shown in Fig. 12-39 can tolerate considerable variation in the amplitude of the triggering pulse.

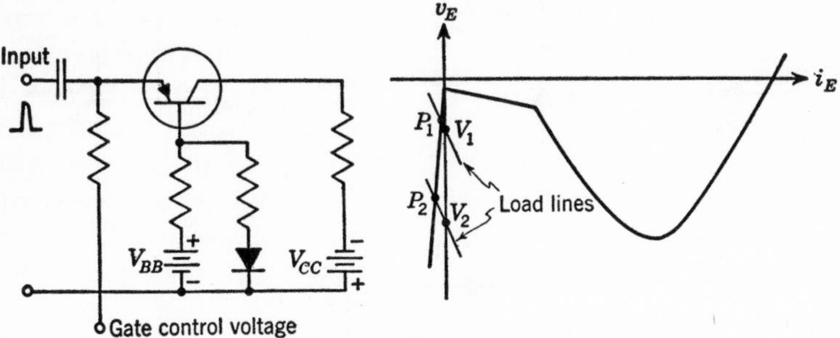

Fig. 12-39. A gated regenerative amplifier.

More elaborate circuits may be formed by associating diode logic circuits with monostable circuits, as shown in Fig. 12-40. Figure 12-40a shows a logical "or" circuit with three input terminals. In the quiescent condition diodes D_4 and D_5 are conducting, holding the emitter at a potential $-V_2$, which leaves the transistor in the cutoff state. A positive input pulse at any terminal, 1, 2, or 3, triggers the circuit into high conduction by raising the potential at A to cut off D_4, permitting the emitter potential to rise toward V_1. Figure 12-40b shows a logical "and" circuit. In the quiescent state D_1, D_2, D_3, as well as D_4, are conducting, thus holding the emitter potential at $-V_2$. Only when all three diodes D_1, D_2, and D_3 are cut off, by applying a positive input voltage to each of the three input terminals simultaneously, can the emitter voltage rise and trigger the circuit into high conduction. Figure 12-40c shows a two-input logical "and" gate with an "inhibition" gate. Without an input at the inhibition terminal 3, the circuit behaves as an "and" gate. With a negative input voltage at the inhibition terminal, the diode D_3 conducts, holding the emitter voltage at $-V_2$ even in the presence of positive pulses at Terminal 1 and Terminal 2. In these three circuits the diode arrangements perform the logic function, while the transistor operates as a regenerative amplifier providing power gain and good signal-to-noise discrimination. The amplitude of the input pulses are not critical so long as they exceed a cer-

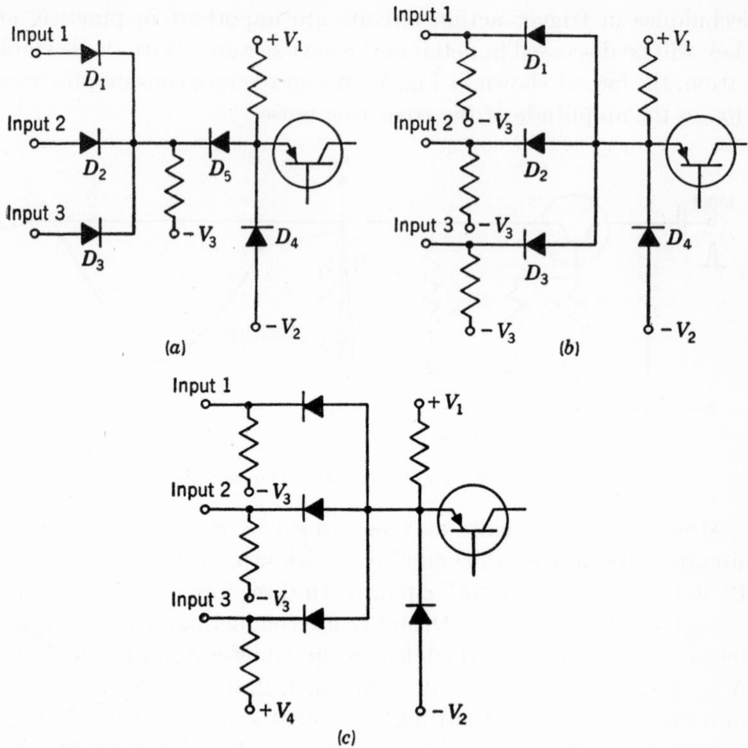

Fig. 12-40. Diode logic circuits: (a) "or" gate; (b) "and" gate; (c) "inhibition" gate.

tain minimum value corresponding to the choice of the diode bias voltages.

12.11 Stabilization of the d-c operating point

In trigger-action circuits, sufficient changes in the d-c operating point, as the result of a change of transistor parameters due to temperature variation or other effects, may render the circuit inoperative. As mentioned earlier, the mode of operation of trigger-action circuits is dictated primarily by the driving-point characteristic. Thus it is important that the characteristic remain unchanged throughout the entire period of operation. While the burden for the solution of this problem lies chiefly in the development of transistors of more uniform and stable characteristics, still certain circuit techniques may be employed to minimize the effects of such changes.

The increase of ambient temperature affects the parameters of a point-contact transistor principally by a decrease of r_c (most significantly shown in the increase of I_{C0}) and the increase of α (especially near saturation). A small-signal measurement of r_c and α in the linear active region as a function of temperature is shown in Fig. 12-41. Other transistor parameters are also affected by temperature variations; r_e and r_b, for example, vary inversely as temperature, but not nearly so much as r_c. The emitter driving-point characteristic of a typical trigger-action circuit under three different ambient temperature conditions is shown in Fig. 12-42. The position of the turnover

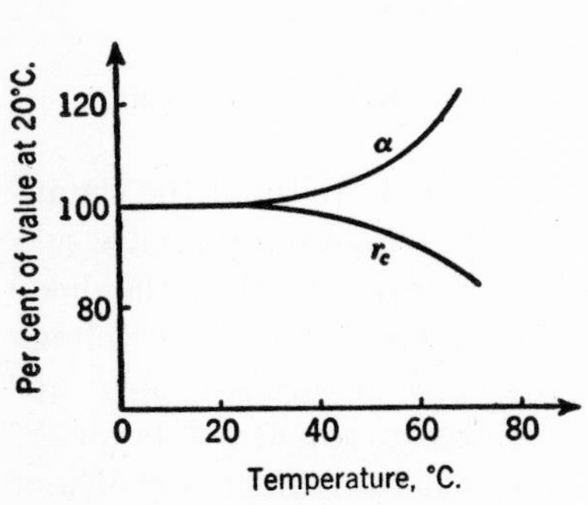

Fig. 12-41. Variations of α and r_c with temperature.

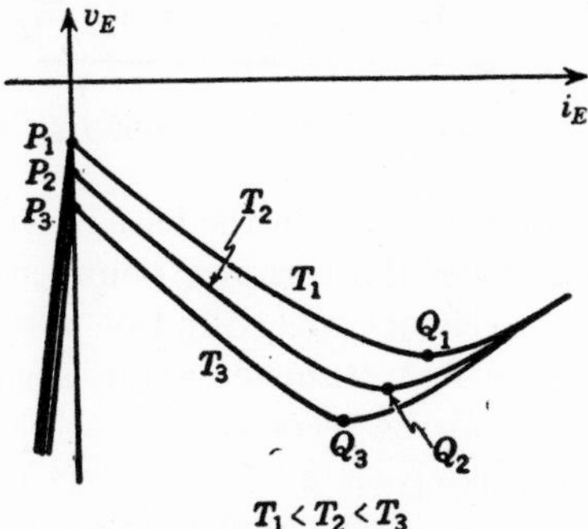

Fig. 12-42. Temperature effect on the emitter driving-point characteristic of a typical trigger-action circuit.

points P and Q, which define the operating regions, together with the load line, determines whether the transistor is in the cutoff state, the saturation state, or the transition state. Hence a prime concern in the design of trigger-action circuits is the stabilization of these turnover points.

Aging may result, in some transistors, in a reduction of both r_c and α. Some transistors also show marked deterioration of characteristics during shelf life, which may be as significant as changes occurring during operation. And finally, one must consider the initial spread in characteristics of quantity produced transistors. Circuit design must allow for characteristics changes as a consequence of all these effects to insure reliable operation.

The well-established technique of *diode clamping* employed in the stabilization of vacuum tube pulse circuits is equally applicable to transistor pulse circuits. As an example, in Fig. 12-43 the effect of

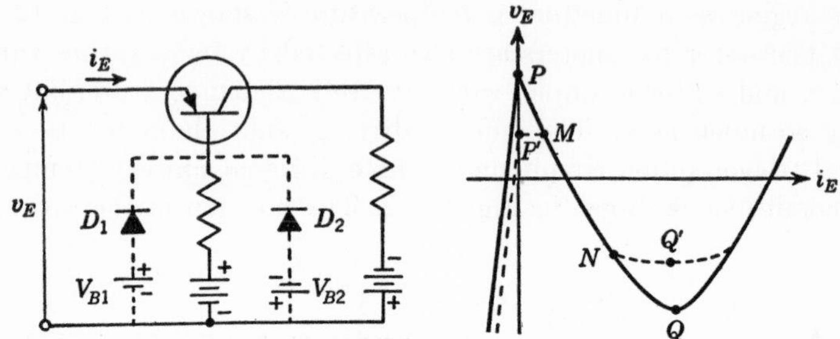

Fig. 12-43. Stabilization by clamping diodes in the base circuit.

clamping diodes in the base circuit is illustrated. Without the clamping diodes the turnover points are P and Q, whose positions are subject to change with variation of transistor parameters. With the diode D_1 the first turnover point is clamped approximately at a voltage V_{B1}; and the second diode D_2 clamps the second turnover point approximately at a voltage V_{B2}. The stabilized turnover points are P' and Q' as shown in the figure. To insure that the segments $P'M$ and NQ' have negative slopes, some resistance may be added in series with the diodes if their forward resistances are not large enough.

In practical circuits, diodes are employed extensively in the emitter and collector circuits, as well as in the base circuit, to serve as voltage or current limiters.[7] This form of stabilization enables the circuits to perform reliably without overrigid selection of transistors and other circuit components.

The linear load line for the basic trigger-action circuit may also be modified to meet specific requirements. The load line for the more simple circuits is usually established by a resistance in series with a bias voltage. In order to insure intersection of the load line at specific points of the driving-point characteristic, diode arrangements may be

[7] F. C. Williams and G. B. B. Chaplin, "A Method of Designing Transistor Trigger Circuits," *Proc. Inst. Elec. Engrs.*, Part III, Vol. 100, pp. 228–247, July 1953.

employed to constitute a *nonlinear load line*. Figure 12-44a shows the ordinary linear load line. In Fig. 12-44b a single diode is employed as an emitter load. The merit of this arrangement has been illustrated in Sec. 12.8. The circuit arrangement shown in Fig. 12-44c offers more flexibility with the employment of R and the biasing voltages V_1 and V_2 as well as the diode. In Fig. 12-44d the load line is so arranged that the intersections with the driving-point characteristic take place in the cutoff region and the transition region, but not in

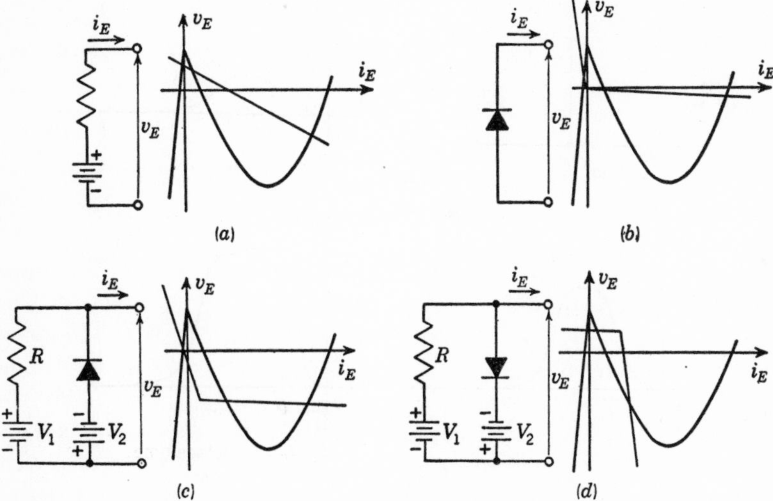

Fig. 12-44. Linear and nonlinear load lines.

the saturation region. The significance of this arrangement will be discussed in Sec. 12.18.

12.12 Transient behavior of point-contact transistors

Up to this point in this chapter the point-contact transistor has been treated as a purely resistive active element. This approximation, although invaluable in illustrating the operation principles of most pulse circuits, does not present a complete picture of the performance of such circuits where transient behavior is an important factor. A more exact representation of the point-contact transistor and the operation of the associated circuits is presented in this and the following sections.

The frequency response of a point-contact transistor, expressed usually in the form of gain-versus-frequency relations, may be obtained by the ordinary small-signal measurements. In pulse circuits, however, the response to an ideal rectangular pulse describes the performance of the transistor in these circuits more directly. For such an investigation, the simple circuit shown in Fig. 12-45a is taken as an example. The input signal at the emitter is a constant-current rectangular pulse (i.e., a voltage pulse in series with a high resistance), and the output signal is taken from a low resistance in the collector circuit. Figure 12-45b shows the response of the transistor to a small input current pulse. In Fig. 12-45c the magnitude of the input current pulse is chosen to be of such value that the transistor is driven close to saturation. In Fig. 12-45d the transistor is driven deep into saturation by a very large input current pulse. The output waveforms display the following important details: (a) *time delay*, t_d, (b) *rise time*, t_r, (c) *decay time*, t_f, and (d) *storage effect* (the persistence of the output waveform for a duration of time after the termination of the input pulse as shown in Fig. 12-45d), which we shall discuss in detail.

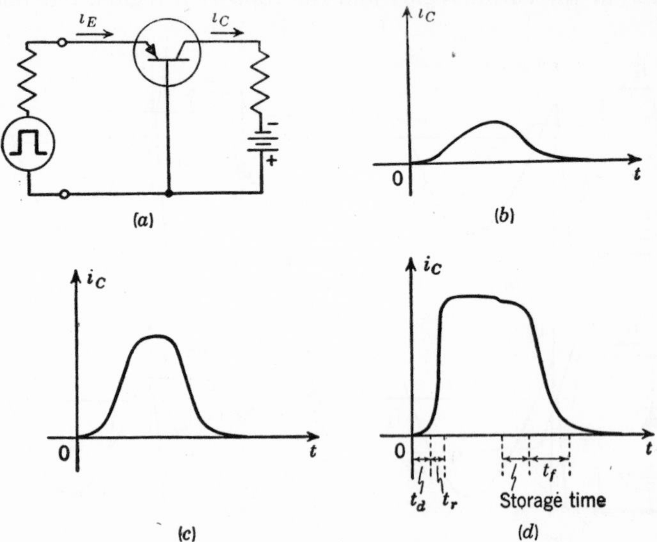

Fig. 12-45. Transient response of a point-contact transistor to a rectangular current pulse.

As explained in Chapter 1, the rise of the collector current in a point-contact transistor is the result of the presence of minority carriers (holes injected at the emitter for n-type material) in the immediate neighborhood of the collector. These minority carriers take a finite length of time to travel from the emitter to the collector, and account for the time delay t_d of the output pulse with respect to the input pulse. All minority carriers do not take the same path in traveling from the emitter to the collector because of the geometry of the transistor and the collisions the minority carriers suffer in traveling through the germanium crystal. Thus all the minority carriers injected into the emitter at the initiation of the input pulse do not arrive at the collector at the same time, but rather arrive spread out over a period of time. This accounts for the rise time. The same reasoning explains the decay time of the output waveform. The *apparent* rise time is improved if the transistor is allowed to be driven to saturation by a large input current. The very short rise time of most trigger-action circuits may be accounted for as the result of overdriven emitter current provided by positive feedback in the circuit.

It is noted that for a large input drive current (Fig. 12-45d) the output current remains at its saturation value for an appreciable time after the termination of the input pulse. This phenomenon is due to the storage of minority carriers in the germanium crystal. The low collector voltage during the saturation state emphasizes the storage effect. Under these conditions a relatively long time is required for the weak electric field in the germanium crystal to sweep the stored minority carriers out of the transistor. The amount of minority carrier storage in the germanium is a function of the magnitude of the input current as well as of the time that the transistor is in the saturation state. The minority carrier storage phenomenon, which imposes a lower limit on the time required for the transistor to return from its saturation state to its cutoff state and which also imposes a more stringent triggering requirement, constitutes a problem of primary importance in the high-speed operation of transistor pulse circuits.

12.13 High-frequency equivalent circuit of the point-contact transistor

The complicated operation mechanism of the point-contact transistor makes it difficult to formulate an elaborate high-frequency equivalent circuit. For many practical applications, however, the low-frequency equivalent circuit may be extended to cover high-frequency operation. Experimental results reveal that all the T equivalent circuit parameters, with the exception of α, are relatively independent of frequency. The value of α on the other hand appears to be a function of frequency in the manner,

$$\alpha = \frac{\alpha_0}{1 + j(f/f_c)} \tag{12-30}$$

where α_0 is the value of α at low frequency, and f_c is the frequency at which the value of α drops 3 db from its low-frequency value. For convenience, the expression may be written in the form,

$$\alpha = \frac{\alpha_0}{1 + \tau s} \tag{12-31}$$

where s is the complex angular frequency, and τ, the transistor time constant, is defined by $\tau \equiv 1/2\pi f_c$. Thus the low-frequency equivalent circuit may be extended to cover high-frequency operation by simply imposing the stipulation that α, instead of being a real constant as in the low-frequency case, is a complex function of frequency defined by Eq. (12-30), and illustrated in Fig. 12-46. For the more common point-contact transistors the cut-off frequency f_c ranges from 2 megacycles for general purpose units to 50 megacycles for high-frequency units.

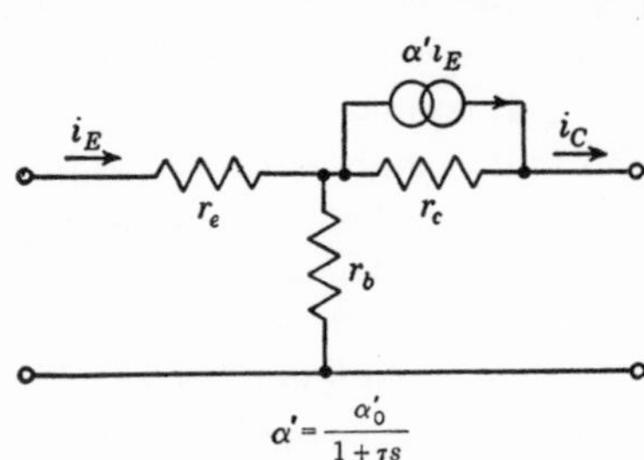

Fig. 12-46. High-frequency equivalent circuit of the point-contact transistor.

The response of the transistor to a step function input current may be readily derived from the simple equivalent circuit of Fig. 12-46 as

$$i_C = \frac{\alpha r_c(1 - \epsilon^{-t/\tau}) + r_b}{R_c + r_c + r_b} I_E$$

Since we are only interested in linear operation in the active region where $r_b \ll r_c$, we have

$$\begin{aligned} i_c &\approx [\alpha r_c I_E/(R_b + r_c)](1 - \epsilon^{-t/\tau}) \\ &= \text{low-frequency amplification} \times (1 - \epsilon^{-t/\tau}). \end{aligned}$$

This expression, based on the simple equivalent circuits, shows the rise time of the output current as a function of the frequency response of the transistor. A more elaborate equivalent circuit, however, is required to show qualitatively the minority carrier storage effect.

As discussed earlier, the highly nonlinear characteristic of the transistor in large-signal operation may be represented by sectionalized linearization; i.e., a linear equivalent circuit for each of the three distinct regions. The frequency response of the transistor is different for the three regions. In the cutoff region the current generator, which is considered to be the sole parameter introducing the reactive components in the transistor, does not appear in the equivalent circuit. Thus the circuit is still purely resistive in this region. In the active region the current generator is a function of complex frequency with a time constant τ as expressed in Eq. (12-31). The value of τ ranges from 0.01 to 0.1 μsec for the more common point-contact transistors. In the saturation region, experimental results reveal that the transistor is highly reactive, much of this reactance being contributed by the minority carrier storage effect. To a certain extent, the situation may be represented by assigning a large value of τ to the current generator in this region. For clear distinction we shall call the time constant in the saturation region τ_s. In the commonly used point-contact transistors τ_s may be as high as 10 μsec.

12.14 Stability criterion of trigger-action circuits

In Sec. 12.4, where the point-contact transistor was treated as a purely resistive active element, the trigger-action circuit is considered

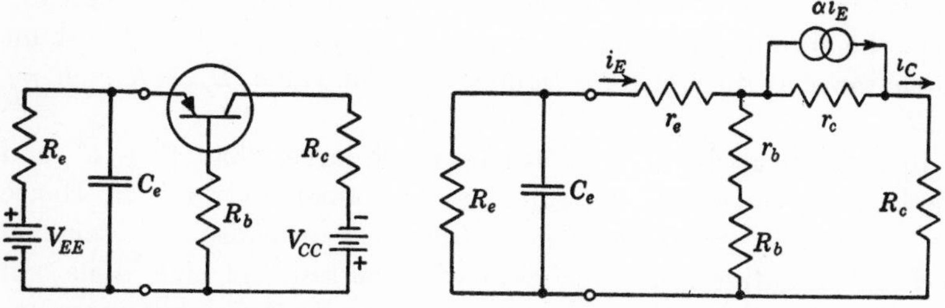

Fig. 12-47. Stability criterion of a basic trigger-action circuit.

to be stable when the operation point lies in the positive-resistance region of the driving-point characteristic, and is considered unstable when the operation point is in the negative-resistance region. Now that the transistor can no longer be treated as a frequency-independent element, the stability criterion also must be revised.

As an illustrative example we shall examine the case of a basic trigger-action circuit with an emitter load consisting of a resistance in parallel with a capacitance (Fig. 12-47). In practice, the resistance R_e represents a high resistance in series with the emitter bias V_{EE} to provide the emitter bias current; and the capacitance C_e represents the distributed stray capacitance plus any intentionally connected capacitance at the emitter. Solving for the condition of stability in the usual manner,[8] the characteristic equation of the circuit reads

$$S^2 + \frac{R_e RC + (R_e + R + R')\tau}{(R + R')R_e C_e \tau} S + \frac{R_e + R}{(R + R')R_e C_e \tau} = 0$$

where
$$R \equiv r_e + (R_b + r_b) \frac{[R_c + r_c(1 - \alpha_0)]}{R_b + r_b + R_c + r_c}$$

$$R' \equiv \frac{(R_b + r_b) r_c \alpha_0}{R_b + r_b + R_c + r_c}$$

The conditions that the characteristic equation may not have positive roots are

$$R_e > -R, \quad \text{and} \quad C_e < \frac{R_e + R + R'}{R_e R} \tau \qquad (12\text{-}32)$$

The following conclusions may be derived from the analysis:

1. The circuit is unconditionally stable if the d-c operating point lies in the positive resistance region of the driving point characteristic.

2. If the d-c operating point lies in the negative resistance region the circuit is stable if (a) the resistance of the emitter load is greater than the absolute value of the negative resistance; *and* (b) the shunt capacitance at the emitter is smaller than the value $(R_e + R + R')\tau / R_e R$.

In a practical circuit R_e is usually much larger than $R + R'$, and the limiting value of C_e for stability is approximately $\tau / -R$. Hence we find that a transistor of good frequency response (i.e., small τ) and high negative resistance (primarily the result of high alpha and large base feedback resistance) tends to make the circuit more unstable when operated in the negative-resistance region. For an ideal transistor with perfect frequency response (i.e., a purely resistive active element as we assumed earlier in this chapter) the circuit

[8] M. F. Gardner and J. L. Barnes, *Transients in Linear Systems*, John Wiley & Sons, Inc., New York, 1942, p. 197.

should always be unstable when operated in the negative-resistance region, since shunting capacitance at the emitter can never be eliminated entirely.

12.15 The emitter driving-point characteristic at high frequency

In Sec. 12.4 the d-c emitter driving-point characteristic was represented as

$$v_E = \left[r_e + \frac{(R_b + r_b)[R_c + r_c(1 - \alpha)]}{R_b + r_b + R_c + r_c} \right] i_E - \frac{R_b + r_b}{R_b + r_b + R_c + r_c} V_{CC} \qquad (12\text{-}1)$$

and which was also written in the abbreviated form,

$$v_E = Ri_E + V \qquad (12\text{–}18)$$

as a sectionalized linear expression, with one set of values of R and V for each of the three linear regions.

To extend the expression to include high-frequency operation, by substituting $\alpha_0/(1 + \tau s)$ for α, the expression becomes

$$v_E = \left[\frac{(R_b + r_b) r_c \tau s \alpha_0/(1 + \tau s)}{R_b + r_b + R_c + r_c} \right] i_E + \left\{ r_e + \frac{(R_b + r_b)[R_c + r_c(1 - \alpha_0)]}{R_b + r_b + R_c + r_c} \right\} i_E + \frac{R_b + r_b}{R_b + r_b + r_c + R_c} V_{CC} \qquad (12\text{-}33)$$

or in the abbreviated form,

$$v_E = R' \frac{\tau s}{1 + \tau s} i_E + Ri_E + V \qquad (12\text{-}34)$$

where $$R' \equiv \frac{(R_b + r_b) r_c \alpha_0}{R_b + r_b + R_c + r_c}$$

and R and V bear the same meanings as in Eq. (12-18).

In terms of network representation the term $R'\tau s/(1 + \tau s)$ may be interpreted as a parallel comination of a resistance R' and an inductance L', following the relation,

$$\tau = \frac{L'}{R'} \qquad (12\text{-}35)$$

The emitter driving point impedance may thus be represented by the two-terminal network shown in Fig. 12-48. This circuit, of course, is not an equivalent circuit of the entire trigger action circuit. It represents only the impedance looking into the emitter terminal, showing the physical significance of the frequency response of the transistor. The stability criterion shown in the last section, however, may be readily derived from this equivalent network.

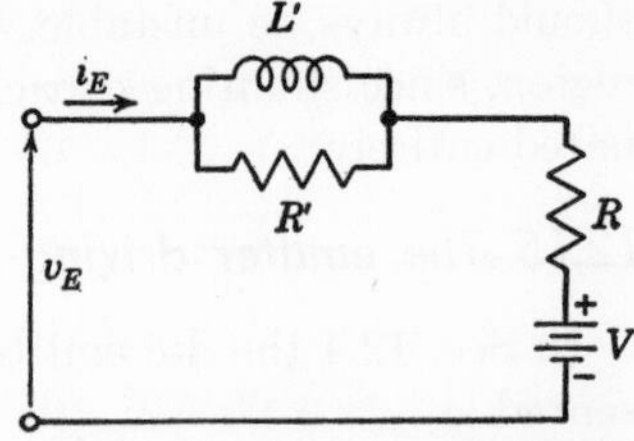

Fig. 12-48. Equivalent network of the emitter driving-point impedance.

12.16 Switching requirements of the basic bistable circuit

In cases where the frequency response of the transistor cannot be overlooked (as in high-speed operation) the requirements placed on the triggering pulse are more involved than those set forth in Sec. 12.10. This problem was studied in detail by Carlson,[9] LeBow, Baker, and McMahon[10] in the design of high-speed switching circuits. The analysis of LeBow *et al.* is presented here in condensed form to illustrate the significance of triggering requirements.

The static large-signal equivalent circuit, recommended by Adler[11] is extended to include high-frequency operation by substituting for the static current generator $\alpha' i_E$ the expression $\alpha_0' i_G$, where

$$i_E = \tau \frac{di_G}{dt} + i_G \tag{12-36}$$

This manipulation inserts the frequency dependence of the transistor into the current i_G and maintains a frequency-independent α_0'. As defined earlier, the transistor is considered to be in the off state when the emitter diode is biased in the reverse direction; and it is considered to be in the on state when the collector diode is conducting in the forward direction (Fig. 12-49).

[9] A. W. Carlson, "A Discussion of Switching in Point-Contact Transistors," *Air Force Cambridge Research Center Report*, 1953.

[10] I. L. LeBow, R. H. Baker, and R. E. McMahon, "The Transient Response of Transistor Switching Circuits," *Technical Report 27*, Lincoln Laboratory, M.I.T., July 1953.

[11] R. B. Adler, *op. cit.*

Referring to the basic trigger-action circuit in Fig. 12-50, consider the circuit to be triggered from the off state to the on state by the application of a triggering voltage at the emitter, which is a step function of amplitude V_t initiated at the time $t = 0$. Since the circuit is considered to be purely resistive in the cutoff region, the triggering voltage will bring the transistor to the active region at the instant $t = 0$. The switching is assumed to be fully initiated when the collector diode begins to conduct in the forward direction; say at a time $t = T_1$; although it still takes some time for the operating point to reach a quiescent stable point in the saturation region. During the time interval $0 < t < T_1$ the operation of the transistor is confined to the active region, and the analysis can be carried out with reference to the linear equivalent circuit of the active region.

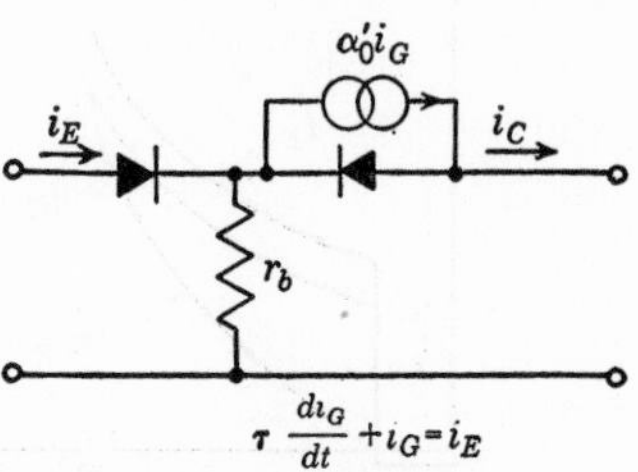

Fig. 12-49. Equivalent circuit of a point-contact transistor in large-signal high-frequency operation.

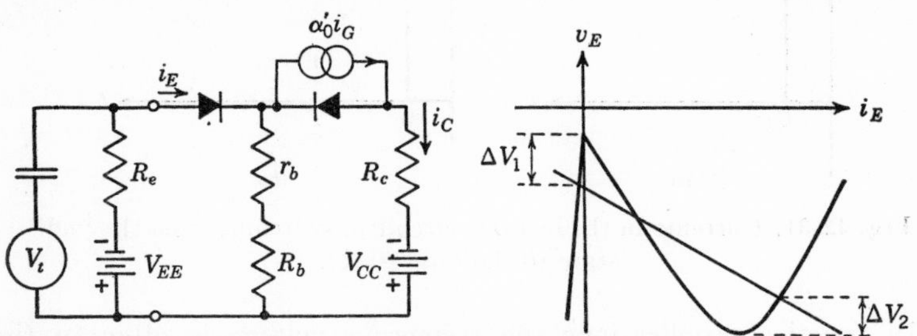

Fig. 12-50. Triggering a bistable circuit at the emitter.

The analysis reveals that the emitter current i_E, the collector current i_C, and the generator current $\alpha_0' i_G$, as a result of the application of the triggering voltage, are functions of time as shown in Fig. 12-51a. It is to be noted that both i_E and i_C take sudden jumps at $t = 0$ and then increase exponentially with time. The generator current $\alpha_0 i_g$, because of the reactive nature of the transistor, does not have the sudden jump, but rather increases exponentially with time from its zero value. At a time T_1, the generator current becomes equal to the collector current. At this time the collector diode begins to conduct in the forward direction, and the transistor is considered to be switched to its on state. The required switching time T_1 is a function of the amplitude of the triggering voltage V_t as well as of the transistor parameters. Effectively, the switching time is proportional to the time constant τ, and decreases with the increase of the triggering voltage and the negative resistance of the circuit.

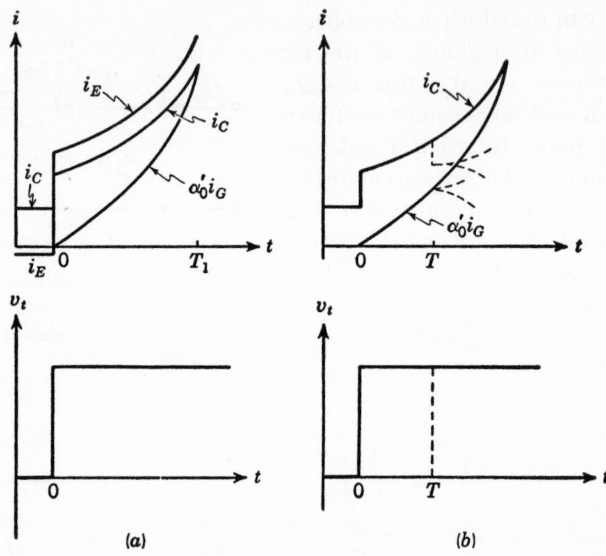

Fig. 12-51. Currents in the bistable circuit in switching from the "off" state to the "on" state.

In practical applications the triggering voltage is often in the form of a pulse which lasts for a duration shorter than the required switching time. Assume the triggering signal to be a rectangular voltage pulse of amplitude V_t and duration T, where $T < T_1$. For the time interval $0 < t < T$ the currents increase with time in the same manner as shown in Fig. 12-51a.[12] At $t = T$, the termination of the triggering pulse causes the collector current to take a sudden drop (Fig. 12-51b). Then both the collector current i_C and the generator current $\alpha_0' i_G$ either increase with time at a slower rate and complete the switching at a later time, or both currents start

[12] Figures 12-51 and 12-52 were taken from the report by LeBow, Baker, and McMahon, *op. cit.*

to decrease with time and return the transistor to its off state. For each value of V_t and for each value of the transistor parameters there is a minimum time duration for the triggering pulse; pulse widths below this time minimum will not assure switching. A plot of minimum pulse amplitude versus pulse duration for successfully switching a typical circuit from off to on is shown in Fig. 12-51a. For large values of pulse duration, the minimum pulse amplitude approaches that of the static value ΔV_1. As the pulse duration approaches zero the minimum pulse amplitude approaches infinity.

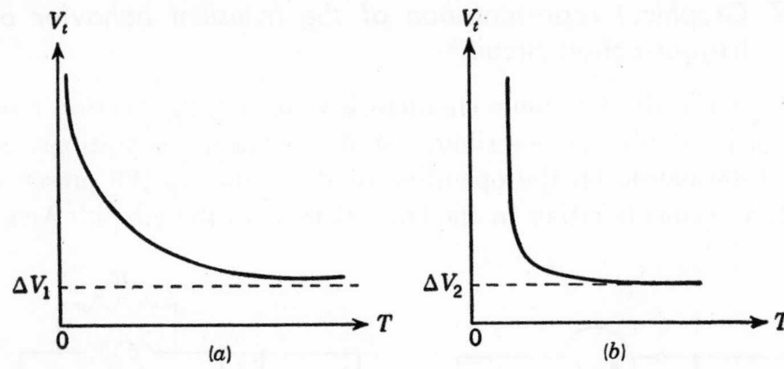

Fig. 12-52. Minimum pulse amplitude vs. pulse duration for triggering a bistable circuit.

Switching the bistable circuit from the on state to the off state follows a similar pattern. However, the operation here is not confined to the active region only. Assume that the circuit has been left in the saturation region for some time and that the operation point has reached the high conduction quiescent point at $t = 0$ when a negative rectangular pulse is applied at the emitter. In the saturation region the current generator is in operation with its large time constant τ_s. Upon the application of the triggering pulse an appreciable time is required for the generator current to decrease to a value less than the collector current in order to reverse the current flow in the collector diode and place the transistor operation in the active region. This time lag is quite long because of the large value of τ_s. Once the transistor is in the active region, the operation is similar to that of the reverse of the operation for switching the circuit from off to on, and a similar analytical procedure applies. The minimum pulse amplitude versus pulse duration relation for this case is shown in Fig. 12-52b. Even for very large values of pulse amplitude an appreciable pulse duration is required for switching. This minimum duration is larger for larger values of τ_s and ΔV_2.

In the analysis above it was assumed that the transistor is allowed to settle to its static condition in the saturation region before the triggering off pulse is applied. If the triggering pulse is applied at an earlier time the triggering requirement is dependent on the length of time the transistor is left in the saturation region. To a certain extent, the longer the transistor is left in the saturation region, the longer is the required triggering pulse duration.

12.17 Graphical representation of the transient behavior of a trigger-action circuit[13]

The static driving-point characteristic of a trigger-action circuit, though invaluable in describing the d-c operating conditions, gives little information on the operation of the circuit in the presence of reactive elements either in the transistor or in the circuit. Analyti-

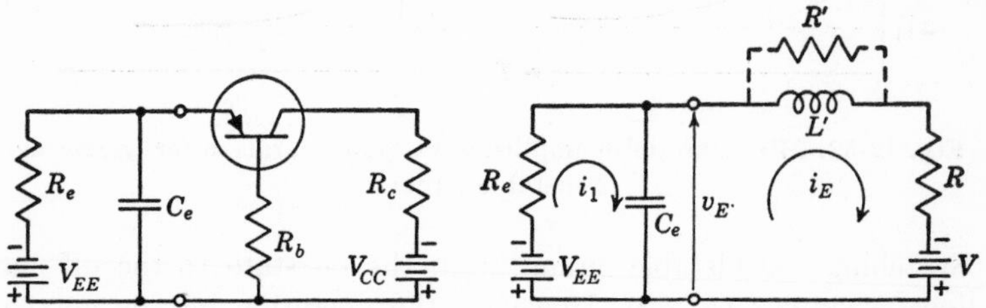

Fig. 12-53. An equivalent circuit for the study of transient response.

cally, the circuit may be represented by differential equations of current and voltage as functions of time. When the number of independent reactive elements in the circuit is not more than two, some form of graphical representation of the differential equations, which describe the operation of the circuit, may be easily made. As an illustrative example let us consider the circuit shown in Fig. 12-53. The only reactive elements in this equivalent circuit are the emitter load capacitance C_e and the equivalent inductance L' by virtue of the frequency response of the transistor. The equivalent

[13] L. W. Hussey, "Pulse Circuit Techniques," A.I.E.E.-I.R.E. Transistor Conference, New York, 1953; B. G. Farley, "Dynamic Transistor Negative-Resistance Circuits," *Proc. I.R.E.*, Vol. 40, pp. 1497–1508, Nov. 1952.

shunt resistance R' is usually large compared with the impedance of L', so that we may omit R' in the analysis. The differential equations of the circuit are therefore

$$-V_{EE} = v_E + R_e i_1 ,$$

$$V = -v_E + L' \frac{di_E}{dt} + R_e i_E ,$$

$$C_e \frac{dv_e}{dt} = i_1 - i_E$$

Eliminating i_1 and t, we have

$$\frac{dv_E}{di_E} = \frac{L'}{R_e C_e} \left(\frac{-V_{EE} - v_E - R_E i_E}{V + v_E - R i_E} \right) \tag{12-37}$$

From Eq. (12-37) and the values of R and V in each of the three distinct regions we are able to map the trajectories in the v_E-i_E plane by recording the slope dv_E/di_E for every point in the plane. Figure 12-54a shows such a graph for a typical bistable circuit. The two

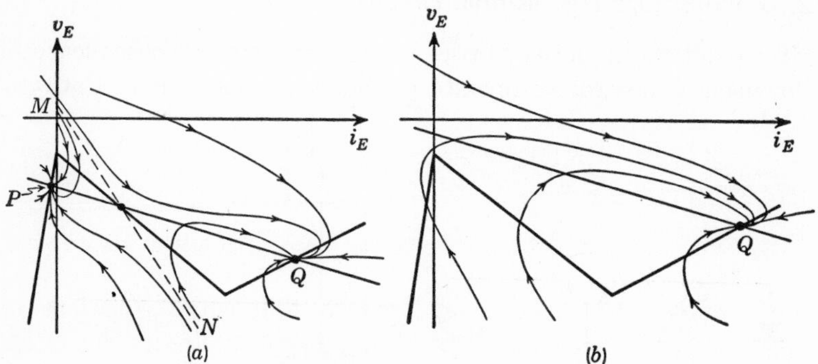

Fig. 12-54. Transient trajectories of a bistable circuit.

stable operation points P and Q are clearly shown to be points where the trajectories converge. After a disturbance, such as that provided by a triggering pulse, the operation point will return either to P or to Q depending on the initial voltage-current condition, as indicated by the different trajectories. It is seen that the dotted line MN divides the plane into two territories; in each territory the trajectories converge to one stable point. To switch the circuit from one state to another the operation point must be carried across this boundary line. This gives some information on the switching requirement. The problem, however, is complicated by the fact that during the triggering the trajectories are modified by the presence of the triggering pulse. Figure 12-54b shows the trajectories when the load line is elevated by the triggering voltage, as in the case where the triggering pulse is applied in series with the load resistance R_e. If the load line is held in this position all the trajectories will naturally converge to the stable point Q. However, it is to be remembered that it takes a finite time for the operation point to travel along the trajectories. If the triggering pulse is applied for a shorter duration, the switching may not be completed. As soon as the triggering pulse terminates, the situation returns to that shown in Fig. 12-54a. If by that time the operation point has not crossed the dividing line MN the trajectory will return to the stable point P and switching will not be completed. This illustrates the requirements imposed on the amplitude and duration of the triggering pulse as discussed in the last section.

12.18 Nonsaturating bistable circuits

To avoid the minority carrier storage effect as a consequence of allowing a transistor to operate in the saturation region, Carlson[14]

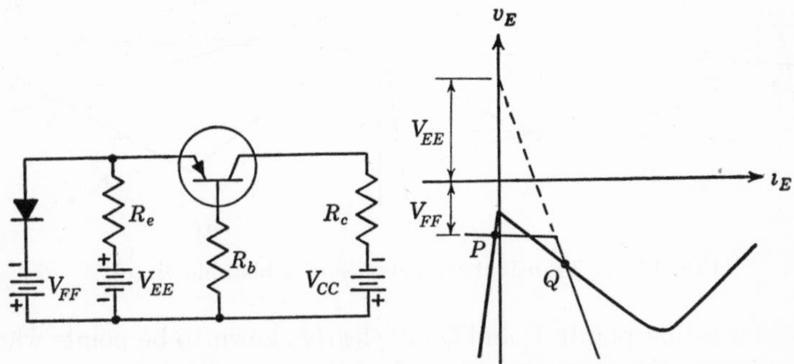

Fig. 12-55. A nonsaturating bistable circuit.

and LeBow[15] suggested several nonsaturating bistable circuits for high-speed applications. One such arrangement is shown in Fig.

[14] A. W. Carlson, *op. cit.*

[15] I. L. LeBow, R. H. Baker, R. E. McMahon, *op. cit.*

12-55. The emitter load line intersects the emitter driving-point characteristic twice; once in the cutoff region and once in the *negative-resistance region*. To insure that the point Q is a stable operation point, the load resistance at that point is kept high by employing a high R_e, and the capacitance in the emitter circuit is kept as low as possible. The triggering pulse is applied at the base, instead of at the emitter, to avoid adding capacitance to the emitter circuit. Reliable operation is possible at repetition frequencies considerably higher than those normally possible with operation in the saturation region.

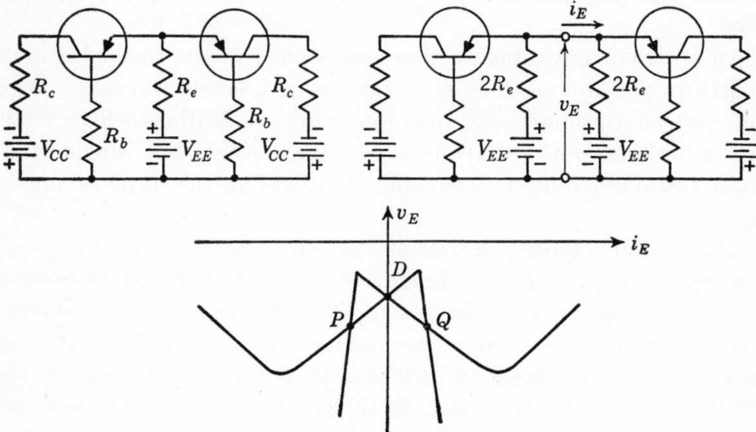

Fig. 12-56. A twin-transistor nonsaturating bistable circuit.

A two-transistor arrangement is shown in Fig. 12-56. One-half of the circuit serves as the load for the other half. The two stable operation points are P and Q, both in nonsaturating regions. The point D is unstable because both halves of the circuit show negative resistance at that point. Pulse steering networks may be incorporated in this basic bistable circuit to form a flip-flop stage.

12.19 Junction transistors in pulse circuits

Up to this point in this chapter we have confined our discussions almost entirely to the application of point-contact transistors in pulse circuits. This is partly because operation of trigger-action circuits using point-contact transistors may be conveniently illustrated and analyzed as two-terminal, negative-resistance networks. The junction transistor offers at this time considerably greater promise for large scale adoption as a switching device. A comparison of the static characteristics of the two devices reveals that the junction transistor more nearly approaches an ideal switch than does the point-contact transistor. In the *off* state the collector-to-emitter resistance of the junction transistor may be in the order of megohms, while in the *on* state, if operated in saturation, the device may have a collector-to-emitter resistance of the order of a few ohms. This, together with the low operating voltage required, indicates that the junction transistor is a good switching device indeed.

An apparent advantage of the point-contact type transistor is its ability to perform bistable operation using a single transistor. This may not be a primary advantage in many applications where a "0" and a "1" output are required simultaneously. The single transistor bistable circuit is incapable of providing this type of operation.

The greater minority carrier storage effect in junction transistors is a concern in pulse circuit design. Once the emitter current exceeds that amount required to drive the collector into saturation, further increase of emitter current succeeds in storing in the transistor large numbers of minority carriers. After the termination of the input pulse the stored carriers must be swept out by the very low collector saturation voltage before the transistor returns to the low conduction state.

However, this problem too diminishes as better switching transistors become available. Finally, if the circuit application demands greater speed, diode clamping techniques can be employed to keep the transistor from saturation as well to limit the collector voltage swing.

In common-base operation, the point-contact transistor can offer a current gain greater than unity, while the input and output signal voltage are in phase. This property is not shared by junction-type transistors. Thus the novel trigger-action circuits discussed in the early part of this chapter do not have a counterpart in circuits using junction transistors. Trigger action circuits using junction transistors more nearly resemble vacuum tube circuits than do they resemble point-contact transistor circuits.

12.20 Large-signal operation of the junction transistor

For operation in the linear active region the response of the junction transistor to a rectangular input pulse may be derived from the high-frequency equivalent circuit described in Chapter 7. In large-signal operation, where the transistor is driven into current saturation, the minority carrier storage effect plays a predominant part. Figure 12-57 shows the output waveforms of a *p-n-p* junction transistor, in the common-emitter configuration, produced by input current pulses of various amplitudes. For a large input current pulse, the transistor may remain in the saturation state for a length of time after the termination of the input pulse. This storage effect is of major concern in the operation of high-speed pulse circuits using junction transistors.

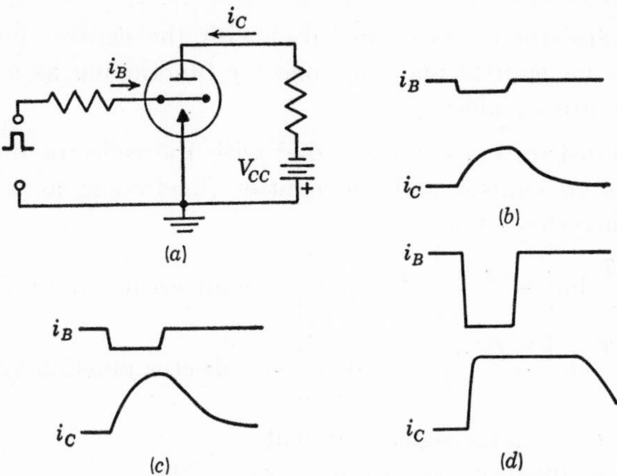

Fig. 12-57. Transient response of a junction transistor to a rectangular current pulse.

The analysis of large-signal operation of the junction transistor follows the same pattern as that of the point-contact transistor. The three distinct regions of operation are defined in much the same manner. The condition of zero emitter current ($i_E = 0$) defines the boundary between the cutoff region (Region I) and the active region (Region II). The boundary between the active region (Region II) and the saturation region (Region III) is conveniently specified by zero collector-to-base voltage ($v_C = 0$) as illustrated in the static characteristics shown in Fig. 12-58. Sectionalized linearization can be applied, and approximate low-frequency equivalent circuits for the three regions may be derived from the static characteristics. Ebers and Moll[16] suggest the more elaborate equivalent circuits reproduced in Fig. 12-59, where:

I_{E0} = saturation current of emitter junction with zero collector current;

I_{C0} = saturation current of collector junction with zero emitter current;

α_N = transistor current gain (d-c) with the emitter functioning as an emitter and the collector functioning as a collector (normal alpha);

α_I = transistor current gain (d-c) with the collector functioning as an emitter and the emitter functioning as a collector (inverted alpha);

$$\Phi_E = \frac{kT}{q} \ln \left[-\frac{I_E + \alpha_I I_C}{I_{E0}} + 1 \right] = \text{emitter junction voltage;}$$

$$\Phi_C = \frac{kT}{q} \ln \left[-\frac{I_C + \alpha_N I_E}{I_{C0}} + 1 \right] = \text{collector junction voltage.}$$

A study of the large-signal transient response of junction transistors by Moll[17] shows that the switching time may be calculated from small-signal equivalent circuits. The *turn-on* time (from the cutoff state to the saturation state) depends on the frequency response of the transistor in the active region. The *turn-off* time (from the saturation state to the cutoff state) consists of two parts: the storage time and the decay time. The storage time represents the time for the operation point to move out of the saturation region and into the active region on ter-

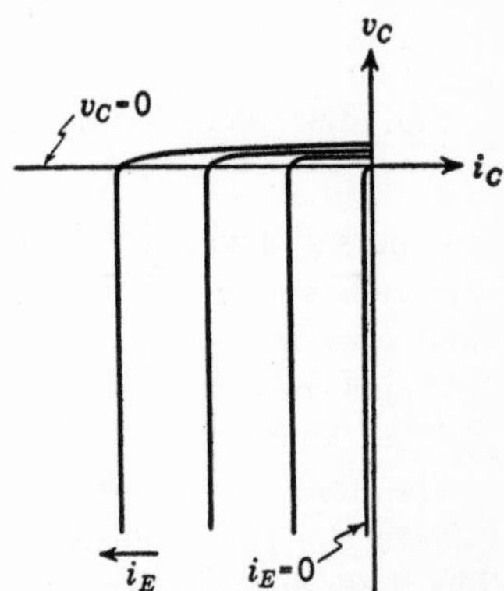

Fig. 12-58. Static characteristics of a junction transistor.

[16] J. J. Ebers and J. L. Moll, "Large-signal Behavior of Junction Transistors," *Proc. I.R.E.*, Vol. 42, Dec. 1954.

[17] J. L. Moll, "Large-signal Transient Response of Junction Transistors," *Proc. I.R.E.*, Vol. 42, Dec. 1954.

mination of the drive current, and is a function of the frequency response of the transistor in the saturation region. The decay time, which follows the storage time in returning the transistor to its cutoff state, depends again on the frequency response in the active re-

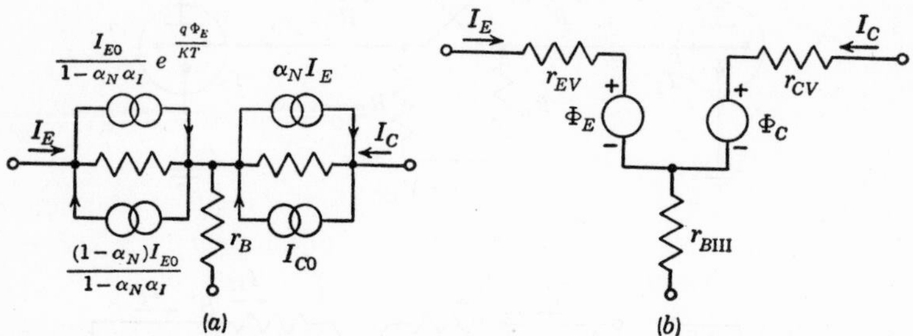

Fig. 12-59. Low-frequency large-signal equivalent circuit of a junction transistor: (a) Regions I and II; (b) Region III.

gion. Formulas for the turn-on time, the storage time, and the decay time of a junction transistor in common-base operation are reproduced here:

$$\text{turn-on time} = \frac{1}{\omega_N} \frac{I_{E2}}{I_{E2} - 0.9 I_C/\alpha_N}$$

$$\text{storage time} = \frac{\omega_N + \omega_I}{\omega_N \omega_I (1 - \alpha_N \alpha_I)} \ln \frac{I_{E2} - I_{E1}}{I_C/\alpha_N + I_{E2}},$$

$$\text{decay time} = \frac{1}{\omega_N} \ln \frac{I_C + \alpha_N I_{E2}}{\frac{1}{10} I_C + \alpha_N I_{E2}}$$

where, α_N, ω_N = normal alpha, and cutoff frequency of normal alpha; α_I, ω_I = inverted alpha, and cutoff frequency of inverted alpha; I_{E1}, I_{E2} = emitter current before, after switching step is applied; I_C = collector current in the saturation state. It is estimated by Moll that switching time in the order of $3/\omega_N$ can be achieved in practice if carrier storage effects are avoided.

12.21 Junction transistor bistable circuits

Bistable circuits using junction transistors follow closely the pattern of the Eccles-Jordan circuit. Fig. 12-60a illustrates a bistable circuit using a pair of *n-p-n* alloy junction transistors. The emitters of the two transistors are kept at ground potential; the base of either

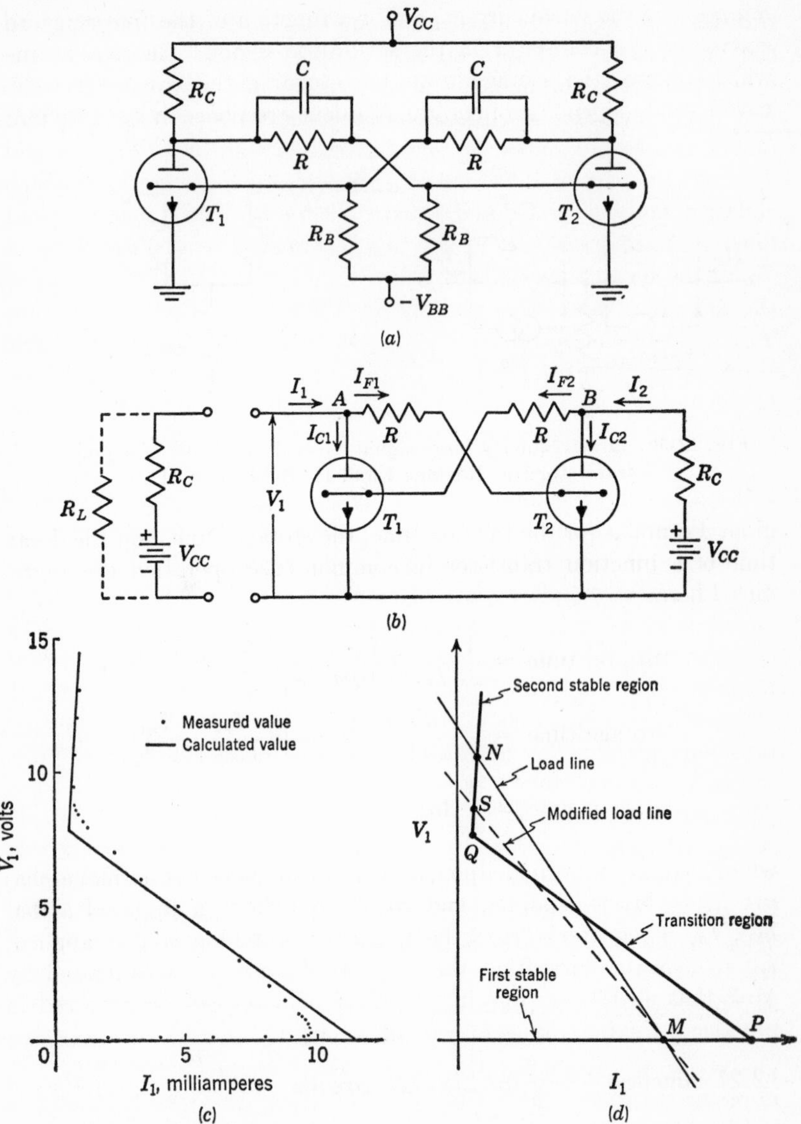

Fig. 12-60. A basic junction transistor bistable circuit: (a) circuit diagram; (b) circuit redrawn as a two-terminal network coupled to a load; (c) driving-point characteristic; (d) sectionally linearized driving-point characteristic and the load-line.

transistor is negatively biased (through the high resistance R_B and the bias voltage $-V_{BB}$) and also coupled to the collector of the other transistor through the cross-coupling RC network. The circuit parameters are so chosen that the circuit can remain in either one of two stable states. In the first stable state (say T_1 is *on* and T_2 is *off*) the base of T_1 is held at a voltage above ground by the high collector voltage of T_2, and thus a sizable base-to-emitter current flows in T_1 and keeps it in the high conduction state. The base of T_2, in the mean time, is held below ground potential on account of the negative bias $-V_{BB}$ and the low collector voltage of T_1; thus T_2 is held in the cutoff state. The circuit switches from one stable state to the other if a negative triggering pulse is applied at the base of the *on* unit, or if a positive triggering pulse is applied at the base of the *off* unit. Triggering at the collectors is also practical.

The operation of the bistable circuit is convienently illustrated and analyzed by examining the driving-point negative-resistance characteristic at some appropriate branch of the circuit, following the technique used earlier in this chapter in the study of point-contact transistor trigger-action circuits.[18] In Fig. 12-60b the bistable circuit is redrawn and expressed as a two-terminal active network coupled to a two-terminal load. Since the value of the base resistor R_B is much larger than that of R and R_C, the biasing circuit may be omitted in examining the operation of the circuit. Looking into the terminals of the active network, the driving-point characteristic (i.e. the I_1–V_1 relation) takes the form of the curve shown in Fig. 12-60c. This curve is readily identified as being the same type of voltage-controlled negative-resistance characteristic shown earlier in Fig. 12-6b. The three distinct regions correspond to the states of the two transistors. In the first stable region T_1 is in the saturation state and T_2 is in the cutoff state. In the second stable region the states of the two transistors are reversed. In the transition region both transistors are in the active state.

Certain approximations may be adapted in deriving a simplified analytical expression for the driving-point characteristic. When T_1 is in the saturation state the internal resistance of the transistor is small compared with the circuit resistances R and R_C; thus V_1 is

[18] T. P. Bothwell, "Junction Transistor Flip-flop Design Methods for Computer Applications," A.I.E.E. Winter General Meeting, New York City, Feb. 1955.

substantially at ground potential, and the characteristic in this region may be expressed approximately as $V_1 = 0$. When T_1 is in the cutoff state and T_2 is in the saturation state, the internal resistance of T_1 is much higher than the resistance R, and the base voltage of T_2 is small compared with the collector voltage of T_1. Thus V_1 is approximately equal to the voltage drop across R; and the I_1–V_1 relation in the second stable region may be expressed as $V_1 = I_1R$. Now in the transition region, where both T_1 and T_2 are in the active state, we have the following relationship:

At node A,

$$I_1 = I_{C1} + I_{F1}$$
$$I_{C1} = \alpha_{CB}I_{F2}$$
$$V_1 = I_{F1}R$$

At node B,

$$I_2 = I_{C2} + I_{F2}$$
$$I_{C2} = \alpha_{CB}I_{F1}$$
$$V_{CC} = I_2R_C + I_{F2}R$$

where α_{CB} is the d-c amplification factor, defined as $\alpha_{CB} = I_C/I_B$. Solving these equations, the I_1–V_1 relation in the transition region is derived as:

$$I_1 = [1 - \alpha_{CB}^2R_C/(R + R_C)]V_1/R + \alpha_{CB}V_{CC}/(R + R_C)$$

Assuming that the transistor parameters remain constant in each of the three distinct regions, the approximate sectionally linearized driving-point characteristic shown in Fig. 12-60d is derived from the analysis. Summarizing, the driving-point characteristic is expressed analytically as,

First stable region: $V_1 = 0$.

Transition region:

$$I_1 = [1 - \alpha_{CB}^2R_C/(R + R_C)]V_1/R + \alpha_{CB}V_{CC}/(R + R_C).$$

Second stable region: $V_1 = I_1R$.

The turn-over points are located at:

Turn-over point P: $V_P = 0$; $I_P = \alpha_{CB}V_{CC}/(R + R_C)$

Turn-over point Q: $V_Q = RV_{CC}/\alpha_{CB}R_C$, $I_Q = V_{CC}/\alpha_{CB}R_C$

In a practical junction transistor the parameter α_{CB} does not re-

states, that transistor T_1 is in the *on* state, and that transistor T_2 is in the *off* state. The collector voltage of T_1 is clamped at ground potential by the diode D_{1a}, and the collector voltage of T_2 is clamped at the potential V'_{CC} by the diode D_{2b}. The diodes D_{1b} and D_{2a} are not conducting. In switching the bistable circuit to the other stable state the transient excursion of voltage and current in the circuit progresses until the diodes D_{1b} and D_{2a} are conducting, and the diodes D_{1a} and D_{2b} are nonconducting. In either stable state the collector voltages are fixed by the respective diode bias voltages.

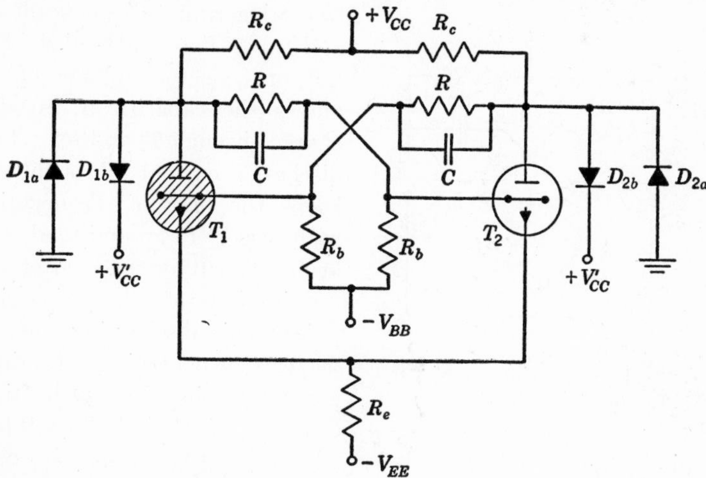

Fig. 12-63. A junction transistor bistable circuit with diode clamping.

The clamping diode D_{1a} (or D_{2a}) keeps the collector at a higher voltage than the base voltage for the transistor in the *on* state, and thus prevents current saturation in the transistor. The clamping diode D_{2b} (or D_{1b}) fixes the collector voltage of the transistor in the *off* state.

In this circuit the stable states are defined by the diode clamping circuits, and are not defined by the nonlinear properties of the transistor as in the unclamped flip-flop. In fact, this type of circuit can be so arranged that the excursions of voltage and current in the transistor are *always* within the linear operation region.[21] The design

[21] J. G. Linvill, "Non-saturating Pulse Circuits Using Two Junction Transistors," to be published.

and analysis of such circuits are greatly simplified since the transistors never reach current saturation or cutoff. The diode clamping techniques are, of course, also readily adaptable in monostable and astable circuits.

12.22 Junction transistor monostable circuits

The basic bistable circuit may be modified to form a monostable circuit in the same manner as in its vacuum tube counterpart. In Fig. 12-64 the transistor T_1 is quiescently biased to high conduction, and the transistor T_2 is biased to cutoff. The application of a negative triggering pulse cuts off T_1 and turns T_2 to conduction. The fall of collector voltage of T_2 allows the capacitor C to discharge through T_2 and R_{b1}. This discharge current through R_{b1} keeps the base of T_1 negative with respect to ground, and thus keeps T_1 cut off even after the termination of the triggering pulse. This discharging current decreases exponentially with time, governed primarily by the time constant of C and R_{b1}. When the discharge current falls below the value that keeps the base voltage of T_1 cut off, T_1 starts to conduct and the circuit triggers back to its quiescent state.

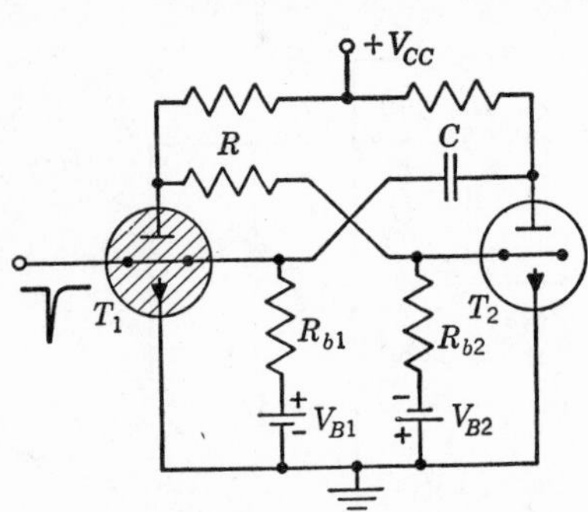

Fig. 12-64. A junction transistor monostable circuit.

12.23 A compound junction transistor unit

In Chapter 1 it was shown that the point-contact transistor may be described as an n-type germanium crystal with a p-type region at the emitter and another p-type region close to, but not in contact with, the collector. This interpretation suggests that a p-n-p junction transistor and an n-p-n junction transistor may be interconnected to form a device similar in characteristic to a point-contact transistor. The arrangement is shown in Fig. 12-65. This compound transistor indeed possesses the unique characteristic of the point-contact transistor of a collector-to-emitter current gain without phase reversal. The α of the compound unit, which is practically the α of the grounded collector stage, is many times more than that which can be expected from a point-contact unit. Furthermore, while the α of a point-contact unit often changes considerably with the emitter current throughout the active region, the compound unit exhibits an α

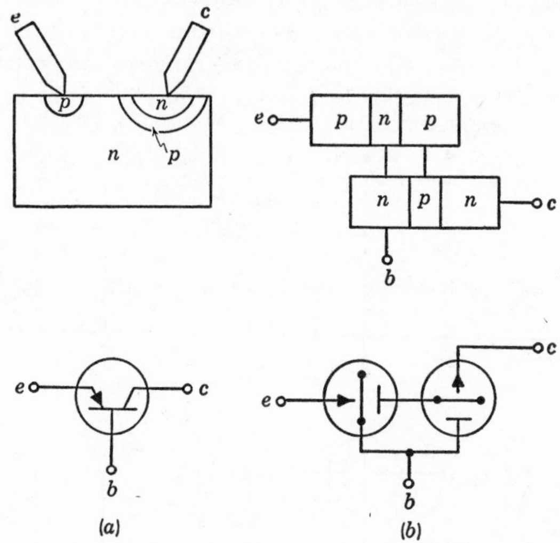

Fig. 12-65. Comparison between (a) point-contact transistor, and (b) compound junction transistor unit.

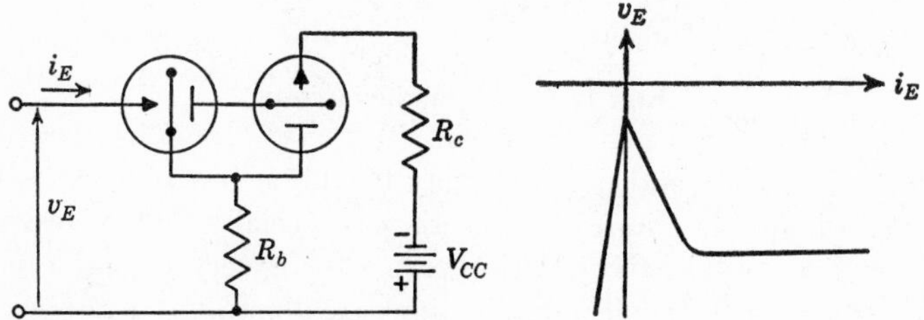

Fig. 12-66. A basic trigger-action circuit employing a compound junction transistor unit.

almost constant in that region. The compound unit therefore can be employed in all the trigger-action circuits discussed in the earlier part of the chapter. Employing the compound unit in a basic trigger-action circuit, the emitter driving-point characteristic is shown in Fig. 12-66. The utilization of the compound unit, however, is quite limited at present by the frequency response of the junction transistor, in particular, the minority carrier storage effect.

12.24 Junction transistor gate circuits[22]

In large-signal operation of alloy junction transistors, the d-c resistance of the transistor can change from a very large value to a very small value over the permissible range of operation. For instance, the emitter-to-collector resistance may be of the order of megohms in the cutoff condition, and may be only a few ohms in saturation. This highly nonlinear characteristic, especially the low resistance at saturation, makes the junction transistor a very desirable gating device. Some of the typical applications are illustrated in this section.

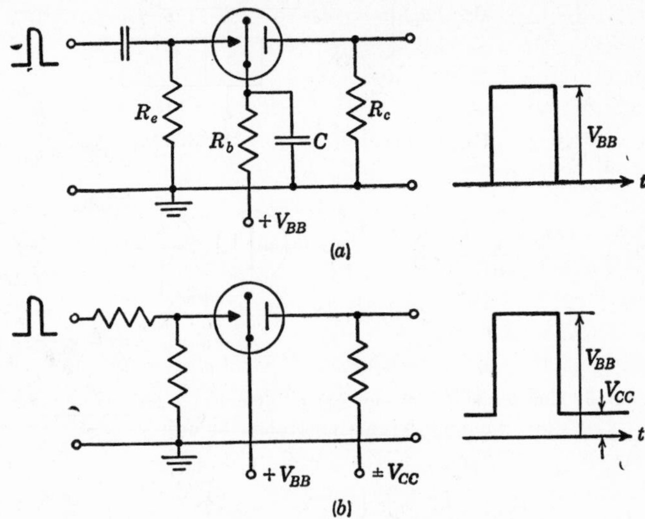

Fig. 12-67. Clamping circuits.

Figure 12-67a shows a pulse amplitude discrimination circuit. The base of the transistor is biased by $+V_{BB}$ so that quiescently a reverse current flows in the emitter junction and the transistor is kept in the cutoff state. An input pulse of amplitude less than $+V_{BB}$ does not develop an output. An input of amplitude slightly higher than $+V_{BB}$ may drive the transistor to saturation; and thus the

[22] D. E. Deuitch, *op. cit.*

input pulse appears at the output terminals with only slight reduction of amplitude.

Figure 12-67b shows a clipping circuit employing an *n-p-n* junction transistor. The emitter junction is biased by a positive voltage $+V_{BB}$ through R_e, provided that V_{BB} is larger than V_{CC}. Quiescently the transistor is in the cutoff condition, as the emitter is biased more negative with respect to the base by V_{BB}. The output terminal is clamped at approximately the voltage V_{CC} (which may be either positive or negative, provided it is smaller than V_{BB}) because of the high value of r_c when the transistor is in the cutoff state. An input voltage less than V_{BB} is not sufficient to drive the transistor out of the cutoff state; thus the output terminal remains at V_{CC}. A larger input voltage may send a positive current into the emitter. This emitter current, if large enough, will saturate the transistor and reduce the collector-to-base resistance to a very small value. Thus the voltage of the output terminal rises to approximately the value of V_{BB}. In this manner an output of prescribed high and low levels is derived from an input voltage provided the input exceeds a certain threshold value. In either the cutoff state or the saturation state the transistor behaves like a passive element, and thus does not give voltage, current, or power gain. Unlike a diode circuit, however, the transistor does give voltage and power gain in the active region when it travels from the cutoff state to the saturation state.

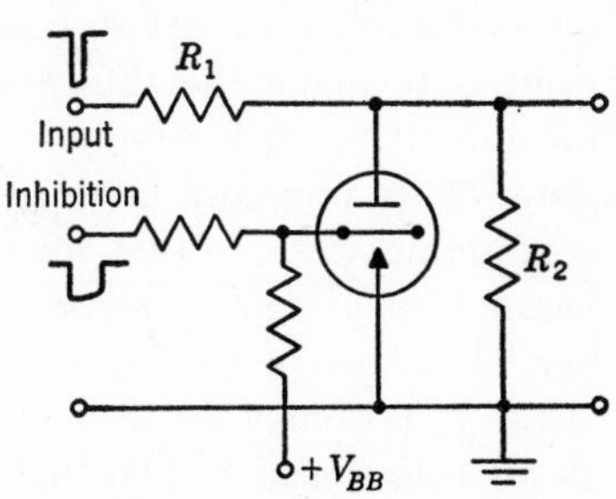

Fig. 12-68. An "inhibition" gate.

In the grounded-emitter configuration, the extremely low emitter-to-collector resistance in the transistor at saturation may be utilized to advantage in logic circuits. Figure 12-68 shows an inhibition gate. Quiescently the transistor is biased to cutoff by $+V_{BB}$, so that the input pulse may appear at the output terminal through the voltage divider composed of R_1 and R_2. In the presence of the inhibition pulse the transistor is biased to saturation so that the input signal is shunted to ground.

A three-input "and" gate is shown in Fig. 12-69. The three transistors are biased to saturation by $-V_{BB}$, thus quiescently the clock pulse does not produce an output pulse. It is only when all the transistors are cut off by applying input pulses 1, 2, and 3 simultaneously that the clock pulse may reach the output terminal. Because of the high collector-to-emitter resistance when the transistor is in the cutoff state, the number of "and" input terminals can be quite large.

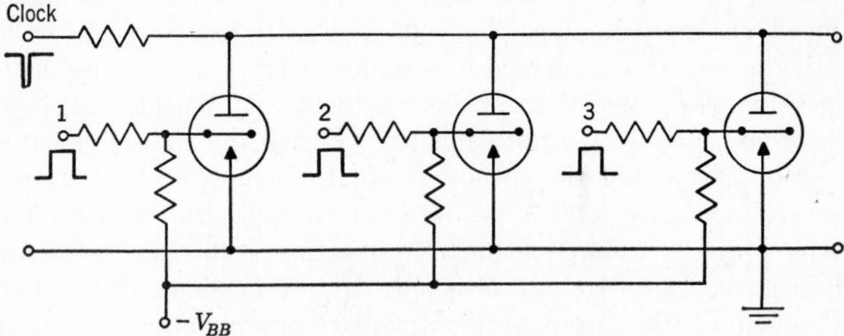

Fig. 12-69. An "and" gate.

The minority carrier storage effect in junction transistors may be utilized to make the transistor a storage device with limited time memory. One such circuit is shown in Fig. 12-70. The *p-n-p* transistor T_1 is normally in the low conduction state, so that the collector is at a high negative voltage. The base of the *n-p-n* transistor T_2 is connected through R_b to the collector of T_1, so that T_2 normally is biased far beyond cutoff. The interrogating pulse is of such amplitude that it cannot drive transistor T_2 out of the cutoff state, and thus produces no output. A "write" pulse applied at the base of T_1 drives the transistor to saturation and stores a quantity of excess minority carriers in it. The stored minority carriers may keep the transistor T_1 in saturation for tens of microseconds. During this time the collector of T_1 is almost at ground potential, and thus the reverse bias at the base of T_2 is re-

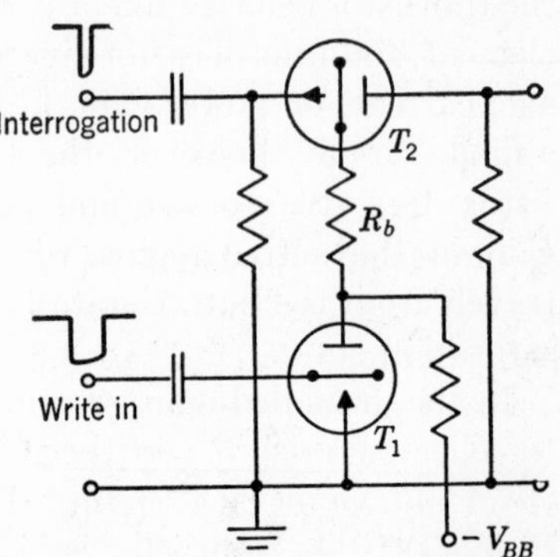

Fig. 12-70. A memory circuit.

duced to a very low value. If the interrogating pulse is applied during this time, the transistor T_2 may be driven to high conduction, and a pulse appears at the output terminal.

PROBLEMS

12-1. Given $R_b = 2000$ ohms, $R_e = 5000$ ohms, $V_{CC} = 45$ v, sketch the emitter driving-point characteristic of the basic trigger-action circuit shown. Use the transistor parameter values listed in Table 12-2.

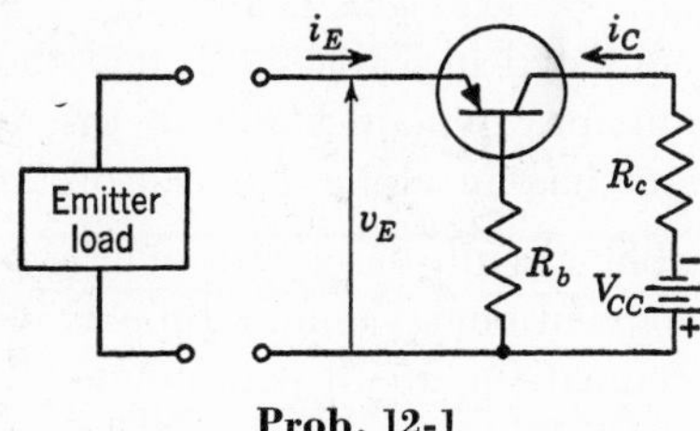

Prob. 12-1

12-2. Repeat Problem 12-1 by using the transistor parameter values listed in Table 12-1. Compare the result with that of Problem 12-1.

12-3. Show the effects of the magnitude of R_b and R_c on the shape of the emitter driving-point characteristic by repeating Problem 12-1 with different values of R_b and R_c.

12-4. The basic monostable circuit shown in Fig. 12-13 is adopted for producing an output voltage pulse of 5 μsec duration and 20 v amplitude. Give the appropriate values of circuit parameters for this operation. Discuss the choice of circuit parameters with respect to circuit recovery time.

12-5. In Problem 12-4 the condenser is replaced by a transmission line (as shown in Fig. 12-20). What are the required characteristics that the transmission line must possess?

12-6. Assume that the diode D_2 in Fig. 12-22a has a forward resistance of 10 ohms and a reverse resistance of 100,000 ohms. Show analytically how the diode arrangement improves the maximum repetition rate of the circuit.

12-7. Explain the shape of the waveforms listed in Fig. 12-22b in terms of the operation of the monostable circuit.

12-8. Referring to Fig. 12-8c, it is suggested that the circuit may perform monostable operation if an inductance is inserted in the base circuit. What is the requirement of the d-c load line in the base circuit? Describe the operation of the circuit with the aid of the base driving-point characteristic.

12-9. In Fig. 12-47 the emitter d-c load line intersects the emitter driving-point characteristic in the negative resistance region. Given $R_b = 2000$ ohms, $R_c = 5000$ ohms, and $R_e = 50{,}000$ ohms, and transistor parameters listed in Table 12-2, find the maximum value of C_e that the circuit may remain stable in the negative resistance region. The transistor has an alpha 3 db cutoff frequency of 5 mc.

12-10. The bistable circuit described in Fig. 12-60 is directly analogous to the conventional vacuum tube Eccles-Jordan circuit. What are the requirements in circuit parameters that the circuit may have two stable states? What are the major differences between the transistor circuit and the vacuum tube circuit?

12-11. What changes in circuit design are necessary to convert the bistable circuit shown in Fig. 12-60 into a free-running multivibrator circuit? Describe in words the operation of the new circuit.

12-12. Derive analytically the duration of the output pulse for the monostable circuit shown in Fig. 12-64. Use approximate values of transistor parameters (one set of parameters for each of the three distinct regions) derived from junction transistor characteristics.

12-13. Express in analytical form, in terms of transistor and circuit parameters, the sectionally linearized driving-point characteristic shown in Fig. 12-66.

INDEX